Reduced Instruction Set Computers
(Second Edition)

REDUCED INSTRUCTION SET COMPUTERS

Second Edition

William Stallings

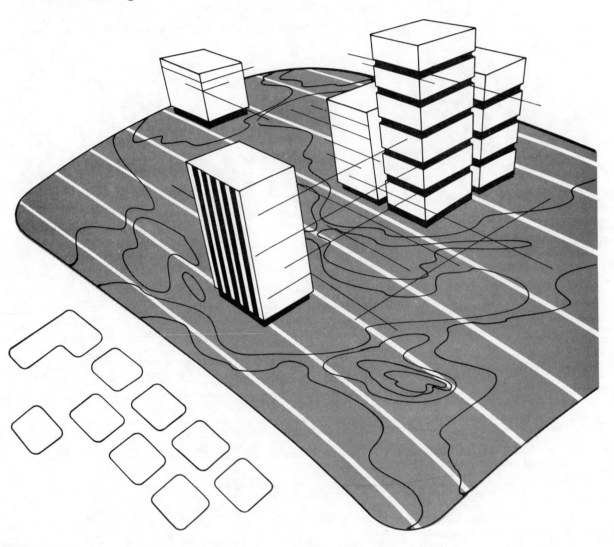

IEEE Computer Society Press Tutorial

Reduced Instruction Set Computers
(Second Edition)

William Stallings

Management Consultant
Computer and Communications Technologies

IEEE Computer Society Press
Los Alamitos, California

• Washington • Los Alamitos • Brussels • Tokyo

Published by

IEEE Computer Society Press
10662 Los Vaqueros Circle
P.O. Box 3014
Los Alamitos, CA 90720-1264

IEEE Computer Society Order Number 1943
Library of Congress Number 89-45996
IEEE Catalog Number EH0295-6
ISBN 0-8186-8943-9 (Casebound)
ISBN 0-8186-5943-2 (Microfiche)

Additional copies may be ordered from:

IEEE Computer Society	IEEE Service Center	IEEE Computer Society	IEEE Computer Society
10662 Los Vaqueros Circle	445 Hoes Lane	13, Avenue de l'Aquilon	Ooshima Building
P.O. Box 3014	P.O. Box 1331	B-1200 Brussels	2-19-1 Minami-Aoyama,
Los Alamitos CA 90720-1264	Piscataway, NJ 08855-1331	BELGIUM	Minato-Ku
			Tokyo 107 JAPAN

THE INSTITUTE OF ELECTRICAL AND ELECTRONICS ENGINEERS, INC.

Preface

Since the development of the stored-program computer around 1950, there have been remarkably few true innovations in the areas of computer organization and architecture. One of the most interesting and, potentially, one of the most important innovations is the reduced instruction set computer (RISC). The RISC architecture is a dramatic departure from the historical trend in CPU architecture and challenges the conventional wisdom expressed in words and deeds by most computer architects. An analysis of the RISC architecture brings into focus many of the important issues in computer organization and architecture. Although most of the work has been on experimental systems, commercial RISC systems have begun to appear.

P.1 Objectives

The objectives of this tutorial text are to (1) provide a comprehensive introduction to RISC and (2) give the reader an understanding of RISC design issues and the ability to assess their importance relative to other approaches. The articles have been selected based on topic and style to support these aims.

P.2 Intended Audience

The tutorial is intended for a broad range of readers who will benefit from an understanding of RISC concepts. These include students and professionals in the fields of computer science and computer engineering, designers and implementers, and data processing managers who now find RISC machines among their available processor choices. A basic, general background in computer architecture is recommended. However, some tutorial material is provided for the reader with little or no background in this area.

P.3 Organization

This tutorial text is a combination of original material and reprinted articles and is organized as follows:

1. *Instruction Execution Characteristics:* This section presents results on studies of the execution characteristics of compiled high-level language instructions. These results form the base on which the RISC approach has evolved.

2. *RISC Overview:* This section introduces the concept of RISC and provides an overview of its key characteristics.

3. *Optimized Register Usage:* One of the major design goals for RISC is to maximize the use of registers and minimize memory reads and writes. Several approaches to optimization have been explored by RISC designers.

4. *RISC Compilers:* A vital element in achieving high performance on a RISC system is an optimizing compiler. This section presents reports on three RISC compilers.

5. *Example Systems:* This section surveys systems that have been implemented using the RISC approach.

6. *An Assessment of RISC:* This section explores the relative merits of the RISC approach compared to the more conventional approaches to computer architecture.

7. *GaAs RISC:* One of the most significant recent developments in processor design is the marriage of RISC and Gallium Arsenide (GaAs) technologies. This section explores the reasons for the use of GaAs in RISC designs and provides several examples.

8. *Glossary:* This includes definitions for most of the key terms appearing in the text.

9. *List of Acronyms:* Includes most of the acronyms appearing in the text.

10. *Annotated Bibliography:* Provides a guide for further reading.

P.4 The Second Edition

In the three years since *Reduced Instruction Set Computers* was published, the field has continued to evolve and expand. There is now a large number of commercial products based fully or partly on RISC architecture, and research and development of RISC technology has intensified. Most notably, Gallium Arsenide (GaAs) has emerged as a promising technology for RISC implementation. These developments are reflected in the makeup of this edition, which includes a total of 18 new articles. Among the most noteworthy additions are a complete new section on GaAs RISC. Other changes include new articles on specific example systems and a further development of the analysis of RISC versus CISC. The author hopes that, with these changes, this will continue to be a useful and timely reference for this fascinating field.

Table of Contents

Section 1: Instruction Execution Characteristics

1.1 Background

One of the most visible forms of evolution associated with computers is that of programming languages. As the cost of hardware has dropped, the relative cost of software has risen. Along with that, a chronic shortage of programmers has driven up software costs in absolute terms. Thus the major cost in the life cycle of a system is software, not hardware. Adding to the cost, and to the inconvenience, is the element of unreliability: It is common for programs, both system and application, to continue to exhibit new bugs after years of operation.

The response from researchers and industry has been to develop ever more powerful and complex high-level programming languages (compare FORTRAN to Ada). These high-level languages (HLL) allow the programmer to express algorithms more concisely, take care of much of the detail, and often support naturally the use of structured programming.

Alas, this solution gave rise to another problem, known as the *semantic gap*, the difference between the operations provided in HLLs and those provided in computer architecture. Symptoms of this gap are alleged to include execution inefficiency, excessive program size, and compiler complexity. Designers responded with architectures intended to close this gap. Key features include large instruction sets, dozens of addressing modes, and various HLL statements implemented in hardware. An example of the latter is the CASE machine instruction on the VAX-11. Such complex instruction sets are intended to

- Ease the task of the compiler writer;
- Improve execution efficiency, since complex sequences of operations can be implemented in microcode;
- Provide support for even more complex and sophisticated HLLs.

Meanwhile, a number of studies have been done over the years to determine the characteristics and patterns of execution of machine instructions generated from HLL programs. The results of these studies inspired some researchers to look for an altogether different approach, namely, to make the architecture that supports the HLL simpler, rather than more, complex.

The articles in this section present results on studies of the execution characteristics of compiled HLL instructions. These results form the base on which the RISC approach has

evolved. For the reader unfamiliar with some of the issues in instruction set design, the following subsections provide some background.

1.2 The Machine Instruction Set

The operation of a computer's central processing unit (CPU) is determined by the instructions it executes. These instructions are referred to as *machine instructions* or *computer instructions*. The CPU may perform a variety of functions, and these are reflected in the variety of instructions defined for the CPU. The collection of different instructions that the CPU can execute is referred to as the CPU's *instruction set*.

Most of the details of a computer's organization and implementation are hidden from the user. One boundary where the computer designer and the computer programmer can view the same machine is the machine instruction set. From the designer's point of view, the machine instruction set provides the functional requirements for the CPU: Implementing the CPU is a task that in large part involves implementing the machine instruction set. From the user's side, the user that chooses to program in machine language or assembly language becomes aware of the register and memory structure, the types of data directly supported by the machine, and the functioning of the arithmetic and logic unit (ALU). Today, few programmers employ machine or assembly language. However, the machine instruction set remains of concern to the compiler writer.

1.3 Elements of a Machine Instruction

The basic function performed by a computer is program execution. The central processing unit (CPU) does the actual work by performing the instructions specified by the program. A program consisting of a set of instructions is stored in memory. The CPU typically reads (*fetches*) instructions from memory one at a time, executes each instruction, and then fetches the next instruction. This process is repeated indefinitely. The processing required for a single instruction is called an *instruction cycle* and is depicted in simplified form in Figure 1-1. The figure is in the form of a state diagram. For any given instruction cycle, some states may be null and others may be visited more than once. The states can be described as follows

- *instruction.address.calculation (iac):* Determine the address of the next instruction to be executed. Usually,

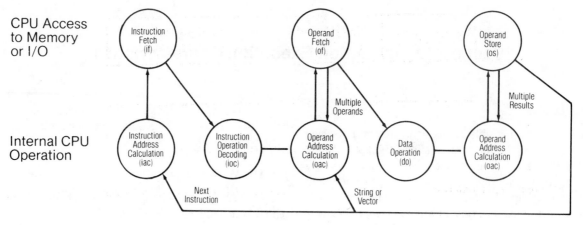

CPU Access to Memory or I/O

Internal CPU Operation

Note: Any state may be null

Figure 1.1: Instruction Cycle State Diagram

this involves adding 1 to the address of the previous instruction.

- *instruction.fetch (if):* Read instruction from its memory location into the CPU.
- *instruction.operation.decoding (iod):* Analyze instruction to determine the type of operation to be performed and operands to be used.
- *operand.address.calculation (oac):* If the operation involves reference to an operand in memory or available via I/O, then determine the address of the operand.
- *operand.fetch (of):* Fetch the operand from memory or read it in from I/O.
- *data.operation (do):* Perform the operation indicated.
- *operand.store (os):* Write the result into memory or out to I/O.

States in the upper part of the diagram involve an exchange between the CPU and either memory or an I/O module. States in the lower part of the diagram involve only internal CPU operations. The oac state appears twice, since an instruction may involve a read, a write, or both. However, the action performed during that state is fundamentally the same in both cases, so only a single state identifier is needed.

Also note that the diagram allows for multiple operands and multiple results, since some instructions on some machines require this. For example, the PDP-11 instruction ADD A,B results in the following sequence of states: iac, if, iod, oac, of, oac, of, do, oac, os.

Finally, on some machines, a single instruction can specify an operation to be performed on a vector (one-dimensional array) of numbers or a string (one-dimensional array) of characters, and this is also reflected in the state diagram.

From Figure 1-1, we can deduce the essential elements of a machine instruction. These elements are

- *Operation code:* Specifies the operation to be per-

formed (e.g., ADD, I/O). The operation is specified by a binary code, known as the operation code, or *opcode*.

- *Source Operand Reference:* The operation may involve one or more source operands, that is, operands that are inputs for the operation.
- *Result Operand Reference:* The operation may produce a result.
- *Next Instruction Reference:* This tells the CPU where to fetch the next instruction after the execution of this instruction is complete.

The next instruction to be fetched is located in main memory or, in the case of a virtual memory system, in either main memory or secondary memory (disk). In most cases, the next instruction to be fetched immediately follows the current instruction, and there is no explicit reference to the next instruction. When an explicit reference is needed, then the main memory or virtual memory address must be supplied. The form in which that address is supplied is discussed below.

Source and result operands can be in one of three areas

- *Main or Virtual Memory:* As with next instruction references, the main or virtual memory address must be supplied.
- *CPU Register:* With rare exceptions, a CPU contains one or more registers that may be referenced by machine instructions. If only one register exists, reference to it may be implicit. If more than one register exists, then each register is assigned a unique number, and the instruction must contain the number of the desired register.
- *I/O Device:* The instruction must specify the I/O module and device for the operation. If memory-mapped I/O is used, this is just another main or virtual memory address.

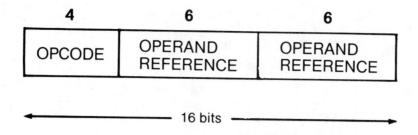

4	**6**	**6**
OPCODE	OPERAND REFERENCE	OPERAND REFERENCE

◄─────── 16 bits ───────►

Figure 1.2: A simple Instruction Format

1.4 Instruction Representation

Within the computer, each instruction is represented by a sequence of bits. The instruction is divided into fields, corresponding to the constituent elements of the instruction. This layout of the instruction is known as the *instruction format*. A simple example is shown in Figure 1-2. With most instruction sets, more than one format is used. During instruction execution, an instruction is read into an instruction register (IR) in the CPU. The CPU must be able to extract the data from the various instruction fields to perform the required operation.

It is difficult both for the programmer and for the reader of textbooks to deal with binary representations of machine instructions. Thus it has become common practice to use a *symbolic representation* of machine instructions.

Opcodes are represented by abbreviations, called mnemonics, that indicate the operation. Common examples are

ADD   Add
SUB   Subtract
MPY   Multiply
DIV   Divide
LOAD   Load data from memory
STOR   Store data to memory

Operands are also represented symbolically. For example, the instruction

ADD R, Y

may mean add the value contained in data location Y to the contents of register R. In this example, Y refers to the address of a location in memory, and R refers to a particular register.

1.5 Instruction Types

Consider a high-level language instruction that could be expressed in a language such as BASIC or FORTRAN. For example

$X = X + Y$

This statement instructs the computer to add the value stored in Y to the value stored in X and put the result in X. How might this be accomplished with machine instructions? Let us assume that the variables X and Y correspond to locations 513 and 514. If we assume a simple set of machine instruc-

tions, this operation could be accomplished with three instructions

1. Load a register with the contents of memory location 513.

2. Add the contents of memory location 514 to the register.

3. Store the contents of the register in memory location 513.

As can be seen, the single BASIC instruction may require three machine instructions. This is typical of the relationship between a high-level language and a machine language. A high-level language expresses operations in a concise algebraic form, using variables. A machine language expresses operations in a basic form involving the movement of data to or from registers.

With this simple example to guide us, consider the type of instructions that must be included in a practical computer. A computer should have a set of instructions that allows the user to formulate any data processing task. Another way to view it is to consider the capabilities of a high-level programming language. Any program written in a high-level language must be translated into machine language in order to be executed. Thus the set of machine instructions must be sufficient to express any of the instructions from a high-level language. With this in mind we can list some of the most important types of instructions

- *Data Transfer:* This is the most fundamental type of machine instruction and results in the movement of data from one location to another. The data transfer instruction must specify the location of the source and destination operands and the length of data to be transferred.

- *Arithmetic:* These provide computational capabilities for processing numeric data (e.g., add, subtract, multiply, divide).

- *Logic:* These operate on individual bits of data and include boolean functions (e.g., AND, OR, NOT) and shifting functions.

- *Input/Output:* I/O instructions are used to transfer programs and data into main memory and results back out to the user or the secondary memory.

- *Transfer of Control:* These instructions are used to

cause the CPU to continue execution from a different point in the program rather than the next instruction in sequence.

1.6 Number of Addresses

One of the traditional ways of describing processor architecture is in terms of the number of addresses contained in each instruction. This dimension has become less significant with the increasing complexity of instruction set design. Nevertheless, it is useful at this point to draw and analyze this distinction.

What is the maximum number of addresses one might need in an instruction? Evidently, arithmetic and logic instructions will require the most operands. Virtually all arithmetic and logic operations are either unary (one operand) or binary (two operands). Thus we would need a maximum of two addresses to reference source operands. The result of an operation must be stored, suggesting a third address. Finally, after completion of an instruction, the next instruction must be fetched, and its address is needed.

The above line of reasoning suggests that an instruction could plausibly be required to contain four address references: two source operands, one result, and the address of the next instruction. In practice, four-address instructions are extremely rare. Most CPU's are of the one-, two-, or three-address variety, with the address of the next instruction being implicit (the next instruction in sequence).

Figure 1-3 compares typical one-, two-, and three-address instructions that could be used to compute $Y = (A - B) \div (C + D * E)$. With three addresses, each instruction specifies two operand locations and a result location. Because we would like to not alter the value of any of the operand locations, a temporary location, T, is used to store some intermediate results. Note that there are four instructions and that the original expression had four operands.

Three-address instruction formats are not common because they require a relatively long instruction format to hold the three address references. With two-address instructions, and for binary operations, one address must do double duty as both an operand and a result. Thus the instruction SUB Y, B carries out the calculation Y - B and stores the result in Y. The two-address format reduces the space requirement, but also introduces some awkwardness. To avoid altering the value of an operand, a MOVE instruction is used to move one of the values to a result or temporary location before performing the operation. Our sample program expands to six instructions.

Simpler yet is the one-address instruction. For this to work, a second address must be implicit. This was common in earlier machines, with the implied address being a CPU register known as the accumulator, or AC. The accumulator contains one of the operands and is used to store the result. In our example, eight instructions are needed to accomplish the task.

Instruction	Comment
SUB Y,A,B	$Y \leftarrow A - B$
MPY T,D,E	$T \leftarrow D \times E$
ADD T,T,C	$T \leftarrow T + C$
DIV Y,Y,T	$Y \leftarrow Y \div T$

(a) Three-Address Instructions

Instruction	Comment
MOVE Y,A	$Y \leftarrow A$
SUB Y,B	$Y \leftarrow Y - B$
MOVE T,D	$T \leftarrow D$
MPY T,E	$T \leftarrow T \times E$
ADD T,C	$T \leftarrow T + C$
DIV Y,T	$Y \leftarrow Y \div T$

(b) Two-Address Instructions

Instruction	Comment
LOAD D	$AC \leftarrow D$
MPY E	$AC \leftarrow AC \times E$
ADD C	$AC \leftarrow AC + C$
STOR Y	$Y \leftarrow AC$
LOAD A	$AC \leftarrow A$
SUB B	$AC \leftarrow AC - B$
DIV Y	$AC \leftarrow AC \div Y$
STOR Y	$Y \leftarrow AC$

(c) One-Address Instructions

Figure 1.3: Programs to Execute
$Y = (A - B) \div (C + D \times E)$

It is, in fact, possible to make do with zero addresses for some instructions. Zero-address instructions are applicable to a special memory organization, called a stack. A stack is a last-in first-out set of locations. The stack is in a known location and, often, at least the top two elements are in CPU registers. Thus zero-address instructions would reference the top two stack elements.

The number of addresses per instruction is a basic design decision. Fewer addresses per instruction results in more primitive instructions, which requires a less complex CPU. It also results in instructions of shorter length. On the other hand, with fewer addresses per instruction, programs contain more total instructions, which in general results in longer execution times and longer and more complex programs. Also, there is an important threshold between one-

Table 1.1: Basic Addressing Modes

Mode	Algorithm	Principal Advantage	Principal Disadvantage
Immediate	Operand = A	No Memory Reference	Limited Operand Magnitude
Direct	EA = A	Simple	Limited Address Space
Indirect	EA = (A)	Large Address Space	Multiple Memory References
Register	EA = R	No Memory Reference	Limited Address Space
Register Indirect	EA = (R)	Large Address Space	Extra Memory Reference
Displacement	EA = A + (R)	Flexibility	Complexity
Stack	EA = Top of Stack	No Memory Reference	Limited Applicability

address and multiple-address instructions. With one-address instructions, the programmer generally has available only one general-purpose register, the accumulator. With multiple-address instructions, it is common to have multiple general-purpose registers. This allows some operations to be performed solely on registers. Since register references are faster than memory references, this speeds up execution. For reasons of flexibility and ability to use multiple registers, most contemporary machines employ a mixture of two- and three-address instructions.

The design tradeoffs involved in choosing the number of addresses per instruction are complicated by other factors. There is the issue of whether an address references a memory location or a register. Since there are fewer registers, fewer bits are needed for a register reference. Also, as we shall see below, a machine may offer a variety of addressing modes, and the specification of mode takes one or more bits. The result is that most CPU designs involve a variety of instruction formats.

1.7 Addressing Modes

The address field or fields in a typical instruction format is quite limited. We would like to be able to reference a large range of locations in main memory or, for some systems, virtual memory. To achieve this objective, a variety of addressing techniques have been employed. They all involve some tradeoff between address range and/or addressing flexibility on the one hand and the number of memory references and/or the complexity of address calculation on the other.

Table 1.1 summarizes the most common addressing modes in use in various instruction sets. The table uses the following notation

A = contents of the (an) address field in the instruction

EA = actual (effective) address of the location containing the referenced operand

(X) = contents of location X

Briefly, the modes are

- *Immediate:* The operand is actually present in the instruction. This mode can be used to define and use constants or set initial values of variables.

- *Direct:* The address field in the instruction contains the effective address of the operand. This is a very simple form of addressing. Its limitation is that the size of memory (range of addresses) is limited by the length of the address field in the instruction.

- *Indirect:* Indirect addressing expands the range of addresses by having the address field refer to the address of a word in memory which in turn contains a full-length address of the operand. The disadvantage of this approach is that two memory accesses are required to access the operand.

- *Register:* The address field refers to a register. This saves time, since register access is faster than memory access, and also saves bits in the instruction format, since there are fewer registers than memory locations. However, because there are few registers, this technique has limited applicability.

- *Register Indirect:* The address field refers to a register that contains a full-length memory address of the operand. As with indirect, this mode provides for a large address range, yet it only requires one memory access.
- *Displacement:* In this mode, the effective address consists of the sum of the contents of a register plus a displacement value. The displacement value may be in another instruction address field or in another register. This powerful mode of addressing is used for a variety of functions, including segmentation of memory and indexing.
- *Stack:* The address is implicit and refers to the top of a stack. This is a useful but specialized mode.

To complete this discussion, two comments need to be made. First, virtually all instruction sets provide more than one of the addressing modes listed above. The question arises as to how the CPU can determine which address mode is being used in a particular instruction. Several approaches are taken. Often, different opcodes will use different addressing modes. Alternatively, one or more bits in the instruction format can be used as a *mode field*. The value of the mode field determines which addressing mode is to be used.

The second comment concerns the interpretation of the effective address (EA). In a system without virtual memory, the *effective address* will either be a main memory address or a register. In a virtual memory system, the effective address is a virtual address or a register. The actual mapping of a virtual address to a physical address is a function of the paging mechanism and is invisible to the programmer.

1.8 Instruction Formats

An instruction format defines the layout of the bits of an instruction, in terms of its constituent parts. An instruction format must include an opcode and, implicitly or explicitly, one or more operands. Each explicit operand is referenced by using one of the addressing modes described above. The format must, implicitly or explicitly, indicate the addressing mode for each operand. For most instruction sets, more than one instruction format is used.

The design of an instruction format is a complex art, and an amazing variety of designs have been implemented. In this section, we look at some of the key design issues.

1.8.1 Instruction Length

The most basic design issue to be faced is the instruction format length. This decision affects, and is affected by, memory size, memory organization, bus structure, CPU complexity, and CPU speed. This decision determines the richness and flexibility of the machine as seen by the assembly-language programmer.

The most obvious tradeoff here is between the desire for a powerful instruction repertoire versus a need to save space. Programmers want more opcodes, more operands, more addressing modes, and greater address range. More opcodes and more operands make life easier for the programmer, since shorter programs can be written to accomplish given tasks. Similarly, more addressing modes give the programmer greater flexibility in implementing certain functions, such as table manipulations and multiple-way branching. And, of course, with the increase in main memory size and the increasing use of virtual memory, programmers want to be able to address larger memory ranges. All of these things (opcodes, operands, addressing modes, address range) require bits and push in the direction of longer instruction lengths. But longer instruction length may be wasteful. A 32-bit instruction occupies twice the space of a 16-bit instruction, but is probably much less than twice as useful.

Beyond this basic tradeoff, there are other considerations. The instruction length should either be equal to the memory-transfer length (in a bus system, data-bus length) or one should be a multiple of the other. Otherwise, we will not get an integral number of instructions during the fetch cycle. A related consideration is the memory transfer rate. This rate has not kept up with increases in processor speed. Accordingly, memory can become a bottleneck if the processor can execute instructions faster than it can fetch them. One solution to this problem is the use of cache memory; another is to use shorter instructions. Again, 16-bit instructions can be fetched at twice the rate of 32-bit instructions, but probably can be executed less than twice as fast.

1.8.2 Allocation of Bits

We have looked at some of the factors that go into deciding the length of the instruction format. An equally difficult issue is how to allocate the bits in that format. The tradeoffs here are complex.

For a given instruction length, there is clearly a tradeoff between the number of opcodes and the power of the addressing capability. More opcodes obviously means more bits in the opcode field. For an instruction format of a given length, this reduces the number of bits available for addressing. There is one interesting refinement to this tradeoff, and that is the use of variable-length opcodes. In this approach, there is a minimum opcode length but, for some opcodes, additional operations may be specified by using additional bits in the instruction. For a fixed-length instruction, this leaves fewer bits for addressing. Thus this feature is used for those instructions that require fewer operands and/or less powerful addressing.

The following interrelated factors go into determining the allocation of bits for addressing

- *Number of addressing modes:* Sometimes, an address mode can be indicated implicitly. For example, certain opcodes might always call for indexing. In other cases, the address modes must be explicit, and one or more mode bits will be needed.
- *Number of operands:* Typical instructions on today's machines provide for two operands. Each operand ad-

dress in the instruction might require its own mode indicator, or the use of a mode indicator could be limited to just one of the address fields.

- *Register versus Memory:* A machine must have registers so that data can be brought into the CPU for processing. With a single user-visible register (usually called the accumulator), one operand address is implicit and consumes no instruction bits. However, single-register programming is awkward and requires many instructions. Even with multiple registers, only a few bits are needed to specify the register. The more that registers can be used for operand references, the fewer bits are needed. A number of studies indicate that a total of 8 to 32 user-visible registers is desirable [e.g., article by Lunde in this section].

- *Number of register sets:* A number of machines have one set of general-purpose registers, with typically 8 or 16 registers in the set. These registers can be used to store data and can be used to store addresses for displacement addressing. The trend recently has been away from one bank of general-purpose registers and toward a collection of two or more specialized sets (such as data and displacement). This trend shows up everywhere from single-chip microprocessors to supercomputers. One advantage of this approach is that, for a fixed number of registers, a functional split requires fewer bits to be used in the instruction. For example, with two sets of eight registers, a functional split requires fewer bits to be used in the instruction. For example, with two sets of eight registers, only three bits are required to identify a register; the opcode implicitly will determine which set of registers is being referenced. There seems to be little disadvantage to this approach [LUND77]. In systems such as the S/370, which has one set of general-purpose registers, programmers usually establish conventions that assign about half the registers to data and half to displacement and maintain a fixed assignment.

- *Address range:* For addresses that reference memory, the range of addresses that can be referenced is related to the number of address bits. Because this imposes a severe limitation, direct addressing is rarely used. With displacement addressing, the range if opened up to the length of the address register. Even so, it is still convenient to allow rather large displacements from the register address, which requires a relatively large number of address bits in the instruction.

- *Address granularity:* For addresses that reference memory rather than registers, another factor is the granularity of addressing. In a system with 16- or 32-bit words, the designer can choose that addresses reference a word or a byte. Byte addressing is convenient for character manipulation but requires, for a fixed-size memory, more address bits.

Thus the designer is faced with a host of factors to consider and balance.

1.9 Instruction Set Design

One of the most intersting, and most analyzed, aspects of computer design is instruction set design. The design of an instruction set is very complex, since it affects so many aspects of the computer system. The instruction set defines many of the functions performed by the CPU, and thus has a significant effect on the implementation of the CPU. The instruction set is the programmer's means of controlling the CPU. Thus, programmer requirements must be considered in designing the instruction set.

Some of the most fundamental issues relating to the design of instruction sets remain in dispute. Indeed, in recent years the level of disagreement concerning these fundamentals has actually grown. This dispute is at the core of the research and development effort on RISC design and the controversy that that effort has generated. In this section, we have examined a number of these design issues. To summarize, the most important of these fundamental design issues include

- *Operation repertoire:* How many and which operations to provide, and how complex operations should be.
- *Data types:* The various types of data upon which operations are performed.
- *Instruction format:* Instruction length (in bits), number of addresses, size of various fields, etc.
- *Registers:* Number of CPU registers that can be referenced by instructions, and their use.
- *Addressing:* The mode or modes by which the address of an operand is specified.

These issues are highly interrelated and must be considered together in designing an instruction set. In this tutorial, we will be examining the design choices made by those involved in the design of RISC machines.

1.10 Article Summary

The first article, "Understanding Execution Behavior of Software Systems," presents the case for an analysis of instruction execution characteristics as a guide to the design of new architectures.

Next, "The Nature of General-Purpose Computations" surveys virtually all of the studies on instruction execution characteristics that are relevant to processor design. The author summarizes the key results that lead to a RISC approach.

The final two articles are perhaps the two most important papers on the subject. They have been referenced widely not only in the RISC literature, but in works on computer architecture in general. Lunde examines a set of numeric-computation programs written in five different high-level languages (2 FORTRAN versions, BASIC, Algol, BLISS). Tanenbaum presents measurements, from over 300 procedures used in operating-system programs and written in a language (SAL) that supports structured programming.

Without an understanding of micro- and macro-execution behavior, potential benefits from enhancements of computer architectures will be lost. Models of execution behavior are needed to connect measurement to theory.

Understanding Execution Behavior of Software Systems

James C. Browne, University of Texas at Austin

Modern computer architectures are primarily designed on a basis of compatibility with past architectures, engineering convenience, and limited context analysis of the execution behavior of current architectures. Only the latter has much value for improving the effectiveness of new architectures. Microelectronics technology permits cost-effective implementation and thus permits designers to utilize data or products developed during recent research on the execution behavior of current architectures. Consequently, hardware designers can, with relative ease, implement tremendously complex architectures or simple architectures with greatly increased computational speeds. However, the designer needs sufficient knowledge of or data on the execution behavior of a new architecture to predict the effectiveness of innovations in instruction set design or data access mechanisms. For example, (1) proposed architectures on which operations on complex data objects can be performed are likely to be inefficient unless the architectures are well matched to the workload, and (2) proposed architectures using simple instruction sets will not succeed unless the operations being performed can span the requirements of higher level language systems and efficiently map complex data structures to the architecture.

Our hopes for more effective computer architectures motivate us to establish the foundation for their development. Our goals include

- more economical use of the components of the hardware system; that is, more deliverable computations per dollar invested in hardware;
- simplification of development and maintenance of compilers and other basic software elements; and
- high-level language programs that obtain a greater fraction of the potential execution power of a given architecture for a given problem.

Two major barriers limit the development of innovative and cost-effective architectures. First, architecture designers lack knowledge of the execution structure of programs on existing architectures. (The execution structure of a program is determined by the way the logical operations and data structures of the program are bound to the instruction set and by the type of data storage facilities implemented in the architecture.) Second, any new architecture will be commercially important only when a useful body of software for it is available. The cost and time required for the development of such software will surely greatly exceed the cost for the development of the architecture itself; in fact, longer than typical lags in software availability may result because of the possible need for establishing techniques for utilizing innovative developments in software. Therefore, we should expect only limited enthusiasm for any truly innovative architectures.

Improvements in software development technology are, however, lessening the time and effort for development of software for new architectures. Parser and compiler generator systems and the trend towards writing basic software in higher level languages have aided in reducing the problems just cited. The porting of Unix to many different architectures is a good example of improved portability—from a clean system structure implemented in a higher level language. There are, however, avenues for more direct, short time-delay applications of significant new concepts in architectures or instruction sets. For instance, many major architectures are at least partially founded on microcoding; therefore, new capabilities can be added through microcoding while retaining compatibility with all current capabilities. Also, special-purpose or dedicated function units can be added to bus-based architectures to quickly implement useful new functions in an existing architecture.

In this article, no single form of instruction set is promoted; nor is one side or the other supported in the controversy involving proponents of the reduced instruction

Reprinted from *Computer*, July 1984, pages 83–87. Copyright © 1984 by The Institute of Electrical and Electronics Engineers, Inc. All rights reserved.

set[1] versus the complex instruction sets[2] controversy (see Jensen's article[3]). Rather, it is essential to recognize that proposals for new architectures should be based on an in-depth knowledge of the execution patterns of a spectrum of significant computation structures. This article investigates models of computation that can guide both the experimental analysis of execution behavior and the design of new generations of architectures.

Models of computation, architectures, and execution behavior

An algorithm or a computation can be described in terms of the model of computation required for execution, while a computer architecture can be described by the model of computation it implements. The cost-effectiveness of an architecture for execution of an algorithm is heavily influenced by the mapping between the models of computation of the algorithm and the architecture. A model of computation is defined by specification of at least the following properties:

- The primitive units of computation;
- The rules for turning the primitive units of computation into computation structures;
- The rules for constructing address spaces in which the complex computation structures execute;
- The modes of synchronization of parallel executions; and
- The modes of communication between computation structures and their address spaces.

The primitive units of computation for an architecture are defined by the instruction set of the processor. An instruction expresses an operation on some data structure or tuples of data structures and the operators of most architectures—arithmetic and logic—are applied to tuples of scalars or vectors of operands.

The common rule for turning primitive operations (instructions) into logical computation structures is to apply a stream of instructions—in some sequence which will usually be data dependent—to some set of basic storage units such as words or bytes. Parallel architectures may simultaneously process parallel streams of data and/or instructions.

An address space is the set of information (program and data) reachable by a composed unit of computation. It is determined in most computations by the specification of the set of memory cells that the currently executing instruction stream can address.

Synchronization is a concept brought into models of computation by the use of parallel instruction streams to execute a single logical computation. These instruction streams must often be executed in a specific sequence in order to implement the computation.

Communication mechanisms move information between the address spaces associated with distinct instruction streams: either the serially occurring instruction streams of sequential computation or the concurrently executing instruction streams of parallel computation structures.

Fundamental questions regarding the features of any architecture are "Which operators and operands should be selected and what are their capabilities for accessing memory in logical patterns?" To answer these questions requires that we first notice the relationship between operations, memory, and data structures; their interrelationship is determined by the time and mode of binding a computation structure to a sequence of elementary operations and a set of memory cells. Current conventional architectures bind structure to operators, at both compile time and execution time, by inserting data movement instructions between primitive instructions to do such things as map implicitly stored structures to registers. An object-based architecture such as a vector processor binds structures to operands in memory when the object is loaded in memory. This early binding is necessary to obtain the predictable behavior on which successful vector streaming operations depend.

Current architectures and research issues

Most current architectures execute their operations based on operands held in registers. Operand registers—in essence, caches for functional units—are introduced into the architectures because logic is faster than memory. The registers tend to limit the range of data structures to which operations can be applied, however, because they typically have simple structures. This limitation may be overcome by microelectronics, particularly by incorporating very large register sets into processor architectures. Programmers (and compilers) can then explicitly compose complex computations based on data held in fast registers.

Registers have a major impact on the instruction set of a processor. Instruction counts are strongly influenced by the movement of data structures between registers and memory. Instruction counts for register-oriented architectures are also skewed by sequence control and counter management instructions, which result from the mapping of complex data structures to operations on scalar registers. The logical structure of the computations executed on register-oriented machines may be obscured by the volume of register operations in instruction traces, unless the effects of the register operations are carefully characterized.

Composition sequencing rules determine how code for operations on complex structures will be produced from the code for the same operation on simple or scalar systems architectures. The composition rules and resulting execution structures could be simplified if instructions and high-level languages could be introduced into architectures to allow execution against objects closer to the object types of algorithms. There are several avenues of approach. One is to extend the application of operators to complex, conformable structures. Another is to introduce data structures into the architecture, then implement appropriate, preferably simple operations for execution against these data structures. In short, since faster execution will be attained only if the mapping between the operations of the algorithm and architectures are effective, analysis of algorithms and architectures on the same basis is very important. The direct-execution Lisp machines[4] testify to the results of an effective match of architecture to computations.

Synchronization among instruction streams depends on the characteristics of the units of computation and the data structures against which they are defined. However, though operating system[5] and database researchers have developed a large number of constructs for synchronization, there has been little systematic study of the effectiveness of mechanisms for coordination of computation structures with a variety of characteristics.

Communication among units of computation is commonly recognized as a concern only for parallel models of execution. Even in serial computation structures, however, the results from one operation on a tuple of operands must be made available (and sometimes reformatted) for the next sequenced or composed operation, a procedure that may involve movements among registers or storing in data structures held in memory. Communication between logical units of computation which execute in different address contexts also engenders execution costs. Reliable software isolates the address spaces of logical units of computation, so execution sequences at this level require either multiple bindings of addresses to names or the movement of values between address spaces. The communication costs of procedure calls can be a substantial fraction of the execution cost for highly modular programs.

An instruction set should provide clean and simple links between its instructions and the stream of control. A requirement for register shuffling or excessive storing and fetching from memory between computational or logical instructions can run up instruction counts to complete a logical unit of computation. Most data movement in sequential computation is caused by the need to compose operations on logical operands from operations on scalars.

A programming language also implements some spectrum of models of computation. Perhaps even more important than the links between the models of computation of algorithms and architectures are those between the models of computations of algorithms and programming languages, and those between programming languages and architectures. Since direct mapping from algorithms to architectures (assembly language programming) is rare, the representations of the models of computations of algorithms are realized in a programming language representation, which is actually executed on an architecture. This situation is sketched in Figure 1.

Analysis of previous research

The approach common in previous research is to analyze the execution of actual programs on existing architectures, then extrapolate from this information. Industry uses this approach to improve the effectiveness of instruction sets across generations of similar processors. Analysis involves counts of instruction frequency both by static occurrence in codes and dynamic occurrence in code execution sequences, as well as architecture dependent searches for patterns such as increment index and store. There are numerous papers and technical reports reporting

the results of such analyses. They often provide insights into execution patterns at a micro-level for a specific architecture, but they seldom relate the observations to the characteristics of the algorithms being executed, or apply the measurements to more abstract models of computation, or assess execution behavior on alternate architectures. The enhancement of operating system performance in the IBM 370 architecture is an obvious success of this approach.

Numerous recent projects in universities have also provided architectures with careful micro-level design, for instance, the MIPS project at Stanford.[6] Major industrial projects have also generated architectures based on detailed micro-level analyses. These include the 801 project at IBM[7] and the Bellmac project at Bell Laboratories.[8]

It is also appropriate to mention the research focused on major issues in models of computation: the Intel-432[9] and the Bellmac, which integrates data structures and instructions for implementation of processes. In addition, Lampson provides an example of a macro-level problem followed by modeling analysis and implementation design.[10]

An important omission in most of these studies has been analysis of patterns of access to memory. This omission has delayed extending analyses to more abstract models of computation. For example, it is difficult to define effective, complex memory structures without knowledge of the access of patterns of reference to data. It has been impossible to predict the behavior on significantly different architectures. There are exceptions, of course, in the work of Davidson and his students,[11,12] Batson and his students,[13] J. E. Smith,[14] and Cook and Donde.[15] The analysis of reference string behavior for support of virtualization of paged memory architectures is, of course, a notable body of experimental literature which is too large to detail here. The work on locality patterns and cache design is another significant body of work.[16]

Goals and directions for future research

Research in architecture should be structured by the scientific approach of constructing models, designing ex-

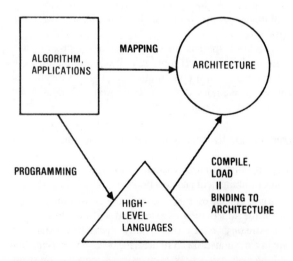

Figure 1. The interrelationships of models of computation.

periments, and measuring in well-understood environments with feedback into new models and experiments. Measurements have frequently been made without the beneficial structuring of models, and they are rarely compared to similar measurements on other architectures. More insight will result from analysis of models of execution behavior at a more macro-level than the instruction level of current-day architecture. There also remains a need for more consideration of the elements that comprise models of computation. Studies of execution of compiler-generated code seldom include implementation of protection structures and vice versa.

It is worthwhile to consider more sophisticated analyses of instruction-level data. A substantial set of analytical tools for determining the properties of graphs, and subgraphs constructed according to various algorithms, and direct construction of graph partitions of specified properties serve as a point of departure. A graph where the nodes represent application of primitive instructions to elementary data structures and the arcs are flow of control may represent a logical unit of computation. Analysis of commonly occurring or logically coherent sequences should reveal the logical elements of the computation. Then conversion of instruction streams to graph models, each representing a computation in terms of primitive computations and data movement in a given architecture, may suggest new instructions or define new data or memory structures.

Complementary research on real architectures could involve execution of abstract algorithms or representations of computations on paper architectures implementing interesting occurrences of significant models of computation. Since the computer industry encourages researchers to establish valid gate-level and micro-level architectures, why not support a similar thrust in the design of macro architectures?

Another major focus might be the organizational structures of modern software development and the increasing need for reliable, robust systems. Defining and maintaining separate address spaces for logical units of computation is a major problem which is neither well characterized nor well explored. For example, architectural suport for an access-list-based protection scheme has not been seriously discussed in the literature, although capability-based architectures have been extensively explored. [17]

Likewise the interaction among architectures, high-level languages, and their compilers is an interesting problem that has already received a great deal of attention. Wulf lists a set of principles for efficiently supporting higher level languages. [18] Still remaining to resolve are the differences between execution patterns for identical computations when the programs are prepared and compiled in different high-level language systems. A comparison might be made of the instruction sequences arising from execution of the same algorithm programmed in one language system using static memory allocation and the other using dynamic memory allocation. Interesting results should also come from a comparison between languages with rich data structuring and with limited data declarational power for their efficiency to execution of operations on complex data structures. The results might

resemble the RISC/CISC analyses, but at a slightly higher level of abstraction.

Other areas of controversy are the interactions between translation techniques for higher level languages and the conceptual gaps between the models of computation specified in high-level languages on the one hand, and those realized in architectures, on the other. The RISC approach argues for increasing the conceptual distance while simplifying the interface. The CISC approach argues for decreasing the conceptual gap while making the interface more complicated. Experiments on translation to the two targets are needed.

I/O architecture is likewise an area hardly touched in previous measurements. What, for example, is the pattern of use of data transferred to executable memories in fixed size pages?

The increasing representational power of microelectronic devices opens opportunities for innovations in architecture, which can lead to much more cost-effective, reliable, and easy-to-use computer systems. Progress must, however, be founded on an in-depth knowledge of the logical execution patterns of a spectrum of significant algorithms on realized and realizable computation architectures. Ultimately it can be the basis for design of more effective computer architectures. *

Acknowledgments

This research was sponsored in part by the Department of Energy (under grant DE-AS05-81-ER10987) and by the National Science Foundation (under grant MCS-8116099).

References

1. D. A. Patterson and C. H. Seguin, "RISC-I: A Reduced Instruction SET VLSI Computer," *Proc. Eighth Annual Symp. on Computer Architectures,* May 1981, pp. 443-458.

2. D. W. Clark and W. D. Strecker, "Comments on the Case for the Reduced Instruction Set Computer," *Computer Architecture News,* Aug. 1980, pp. 34-38.

3. E. D. Jensen, R. P. Colwell, and C. Y. Hitchcock, "Peering Through the RISC/CISC Fog," *Computer Architecture News,* Nov. 1982.

4. D. Weinreb and D. Moon, *LISP Machine Manual,* Symbolics Inc., Cambridge, Mass., 1981.

5. J. Bloom, "Evaluating Synchronization Primitives," *Proc. Seventh Symp. Operating Systems Princicples,* 1979, pp. 24-32.

6. J. Hennessy et. al, "Hardware/Software Tradeoffs for Increased Performance," *Proc. Symp. on Architectural Support for Programming Languages and Operating Systems,* Mar. 1982, pp. 2-11.

7. G. Radin, "The 801 Minicomputer," *Proc. Symp. Architectural Support for Programming Languages and Operating Systems,* Mar. 1982, pp. 39-47.

8. A. Berenbaum, M. Condry, and P. Lu, "The Operating System and Language Support Features of the BELL-MAC-32," *Proc. Symp. Architectural Support for Programming Languages and Operating Systems,* Mar. 1982, pp. 30-38.

9. J. Rattner and G. Cox, "Object-Based Computer Architectures," *Computer Architecture News,* Aug. 1980, pp. 4-11.

10. B. W. Lampson, "Fast Procedure Calls," *Proc. Symp. Architectural Support for Programming Languages and Operating Systems,* Mar. 1982, pp. 66-76.

11. D. W. Hammerstrom and E. S. Davidson, "Information Content of CPU Memory Referencing Behavior," *Fourth Annual Symp. Computer Architectures,* Mar. 1977, pp. 184-192.

12. A. R. Pleszkun and E. S. Davidson, "Structured Memory Access Architecture," *Proc. Int'l Conf. Parallel Processing,* Aug. 1983, pp. 461-471.

13. A. W. Madison and A. P. Batson, "Characteristics of Program Localities," *Comm. ACM,* Vol. 18, 1975, pp. 285-294.

14. "Decoupled Access/Execute Computer Architectures," *Proc. Ninth Annual Symp. on Computer Architecture,* 1982, pp. 112-119.

15. R. P. Cook and N. Donde, "An Experiment to Improve Operand Addressing," *Proc. Symp. on Architectural Support for Programming Languages and Operating Systems,* Mar. 1982, pp. 87-95.

16. A. J. Smith, "Cache Memories," *Computing Surveys 14,* 1982, pp. 473-530.

17. M. V. Wilkes, "Hardware Support for Memory Protection," *Proc. Symp. on Architectural Support for Programming Languages and Operating Systems,* Mar. 1982, pp. 107-116.

18. W. A. Wulf, "Compilers and Computer Architecture," *Computer,* Vol. 14, No. 7, July 1981, pp. 41-47.

James C. Browne received a BA degree from Hendrix College, Conway, Arkansas, in 1956 and a PhD in physical chemistry from the University of Texas at Austin in 1960. From 1960 to 1964, he was an assistant professor of physics, University of Texas at Austin, carrying out quantum mechanical calculations of small molecules, and research and development work on operating systems. From 1964 to 1965, he was an NSF postdoctoral fellow at Queen's University of Belfast, Northern Ireland, and from 1965 to 1968, professor of computer science and director of the computation laboratory at Queen's University. In 1968, he returned to the University of Texas at Austin as professor of computer science and physics, and served as chairman of the Dept. of Computer Sciences. His research interests include operating systems, systems modeling and design, performance evaluation of computer systems, and parallel computing. He is a fellow of the American Physical Society and the British Computer Society, and a member of the Association of Computing Machinery. He can be contacted at the Dept. of Computer Sciences, University of Texas, Austin, TX 78712.

The Nature
of General-Purpose Computations

In the design of a computer system, two issues must be studied carefully:

(1) FUNCTION: What is the purpose of the computer system? What is the nature of the computations it will perform? What are the necessary features that will enable it to perform those computations with high efficiency?

(2) COST: Can the desirable architectural features be implemented at a reasonable cost and with a reasonable performance, in a particular technology? What are the trade-offs imposed by the constraints of a given implementation technology?

This chapter focuses on the first question of what it is that computer systems usually do, leaving the bulk of the discussion on implementation issues for the next chapters. We are interested in "general-purpose computer systems". Although it is difficult to define this term, we use it to refer to systems not biased towards the execution of a particular algorithm, and, specifically, systems that execute a mix of word processing, data base applications, mail and communications, compilations, CAD, control, and numerical applications. The chapter will assemble a picture of the nature of such "general-purpose" computations, by collecting program measurements from the literature, and by studying the critical loops of some representative programs. The resulting picture will be used in the next chapters.

2.1   Goal and Methods of Program Measurement

The main vehicle for a qualitative and quantitative understanding of the nature of computations is the measurement of the important properties on some real programs. It is very difficult for such a study to be made *abstractly* -- not in connection with a particular model of computers and computations, because real programs and programming languages *are* written and defined with a particular model in mind, and because the properties to be measured depend on this model.

Throughout this dissertation, a *von Neumann model* of computers and computations is assumed. Programs written in corresponding languages are considered in this chapter. C and FORTRAN program fragments are studied, and measurements from the literature are reported, which were collected by looking at programs written in FORTRAN, XPL, PL/I, Algol, Pascal, C, BLISS, Basic, and SAL. This section identifies the main properties of computations which are important in the design of von Neumann architectures, and lists tools and methods for their measurement.

2.1.1 Architecturally Important Properties of Computations

In the von Neumann model, computations are performed by sequentially executing operations on operands which are kept in a storage device. The sequence of

Reprinted with permission from *Reduced Instruction Set Computer Architectures for VLSI*, edited by M. Katevenis, 1985, pages 9–41, Copyright © 1985 by MIT Press.

operations is dynamically controlled by operand values. Thus, the properties of computations that will interest us are:

- **Operands used.** Their type, size, structure, and the nature of their usage determines the storage organization for keeping them and the addressing modes for accessing them. In particular:

  - Constant or variable operands.
  - Types of operands: integers, floating-point, characters, pointers.
  - Structure of operands: scalars, arrays, strings, structures of records.
  - Declaration of operands: globals, procedure arguments, procedure locals.
  - Number of operands, sizes, and frequency of accesses for the above categories.
  - Amount and nature of locality-of-reference, possibly determined individually for each one of the above categories, for example, for scalars, arrays, (dynamic) structures, globals, and procedure activation records.

- **Operations performed.** These will determine the required operational units, and their connection to the storage units. The relative frequency of operations such as the ones listed below is important, and the variation of those frequencies with the operands' categories is also of interest.

  - Test, compare, add, subtract, multiply, divide, and so on.
  - Operation type, such as integer, floating-point, or string.
  - Higher level operations, such as I/O, buffer, list, and so forth.

- **Execution sequencing.** This will determine the control and pipeline organization:

  - Control transfers: conditional/unconditional jumps, calls, returns. What is their frequency, distance, conditions, predictability, and earliness of condition resolution.
  - Amount and nature of extractable parallelism. This is a very general and important question; for von Neumann architectures, we are interested in low-level parallelism.

While quantitative measurements are essential, the large number of properties to be measured -- especially if correlation among them is also studied -- makes a qualitative understanding of the global picture equally important. Methods for both kinds of analysis are presented below.

2.1.2 Static and Dynamic Measurements

Program measurements are usually collected by running the program under study through a suitable filter, or by executing it in a suitable environment. In both cases the result of this processing is a count of the numbers of times that some feature has appeared or that some particular property has held true in the text of the program or in its execution.

Measurements referring to the text of a program are called static. They give no useful information on performance, because they are not weighted relative to the number of times each statement was executed. They can show the size of storage required for the machine code and for the statically allocated objects, and they can show what the compiler has to deal with. Under crude assumptions, the static characteristics of programs can also give some indication on their dynamic behaviour.

Measurements referring to the execution of a program are called dynamic. Execution of the program requires previous compilation into object code for some machine, except if expensive interpretation is used. Thus, dynamic measurements usually refer to machine rather than source code, introducing another - often unwanted - parameter into the study. Machine code can be correlated back to source code, so that dynamic measurements at the source level can be inferred. However, this correlation is not always easy or precise.

Static and dynamic program measurements have frequently appeared in the literature, and have also been collected early in the RISC project (spring 1980). Section 2.2 reviews some of them.

2.1.3 Source-Code Profiling and Studying

Because the list of important properties of computations is very long, and because several of them are difficult to quantify or to measure, the static and dynamic program measurements have some limitations. There is another method of looking at the nature of computations which is less quantitative but more qualitative, and which can complement these measurements or give a better idea of what specific other measurements should be taken. That method is to carefully study the source code of a program and, if possible, the underlying algorithms, concentrating on those portions of it which account for most of the execution time.

It has been observed, time and again, that programs spend most of their execution time in small portions of their code, the so-called "critical loops". This makes it feasible and worthwhile to study those portions in detail, to understand the nature and properties of the computation that is carried out. The critical loops can be identified by profiling the program during execution. Profiling is the dynamic measurement of how much of the execution "cost" is spent at each place in the program's code. The "cost" may be:

- time spent,
- number of source-code lines executed,
- number of memory accesses, and so forth.

In section 2.3 we will study some critical loops that have been identified by other researchers. Section 2.4 studies some more critical loops, which were identified by this author using two profiling systems. The first was the standard profiling facility of UNIX: compilation using the -p or -pg switch, execution, and then interpretation of the results by the prof or gprof program. This method arranges that the program-counter of an executing process be sampled at "random" intervals (on clock interrupts, every 1/60th of a second). The sampled value is used to determine which procedure was executing at that time. If a program runs for a long time, the above samples can be used to construct estimates of how much time was spent in each of the program's procedures. There is no straightforward way to find out the time spent in executing any smaller program portions.

The second profiling system that was used, for programs written in C, belongs to Bell Laboratories (Murray Hill), and was used under special authorization [Wein]. It counts the number of times that each source-code line is executed (but gives no indication as to how long its execution takes). A special version of the C compiler is used, which inserts code at appropriate locations to increment appropriate counters. At the end of execution the counts are saved in a file. Another program is then invoked to correlate those counts with the original source code, and to generate an annotated program listing †.

2.2   Review of some Program Measurements from the Literature

In this section interesting program measurements from the literature are reviewed. Measurements on all properties mentioned in section 2.1.1 are not present here, because some of them either have not received enough attention in the literature, or were difficult to measure. The measurements were selected from:

[AlWo75]: Alexander and Wortman collected static and dynamic measurements from 19 programs (mostly compilers), written in XPL and executed on the IBM/360 architecture.

[Elsh76]: Elshoff presented static measurements of 120 commercial, production PL/I programs for business data processing.

[HaKe80],

[TaSe83]: Halbert and Kessler, in their study of multiple overlapping windows early during the RISC project, collected dynamic measurements on the number of arguments and local scalars per procedure, and on the locality property of procedure-nesting-depth. They measured the C compiler, the Pascal interpreter, the troff typesetter, and 6 other smaller non-numeric programs (all written in C). Tamir and Séquin collected some more dynamic data on the locality of nesting depth, measuring the RISC C compiler, the towers-of-Hanoi program, and the Puzzle program (all written in C).

[Lund77]: Lunde used the concept of "register-lives" in his measurements. He analyzed half a dozen numeric-computation programs written in 5 different HLL's (2 FORTRAN versions, Basic, Algol, BLISS), plus some compilers, all running on a DECsystem10 architecture.

[Shus78]: Shustek studied the usage made of the PDP-11 addressing modes, by statically measuring 10,000 lines of code of an operating system.

[PaSe82]: Patterson and Séquin presented the most important measurements collected during the early stages of the RISC project, in spring 1980,

---

† the count is not always what one would expect for lines like: " } else { ". The listings in section 2.4 have been corrected by hand in those situations.

in collaboration with E. Cohen and N. Soiffer. Measurements are dynamic, and were collected from compilers, typesetters, and programs for CAD, sorting, and file comparison. Four of those were written in C, and the other four in Pascal.

[Tane78]: Tanenbaum published static and dynamic measurements of HLL constructs, collected from more than 300 procedures used in operating-system programs and written in a language that supports structured programming (SAL).

2.2.1 Measurements on Operations

The operations performed by programs are the most frequent object of measurement, in the form of statement types (source level) or opcodes (machine level). The following tables summarize such measurements.

Property:	Measurement:	Reference:
Dynamically executed instructions:		
moves between registers and memory	40 %	[Lund77,p.149]
branching instructions	30 %	(numeric &
fixed-point add/sub's	12 %	compilers)
load, load address	33 %	[AlWo75]
(more than normal, due to 360 archit.)		(mostly compil.
store	10 %	in XPL
branch	14 %	on IBM/360)
compare	6 %	
Statically counted HLL statements:		
assignments	42 %	[AlWo75]
if	13 %	(mostly compil.
call	13 %	in XPL)
Dynamically executed HLL statements:		
assignments	42 ± 12 %	[PaSe82]
if	36 ± 15 %	(non-numeric,
call/return	14 ± 4 %	in C & Pascal)
loops	4 ± 3 %	
....weighted with the number of machine instructions executed for each:		
loops	37 ± 5 %	[PaSe82]
call/return	32 ± 12 %	(non-numeric,
if	16 ± 7 %	in C & Pascal)
assign	13 ± 4 %	
....weighted with the number of memory accesses necessary for each:		
call/return	45 ± 16 %	[PaSe82]
loops	30 ± 4 %	(non-numeric,
assign	15 ± 5 %	in C & Pascal)
if	10 ± 4 %	

More on procedure calls:

procedure calls as percentage of dynamically executed HLL statm.	12 %	[Tane78] (O.S., structured pr.)
procedure call administration as percentage of execution time	25 %	[Lund77,p.151] (BLISS compiler)
an amazing exception case:		[Elsh76] (PL/I business prog., static)
procedures def. within 100 K statm.	83 (only!)	
perc. of calls relative to all statem.	2 % (!)	

Other frequent high-level operations:

• vector operations (inner product, move, sum, search,...)	[Lund77]
• character-string ops (table-controlled substitute, delete, branch)	
• loop control (incr. a reg., compare it to another reg., and branch)	

Jump distance, measured dynamically:

< 128 bytes	55 %	[AlWo75]
< 16 Kbytes	93 %	

Jump conditions, measured dynamically:

unconditional jumps as % of all jumps	55 %	[AlWo75]
..."the comparison of two non-zero values is about twice as common as compr. with zero".		[Lund77]

Expressions, register lives:

one-term expressions in assignments†	66 %	[Tane78]
two-term expressions in assignments†	20 %	(dynamic)
operators per expression (average)	0.76	[AlWo75](st)
relative to all register lives:		
lives w. no arithm. performed on them	50% (20-90%)	[Lund77]
lives w. max†† integer add/sub on them	25% (1-70%)	(dynamic,
lives w. max†† integer mult/div on them	5% (2-20%)	numeric &
lives used in floating-point operations	15% (0-40%)	compilers)
lives used for indexing	40% (20-70%)	[Lund77]

† on the right-hand-side of assignments.

†† "maximum-complexity" operation performed on the register,
    where int-add/sub < int-mult/div < floating-point-op.

These measurements are not very helpful in understanding the high-level nature of computations, but they do show:

- The importance of the procedure call mechanism, since so much time is spent in it.

- The importance of the sequencing control mechanism (compare and branch), since loops and if's are so frequent.

- The importance of simple arithmetic and of addressing, accessing, and moving operands around, since expressions are usually very short, and since half of the operands appearing in registers ("register lives" in [Lund77]) have no arithmetic performed on them.

2.2.2 Measurements on Operands

Measurements on the operands in programs have not been so frequent in the literature, even though this subject is very important. Lunde [Lund77] measured on a DECsystem10 that each instruction on the average references 0.5 operands in memory and 1.4 in registers dynamically. These figures depend highly on the architecture and on the compiler, but they do illustrate, nevertheless, the importance of fast operand accessing, since that occurs so frequently.

Property:	Measurement:	Reference:
Dynamic percentage of operands (HLL):		
integer constants	20 ± 7 %	[PaSe82]
scalars	55 ± 11 %	(non-numeric,
array/structure	25 ± 14 %	in C & Pascal)
local-scalar references as percentage of all scalar references	> 80 %	[PaSe82]
global-array/structure references as percentage of all arr/str. references	> 90 %	[PaSe82]
Use of PDP-11 addressing modes:		
"The 4 most common modes are perhaps the 4 simplest":		[Shus78]
register	32 %	(static,
indexed (e.g. for fields of structures)	17 %	O.S.)
immediate (constants)	15 %	
PC-relative (direct addressing)	11 %	
all others	25 %	
"The 4 least-used modes are precisely the 4 memory indirect ones (1%)".		
"Half of the move instr. had a register as their dest."		[Shus78]
"Half of the compare/add/subtract instructions had one of their operands be an immediate"		

A property that had attracted very little attention in the past is the high locality of references to local scalar variables. The figures from [PaSe82] given above show that over half of the accesses to non-constant values are made to local scalars. On top of that, references to arrays/structures require a previous reference to their index or pointer, which is again a - usually local - scalar. Most of the time, the number of local scalars per procedure is small.

Tanenbaum [Tane78] found that 98 % of the dynamically called procedures had less than 6 arguments, and that 92 % of them had less than 6 local scalar variables. Similar numbers were found by Halbert and Kessler:

Procedure Activation Records: [HaKe80] Percentage of executed procedure calls with:		
	compiler, interpr. and typesetter	other smaller programs (non-numer.)
> 3 arguments	0 to 7 %	0 to 5 %
> 5 arguments	0 to 3 %	0 %
> 8 words of arg's & locals	1 to 20 %	0 to 6 %
> 12 words of arg's & locals	1 to 6 %	0 to 3 %

Thus, the number of words per procedure activation is not large. The following measurements show that the number of procedure activations touched during a reasonable time span is not large either. This establishes the locality-of-reference property for local scalars.

Locality of Procedure Nesting Depth: [HaKe80] [TaSe83] Percentage of executed procedure calls which overflow from last span of nesting depths:		
(assuming that the span of nesting depths has constant size, and that its position moves by one on every over/under-flow; this corresponds to a RISC register file with as many windows as the span size, and with no window reserved for interrupts. See section 3.2).		
	2 compilers, interpr. typesetter, Hanoi	6+1 other smaller programs (non-numeric)
span sz = 4 (4 wind.)	8 to 15 %	0 to 2.5 %
span sz = 8 (8 wind.)	1 to 3 %	0 to 0.2 %

2.3 Study of some Critical FORTRAN Loops (collected mostly by Knuth)

Knuth, in [Knut71], presents a study of where FORTRAN programs spend most of their time. The programs he measured varied from text-editing to scientific number-crunching programs. Dynamic measurements of the HLL statements executed showed that:

- 67% were assignments,
- one third of those assignments were of the type A=B,
- 11% were IF, 9% were GOTO, 3% were DO,
- 3% were CALL, and 3% were RETURN,
- More than 25% of the execution time was spent in I/O formatting.

However, what is most interesting for our study is that he gives the actual code fragments where 17 of those programs (chosen at random) spent most of their time. He used those fragments ("examples") to test the effectiveness of various techniques for optimization of compiled code. We will briefly study those same examples from our point of interest: understanding the nature of computations, and in particular answering the questions of section 2.1.1. The 17 examples have been classified in three categories of array-numeric, array-searching, and miscellaneous style examples. Their code (or a summary of it) is given below in a modernized-FORTRAN format. An eighteenth example of a critical loop, collected by the author of this dissertation, was added to the first category. It is the main loop of a procedure that inverts a positive-definite symmetric matrix. It was included in the study after two researchers in structural mechanics and in fluid dynamics independently told this author that they felt matrix inversion was the most time-consuming computation done by people in their area.

2.3.1 "Array-Numeric" Style Examples

Example 3:
```
double A, B, D
do 1 k=1,N
1   A = T[I-k, 1+k] ;  B = T[I-k, J+k] ;  D = D - A*B
```

Example 7:
```
do 1 i=1,N
    A = X**2 + Y**2 - 2.*X*Y*C[i]
1   B = SQRT(A) ;  K = 100.*B+1.5 ;  D[i] = S[i]*T[K]
    Q = D[1] - D[N]
    do 2 i=2,M,2
2   Q = Q + 4.*D[i] + 2.*D[i+1]
```

Example 9:
```
do 2 k=1,M
do 2 j=1,M
initialize...
do 1 i=1,M
    N = j + j + (i-1)*M2 ;  B = A[k,i]
1   X = X + B*Z[N] ;  Y = Y + B*Z[N-1]
2 more computations...
```

Example 11: a Fast Fourier Transform. It computes sums and products of floating-point elements of two linear arrays. One array is those same examples from our point of interest: understanding the nature of computations, and in particular answering the questions of section 2.1.1. The 17 examples have been classified in three categories of array-numeric, array-searching, and miscellaneous style examples. Their code (or a summary of it) is given below in a modernized-FORTRAN format. An eighteenth example of a critical loop, collected by the author of this dissertation, was added to the first category. It is the main loop of a procedure that inverts a positive-definite symmetric matrix. It was included in the study after two researchers in structural mechanics and in fluid dynamics independently told this author that they felt matrix inversion was the most time-consuming computation done by people in their area.

2.3.1 "Array-Numeric" Style Examples

Example 3:
```
double A, B, D
do 1 k=1,N
1   A = T[I-k, 1+k] ;  B = T[I-k, J+k] ;  D = D - A*B
```

Example 7:
```
do 1 i=1,N
    A = X**2 + Y**2 - 2.*X*Y*C[i]
1   B = SQRT(A) ;  K = 100.*B+1.5 ;  D[i] = S[i]*T[K]
    Q = D[1] - D[N]
    do 2 i=2,M,2
2   Q = Q + 4.*D[i] + 2.*D[i+1]
```

Example 9:
```
        do 2 k=1,M
        do 2 j=1,M
        initialize...
        do 1 i=1,M
          N = j + j + (i-1)*M2 ;  B = A[k,i]
1         X = X + B*Z[N] ;  Y = Y + B*Z[N-1]
2       more computations...
```

Example 11:   a Fast Fourier Transform. It computes sums and products of floating-point elements of two linear arrays. One array is accessed sequentially, and the other one with a step of N.

Example 12:   a very long inner loop, with counter arithmetic, array accesses (many 3-dimensional arrays, some 2- and 1- dimensional), and floating-point multiplications and additions. There is one expression with 32 operators! In spite of its heavy computation character, this program has no more floating-point operations than it has simple counter and index operations.

Example 15:
```
        do 1 j=i,N
          H[i,j] = H[i,j] + S[i]*S[j]/D1 - S[k+i]*S[k+j]/D2
1         H[j,i] = H[i,j]
```

Example 17:
```
        do 1 i=1,N
1         A = A + B[i] + C[k+i]
```

Example - Matrix Inversion:
Figure 2.3.1 shows the aforementioned critical loop of positive-definite symmetric matrix inversion, in an abstract flow-chart form.

All these critical loops are of the same style: They perform floating-point operations on elements of arrays. Two almost independent "processes" exist. First, array elements are accessed in a *regular* fashion, i.e. in an arithmetic progression of memory addresses; the loop control is related to the array indexes, and does not depend on the array data. The second "process" is that of doing the actual numerical data computations.

2.3.2 "Array-Searching" Style Examples

Example 1:   a search for the maximum of the absolute values:
```
        do 2 j=1,N
          t = ABS( A[i,j] ) ;  if (t>s) then s=t ;
2       continue
```

Example 2:   a search for a match:
```
        do 1 j=38,53
          if (K[i]==L[j]) then goto 2
1       continue
```

Example 10:
```
        do 1 i=L,M
1         if ( X[i-1,j] < Q  and  X[i,j] ≥ Q ) then rare
```

22

Example 13:   a binary search:
    1 j = (i+k)/2
     if (j==i) then goto 2
     if (X[j] == XKEY) then goto 3
     if (X[j] < XKEY) then i=j else k=j
     goto 1

These examples are non-numeric. Most of them access the array(s) in a regular manner, like the examples in 2.3.1. However, the control of their sequencing is *dynamic* in nature: it depends on the actual data being visited, rather than on regularly incremented counters.

2.3.3 "Miscellaneous" Style Examples

Example 4: first a poor quality random-number generator is defined:
    subroutine RAND(R)
    j = i * 65539
    if (j<0) then j = j + 2147483647 + 1
    R = j ; R = R * 0.4656613e-9
    i = j ; k = k+1 ; return
  then it is called:
    do 1 k=M,20
     call RAND(R)
   1 if (R > 0.81) then N[k] = 1
  Knuth comments: "...the most interesting thing here, however, is the effect of subroutine linkage, since the long prologue and epilogue significantly increase the time of the inner loop".

Example 5: this is a long inner loop that does lots of floating-point computations. It contains some simple arithmetic and compare & branch operations on integer counters, sequential addressing of two linear arrays, and several floating-point exponentiations, multiplications, and additions. The loop is badly written, with many large common subexpressions. There is lots of low-level parallelism present, mainly among the floating-point computations, but also between them and the integer ones.

Example 6: a subroutine S is defined:
    subroutine S(A,B,X)
    dimension A[2], B[2]
    X=0 ; Y = (B[2]-A[2])*12 + B[1] - A[1]
    if (Y<0) then goto 1
    X=Y
   1 return
  then W is defined, which is called multiple times, and which calls S:
    subroutine W(A,B,C,D,X)
    dimension A[2], B[2], C[2], D[2], U[2], V[2]
    X=0 ; call S(A,D,X) ; if (X==0) then goto 3
    call S(C,B,X) ; if (X==0) then goto 3
    rarely executed code
   3 return

Example 8:
```
subroutine COMPUTE ; common ....
complex Y[10], Z[10]
R=real(Y[n]) ;  P=sin(R) ;  Q=cos(R)
S = C * 6.0 * (P/3.0 - Q*Q*P)
T = 1.414214 * P * P * Q * C * 6.0
U=T/2.
V = -2.0 * C * 6.0 * (P/3.0 - Q*Q*P/2.0)
Z[1] = (0.0,-1.0)   *  ( S*Y[1] + T*Y[2] )
Z[2] = (0.0,-1.0)   *  ( U*Y[1] + V*Y[2] )
return
```

Example 14:
```
      do 1 i=1,N
    1   C = C/D*R ;  D = D-1 ;  R = R+1
```

Example 16:
```
real function F(X)
Y = X * 0.7071068
if ( Y < 0.0 ) then goto 1
rarely executed code
    1   F = 1.0 - 0.5 * (1.0 + ERF(-Y)) ;  return
```

These examples help us remember that real programs are not always as simple and straightforward as those seen in sections 2.3.1 and 2.3.2. Relative to those simpler ones, these "miscellaneous" programs are characterized by more numeric computations, the same number or fewer array accesses, less index/counter arithmetic, less or unusual-style comparisons and branches, and -- in some cases -- more procedure calls.

2.3.4 The Nature of Numeric Computations

The above examples give a picture of typical numeric computations, which can be summarized as follows:

1. The absolutely predominant data structure is the **array.** Most of the arrays are 1- or 2- dimensional. (Of course, the predominance of arrays over other data-structures can not be deduced by studying FORTRAN programs, since arrays are the only data-structure allowed in that language. However, it is known that the vast majority of numerical computations is performed to solve engineering or other similar problems, where the array arises as the natural data-structure.)

2. In the vast majority of the cases, the array elements are **accessed in regular sequence(s).** There are a few "working locations" in the array(s), and their addresses change as arithmetic progressions. The step is quite often equal to one element size, or, at other times, it is the column size or some other constant.

3. A few integer scalar variables are used as **loop-counters and array-indexes.** The arithmetic performed on them is simple and corresponds to the above "regular sequence" of array accesses: increment by a constant, compare & branch. **Address computations** for multi-dimensional arrays require integer multiplication. Most of the times, it is feasible and advantageous for the optimizing compiler (or the very sophisticated programmer) to replace those integer counters/indexes by actual memory pointers; the address computations

are avoided in this way (see [AhUl77], p.466: Induction Variable Elimination).

4. The numeric computations are usually **floating-point operations** (multiplications and additions/subtractions being the most frequent). Several such operations are performed, but usually not many more in number than the integer operations on counters.

5. **Low-level parallelism** is present in many cases, and has two forms: (1) among various floating-point operations, usually when long expressions are computed, and when a series of assignment statements is executed with no control-transfers in between; and (2) between counter/address calculations and floating-point operations, especially when program sequencing (if's, loop's) depend on the former only. This quite common "static nature" of program sequencing is an important characteristic of programs which perform a certain computation on all elements of a vector or of an array.

6. The last property also gives to these programs significant amounts of **higher-level parallelism.** Subsequent loop iterations are independent and could proceed in parallel. Some times, they are completely independent (Example 15 of section 2.3.1), so that a highly pipelined von Neumann processor could take advantage of them. Other times, they are less independent (Example 17 in section 2.3.1 would require a tree-organized addition); von Neumann architectures and languages typically cannot exploit that parallelism.

2.4 A Study of four C Programs for Text Processing and CAD of IC's

In this section we study the critical loops of four non-numeric programs, written in C and taken out of the Berkeley UNIX† and CAD environment:

fgrep   the UNIX program which searches a file for occurrences of fixed strings,

sed   the UNIX stream (batch) text editor,

sort   the UNIX program to sort the lines in a file, and

mextra   a circuit extractor [FitzMe] which, given a description of the IC's geometry, generates a list of the transistors and their interconnections present in an integrated circuit. It works by first reading-in the description of the geometry and building a corresponding dynamic data structure, and then "scanning" the IC following horizontal scan-lines of gradually increasing y-coordinate. It may be considered an example of a program that *manipulates a non-trivial dynamic data structure.*

As an argument in support of the representativeness of the above sample of programs, let us look at a typical compiler. Kessler's Pascal compiler spends

---

†UNIX is a trademark of Bell Laboratories.

most of its time [Kess82] scanning the input (i.e. reading and recognizing characters), generating assembly code (i.e. character I/O), and walking through tree structures and interrogating them. These functions are similar to what *fgrep, sed,* and *mextra* do.

The tools described in section 2.1.3 were used for locating the critical loops. Below, wherever code is shown, the number on the left of each line is the count of how many times the line was executed during the test run.

2.4.1 FGREP: a String Search Program

In the test run, *fgrep* was used to search for occurrences of the string "kateveni" in a file of size ≈ 230 KBytes (there were a few hundred such occurrences). The run took about 6 seconds CPU time, allocated as follows:

- ≈ 87% in the procedure *execute()*,
- ≈ 11% in *_read* (i.e. in the operating system),
- ≈ 2% in everything else.

The procedure *execute()* follows:

---

fgrep: execute() [87%]:

```
        | # define ccomp(a,b) (yflag ? lca(a)==lca(b) : a==b)
        | # define lca(x) (isupper(x) ? tolower(x) : x)
        |
        | struct words {
        |       char inp, out;
        |       struct words *nst, *link, *fail;
        | } w[MAXSIZ];
        | int    yflag;
        |
        | ....
        |
      1 | execute(file)   char *file;
        | { register struct words *c;
        |   register int ccount;
        |   register char ch, *p;
        |   char buf[2*BUFSIZ];
        |   int f, failed; char *nlp;
        |
      1 |       .... Initial Set-Up Work ....
 229253 |       for (;;)
 229253 |           { if (--ccount <= 0)
    226 |               { read-in a new 1Kbyte block or exit loop }
        |             nstate:
 229252 |             if (ccomp(c->inp, *p))    /* in-line expansion */
    923 |                 { c = c->nst; }
 228329 |             else if (c->link != 0)
      0 |                 { c = c->link; goto nstate; }
        |             else
```

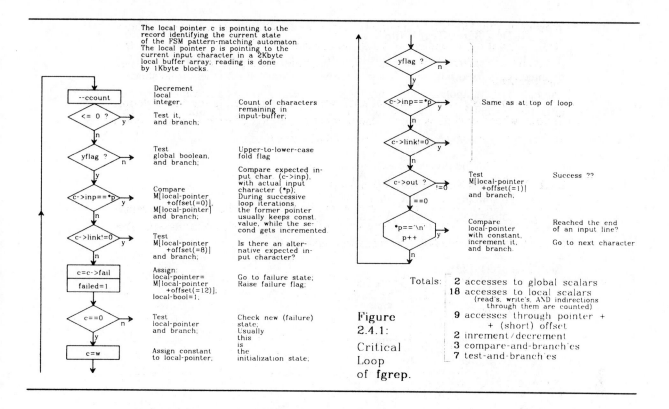

The local pointer c is pointing to the record identifying the current state of the FSM pattern-matching automaton. The local pointer p is pointing to the current input character in a 2Kbyte local buffer array; reading is done by 1Kbyte blocks.

Figure 2.4.1: Critical Loop of fgrep.

Totals:
2 accesses to global scalars
18 accesses to local scalars (read's, write's, AND indirections through them are counted)
9 accesses through pointer + + (short) offset
2 inrement/decrement
3 compare-and-branch'es
7 test-and-branch'es

```
228329 |        { c = c->fail;
228329 |            failed = 1;
228329 |            if (c==0)
228329 |                { c = w;
       |                istate:
228329 |                if (ccomp(c->inp,*p)) /*in-line exp*/
     0 |                    { c = c->nst; }
228329 |                else if (c->link != 0)
     0 |                    { c=c->link; goto istate; }
       |                }
     0 |            else goto nstate;
       |                }
229252 |        if (c->out)
    48 |            { Code for Success }
229204 |        if (*p++ == '\n')
  4237 |            { Code for End-of-Line }
       |        }
     1 |    .... Final Wrap-Up Work ....
       | }
```

Figure 2.4.1 contains a flow-chart of the critical loop of this run of *fgrep*. The vast majority of the operations performed are simply:

• accesses to scalars (mostly locals) and indirections through them to access fields of structures to which they are pointing, and

• comparisons (mostly to zero) & subsequent branches. The high frequency of compare-&-branches is in part a result of the nature of the program (pattern matching), but is also a general characteristic of the non-numeric programs, as the next examples will show.

2.4.2 SED: a Batch Text Editor

In our test run, *sed* copies a 2.2 Mbyte file to output, searching for occurrences of three short fixed patterns. It replaces two of them with 2 others (one shorter, one longer), and upon encountering the third one, it appends a specified new line after the current one. The run took about 160 sec CPU time, allocated as follows:

- ≈ 23% in the procedure *execute()*,
- ≈ 23% in the procedure *match()*,
- ≈ 16% in the procedure *gline()*, and
- all other procedures accounted for < 8% each.

---

sed: execute() [23%]:

```
      1 | execute(file)      char *file;
        | { register char *p1, *p2;
        |   register union reptr *ipc;
        |   int c;   char *execp;
        |
      1 | .... Initial Set-Up Work...
  52820 | for(;;)
  52820 |    { if((execp = gline(linebuf)) == badp) { rare }
  52819 |      spend = execp;
 158457 |      for(ipc = ptrspace; ipc->command; )
 158457 |         { p1 = ipc->ad1;
 158457 |           p2 = ipc->ad2;
 158457 |           if(p1)
  52819 |              { if(ipc->inar) { never }
  52819 |                else if(*p1 == CEND) { never }
  52819 |                else if(*p1 == CLNUM) { never }
  52819 |                else if(match(p1, 0)) {22,000 if's exct'd}
  30899 |                else {62,000 stmnts exect'd; continue;}
        |              }
 127558 |           if(ipc->negfl) { never }
 127558 |           command(ipc);
 127558 |           if(delflag) { never }
 127558 |           if(jflag) { never }
 127558 |           else ipc++;
        |         }
  52819 |      if(!nflag && !delflag)
2143025 |         { for(p1 = linebuf; p1 < spend; p1++)
        |                  /*''spend'' is a global pointer*/
2143025 |              putc(*p1, stdout);
```
/*Note: in-line expanded to: */
/* (--_iob[1]._cnt>=0 ? *(_iob[1]._ptr)++ = *p1 : {rare}) */
/* _iob[1]._cnt, _iob[1]._ptr are global scalars (compiler knows their addr.)*/
```
  52819 |              putc('\n', stdout);
        |         }
```

```
52819 |      if(aptr > abuf) { 22,000 calls: arout(); }
52819 |      delflag = 0;
      |    }
      | }
```

Here, we have:

- 0.26 M procedure calls,
- 2.35 M compare-&-branch,
- 3.10 M test-&-branch,
- 4.40 M incrementations, and
- 0.50 M assignments with no operation (move-type).

The vast majority of operands are accessed indirectly, through local pointers with a zero or small offset. Other accesses are to local and global scalars. Certainly, a lot of this procedure's time is spent in the tight **for** loop that copies characters to standard output.

---

sed: match() [23%]:

```
161106 | match(expbuf, gf)    char *expbuf;
       | { register char      *p1, *p2, c;
       |
161106 |      if(gf) { Execute ≈ 150,000 statements }
158457 |      else { p1 = linebuf; locs = 0; }
161106 |      p2 = expbuf;
161106 |      if(*p2++) { never }
       |      /* fast check for first character: */
161106 |      if(*p2 == CCHR)
161106 |          { c = p2[1];
5242476 |            do  { if(*p1 != c) continue;
269623 |                  if(advance(p1, p2)) { infrequent }
5189445 |                } while(*p1++);
108075 |            return(0);
       |          }
     0 |      ...Various  others, never executed...
       | }
```

---

sed: gline() [16%]:

```
52820 | char *gline(addr)    char *addr;
      | { register char *p1, *p2;   register c;
      |      ...Initial Set-Up Work (100,000 statements total)...
2174691 |     for (;;)
2174691 |       { if (p2 >= ebp) { rare }
2174690 |         if ((c = *p2++) == '\n') { infrequent }
2121871 |         if(c) if(p1 < lbend)
2121871 |             *p1++ = c;
```

```
|        }
|      ...Final  Wrap-Up Work (200,000 statements total)...
| }
```

These two procedures spend most of their time scanning characters. *Match()* scans characters searching for some particular one. *Gline()* scans characters copying and checking them.

2.4.3 SORT: an Extreme, but Real Case

The particular sorting program that was studied, namely the one installed on our UNIX machines, spent one third of the test run time in its calls to a trivial procedure *blank()* used to scan over blanks. Obviously, it is preferable that *blank()* were defined as a macro, so that it be expanded in-line. The test run consisted of sorting a 2.2 Mbyte file, relative to the second-in-line field and with elimination of duplicates. It took half-an-hour of CPU time.

sort: blank() [31%]:

```
26087970 | blank(c)
26087970 | { if(c==' ' || c=='\t')
 6279488 |            return(1);
19808482 |      else  return(0);
         | }
```

In general, text-processing programs spend a lot of their time in inner loops where they sequentially "walk" through the characters in buffers, copying, comparing, or testing various things.

It is important to notice that programs dealing with text waste a lot of memory bandwidth in the usual architectures, where a full memory word is accessed each time a byte transaction takes place.

Exploitation of parallelism is difficult in these programs, because of the high frequency of conditional branches. The amount of work done between two consecutive branches is usually quite small, with limited parallelism. Parallelism is often available between operations in two different blocks B1 and B2 separated by a conditional branch, where the branch *usually* follows the path that makes B2 execute after B1. Programs are usually written in such a way that execution of B2 cannot start before it is certain that it should start. The programmer could rearrange the code and introduce temporary variables to hold tentative results, but doing so would lead to complicated and hard to maintain programs.

2.4.4 MEXTRA: a Circuit Extraction Program

Mextra's test run consisted of extracting the circuitry in the control section of the RISC II chip. It took 330 sec CPU time, allocated as follows:

- ≈ 14% in the procedure *ScanSubSwath()*,
- ≈ 11% in the procedure *Propagate()*,
- ≈ 10% in the procedure *alloc()*,
- ≈ 8% in the procedure *EndTrap()*,
- ≈ 5% in the procedure *Free()*, and
- the remaining procedures took < 4% of the total time each.

mextra: ScanSubSwath() [14%]:

```
  771 | ScanSubSwath(bin)    int bin;
       | {   int i, newCount, n;
       |     register edge *new,*old,*last, *oldList,*newList;
       |
       |       ...Initial Set-Up Work (30,000 statements)...
353237 |       while(new != NIL && old != NIL)     /* NIL is 0 */
352466 |         { if(new->bb.l < old->bb.l) { infrequent }
       |           else
302554 |             {  if(n < old->bb.t)
254342 |                   { if(last == NIL) { rare }
253628 |                     else {last->next=old; last=old;}
254342 |                     old = oldList;
254342 |                     if (old!=NIL) oldList=old->next;
       |                   }
 48212 |               else { infrequent }
       |             }
304254 |           if(depth[last->layer] == 0)
140442 |               StartTrap(last->layer,last);
304254 |           if((depth[last->layer] += last->dir) == 0)
139794 |               EndTrap(last->layer,last);
304254 |           nextEnd =
       |             (nextEnd<last->bb.t ? nextEnd : last->bb.t);
       |         }
       |       ...Final Wrap-Up Work (250,000 statements)...
       | }
```

This procedure performs extensive list operations, using local pointers. The total operations performed in its critical loop are:

- 0.6 M procedure calls;
- 0.3 M additions (not counting address computations).
- 1.8 M test-&-branches;
- 1.0 M compare-&-branches;
- ≈ 0.6 M accesses to a global scalar (nextEnd);
- 6.5 M accesses to locals (96% of them to pointers)
    (these include accesses for indirecting through them);
- 3.1 M accesses to fields of structures via a local pointer, and
- 1.0 M (random) accesses to a small array *depth[10]*.

The basic pattern of memory accesses is the list traversal, which places a corresponding limit on locality-of-reference. However, during each loop iteration there are 11 accesses to fields of the structures pointed to by "old->" and by "last->". Accesses to various fields of the same structure are obviously accesses to neighboring memory locations, since the structure nodes here have a size of 8 words. Moreover, there are repeated accesses to the same field of the same structure, for example ≈ 4 accesses per iteration to "last->layer".

The available parallelism, is again limited by the high frequency of conditional branches. Some parallelism can be seen between accessing a memory location and computing the effective address for a subsequent memory access. For example:

```
if ( new->bb.l < old->bb.l )
if ( (depth[last->layer] += last->dir) == 0)
```

---

mextra: Propagate() [11%]:

```
   773 | Propagate(y,yNext)   int y, yNext;
        | { int  layer, height, tempx,tempy;
        |   register segment *above, *below, *next, *poly, *diff;
        |
        |       ...Initial Set-Up Work (8,000 statements)...
        |       for( above=Above[layer]; above!=NIL;
        |               above=above->next )
 141443 |           {
        |               for(    ; below!=NIL &&
        |                        below->right < above->left;
        |                   below=below->next)
 138000 |                   if(below->area != 0) { rare }
        |               for( next=below;
        |                   next!=NIL && next->left <= above->right;
        |                   next=below->next)
 136083 |                   { below = next;
 136083 |                       if(above->node == 0)
        |                           {
 135024 | above->node = below->node;
 135024 | above->area = below->area +
        |               height*(above->right – above->left – 1)/100;
 135024 | above->perim = below->perim +
        |               2 * (height + above->right – above->left –
        |               MIN(above->right,below->right) +
        |               MAX(above->left,below->left) ) / 10;
        |           /* Note: In-line expansions:  */
        |           /*   MIN(x,y) into: (x<y ? x : y) */
        |           /*   MAX(x,y) into: (x<y ? y : x) */
 135024 | below->perim = below->area = 0;
        |                           }
        |                       else { rare }
 136083 |                       if(below->area != 0) { never }
        |                   }
 141443 |               if(above->node == 0) { rare }
        |           }
        |       ...Final Wrap-Up Work (500,000 statements)...
        | }
```

Here again, extensive list operations are performed. The list-nodes have a size of 8 words, and are accessed via local pointers. During each loop iteration, 16 accesses are made to fields of a certain list-node, and 15 to fields of another. Each individual field is accessed an average of 3 times. This procedure has more numeric computations than the other procedures in this section, but these are still not the dominant factor.

---

mextra: alloc() [10%]:

```
283165 | alloc(n)
       | { register int tmp; register struct cell *ptr;
       |
283165 |     if(n<CELLSIZE-4) { rare }
283165 |     n = (n+WORDSIZE-1)/WORDSIZE;
       |                 /* WORDSIZE is 2 in this example */
283165 |     if(TBLSIZE<=n) { rare }
283138 |     else if(FreeTbl[n]!=0)
258662 |         { ptr = FreeTbl[n];
258662 |           FreeTbl[n] = ptr->next;
258662 |           --FreeCnt[n];
258662 |           if(ptr->status!=FREE || ptr->count!=n) {never}
258662 |           if(FreeCnt[n]!=0)
241417 |               { if(FreeTbl[n]->status!=FREE) {never}
241417 |                 if(FreeTbl[n]->count!=n) {never}
       |               }
       |           else { rare }
       |         }
       |     else { infrequent }
283165 |     ptr->status = ALLOC;
283165 |     ptr->count = n;
283165 |     tmp = (int) ptr;
283165 |     if (n<TBLSIZE) AllocCnt[n]++;
283165 |     return(tmp+4);
       | }
```

This last procedure has no loop; it is entered many times, and does a little work each time. Besides accessing fields of structures via pointers, it also makes many references to the n-th elements of several arrays. These latter are *not* sequential array-element accesses. However, if the information were kept in a single array of structures, instead of in multiple simple arrays, then the above accesses would all be to neighboring memory locations. Slightly more parallelism can be found here, for example:

{ptr->status=ALLOC; ptr->count=n; tmp=(int)ptr; if(n<TBLSIZE)}

Also, notice that the *if*s that lead to *then-clauses* which never get executed are consistency checks, and they could all be done in parallel if the language allowed some way of expressing that.

The overall picture from this CAD program is one of many conditional branches and of many accesses to fields of structures using local pointers pointing to them. Although the application has some arithmetic that needs to be done, it does not play a dominant role. There are very few increment operations, contrary to the previous programs studied in earlier sections, because this program deals with dynamic data structures. The locality-of-references to the elements of the data structures stems from the computation pattern of performing several accesses to various fields of a few structure instances, before interest shifts to some new such instances.

2.5   Summary of Findings

In this chapter, we first reviewed static and dynamic program statistics collected by other researchers. Their results indicate that the simplest operations are also the ones that are executed most of the time.

Then, we looked at several FORTRAN programs, most of them doing numerical computations. We observed that they perform primarily floating-point arithmetic operations on operands which frequently are elements of arrays. The inner loops usually traverse the arrays in a "regular" fashion, using indexes that are incremented by a constant amount and compared to a limit. The use of pointers rather than indexes, by the programmer or by the optimizing compiler, would be advantageous.

Then, we studied some text-processing programs written in C, and saw that they spend a large fraction of their time running sequentially through character buffers. These are array elements, again, but here programmers usually access them indirectly through local pointers. The dominant operations are not arithmetic any more -- they are tests or comparisons for branching and mere copying.

Finally, we analyzed a program for CAD of IC's, which manipulates a nontrivial dynamic data structure. The fields of a few nodes (structures) are accessed several times indirectly through local pointers, before the program shifts its attention to some other nodes linked to the previous ones. Again, we found high frequencies of test/compare-&-branch and of copying.

In all cases, we saw that programs are organized in procedures and that procedure calls are frequent and costly in terms of execution time. Procedures usually have a few arguments and local variables, most of which are scalars, and are heavily used. The nesting depth fluctuates within narrow ranges for long periods of time.

We found low-level parallelism although usually in small amounts, mainly between address and data computations. The frequent occurrence of conditional-branch instructions greatly limits its exploitation.

General-purpose computations, as usually expressed in von Neumann languages, are carried out by walking through static or dynamic data structures in some - usually regular - path. Operand addressing, copying, and comparing for decision making, are factors of prime importance. Procedures are heavily used for hierarchical organizations. Numeric computations are frequent and expensive in some applications.

In the next chapters, possible architectural features for exploiting these program characteristics will be presented.

Computer
Systems

G. Bell, D. Siewiorek,
and S.H. Fuller, Editors

Empirical Evaluation of Some Features of Instruction Set Processor Architectures

Åmund Lunde
Carnegie-Mellon University

This paper presents methods for empirical evaluation of features of Instruction Set Processors (ISPs). ISP features are evaluated in terms of the time used or saved by having or not having the feature. The methods are based on analysis of traces of program executions. The concept of a register life is introduced, and used to answer questions like: How many registers are used simultaneously? How many would be sufficient all of the time? Most of the time? What would the overhead be if the number of registers were reduced? What are registers used for during their lives? The paper also discusses the problem of detecting desirable but non-existing instructions. Other problems are briefly discussed. Experimental results are presented, obtained by analyzing 41 programs running on the DECsystem10 ISP.

Key Words and Phrases: computer architecture, program behavior, instruction sets, opcode utilization, register structures, register utilization, simultaneous register lives, instruction tracing, execution time
CR Categories: 6.20, 6.21, 6.33

This work was supported in part by the Advanced Research Projects Agency of the office of the Secretary of Defense (F44620-73-C-0074) monitored by the Air Force Office of Scientific Research, in part by The Norwegian Research Council for Science and the Humanities (Norges Almenvitenskapelige Forskningsråd). Author's present address: EDB-sentret, Universitetet i Oslo; P.O. Box 1059, Blindern, Oslo 3, Norway.
* Notes for this article appear on p. 152.

1. Introduction

A quick survey of current computers reveals a great variation in the structure of Instruction Set Processors.[1]* This observation is true even for computers intended for the same general market. Current ISPs designed with the scientific market in mind, for example, have word lengths ranging from 24 to 64 bits; the number of different instructions varies from about 70 to over 400; register structures span the area from one accumulator plus a few index registers, through designs with 8 to 24 general or specialized registers, to designs with up to 64 registers, again relatively general. A natural conclusion from such a survey is that very little is known about the optimal structure of ISPs. Further study reveals that very little has been published about measuring techniques or other methods designed to obtain such knowledge.

This paper presents a step towards the development of such measuring techniques. It describes methods designed to study the detailed behavior of programs as they are executing on some ISP. Experimental results are presented which reflect the behavior of one particular set of programs on one particular ISP.

The need for such measures and their utility is vindicated by the results found by the designers of the Burroughs B1700 central processor [14, 15]. These results clearly show the dependence of program efficiency on a good ISP.

Previous authors have measured the frequency of execution of the individual instructions or groups of instructions [7 (The Gibson mix), 8, 4, 12, and 9]. Only a few more comprehensive studies are known to this author: Foster et al. [5, 6] have developed measures of opcode utilization and studied alternative encodings of the opcodes into fewer bits than those required by a conventional encoding. Similar results are presented by Wilner [15]. Winder [16, 17] has gathered miscellaneous statistics on ISP usage. Alexander [1] has made extensive study of how one particular programming language uses ISP features.

None of the above studies report on ISP behavior reflecting more than two or three consecutive instructions. Also, register use is barely touched upon. The methods described in this paper improve this situation. They are only to a small extent, or not at all, restricted to the study of a small fixed length sequence of instructions. On the contrary, we may follow a phenomenon for as many instructions as seems relevant, while at the same time retaining full knowledge about every instruction executed.

2. Basic Methodology

The basic idea of the methods is to analyze traces of a representative set of programs, the *subject set*, written as these are executed by an interpreter for the ISP being studied. Information is recorded for every instruction executed by the *subject program*. The major advantages of this approach are:

—ISP behavior may be studied in great detail.
—The methods are not restricted to special languages or compilers.
—Analysis programs are easily written, and programs for new analysis methods may be developed after the data have been collected.
—All analyses of the same program (trace) see exactly the same instruction stream; hence the results are not perturbed by random influences caused by external devices or by multiprogramming of jobs.

Each individual analysis, therefore, studies the behavior of a user program running on the user ISP and the suitability of this ISP to that particular program, as opposed to studying the suitability of the full ISP to a collection of multiprogrammed programs. For the latter purpose a device is needed to trace executive mode programs, probably at full speed. Statistical validity comes from studying many programs individually.

The methods are easily modifiable to apply to all register structured ISPs, and to some extent even to stack ISPs or other ISPs. The specific results obtained are, however, strongly dependent on the structure of the ISP analyzed. The extent to which they can be applied to similar ISPs depends on the degree of similarity and on the result in question. On the other hand, the results are relatively independent of technology; hence they may be used by ISP architects to compare the cost/utility ratios of different structures across different technologies.

Our methods evaluate ISP features in terms of their associated time cost, i.e. the change in execution time or instruction count caused by including or removing the feature. Of these, the instruction count is most independent of technology, but it hides the fact that certain operations take a longer time than others, regardless of technology. Hence execution time is also computed in some cases by summing the individual instruction execution times.

Other relevant costs are the space occupied in primary memory by program and data, and the cost of designing, coding, and debugging programs. Both of these are highly dependent on the ISP, and are as important to a good design as the time cost. They are not, however, measured by our methods, but should be otherwise measured or estimated by the ISP architect before he makes his decisions.

3. Experimental Environment

3.1 ISP Studied
The emphasis of our experimental work was on studying the methods, and estimating the dependence of the results on the major parameters of the subject set. In order to reduce the work, experiments were performed on one ISP only: the DECsystem10 (KA-10). The structure of this ISP is unusually general; some of its properties are:

(1) It has a large instruction repertoire of about 420 user instructions including:
—A rich set of instructions for arithmetic and bitwise comparison. These compare memory, register, immediate or implicit (0) operands, and all 6 arithmetic conditions are available.
—Programmer defined stacks.
—Three different mechanisms for subroutine calls.
—All 16 Boolean functions of two variables.
—Immediate operands and several result destinations (register, memory or both) for arithmetic and logic instructions.
—31 Monitor calls and 32 user-definable trap instructions (UUOs).

(2) The register structure is equally general. The 16 registers are part of the memory address space. All of them may be used for all standard purposes with only insignificant exceptions.

(3) Indirection may be carried to any depth, with indexing at each level.

Hence this ISP is a good starting point for detection of unnecessary generality or superfluous features. This is vindicated by our results reported here and in [10]. We did, however, also discover features which we would like to see incorporated into this ISP. Some of these have, in fact, been included in later processors of the DECsystem10 family.

3.2 Subject Set
Another restriction on our experiments was that we analyzed programs only from a scientific environment. On the other hand, we tried to choose a subject set which would show the influence of the choice of algorithm, programming language, and compiler.

Hence one part of our subject set consisted of six algorithms from *Collected Algorithms of the ACM* (CALGO). These were selected to contain as many as possible of the commonly used program structures, and to give a reasonable covering of the modified SHARE classification for algorithms. Each of these algorithms was coded in four languages: ALGOL, BASIC, BLISS, and FORTRAN. Two different FORTRAN systems were used. BLISS [18] is a high-

Table I. Distribution of Lives by Lifelength, Unweighted Sum of All Programs—Logarithmic Table Division.

Length	No. of lives	Fraction	Cum. fraction
1 - 1	174927	0.09	0.09
2 - 3	728346	0.38	0.48
4 - 7	547072	0.29	0.77
8 - 15	252508	0.13	0.90
16 - 31	116404	0.06	0.96
32 - 63	41673	0.02	0.98
64 - 127	17790	0.01	0.99
128 - up	15603	0.01	1.00
Total number of lives	1894323		

level language for systems programming. The other languages should be well known. The six algorithms were:

No. 30: Polynomial roots by Bairstow's method (Bairstow)

No. 43: Linear equations by Crout's method (Crout)

No. 113: Treesort

No. 119: PERT

No. 257: Numerical integration by Håvies method (Håvie)

No. 355: Generation of Ising configurations (Ising).

The latter could not easily be coded in BASIC, hence that version was omitted.

To investigate the influence of coding style, we included an algorithm for polynomial interpolation (Aitken) as coded in BLISS by four different programmers, plus a carefully tuned version of this algorithm. These are denoted E (efficient), B, A, L, and G. A medium-sized numeric FORTRAN program, SEC, was also analyzed. Again both FORTRAN systems were used. Finally we analyzed the five compilers used for the CALGO set: these are denoted ALGOL, BASIC, BLISS, FORFOR, and FORTEN. ALGOL, BASIC, and FORFOR are written in MACRO (the assembly language), BLISS and FORTEN are written in BLISS.

Thus our final subject set consisted of 41 programs, comprising about 5.3 million instructions or 16.8 seconds of CPU time. 38 of these were written in high-level languages. One would a priori expect that such programs do not make as good use of the ISP as do assembly language programs. On the other hand, we are already restricted to the user ISP, and certainly the majority of user programs are written in high-level languages.

4. Register Structure

Methods were developed for two problems connected with register structure:

—How many registers are used efficiently?

—What is the need for generality of registers?

Both are attacked through the concept of a *register life*. A register life consists of all activity associated with a given register during a period of time starting with a load into that register, and terminating with the last use of the register before the next load into it. A register is *loaded* when a new value is brought into it which is unrelated to its old value. Use of the old value during address calculation is not considered a relation in this context.

The start of a register life is analogous to the "open effects" situation described by Tjaden and Flynn [13]. The terms *live* and *dead* now have obvious meanings. A register is *dormant* when it is live but not used. The resolution of our time measure is one instruction. Hence two successive lives of the same register may overlap if the old value is used to load the new one. Usually there will be a dead period between two consecutive lives of a register. Finally we note that for a machine with several registers, any number of them may be live at any given time.

It seems unreasonable to use these concepts unmodified for registers which have long dormant periods. Hence the results below were obtained under the assumption that a register was dead when it had been dormant for 200 or more instructions. This is discussed further below.

4.1 Analysis Program

The analysis program detects register lives, classifies them according to the operations they contain, and finds the number of live registers at each point in time during program execution.

As the trace is read, one can not in general tell whether a register is dead or live until the next LOAD into it is encountered. This may be any length of time after the register actually died. Hence the analysis of register usage is a two-phase process. In the first phase register lives are detected and classified. Phase I also writes a file of descriptions of each life which is used by phase II. Phase II then finds how many registers were live at each point in time, and computes various results based on this.

In the analysis a relatively fine classification was used for the lives. For purposes of presentation the following seven classes were considered:

—All lives (the total class—TOT).

—Lives used for indexing (INX).

—Lives used for temporary storage only (TMP).

—The four classes defined by the "strongest" arithmetic used:

   No arithmetic (NOA).

   Fixed-point additions and subtractions (FAS).

   Fixed-point multiplications and divisions (FMD).

   Floating-point operations (FLO).

The latter four classes are disjoint and their union is the class TOT.

4.1.1 Phase I. As the trace is read, phase I keeps track of the times of the most recent load and the most recent use of each register. Hence each time a register

Table II. Average Lifelength in Instructions.

Language:	ALGOL	BASIC	BLISS	FORFOR	FORTEN	Mean
Bairstow	12.3	12.3	11.2	12.9	12.9	12.3
Crout	13.6	11.3	18.2	15.1	15.9	14.8
Treesort	6.1	11.9	9.0	4.2	5.8	7.4
PERT	10.9	11.4	8.4	5.0	7.9	8.7
Havie	16.6	11.2	13.5	14.3	20.0	15.1
Ising	16.5	-	9.7	5.5	9.2	10.2
Secant	-	-	-	8.1	9.6	8.9
Programmer:	E	B	A	G	L	Mean
Aitken	14.3	14.7	13.0	8.9	11.9	12.6
Compiler:	ALGOL	BASIC	BLISS	FORFOR	FORTEN	Mean
	17.4	23.8	9.7	14.9	11.4	15.4

Language:	MACRO	ALGOL	BASIC	BLISS	FORFOR	FORTEN	Mean
Mean	18.7	12.7	11.6	11.8	9.3	11.6	11.9

Table V. Memory References per Instruction Excluding Instruction Fetches.

Language:	ALGOL	BASIC	BLISS	FORFOR	FORTEN	Mean
Bairstow	.61	.52	.50	.62	.60	.57
Crout	.44	.59	.50	.55	.64	.54
Treesort	.65	.50	.51	.57	.63	.57
PERT	.51	.47	.53	.69	.63	.57
Havie	.30	.45	.31	.44	.35	.37
Ising	.40	-	.60	.67	.60	.57
Secant	-	-	-	.60	.53	.57
Programmer:	E	B	A	G	L	Mean
Aitken	.45	.48	.52	.50	.53	.50
Compiler:	ALGOL	BASIC	BLISS	FORFOR	FORTEN	Mean
	.40	.32	.45	.42	.40	.40

Language:	MACRO	ALGOL	BASIC	BLISS	FORFOR	FORTEN	Mean
Mean	.38	.49	.51	.48	.59	.57	.51

Table III. Usages per Register Life.

Language:	ALGOL	BASIC	BLISS	FORFOR	FORTEN	Mean
Bairstow	4.6	3.6	4.6	4.6	4.4	4.4
Crout	3.8	3.7	6.6	3.7	3.9	4.3
Treesort	3.9	3.5	4.8	2.9	2.9	3.6
PERT	4.1	3.4	3.8	3.1	3.2	3.5
Havie	4.4	3.7	5.8	5.4	5.2	4.9
Ising	4.0	-	4.5	3.1	3.3	3.7
Secant	-	-	-	3.8	3.8	3.8
Programmer:	E	B	A	G	L	Mean
Aitken	5.4	5.5	5.2	3.9	5.2	5.0
Compiler:	ALGOL	BASIC	BLISS	FORFOR	FORTEN	Mean
	3.7	6.0	3.5	4.1	3.2	4.1

Language:	MACRO	ALGOL	BASIC	BLISS	FORFOR	FORTEN	Mean
Mean	4.6	4.1	3.6	4.8	3.8	3.8	4.2

Table VI. Register References per Instruction.

Language:	ALGOL	BASIC	BLISS	FORFOR	FORTEN	Mean
Bairstow	1.66	1.05	1.58	1.35	1.37	1.40
Crout	1.67	1.21	1.67	1.56	1.46	1.51
Treesort	1.62	1.04	1.65	1.28	1.32	1.38
PERT	1.59	1.05	1.61	1.25	1.22	1.34
Havie	1.57	1.14	1.61	1.36	1.16	1.37
Ising	1.58	-	1.66	1.11	1.13	1.37
Secant	-	-	-	1.39	1.33	1.36
Programmer:	E	B	A	G	L	Mean
Aitken	1.66	1.67	1.69	1.69	1.64	1.67
Compiler:	ALGOL	BASIC	BLISS	FORFOR	FORTEN	Mean
	1.09	1.13	1.32	1.39	1.17	1.22

Language:	MACRO	ALGOL	BASIC	BLISS	FORFOR	FORTEN	Mean
Mean	1.20	1.61	1.10	1.59	1.33	1.28	1.40

Table IV. Average Number of Live Registers, Computed as ⟨Sum of Lifelengths⟩/⟨Program Length⟩.

Language:	ALGOL	BASIC	BLISS	FORFOR	FORTEN	Mean
Bairstow	4.4	3.6	3.8	3.8	4.0	3.9
Crout	6.0	3.7	4.7	6.4	6.0	5.4
Treesort	2.5	3.5	3.1	1.8	2.7	2.7
PERT	4.2	3.6	3.6	2.0	3.0	3.3
Havie	6.0	3.5	3.7	3.6	4.5	4.3
Ising	6.5	-	3.6	1.9	3.2	3.8
Secant	-	-	-	3.0	3.4	3.2
Programmer:	E	B	A	G	L	Mean
Aitken	4.4	4.5	4.2	3.9	3.7	4.1
Compiler:	ALGOL	BASIC	BLISS	FORFOR	FORTEN	Mean
	5.1	4.5	3.6	5.1	4.2	4.5

Language:	MACRO	ALGOL	BASIC	BLISS	FORFOR	FORTEN	Mean
Mean	4.9	4.9	3.6	3.9	3.2	3.8	3.9

Table VII. Fraction of Lives with No Arithmetic.

Language:	ALGOL	BASIC	BLISS	FORFOR	FORTEN	Mean
Bairstow	.213	.637	.574	.494	.470	.478
Crout	.528	.716	.214	.349	.440	449
Treesort	.315	.686	.257	.784	.565	.521
PERT	.597	.735	.547	.457	.416	.550
Havie	.628	.680	.482	.496	.412	.540
Ising	.695	-	.620	.744	.622	670
Secant	-	-	-	.263	.266	.265
Programmer:	E	B	A	G	L	Mean
Aitken	.317	.390	.402	.475	391	.395
Compiler:	ALGOL	BASIC	BLISS	FORFOR	FORTEN	Mean
	.844	.744	.921	.802	.886	.839

Language:	MACRO	ALGOL	BASIC	BLISS	FORFOR	FORTEN	Mean
Mean	.797	.496	.691	.498	.512	.456	.538

is loaded, the endpoints of its previous life are immediately available. For each register life, phase I determines its class, and also the number of references to it. Finally phase I computes the total number of register references and memory references. The data items written on the file for phase II contain most of this information, together with the register name.

Some results from phase I are given in Tables I through XII. Results are given for each individual program, as well as the averages for each algorithm, for all the compilers, and for all programs written in each language. All the programs are equally weighted in these averages.

We note that most lives (68% of the total) are between 2 and 7 instructions long. Only 4% are 32 instructions or longer. For each individual program over half the lives are less than 8 instructions long. Only 3 programs have more than 10% of their lives 32 instructions or longer. The average lifelength is 11.9 instructions, but ranges from 4 to 24 instructions for the individual programs. The average number of references to a life is 4.2, it ranges between 3 and 7 for the individual programs. The average number of simultaneously live registers ranges between 2 and 6. Operands, including indices and nominators (indirect addresses), are found in registers 2 to 4 times as often as in primary memory.

The classes FLO and FMD are significant only for those algorithms that use floating-point arithmetic, or where FMD arithmetic is used to access data. This is as one would expect. Even for highly numeric programs at most 50% of the lives are in class FLO, less than

Table VIII. Fraction of Lives with Fixed Point Add/Subtract.

Language:	ALGOL	BASIC	BLISS	FORFOR	FORTEN	Mean
Bairstow	504	.106	.054	.118	.141	.185
Crout	.304	.009	.096	.186	.122	143
Treesort	.355	.103	.710	.208	.056	.286
PERT	.380	.122	.397	.516	.552	393
Hävie	.278	.085	.149	.123	.156	.158
Ising	.300	–	.373	.250	.370	323
Secant	–	–	–	.359	.303	331
Programmer:	E	B	A	G	L	Mean
Aitken	.210	.202	.302	.423	.389	.305
Compiler:	ALGOL	BASIC	BLISS	FORFOR	FORTEN	Mean
	.130	.234	.074	.190	.108	.147
Language:	MACRO	ALGOL	BASIC	BLISS	FORFOR	FORTEN	Mean
Mean	.185	.354	.085	.268	.251	.243	.245

Table IX. Fraction of Lives with Fixed Point Multiply/Divide.

Language:	ALGOL	BASIC	BLISS	FORFOR	FORTEN	Mean
Bairstow	.009	.001	.018	.042	.019	.018
Crout	.006	.064	.433	.156	.142	.160
Treesort	.317	.000	.011	.000	.370	.140
PERT	.002	.000	.004	.006	.006	.004
Hävie	.002	.001	.031	.018	.015	.013
Ising	.006	–	.007	.006	.008	.007
Secant	–	–	–	.175	.199	.187
Programmer:	E	B	A	G	L	Mean
Aitken	.000	.000	.000	.000	.035	.017
Compiler:	ALGOL	BASIC	BLISS	FORFOR	FORTEN	Mean
	.026	.019	.005	.009	.008	.013
Language:	MACRO	ALGOL	BASIC	BLISS	FORFOR	FORTEN	Mean
Mean	.018	.057	.013	.046	.058	.108	.054

Table X. Fraction of Lives with Floating Point Arithmetic.

Language:	ALGOL	BASIC	BLISS	FORFOR	FORTEN	Mean
Bairstow	.274	.256	.354	.347	.369	.320
Crout	.163	.211	.257	.306	.296	.247
Treesort	.014	.211	.022	.008	.009	.053
PERT	.021	.143	.053	.021	.026	.053
Hävie	.092	.233	.339	.353	.418	.289
Ising	.000	–	.000	.000	.000	.000
Secant	–	–	–	.203	.232	.218
Programmer:	E	B	A	G	L	Mean
Aitken	.473	.408	.296	.102	.136	.238
Compiler:	ALGOL	BASIC	BLISS	FORFOR	FORTEN	Mean
	.000	.003	.000	.000	.000	.001
Language:	MACRO	ALGOL	BASIC	BLISS	FORFOR	FORTEN	Mean
Mean	.001	.094	.211	.188	.178	.193	.162

40% in all but two programs. In spite of the fact that all variables in BASIC are floating point, the percentage of FLO lives in the BASIC programs is never above 25.

For the classes FAS and NOA, the dependence on language is larger than the dependence on algorithm. This is in particular true for ALGOL and BASIC, which enforce a stronger regimen on programs than do the other languages.

Between 18% and 68% of the lives, 39% on the average, are used for indexing.

4.1.2 Phase II. Phase II reads the file written by phase I in reverse order, and simulates a backwards execution of the subject program. Initially the descriptions of the last lives of each register are read. For each register the program keeps the description of one life, viz. that which is now valid, or will next be valid, during the backwards simulation. The loading and final uses of each register are entered in a list sorted by decreasing time. This list is processed in order, and a counter of live registers is suitably updated.

Each time a loading use of a register is processed, all information about that life may be discarded. The program is then ready to receive the description of the previous (at execution) life for that register. This description was written by phase I as it processed the same load instruction which is now being processed by phase II. Hence the desired data item is in the correct position to be read off the file.

We now know exactly how many registers were live at each point in time, and the fraction of the total time when exactly N registers were live can easily be computed for each N. Since the usage class was written on the intermediate file, this analysis may be done simultaneously for any suitably defined classes of lives. The results for the 7 classes previously defined are given in Tables XIII through XV.

As is seen, no program uses more than 15 registers simultaneously. 17 of the 41 programs would get by with 10 or fewer registers. This maximum is only used for short periods of time. Thus 10 registers would suffice 90% of the time for all 41 programs, 98% of the time for 36 of the 41 programs. The results for the compilers and for the BLISS programs (BLISS has a highly optimizing compiler) show that neither the size and complexity of the programs nor their efficiency imply the use of many registers. On the contrary, the BLISS results seem to indicate the opposite conclusion. Hence we would attribute the relatively high number of live registers for the other compilers to the fact that these are written in assembly language. If specialized registers were to be used, it would seem appropriate to have 2 floating point accumulators, 2 fixed-point accumulators, and 8 index registers with simple fixed-point operations.

4.2 Reducing the Register Block

The results just presented suggest that programs might run almost equally time-efficiently on an ISP with fewer registers than the one analyzed, but otherwise having the same structure. Increased execution time would ensue from having to store and reload registers whenever the number of lives in the original version was too high. We use two methods, called *interleaving* and *bedding*, to compute an upper bound on this increase in execution time.

4.2.1 Interleaving. Interleaving is applied in phase II. Assume that our reduced ISP has M registers. For each period when the program requires N registers, $N > M$, we select the $N - M$ least useful lives as described below, and assume the associated values to be stored in memory. Each time one of these values is

Table XI. Fraction of Lives Used as Temporaries Only.

Language:		ALGOL	BASIC	BLISS	FORFOR	FORTEN	Mean
Bairstow		.028	.067	.179	.101	.121	.099
Crout		.018	.101	.049	.137	.142	.098
Treesort		.001	.107	.000	.000	.001	.022
PERT		.016	.128	.188	.069	.104	.101
Hàvie		.072	.279	.062	.250	.019	.136
Ising		.059	–	.086	.147	.067	.090
Secant		–	–	–	.041	.030	.036
Programmer:		E	B	A	G	L	Mean
Aitken		.062	.078	.092	.112	.015	.072
Compiler:		ALGOL	BASIC	BLISS	FORFOR	FORTEN	Mean
		.096	.089	.180	.151	.153	.134
Language:	MACRO	ALGOL	BASIC	BLISS	FORFOR	FORTEN	Mean
Mean	.112	.032	.136	.097	.106	.069	.090

Table XII. Fraction of Lives Used for Indexing.

Language:		ALGOL	BASIC	BLISS	FORFOR	FORTEN	Mean
Bairstow		.513	.407	.226	.341	.251	.347
Crout		.519	.374	.520	.195	.244	.370
Treesort		.482	.412	.683	.431	.476	.497
PERT		.592	.421	.556	.445	.497	.502
Hàvie		.524	.365	.387	.278	.203	.351
Ising		.571	–	.484	.267	.249	.393
Secant		–	–	–	.376	.406	.392
Programmer:		E	B	A	G	L	Mean
Aitken		.185	.196	.232	.318	.474	.281
Compiler:		ALGOL	BASIC	BLISS	FORFOR	FORTEN	Mean
		.401	.364	.341	.509	.313	.386
Language:	MACRO	ALGOL	BASIC	BLISS	FORFOR	FORTEN	Mean
Mean	.425	.534	.396	.378	.333	.332	.391

needed, some register has to be temporarily stored, and the required value loaded into it. Hence each reference to one of the selected lives costs at most two STORE LOAD pairs.

The following four criteria were used for usefulness of lives:
—The number of references to the life was high.
—The density of references to the life was high.
—The life was long.
—The life was short.

The fourth criterion never gave the lowest cost. The third one rarely gave a low cost, the first two gave the lowest cost almost equally often. Furthermore the criterion that gave the lowest cost often changed with M within the same analysis. The interleaving cost is computed only when needed, i.e. when $N > M$. On the other hand, neither the selection of useless lives nor the cost computation takes local properties of the lives into account; both are based on their global characteristics.

4.2.2 Bedding. The bedding method, on the other hand, is based on the local properties of lives. The idea is to store ("bed") registers in memory when they have long dormant periods. In each such period the number of live registers is reduced by one, at the cost of one STORE LOAD pair. Such periods are known during phase I, but the information is not easily carried into phase II. In phase I, however, we do not know when registers are scarce ($N > M$). Hence bedding must

be applied each time a life has been dormant longer than some time K, regardless of the need for registers during that time.

Our results were obtained using a hybrid method. Registers were bedded by phase I whenever they were dormant more than 200 instructions, and interleaving was used in phase II. The results, given as relative increase in instruction count, are displayed in Table XVI. As is seen, the increase caused by a reduction to 8 registers is less than 1% for 21 of the 41 programs, less than 5% for 30 of them, but runs as high as 50% or more in a few cases. The average increase is 7.9%.

We investigated the bad cases further by using lower values for K, i.e. lives were bedded when they had been dormant for as little as 22 instructions (in one case). Interleaving was applied in phase II as before. As K is reduced the interleaving cost decreases, since there are fewer periods when $N > M$. On the other hand, the bedding cost increases since there are more dormant periods. We have at present no way of telling which K will give the best result. In fact, in a similar analysis of two programs where the cost for $K = 200$ was already low, we found that the cost was lower for $K = 200$ in one case, $K = 100$ in the other. To produce the results given in Table XVII, different values of K were tried until a minimum seemed close. As is seen, the cost has been dramatically reduced for all of the programs, although it still is high for some. These results would reduce the mean of Table XVI from 7.9% to 2.7%.

The values obtained by bedding and interleaving are upper bounds, in the sense that any satisfactory compiler or programmer, knowing the local properties of the program, will select better "useless" lives, and only store them when N is high. He will also avoid unnecessary STOREs. On the other hand, the results were obtained using complete knowledge of the path taken through the program. When the code is written, all possible paths have to be provided for. This implies a less than optimal use of registers in each particular execution. In view of the fact that most lives are short, it is reasonable to assume that the gain by the former factor far outweighs the loss by the latter.

5. Operator Utility

We also used traces to study the utility of data types, data operators, and control operators. For existing operators and types, frequency counts were used. Some desirable but nonexisting operators were detected by observing frequencies of dynamic sequences of instructions.

Frequency studies for individual instructions or groups of instructions have been reported by various authors [1, 2, 4, 8, 9, 12, 16, 17]. Our results agree well with those of Gibson [7] (the Gibson mix), which

Table XIII. Number of Registers Sufficient 100%, 98%, and 90% of the Time (K = 200).

Language:		ALGOL	BASIC	BLISS	FORFOR	FORTEN	Mean
Bairstow	100%	13	10	9	13	12	11.4
	98%	11	7	6	10	9	8.6
	90%	8	6	5	9	7	7.0
Crout	100%	13	7	7	13	12	10.4
	98%	11	7	7	12	8	9.0
	90%	10	6	6	10	7	7.8
Treesort	100%	14	7	6	4	12	8.6
	98%	4	7	5	4	5	5.0
	90%	3	6	5	3	4	4.2
PERT	100%	14	10	7	11	12	10.8
	98%	10	7	6	8	8	7.8
	90%	8	6	5	3	5	5.4
Hávie	100%	14	10	9	10	13	11.2
	98%	11	6	6	6	9	7.6
	90%	9	5	5	5	5	5.8
Ising	100%	14	–	7	11	12	11.0
	98%	11	–	5	7	9	8.0
	90%	10	–	5	3	6	6.0
Secant	100%	–	–	–	13	12	12.5
	98%	–	–	–	6	6	6.0
	90%	–	–	–	5	5	5.0
Programmer:		E	B	A	G	L	Mean
Aitken	100%	7	7	8	7	8	7.4
	98%	7	7	7	7	7	7.0
	90%	7	7	6	6	7	6.4
Compiler:		ALGOL	BASIC	BLISS	FORFOR	FORTEN	Mean
	100%	15	11	13	13	11	12.6
	98%	10	9	6	8	8	8.2
	90%	8	7	5	7	6	6.6
Language:	MACRO	ALGOL	BASIC	BLISS	FORFOR	FORTEN	Mean
Mean 100%	13.0	13.7	8.8	8.2	10.7	12.1	10.4
98%	9.0	9.7	6.8	6.5	7.6	7.7	7.6
90%	7.3	8.0	5.8	5.7	5.4	5.6	6.1

Table XIV. Number of Registers Sufficient 90% of the Time for the Arithmetic Classes FLO, FMD, and FAS (FLO = Floating, FMD = Fixed Mul/Div, FAS = Fixed Add/Sub).

Language:		ALGOL	BASIC	BLISS	FORFOR	FORTEN	Mean
Bairstow	FLO	2	1	2	2	2	1.8
	FMD	1	0	0	1	0	0.4
	FAS	4	2	2	1	2	2.2
Crout	FLO	1	1	1	3	2	1.6
	FMD	0	1	2	4	2	1.8
	FAS	5	1	3	3	3	3.0
Treesort	FLO	0	1	0	0	0	.2
	FMD	1	0	0	0	1	.4
	FAS	1	2	3	1	2	1.8
PERT	FLO	0	1	1	0	0	.4
	FMD	0	0	0	0	0	.0
	FAS	4	2	3	2	3	2.8
Hávie	FLO	1	2	2	2	2	1.8
	FMD	0	0	1	0	0	.2
	FAS	5	2	2	2	3	2.8
Ising	FLO	0	–	0	0	0	.0
	FMD	0	–	0	0	0	.0
	FAS	5	–	4	1	3	3.3
Secant	FLO	–	–	–	2	1	1.5
	FMD	–	–	–	1	1	1.0
	FAS	–	–	–	2	4	3.0
Programmer:		E	B	A	G	L	Mean
Aitken	FLO	2	2	2	2	2	2.0
	FMD	0	0	0	0	1	.2
	FAS	3	2	3	4	3	3.0
Compiler:		ALGOL	BASIC	BLISS	FORFOR	FORTEN	Mean
	FLO	0	0	0	0	0	.0
	FMD	0	1	0	0	0	.2
	FAS	3	2	2	2	2	3.2
Language:	MACRO	ALGOL	BASIC	BLISS	FORFOR	FORTEN	Mean
Mean FLO	.0	.7	1.2	1.2	1.3	1.0	1.0
FMD	.3	.3	.2	.3	.9	.6	.4
FAS	2.3	4.0	1.8	2.8	1.7	2.9	2.4

should be well known. We refer the reader to [10] and [11].

274 of the over 400 instructions were used by our subject set. 75% of the instructions executed were accounted for by the 29 most executed instructions. 133 instructions accounted for 99% of the executed instructions. Over 40% of the executed instructions were moves between registers and primary memory, almost 30% were branching instructions, 12% were fixed-point adds or subtracts. The other categories of [7] each accounted for less than 5%.

We would also point out one particular result, relating to the addressing problem for tests, where the rich set of test instructions on the DECsystem10 permitted some possibly new observations. The test instructions were divided into groups according to the form of their operands, as seen in Table XVIII. Similarly, the programs were divided into three obvious groups. The programs were weighted in inverse proportion to their instruction count, and the distribution of the different groups of test instructions was observed.

Table XVIII clearly shows that comparison of two nonzero values is twice as common as comparison with zero. This is particularly true for recently computed values (contained in registers), in which case the factor is 3. Hence one is led to doubt the utility of condition codes as compared with the more general test instructions. Also noteworthy is the fact that compilers frequently test against small values known when the compiler was written (immediate operands).

5.1 Instruction Sequences

We now describe our attempt to detect data types and operators that could be included in the ISP at a benefit. Such operators manifest themselves as sequences of instructions, viz. those sequences used to interpret the desirable instructions in terms of the existing instruction set. Since such sequences may be of considerable length, a major difficulty is to limit the space and time used by the analysis program. Thus, for one of our subject programs, the number of different pairs of instructions was as high as 2000. If all these were to be extended to triples, quadruples or longer sequences, both space and time required for the analysis would be prohibitive.

We avoided this problem by using a multipass algorithm. Each pass scanned the whole trace; the first pass built the pairs, successive passes extended the existing sequences by one. After each pass the data structure was pruned; only those sequences thought to be significant were retained. The program ran until no sequences were retained, or until an arbitrary preset length of 20 was reached (after 19 passes). Before the results were printed, the counts for all those sequences which had been extended were reduced by the counts of the extensions. Hence only the unextendable fraction of each sequence was included in the final counts.

Five heuristics were used to detect candidates for deletion:

—All sequences whose counts were low compared to the most frequent sequence of the same length were deleted.

—All sequences that were not a significant extension of their leading and trailing longest subsequences were deleted. The intent was to isolate the common part of overlapping sequences as the interesting part.

—By the algorithm used, loops of length L may be represented at L different places in the data structure. When sequences of length $L + 2$ had been generated, all those for which the two last and two first instructions were the same, and which contained a jump instruction, were assumed to be loops of length L. One representation of such loops was retained, the others deleted.

—An attempt was made to detect all but one of several overlapping sequences representing the same longer sequence. Assume that the sequence A B C D E F G occurs frequently in the trace. At the end of pass 4 the sequences A B C D E, B C D E F, and C D E F G are observed to have approximately the same count. The latter two may be deleted, since the former will be extended in later passes.

—An attempt was made to detect all but the most frequent of long sequences with a large degree of overlap.

Using these pruning heuristics, about half the analyses produced one or more sequences of length 20. All analyses produced sequences of length 10 or more.

The heuristics above, as used in our experiments, were not as good as one might desire. In particular, in most analyses several of the sequences obviously overlapped. This caused the reduced counts for the overlapping parts to be much too low. Other sequences were extended too much, or they included only part of what was known from other considerations to be "the right" sequence. Hence a manual, and therefore subjective, analysis was necessary to extract significant results. This was also needed to relate the results back to program fragments with more or less intuitive meaning. During this analysis, the final results were compared with the unreduced counts printed after each pass. This manual analysis could be reduced by improving the existing heuristics and devising new ones. More accurate counts could be obtained by running a second analysis, observing only predetermined sequences or classes of sequences. This was, however, not done.

5.2 Sequence Results

Specific results are presented in [10]. Below we give a survey of those that seemed most important, and a few specific examples.

5.2.1 Subroutine calling sequences.
Calling sequences for subroutines should be better supported by suitable

Table XV. Number of Registers Sufficient 90% of the Time for the Classes NOA, INX, and TOT (NOA = No Arithmetic, INX = Indexing, TOT = Total Class).

Language:		ALGOL	BASIC	BLISS	FORFOR	FORTEN	Mean
Bairstow	NOA	4	4	3	7	5	4.6
	INX	6	3	2	5	5	4.2
	TOT	8	6	5	9	7	7.0
Crout	NOA	6	4	2	3	5	4.0
	INX	9	3	3	2	3	4.0
	TOT	10	6	6	10	7	7.8
	NOA	2	4	2	2	2	2.4
	INX	2	3	3	2	2	2.4
	TOT	3	6	5	3	4	4.2
PERT	NOA	4	4	2	2	3	3.0
	INX	7	3	3	2	2	3.4
	TOT	8	6	5	3	5	5.4
Håvie	NOA	5	3	2	2	2	2.8
	INX	8	3	2	2	2	3.4
	TOT	9	5	5	5	5	5.8
Ising	NOA	6	–	2	2	4	3.5
	INX	9	–	2	2	4	4.3
	TOT	10	–	5	3	6	6.0
Secant	NOA	–	–	–	2	2	2.0
	INX	–	–	–	2	2	2.0
	TOT	–	–	–	5	5	5.0
Programmer:		E	B	A	G	L	Mean
Aitken	NOA	4	4	4	3	2	3.4
	INX	4	3	3	2	5	3.4
	TOT	7	6	6	6	7	6.4
Compiler:		ALGOL	BASIC	BLISS	FORFOR	FORTEN	Mean
	NOA	6	5	4	6	4	5.0
	INX	4	4	2	4	2	3.2
	TOT	8	7	5	7	6	6.6

Language:		MACRO	ALGOL	BASIC	BLISS	FORFOR	FORTEN	Mean
Mean	NOA	5.7	4.5	3.8	2.9	2.9	3.3	3.5
	INX	4.0	6.8	3.0	2.9	2.4	2.9	3.5
	TOT	7.3	8.0	5.8	5.7	5.4	5.6	6.1

Table XVI. Sum Interleaving and Bedding Costs for $K = 200$ When the Number of Registers is Reduced to 10, 8, or 7, Given as Relative Increase in Instruction Count.

Language:		ALGOL	BASIC	BLISS	FORFOR	FORTEN	Mean
Bairstow	10 rg	.057	.000	.005	.017	.009	.018
	8 rg	.231	.001	.005	.136	.095	.094
	7 rg	.371	.002	.009	.254	.184	.164
Crout	10 rg	.077	.000	.004	.440	.016	.107
	8 rg	.385	.000	.004	.757	.022	.234
	7 rg	.773	.000	.004	1.046	.097	.384
Treesort	10 rg	.002	.000	.011	.000	.015	.006
	8 rg	.005	.000	.011	.000	.016	.006
	7 rg	.007	.000	.011	.000	.016	.007
PERT	10 rg	.017	.000	.000	.004	.004	.005
	8 rg	.133	.000	.000	.036	.038	.041
	7 rg	.213	.001	.000	.053	.067	.070
Håvie	10 rg	.060	.000	.002	.001	.006	.014
	8 rg	.575	.001	.003	.005	.045	.126
	7 rg	.734	.003	.008	.018	.072	.167
Ising	10 rg	.068	–	.005	.002	.005	.020
	8 rg	.438	–	.005	.010	.052	.127
	7 rg	.998	–	.005	.031	.106	.285
Secant	10 rg	–	–	–	.004	.005	.005
	8 rg	–	–	–	.012	.017	.015
	7 rg	–	–	–	.018	.023	.021
Programmer:		E	B	A	G	L	Mean
Aitken	10 rg	.003	.003	.002	.001	.002	.002
	8 rg	.003	.003	.002	.001	.002	.002
	7 rg	.003	.003	.013	.001	.005	.005
Compiler:		ALGOL	BASIC	BLISS	FORFOR	FORTEN	Mean
	10 rg	.031	.004	.000	.013	.008	.011
	8 rg	.081	.040	.002	.072	.016	.042
	7 rg	.134	.085	.010	.225	.030	.097

Language:		MACRO	ALGOL	BASIC	BLISS	FORFOR	FORTEN	Mean
Mean	10 rg	.016	.047	.000	.004	.067	.009	.035
	8 rg	.064	.295	.000	.004	.136	.041	.079
	7 rg	.148	.516	.001	.007	.202	.081	.137

instructions to handle parameter transmission, return addresses, and to save and restore registers and other parts of the runtime representation.

The cost of call administration is easily detected for BLISS programs, since stack instructions are used only in this context. There is, however, no reason to believe that this cost is less for other languages usually considered to be "efficient."

The BLISS compiler, which is written in BLISS, and which contains many small subroutines for trivial bookkeeping tasks, spent approximately 25% of its time (to compile the BLISS version of Treesort) in call administration. For one of the FORTRAN compilers, which is also written in BLISS, the same number was approximately 15%.[2]

About $\frac{1}{8}$ of the instructions executed by the BLISS compiler could be saved if the subroutine call and exit instructions (PUSHJ and POPJ) were extended to manipulate the run-time registers, and to remove parameters from the stack on exit.

This would reduce 6 or 8 instructions to 2, and 10 or 12 memory cycles to 5, for each subroutine call. This improvement would fit well into the existing instruction format. In the case of FORTRAN programs it would be useful if parameter descriptors were recognized by the hardware, so that local copies of the actuals could be made by the calling instructions.

The suggested improvements would force representations on the language implementors, and hence reduce flexibility. However, such representations are rarely changed once they are decided, so this would not be a serious objection, particularly not if the instruction set were microprogrammed.

Another observation is interesting in this context: From observing the use of the stack instructions, we know that the BLISS compiler saves and restores about 16,000 registers per second (about 1.15 per routine call). This is the same number as would be saved and restored by 1,000 complete process swaps per second. We believe this to be a high frequency of process swaps for the KA-10 processor. Hence it seems that the cost of register saving caused by routine calls may be considerably larger than the corresponding cost caused by interrupts.

One remark is in order: the BLISS compiler has very many small and frequently called subroutines, and is not typical of common or garden programs. We do not, however, consider this a deficiency. Subroutines are an important ingredient in structuring programs, and should be cheap to use. The experimental results support our plea for more efficient hardware to handle registers and state information in calling mechanisms.

5.2.2 Vector descriptors and operands. A vector type should be introduced. This is motivated not only by the importance of vectors as a mathematical structure, but also by the vector structure of central memory and the effect this has on program structure in general. A vector descriptor should be provided. This should

Table XVII. Best Upper Bound for Relative Increase in Instruction Count, Selected Subject Programs, Best K Tried.

Language:	ALGOL	FORFOR	ALGOL	FORFOR
Algorithm	Bairstow	Bairstow	Crout	Crout
Bedding cost	.049	.017	.078	.114
Interleaving cost	.007	.011	.001	.015
Total cost	.056	.028	.079	.129
K where obtained	25	40	27	22
Same cost for K = 200	.231	.136	.385	.757

Language:	ALGOL	ALGOL	ALGOL
Algorithm	PERT	Håvie	Ising
Bedding cost	.043	.065	.102
Interleaving cost	.001	.005	.008
Total cost	.044	.070	.110
K where obtained	25	30	27
Same cost for K = 200	.133	.575	.438

Table XVIII. Use of Test Instructions, Percentages of Total Instruction Count.

Program type	Compilers	Non-numeric programs	Highly numeric programs	Total subject set
Instruction form				
Register vs. memory	3.0	4.9	4.5	4.5
Register vs. immediate	7.7	1.7	1.0	2.1
Memory vs. 0	2.3	1.7	.9	1.3
Register vs. 0	2.5	1.8	2.1	2.0

make no distinction between vectors allocated by the compilers, and those allocated at run time. Furthermore, it should permit easy description of both row and column vectors of matrices. Operations should include common mathematical operators such as inner product, and also moves, summation, searches in ordered vectors etc. By permitting vectors of different lengths, and in particular length 1, interesting specializations may be obtained, such as initialization by a constant value.

Vector types would, in the extreme, change the ISP radically, as is exemplified by the CDC STAR. We do think, however, that some vector operations would be useful even in more conventional ISPs. Examples are frequent in our programs, although none are as dramatic as the others cited in this section.

5.2.3 String handling. Introduction of a "character string" type would speed up the compilers by a significant amount. Instructions operating on this type should be controlled by a table, indexed by the set of possible characters. The options for each character should include substitution, removal, branching to a special action routine, and termination of the instruction. It should be easy to use these instructions to change encodings, move strings, remove multiple blanks, remove extraneous characters etc. Analysis of routines for I/O formatting, and of COBOL programs, would suggest further options. Typical examples which illustrate the need for such instructions come from the compilers, particularly from BASIC.[3]

5.2.4 Run-time support for languages. The routines for run-time space management, parameter transmis-

sion and similar functions in ALGOL and similar languages are exceedingly expensive. They may consume as much as 50% of the execution time of some ALGOL programs.[4]

5.2.5 Miscellaneous data operators. Other data operators which could be included are: memory to memory moves (unless subsumed under the vector type), type conversions, and packing and unpacking of partwords. Some of these are already in the DECsystem10 ISP, but are not accessible to high-level language programmers. Hence this is a language problem as much as an ISP problem.[5]

5.2.6 Loop control. There should be an instruction for loop control which increments a fullword counter in one register and tests it against a fullword upper bound in another register. This instruction is also easily accommodated within the DECsystem10 ISP structure. It would save up to 5% of the execution time of some programs, reduce program size, and increase readability.[6]

6. Conclusions

In spite of the restricted set of experiments performed, we believe some of the results produced to be valid, not only for the DECsystem10, but for all register structured ISPs. This is in particular true for the results on simultaneous use of registers, and on the cost of subroutine calls.

It seems, for instance, that eight registers would be sufficient for a general register ISP similar to the DECsystem10. The result is no longer valid when the registers are used for other tasks than in this ISP, such as base register addressing, program counter, hardware defined stacks, etc.

Similarly the results on overhead in subroutine calling are both important and portable. Results from other ISPs would often exhibit an even worse situation, since the handling of return linkages for recursive or reentrant subprograms is more cumbersome. On the other hand, the situation can easily be improved by introducing instructions tailored to the needs of the commonly used languages. An ideal solution would be to permit a restricted form of writable microprogram, defining special instructions for each language. This would also be helpful with respect to run-time support for ALGOL and other languages.

Some of the results presented here and in [10], particularly those stemming from unnecessary generality, might seem like a severe criticism of the DECsystem10. This is a consequence of the deplorable fact that our methods only measure the time cost of ISP features. The richness and generality of the DECsystem10 ISP make it a good ISP to program for, and contribute to a low programming cost and a low memory space for programs. For our other points of

criticism we note that although the DECsystem10 leaves room for improvement, the problems we point out are not solved in a better way in other common ISPs.

Our work has barely scratched the surface of a large area of investigation. In particular, it would be interesting to study information used for address calculation and information used for control purposes. We would like to know more about how such information is computed, and how the two kinds interact. We hope to make this the subject of further research. The various solutions to the addressing problem for test instructions should also be investigated.

Acknowledgment. W.A. Wulf provided initial impetus to and considerable support and ideas throughout the project that led to this paper.

Received April 1975, revised January 1976

Notes
1. By an Instruction Set Processor, or ISP [3], we mean the logical processor which processes the instruction set, as divorced from its physical realization. Example: The IBM 360/370 is one ISP which has several physical realizations.

2. This is illustrated by the following sequences from the BLISS compiler:

PUSH PUSHJ JSP PUSH HRRZ	(14.3% of the execution time)
JRST POP POPJ SUB	(7.2% of the execution time)
JRST POP POP POPJ SUB	(3.5% of the execution time)

Only 3 of these 14 instructions are used in connection with parameter transmission; the rest are used for state saving, environment definition, and linkage handling.

3. The sequence:

SKIPE ILDB JRST CAIE CAIN CAIN CAIE CAIN CAIE CAIN CAIG CAIA CAIGE IDPB SKIPE SOSLE AOJA

consumed 20.7% of the compilation time. Its purpose is to move a line while removing extraneous characters like TABs, LINEFEEDS, etc. Similarly the sequence

ILDB CAIN IDPB JRST

moves a line stopping at a RETURN. it consumed 8% of the compilation time.

4. The following example is from the Ising program:

AOBJP MOVE MOVE ADDI HLLZ SETZB ROTC EXCH ROTC ROT ANDI HLRZ HRRZ ANDI LSH ANDI LSH

It consumed 19% of the time. From PERT we have:

XCT PUSHJ PUSHJ MOVE PUSH MOVEI MOVE PUSH HLRZ PUSHJ MOVE ADD MOVE POPJ POP POP TLNE POPJ MOVE POPJ

This is a complete call of a formal parameter by name (thunk), starting at the call within the procedure body (XCT) and ending at the POPJ back into it. The actual parameter is a vector element. Time consumed by this sequence was about 20% of the total.

5. An example is the sequence MOVE IDIV, used to unpack left halfwords, which consumes 45% of the time for the FORTEN version of Treesort. The HLRZ instruction used for the same purpose in the BLISS version consumes only 7.5% of the time of that version. The rest of these routines are about equally efficient.

6. The function shows up as:

ADDI AOJL or GAMGE AOJA MOVEM in FORTRAN
JRST AOS CAMLE in ALGOL,
MOVE FADR JRST CAMLE MOVEM in BASIC, and
AOJA CAMLE in BLISS.

References

1. Alexander, W.G. How a programming language is used. Rep. CSRG-10, Comptr. Res. Group, U. of Toronto, Toronto, Canada, Feb. 1972.

2. Arbuckle, R.A. Computer analysis and thruput evaluation. *Computers and Automation* (Jan. 1966), 12–15 and 19.

3. Bell, C.G., and Newell, A. *Computer Structures, Readings and Examples.* McGraw-Hill, New York, 1971.

4. Connors, W.D., Mercer, V.S., and Sorlini, T.A. S/360 instruction usage distribution. Rep. TR 00.2025, IBM Systems Development Div., Poughkeepsie, N.Y., May 8, 1970.

5. Foster, C.C., Gonter, R.H., and Riseman, E.M. Measures of opcode utilization. *IEEE Trans. Computers C-20*, 5 (May 1971), 582–584.

6. Foster, C.C., and Gonter, R.M. Conditional interpretation of operation codes. *IEEE Trans. Computers C-20*, 1 (Jan. 1971), 108–111.

7. Gibson, J.C. The Gibson mix. Rep. TR 00.2043, IBM Systems Development Div., Poughkeepsie, N. Y., 1970.

8. Gonter, R.H. Comparison of the Gibson mix with the UMASS mix. Pub. No. TN/RCC/004, Res. Comptg. Center, U. of Massachusetts, Amherst, Mass.

9. Herbst, E.H., Metropolis, N., and Wells, M.B. Analysis of problem codes on the MANIAC. *Math. Tables and Other Aids to Comput. 9* (Jan. 1955), 14–20.

10. Lunde, Å. Evaluation of instruction set processor architecture by program tracing. Ph.D. Th., Dep. Comptr. Sci., Carnegie-Mellon U., Pittsburgh, Pa., July 1974 (available as AD A004824 from Nat. Tech. Inform. Service, Springfield, Va).

11. Lunde, Å. More data on the O/W ratios. A note on a paper by Flynn. *Computer Architecture News 4*, 1 (March 1975), 9–13.

12. Raichelson, E., and Collins, G. A method for comparing the internal operating speeds of computers. *Comm. ACM 7*, 5 (May 1966), 309–310.

13. Tjaden, G.S., and Flynn, M.J. Detection and parallel execution of independent instructions. *IEEE Trans. Computers C-19*, 10 (Oct. 1970), 889–895.

14. Wilner, W.T. Design of the Burroughs B1700. Proc. AFIPS 1972 FJCC, Vol. 41, AFIPS Press, Montvale, N.J., pp. 489–497.

15. Wilner, W.T. Burroughs B1700 memory utilization. Proc. AFIPS 1972 FJCC, Vol. 41, AFIPS Press, Montvale, N.J., pp. 579–586.

16. Winder, R.O. Data base for computer performance evaluation. RCA-reprint PE-517, RCA David Sarnoff Res. Ctr., Princeton, N.J., 1971.

17. Winder, R.O. A data base for computer evaluation. *Computer 6*, 3 (March 1973), 25–29.

18. Wulf, W.A., Russell, D.B., and Habermann, A.N. BLISS: A language for systems programming. *Comm. ACM 14*, 12 (Dec. 1971), 780–790.

"Implications of Structured Programming for Machine Architecture" by A.S. Tanenbaum from *Communications of the ACM,* Volume 21, Number 3, March 1978, pages 237–246. Copyright 1978, Association for Computing Machinery, Inc., reprinted by permission.

Computer Systems   G. Bell, S. H. Fuller, and D. Siewiorek, Editors

Implications of Structured Programming for Machine Architecture

Andrew S. Tanenbaum
Vrije Universiteit, The Netherlands

Based on an empirical study of more than 10,000 lines of program text written in a GOTO-less language, a machine architecture specifically designed for structured programs is proposed. Since assignment, CALL, RETURN, and IF statements together account for 93 percent of all executable statements, special care is given to ensure that these statements can be implemented efficiently. A highly compact instruction encoding scheme is presented, which can reduce program size by a factor of 3. Unlike a Huffman code, which utilizes variable length fields, this method uses only fixed length (1-byte) opcode and address fields. The most frequent instructions consist of a single 1-byte field. As a consequence, instruction decoding time is minimized, and the machine is efficient with respect to both space and time.

Key Words and Phrases: machine architecture, computer architecture, computer organization, instruction set design, program characteristics

CR Categories: 4.12, 4.22, 4.9, 6.21

General permission to make fair use in teaching or research of all or part of this material is granted to individual readers and to nonprofit libraries acting for them provided that ACM's copyright notice is given and that reference is made to the publication, to its date of issue, and to the fact that reprinting privileges were granted by permission of the Association for Computing Machinery. To otherwise reprint a figure, table, other substantial excerpt, or the entire work requires specific permission as does republication, or systematic or multiple reproduction.

Author's address: Computer Science Group, Vrije Universteit, Amsterdam, The Netherlands.
© 1978 ACM 0001-0782/78/0300-0237 $00.75

1. Introduction

Information about the way computers are actually used is of great importance to computer architects, programming language designers, and compiler writers. Whether or not a certain semantic primitive should be included in a machine's instruction set, made a language construct, or carefully optimized depends primarily upon its projected frequency of usage. This information can only be obtained empirically, since there is no way to predict a priori, whether, for example, REPEAT . . . UNTIL statements are more useful than CASE statements.

The ways in which certain programming languages are used has already been studied: Knuth [6] has examined Fortran; Salvadori, Gordon, and Capstick [9] have examined Cobol; Alexander and Wortman [1] have examined XPL; Wortman [15] has examined student PL.

In recent years unstructured programs have fallen into disrepute. A growing number of people have come to recognize the importance of structuring programs so that they can be easily understood. Although there is no generally accepted definition of structured programming yet (see [2] for discussion), most programmers intuitively realize that breaking programs up into small, easily understood procedures, and drastically reducing or even eliminating GOTO statements greatly improves readability. We are even beginning to see the development of new programming languages which have been intentionally designed without a GOTO statement [16].

In order to determine what characteristics structured programs have, it is necessary to collect and dissect a number of them. These data can then be used as a basis for designing computer architectures that can execute structured programs efficiently. The next section of this article describes a GOTO-less language we have developed to encourage good programming style. The third and fourth section contain an analysis of a collection of procedures written in this language. The fifth and sixth sections propose and discuss a machine architecture based upon our findings.

2. The Experiment

We have developed a typeless GOTO-less language (SAL) specifically intended for system programming [10]. It has been implemented [11] on a PDP-11/45, and used, among other things, to construct a general purpose time sharing system for that computer. The language resembles BCPL [8]; its control structures are similar to those of Pascal [5]. A summary of the executable statements follows.

Assignment
CALL
IF . . . THEN . . . ELSE . . . FI
RETURN

```
FOR . . . FROM . . . TO . . . BY . . . DO . . . OD
WHILE . . . DO . . . OD
REPEAT . . . UNTIL . . . LITNU
DO FOREVER . . . OD
EXITLOOP
CASE . . . IN . . . . . . . . . . . , OUT . . . ESAC
PRINT
```

Expressions are evaluated strictly left to right, with no precedence or parentheses. ELSE parts in IF statements are optional. RETURN statements exit the current procedure, and optionally return a value, so that a procedure may be used as a function. Procedures not returning an explicit value may terminate by "falling through", i.e. the END statement implies RETURN.

The WHILE statement tests at the top of the loop, whereas the REPEAT statement tests at the end of the loop. DO FOREVER statements are the same as WHILE TRUE DO; they are useful in operating system modules that endlessly get and carry out service requests, the "get" primitive blocking the process in the absence of a message. EXITLOOP is a forward jump out of one level of enclosing loop of any kind (FOR, WHILE, REPEAT, or DO FOREVER). Our experience indicates that this, plus RETURN, is sufficient most of the time. The CASE statement contains an integer expression that selects one of the clauses to be executed, or the OUT clause if the integer is out of range (as in Algol 68 [12]). There is no GOTO statement.

In addition to the above statements, there are a variety of declarations, debugging facilities and compiler directives.

The basic data types are machine words (including the general registers and the i/o device registers, accessible as the top 4K memory words), one-dimensional arrays of words and characters, bit fields, and programmer defined data structures consisting of a collection of named fields, each field being a word, character, bit field, or array. There are two scope levels, local (stack storage, reserved upon procedure entry, and released upon procedure exit), and global (static storage). A program consists of one or more procedures, and zero or more modules that declare and initialize external variables.

The programs examined for this research were all written by the faculty and graduate students of the Computer Science Group at the Vrije Universiteit. All the programmers involved made a very deliberate effort to produce "clean," well structured programs, knowing full well that succeeding generations of students would pore over their code line by line. This is clearly a different situation than one finds in the average, garden variety, computer center.

The amount of memory available on our PDP-11/45 was so small that the initial compiler could not handle procedures much larger than two pages of source code. This defect was remedied by declaring it to be a virtue, and by continually exhorting the programmers to produce short, well structured procedures. (The mean number of executable statements per procedure turned out to be 18.2). The combination of the GOTO-less language, the quality of the programmers, an environment with a long Algol tradition and no Fortran tradition, and our deliberate efforts to produce intelligible programs has resulted in what we believe to be state-of-the-art structured programs.

3. Characteristics of the Programs

For this study we have used a specially instrumented compiler to collect information on more than 300 procedures used in various system programs. Most of these were related to the time sharing system project. The results presented should be interpreted keeping in mind that operating system modules may systematically differ from say, applications programs, in certain ways, e.g. they have little i/o.

Where relevant, both static and dynamic measurements are given. Static measurements were obtained by having the compiler count the number of occurrences of the item in the source text. Dynamic measurements were obtained by having the compiler insert code into the object program to increment counters during program execution. The results are given in Tables I–VIII.

4. Discussion of the Results

According to our data, a typical procedure consists of 8 or 9 assignment statements, 4 calls to other procedures, 3 IF statements, 1 loop, and 1 escape (RETURN or EXITLOOP). Two of the assignment statements simply assign a constant to a scalar variable, one assigns one scalar variable to another, and 3 or 4 more involve only one operand on the right hand size. The entire procedure probably contains only 2 arithmetic operators. Two of the three conditions in the IF statements involve only a single relational operator, probably = or ≠.

The general conclusion that can be drawn from this data is the same as Knuth drew from his Fortran study: programs tend to be very simple. Combining this conclusion with the Bauer principle (If you do not use a feature, you should not have to pay for it), we suggest that most present day machine architectures could be considerably improved by catering more to the commonly occurring special cases. This will be discussed in detail in the next section. First we have a few more comments about the measurements.

In some cases there are significant differences between the static and dynamic measurements. Some of these differences are genuine, e.g. the operating system is constantly looking for internal inconsistencies in its tables. If an error is detected, an error handling

Table I. Percent Distribution of Executable Statements.

Statement Type	Static	Dynamic
Assignment	46.5	41.9
CALL	24.6	12.4
IF	17.2	36.0
RETURN	4.2	2.6
FOR	3.4	2.1
EXITLOOP	1.4	1.6
WHILE	1.1	1.5
REPEAT	0.5	0.1
DO FOREVER	0.5	0.8
CASE	0.3	1.2
PRINT	0.3	<0.05

Table II. Percent Distribution of Assignment Statement Types.

Type	Static	Dynamic
variable=constant	21.7	19.2
variable=variable	9.5	9.1
variable=function call	4.4	1.9
variable=array element	4.3	3.3
array element=constant	4.1	2.8
array element=variable	4.1	2.9
array element=array element	0.9	1.8
array element=function call	0.5	0.1
other forms with 1 rhs term	30.5	25.2
forms with 2 rhs terms	15.2	20.4
forms with 3 rhs terms	3.0	6.9
forms with 4 rhs terms	1.5	5.9
forms with ≥5 rhs terms	0.3	0.3

Table III. Percent Distribution of Operand Types

Type	Static	Dynamic
constant	40.0	32.8
simple variable	35.6	41.9
array element	9.3	9.2
field of structure	7.1	11.1
function call	4.8	1.6
bit field	3.2	3.3

Table IV. Percent Distribution of Arithmetic Operators.

Operator	Static	Dynamic
+	50.0	57.4
−	28.3	25.5
×	14.6	13.2
/	7.0	3.8

Table V. Percent Distribution of Relational Operators.

Operator	Static	Dynamic
=	48.3	50.6
≠	22.1	18.6
>	11.8	10.2
<	9.5	9.0
≥	4.5	8.4
≤	3.8	3.3

Table VI. Percent of all Procedures with N Formal Parameters.

N	Static	Dynamic
0	41.0	21.2
1	19.0	27.6
2	15.0	23.3
3	9.3	10.8
4	7.3	8.8
5	5.3	6.6
6	2.3	0.6
7	0.3	0.2
8	0.3	<0.05
≥9	<0.05	1.0

Table VII. Percent of all Procedures with N Local Scalar Variables.

N	Static	Dynamic
0	21.5	30.7
1	17.2	26.5
2	19.8	15.4
3	13.5	4.2
4	8.3	4.9
5	5.3	10.0
6	4.6	1.6
7	3.6	1.0
8	1.3	1.6
9	1.0	0.8
10	0.7	<0.05
≥11	3.3	3.0

Table VIII. Percent Distribution of Number of Statements in "THEN" Part of IF Statements.

Statements	Static
1	47.4
2	20.5
3	9.9
4	5.8
5	2.3
6	3.4
7	1.2
8	1.1
9	2.0
≥10	6.1

procedure is called. During normal operation there are no inconsistencies, so these error handlers are not called. These CALL statements increase the static number of CALL's but not the dynamic number.

Furthermore, an IF statement containing a single CALL statement in its THEN part and a single CALL statement in its ELSE part will be counted as one IF and two CALL's in the static statistics, but one IF and one CALL in the dynamic statistics, since only one branch is actually taken per execution. This effect increases the proportion of IF statements relative to other statements in the dynamic statistics.

On the other hand, a single loop executed 10,000 times gives grossly disproportionate weight to the statements in the loop in (only) the dynamic statistics. Thus the dynamic statistics may in fact be based on a very

much smaller sample than the more than 10,000 lines of source text used to derive the static statistics. For this reason the static statistics are probably more meaningful. In the remainder of this paper we will use the static statistics.

From the fact that 5.5 percent of the statements are loops, and 1.4 percent are EXITLOOP's, we estimate that at least 25 percent of the loops are "abnormally" terminated. (In addition, an unknown number of loops are terminated by RETURN). The

Table IX. Comparison of Static Executable Statement Distribution (percent).

Statement type	SAL	XPL	Fortran
Assignment	47	55	51
CALL	25	17	5
IF	17	17	10
Loops	6	5	9
RETURN	4	4	4
GOTO	0	1	9

Table X. Summary of EM-1 Instructions and Number of Opcodes Allocated to Each.

Instruction description	Format 1	2	3A
push constant onto stack	3	2	
push local onto stack	12	1	
push external onto stack	8	1	
pop local from stack	12	1	
pop external from stack	8	1	
zero address ADD, SUB, MUL, DIV	4		
increment local	12	1	
zero local	12	1	
increment top word on stack	1		
push array element onto stack		2	
pop array element from stack		2	
call		1	
load address		1	
load indirect		1	
mark	3	1	
advance stack pointer		1	
return	1		
for instruction			2
branch forward unconditionally	34	1	
branch backward unconditionally		1	
branch if operand 1=operand 2	12	1	
branch if operand 1≠operand 2	20	1	
branch if operand 1≤operand 2	8	1	
branch if operand 1≥operand 2	8	1	
branch if operand 1<operand 2	4	1	
branch if operand 1>operand 2	4	1	
branch if operand=0	12	1	
branch if operand≠0	20	1	
branch if operand≤0	8	1	
branch if operand≥0	8	1	
branch if operand<0	4	1	
branch if operand>0	4	1	
opcode 255 (i.e. use formats 3B, 4)	1		

discussion currently raging in the literature [7] about how premature loop termination should be incorporated into language syntax is not irrelevant.

Since measurements of the type presented in this paper are obviously very sensitive to idiosyncracies of one's programming style, it is interesting to compare our results to previously published work. Table IX compares executable statement distribution for 3 studies cited in Section 1. One difference between Fortran and the other languages stands out immediately: Fortran programs have relatively few procedure calls. This suggests that they are not well modularized. From Knuth's data (his Table I) we compute that the average Fortran subroutine has 86.3 executable statements, vs. 28.6 for XPL and 18.2 for SAL, which agrees with this hypothesis.

Our data gives an average of 0.45 arithmetic operators per expression, which agrees well with Alexander's and Wortman's figure of 0.41. Likewise, our measurement of 1.22 operators per conditional expression agrees with their value of 1.19 logical plus relational operators. Such good agreement enhances one's confidence in the universality of the results.

5. A Proposal for a Machine Architecture

Most present day computers have an architecture designed in the early 1960's. They have remained substantially unchanged for a decade in the name of compatibility in spite of their obstacles to generating efficient code from high level languages. A machine architecture based on the characteristics of the programs described in the previous sections is sketched below. The architecture is specifically intended for block structured languages that permit recursion, i.e. Algol-like languages.

Our architecture has two explicit goals: 1. minimizing program size, and 2. providing a target language to which compilation is straightforward. We choose to minimize program size rather than maximize execution speed for several reasons. First, execution speed depends not only on the raw clock rate, but also on the characteristics of the underlying microinstruction set. Given a high level language benchmark program and two proposed instruction sets, it is possible to determine unambiguously which object program is smaller, but not which is faster. (By hypothesizing a faster clock or better microarchitecture either machine can be speeded up). In other words, minimizing size is a more clearly defined goal than maximizing speed.

Second, size and speed are highly intertwined. All other factors being equal, a shorter program will execute faster than a longer one since fewer bits need be processed. If the memory bandwidth is N bits/sec and the mean instruction size is L bits, the maximum instruction execution rate will be N/L instructions/sec. The smaller L is, the faster the machine can be. Furthermore, on a machine with virtual memory, reducing program size reduces the number of page faults, which, in turn, reduces the time required to process the page faults, thereby speeding up execution.

Third, on large computers with sophisticated multiprogramming systems, a decrease in program size means an increase in the degree of multiprogramming, hence a higher CPU utilization, as well as less swapping.

Fourth, the small amount of memory available on minicomputers is often a serious limitation. Making the program fit into the memory may take precedence over all other considerations.

Fifth, on mini and micro computer systems, the cost of memory frequently is much larger than the CPU cost. Reducing memory requirements has a much greater effect on total system cost than reducing execution time.

The fact that few compilers for third generation computers can produce code that even comes close to what a skilled assembly language programmer can generate argues strongly for redesigning machine architectures so that compilers can do their job better. (See [11] for some statistics). It is for this reason that we consider a stack machine, since generating efficient reverse Polish is simpler than generating efficient code for a register oriented machine. We assume the presence of a cache to eliminate the need for memory cycles when referencing the stack.

The design described below is intended for implementing modern programming languages such as Algol 60, Algol 68, Pascal, XPL, BCPL, SAL, and others of this genre, since they tend to facilitate rather than hinder the writing of well structured programs.

The proposed machine, which we shall call EM-1 (Experimental Machine-1) has a paged, segmented virtual memory. The program and data reside in different address spaces (like the PDP-11/45), so that instruction space segment 0 is distinct from data segment 0. An instruction space segment is a sequence of 8-bit bytes, each with a unique address. A data space segment is a sequence of words of N bits each (N is left unspecified here). The word length for data space segments may be different from that of instruction space segments. (See Table X.)

One data space segment is special: the stack. The stack has associated with it a stack pointer register (SP) that points to the top word on it. Whenever a procedure is entered, a new frame is allocated on the stack for the administration, actual parameters, and locals. The frame is released upon procedure exit. Figure 1 depicts the stack for the following Algol 60 program.

```
begin integer e1, e2, e3; integer array e4[1:3];
  proc p1;
  begin integer k1, k2; p2(k1, k2)
  end;
  proc p2(formal1, formal2);
  begin integer k1, k2; p2(k1, k2)
    integer array n5[1:4], n6[0:1];
    comment snapshot of Figure 1 taken here;
  end;
  p1
end
```

When p2 returns, SP will be reset to point to k2, thus removing that part of the stack marked "current stack frame" in Figure 1.

The stack frame for a procedure consists of 4 areas: (1) the administration information; (2) the actual parameters; (3) the local scalar variables and array descriptors; and (4) the elements of local arrays. The sizes of areas (1–3) are always known at compile time; the size of area (4) may not be known until run time.

A special hardware register, LB (Local Base) points

Fig. 1.

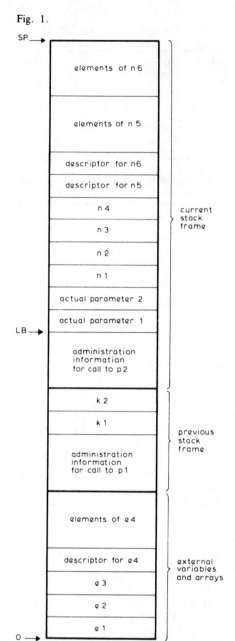

to the beginning of the local variables. Local variables are specified by giving their positions relative to LB.

The administration area contains the calling procedure's return address, the previous value of LB, and other (language dependent) information. It is assumed that the microprogram knows the size and organization of the administration area; a special instruction could be executed at the beginning of each program to tell it. Actual parameters can be addressed by giving their distance from LB, just as locals. Note that the administration area is not counted in order to reduce the size of the constants needed.

A procedure call takes place in the following steps:

1. A MARK instruction is executed to deposit the static and dynamic links on the stack. The MARK instruction has one operand which tells how much the static depth of nesting is increased or decreased.

This is needed to update the static chain. The MARK instruction also reserves space for the return address to be deposited subsequently.

2. The calling procedure pushes the actual parameters onto the stack.
3. A call instruction is executed, transferring control to the called procedure. The call instruction has as operand the index of a procedure descriptor, discussed later. This instruction must deposit the return address in the place reserved for it by the MARK instruction, update LB and transfer control.
4. The called procedure executes a single instruction that increments SP to reserve as much local storage as is initially needed; this instruction could also initialize the local variables to 0 or a special "undefined" value such as 1000 . . . 000 (two's complement -0). If more local storage is needed during execution of the procedure, e.g. for an Algol 68 local generator, SP can simply be advanced again.

We propose an addressing mechanism with distinct instructions for the 2 most important cases: local and external variables. Each instruction must provide an integer offset telling which variable is intended. Locals are offset above LB, and externals are offset from address 0 of the stack segment. For the purposes of addressing, procedure parameters are the same as locals.

Two other addressing forms are needed but are much less important. One is for full virtual addresses consisting of a segment and word within the segment. The other is for accessing intermediate lexicographical levels in block structured languages by means of a (relative lexicographical level, offset) pair. Rather than using a display, which must be frequently updated at considerable cost, we propose that at some position within the administration area known to the microprogram is the LB value of the most recent incarnation of the procedure in which the current procedure is nested (i.e. the static link). Given a (relative lexicographical level, offset) pair, the microprogram can follow the chain and locate variables at any outer static level. Note that the penalty for accessing intermediate levels is only a few microinstructions and one memory reference for each level of nesting followed. The combination of infrequent usage and a small penalty per use makes this method attractive since it reduces procedure call overhead, which is far more crucial.

The stack is also used for all arithmetic and logical operations, shifting, etc. An assignment is performed by first pushing the value to be assigned onto the stack (or perhaps its descriptor, if provision is made for assigning entire arrays in one instruction), and then popping it to its destination, a total of 2 instructions. The statement $A = B \times C$ is handled by 4 instructions: PUSH B; PUSH C; MULTIPLY; POP A.

The advantage of a stack type architecture for arithmetic is clear: compilers can translate expressions to reverse Polish very simply, with no complicated

register optimization needed. High execution speed can be attained by a hardware cache memory that retains the most recently referenced words (i.e. the top of the stack) in high speed storage, or by having the microprogram keep them in its scratchpad memory. If the arithmetic expressions evaluated are simple, little cache or scratchpad storage will be needed. Our data indicate that 80 percent of all expressions consist of a single term, 95 percent consists of 1 or 2 terms and 99.7 percent consists of 4 or fewer terms, meaning that rarely will more than 4 operands be on the stack simultaneously.

Most of the instructions require an opcode and a small constant, which we call the "offset." The offset is generally used to select one of the local variables, one of the external variables, the number of bytes to skip (branch instructions), etc. The following five instruction formats are used by EM-1.

Format	Bytes	Description
1	1	byte 1 = opcode + offset (arithmetic sum)
2	2	byte 1 = opcode, byte 2 = offset
3A	3	byte 1 = opcode, bytes 2,3 = offset
3B	3	byte 1 = 255, byte 2 = opcode, byte 3 = offset
4	4	byte 1 = 255, byte 2 = opcode, bytes 3,4 = offset

The choice of machine instructions, and their assignment to formats, should be carefully arranged to minimize program size (based on the data of Section 3). In particular, an effort should be made to insure that the most common statements can be translated into 1 byte instructions most of the time. The scheme described below is constrained by the fact that the total number of format 1 instructions plus format 2 instructions plus format 3A instructions must not exceed 255. Some instructions, may occur several times in the order code, e.g. push constant onto the stack occurs in formats 1, 2, and 4, with a different range of constants provided in each form.

The idea of using shorter bit patterns for common instructions and longer bit patterns for infrequent instructions is not new. Huffman [4] gives a method for encoding items whose probabilities of occurrence are known, in the minimum number of bits. An approximation of this technique has been used in the design of the Burroughs B1700 S-machines (Wilner, [13, 14]). In the SDL S-machine, opcodes can be 4, 6, or 10 bits, and addresses 8, 11, 13, or 16 bits. A single address instruction can have a length of 12, 14, 15, 17, 18, 19, 20, 21, 22, 23, or 26 bits. Since the B1700 microarchitecture is extremely flexible (among other things being able to read an arbitrary length bit string—up to 24 bits—out of memory beginning at an arbitrary bit, in a single microinstruction) the use of peculiar length instructions does not slow down interpretation.

However, nearly all other computers are based upon a memory organization using fixed length words. For a microprogram with internal registers, bus widths etc. of 8, 16, or 32 bits interpreting a "machine" language whose instructions came in units of 12, 14, 15, 17, 18, 19, 20, 21, 22, 23, or 26 bits would be unbearably slow, since nearly every instruction would straddle word or byte boundaries, necessitating time consuming shifting and masking operations to extract the opcode and address fields. The scheme described by Wilner is only feasible if every single bit in memory has a unique address, a situation which is rarely the case.

The instruction set of EM-1, in contrast, also provides a very efficient method for encoding instructions, but is based on a memory in which every 8-bit byte has a unique address, rather than every bit having a unique address. This makes the principles of the EM-1 design applicable to a much larger number of computers than one utilizing arbitrary length bit fields.

From Table I we see that the assignment, IF, CALL, RETURN and FOR statements together account for 96 percent of the source statements. Therefore we will design an instruction set to handle the object code from these statements efficiently. To push local variables (including parameters) onto the stack, we propose 12 distinct 1-byte (format 1) opcodes, one each for offsets 0–11. Twelve instructions allow access to all the locals (and parameters) in 94.6 percent of the procedures, and to more than 50 percent of the locals in the remaining procedures. For example, opcodes 114–125 might be used for PUSH LOCAL 0, PUSH LOCAL 1, . . . , PUSH LOCAL 11. There is no need to have distinct "opcode" and "address" bits.

Eight opcodes will be allocated to stacking the 8 external variables at the base of the stack segment. Since 81.4 percent of the constants in our data were either 0, 1, or 2, we allocate 3 opcodes for pushing these constants onto the stack.

At this point 23 of the 255 available 1 byte instructions have been used. Another 20 are needed for popping values from the stack. To handle programs with up to 256 locals, or externals, 4 format 2 instructions are needed: 2 push and 2 pop. Two more opcodes (format 2) are needed to push positive and negative constants up to 256 onto the stack. Format 4 (16 bit offset) can contain instructions with larger offsets for truly pathological programs. By including zero address (stack) instructions for add, subtract, multiply, and divide, we have sufficient instructions to evaluate most scalar expressions, using 53 of the opcodes.

Setting local variables to zero, and incrementing them by 1, are so common that we allocate 24 format 1 and two format 2 opcodes for this purpose. Incrementing the top of the stack is also worth an opcode.

Array accesses are accomplished using descriptors on the stack. Each descriptor (which may be 1 or more words, depending on N, the word length) contains the bounds and strides, S_i, for the array. For example, the address of $A[i, j, k]$ can be found from

$$\text{address} = S_0 + S_1 \times i + S_2 \times j + S_3 \times k$$

where the strides can be computed once and for all as soon as the bounds are known, at compile time in many cases, and at run time in the others. The descriptor must also contain the number of dimensions and the element size (and the segment number, for nonlocal arrays).

Array elements are accessed as follows. First the subscripts are stacked, requiring at least one instruction per subscript. Then a PUSH ELEMENT instruction is executed, specifying the offset of the descriptor from LB. This instruction removes all the subscripts from the stack, and replaces them with the selected element. The instruction also performs all bounds checking (unless disabled) and traps upon detecting a subscript error. A second opcode is needed for a POP ELEMENT instruction that first pops the subscripts and then the value. With these two instructions, the statement $A[I] := B[J]$ can usually be compiled into only 6 bytes of object code, including all bounds checking (PUSH J; PUSH ELEM; PUSH I; POP ELEM). This is a substantial improvement over most conventional designs. Four format 2 instructions are needed for pushing and popping local and external array elements.

Note that this addressing scheme is not affected by the size of the arrays. Assuming that a descriptor can fit in a single machine word, a procedure with ≤ 256 large arrays could nevertheless perform all array accesses using exclusively format 2 instructions.

For calling procedures, we envision one format 2 instruction whose offset is an index into a table held in a special data segment. Each table entry could contain the segment and address of the object code, possibly a "not yet linked" bit, to implement dynamic linking as in MULTICS, and possibly some protection machinery to keep less privileged procedures from calling more privileged ones. The symbolic name might also be present for debugging purposes and a counter to be incremented by the microprogram upon each call might be provided for performance monitoring.

To allow the instruction to locate the administration area in order to deposit the return address there, and to update LB, the number of words of parameters is also needed. For programs with up to 256 procedures, the call instruction will be 2 bytes, although a method to reduce this to 1 byte in most cases will be described below.

No additional instructions are needed for call-by-value. For call-by-reference an additional format 2 instruction to push an address onto the stack would be useful, along with one to fetch a parameter passed by reference (i.e. load indirect). The three most common types of procedure calls are to increase the depth of static nesting by 1, leave it unchanged, and decrease it by 1. Three opcodes are devoted to the three corresponding MARK instructions.

After a MARK instruction the distribution of the next few instructions is radically more different than the normal one. This fact can be exploited to reduce the procedure call instruction to 1 byte in many cases, using a generalization of the idea of Foster and Gonter [3]. The only instructions than can follow a MARK instruction are those needed to pass the parameters, if any, and the CALL itself. Most parameters are constants, variables, or simple expressions, which can usually be passed using only a limited number of different instructions, mostly load type instructions. About 200 opcodes could be reserved for CALL's, each corresponding to a specific procedure descriptor. These CALL instructions would each require only 1 byte.

The simplest way to implement this would be to have the microprogram maintain the microaddress of the start of the instruction fetch loop in one of its registers. At the end of the execution phase of each interpreted instruction the microprogram would jump indirectly to this register. The MARK instruction would reload this register with the address of an alternative fetch loop, which would merely use a different branch table, in effect temporarily remapping the opcodes. The CALL instruction could restore the normal opcodes by resetting just one internal register. The use of opcode remapping can also be used in any other context with explicit first and last instructions.

An instruction with a 1-byte offset is needed by the called program to advance SP. The return instruction, which needs no offset, restores the stacked program counter and previous LB value (which are at known positions below the current LB) and resets SP.

Our proposed FOR statement instructions are based upon our measurement that 95 percent of the loops have a BY part of +1 or −1. Before the loop, the controlled variable is initialized, and the TO part is evaluated and pushed onto the stack. The EM-1 FOR instruction reads the TO part and the controlled variable. If the termination condition is met, a forward branch out of the loop occurs. Otherwise the controlled variable is updated and the next instruction is executed. The TO part is only removed from the stack when the loop is terminated. To allow both tests for both upward and downward counting, two opcodes are needed. (For languages in which the TO and BY parts may change during execution of the loop, variants of these instructions will be needed). Both instructions use format 3A. The offset of the controlled variable is in the second byte of the instruction, and the forward branch distance is specified in the third byte. The body of the loop is terminated by an unconditional branch backward to the FOR instruction.

At this point we must devise instructions to handle IF statements. A number of third generation machines perform conditional branching by first setting condition code bits, and then testing them in a subsequent instruction. EM-1, in contrast, combines these functions, and eliminates the need for condition codes.

There are three types of branch instructions, distinguished by the number of operands they remove from the stack. The unconditional branch forward and backward instructions do not remove any operands from the stack. The second group removes one operand and compares it to zero, branching forward if the condition specified by the opcode ($=, \neq, <, >, \leq,$ or $\geq$) is met. This group is useful for statements such as IF N = 0 THEN . . . If Boolean variables represent FALSE by 0 and TRUE by 1, this group can also be used for statements such as IF FLAG THEN. . . .

The third group of branch instructions removes two operands from the stack, compares them, and branches forward if the specified condition is met. Backward conditional branches are not needed for translating IF statements (or WHILE statements either).

Each branch instruction specifies an offset which is the branch distance in bytes relative to the instruction itself. (Offset = k means skip $k + 1$ bytes.) Intersegment branches are prohibited, so that the procedure call mechanism can be used to limit access to privileged procedures. The size of the offsets required can be estimated from the data of Table VIII. Based upon the design proposed above, we estimate that the average source statement will require not more than 4 bytes of object code. This means that an offset with a range of 0–3 (i.e. 4 instructions) is sufficient for nearly half the IF statements, and a range of 0–15 (i.e. 16 instructions) is sufficient for more than $4/5$ of the cases. We need 14 opcodes to provide format 2 instructions for the unconditional branch, 1 operand conditional branch, and 2 operand conditional branch instructions.

This leaves 141 opcodes over for the format 1 opcodes. A possible allocation covering most of the frequently occurring cases is given in the summary of opcode usage below. If the average statement needs 4 bytes of object code, the division proposed below will handle 77 percent of the IF tests in a single byte. Note that "IF $A = B$" compiles into a branch NOT equal instruction to skip over the THEN part.

We will not discuss the instruction set further here. Suffice to say that all the instructions that could not be included in format 1 or format 2 for lack of encoding room, are included in format 3B. Also versions of all the above instructions should be provided as format 4 instructions (16-bit offset). Instructions needed, but not discussed above, e.g. accessing intermediate lexicographical levels of block structured languages should also be provided as format 3B and 4 instructions. There should also be instructions for multiple precision arithmetic, floating point, shifting, rotating, Boolean operations, etc.

It should be obvious that our design is not optimal in the information theory sense. More data and detailed simulation are needed to fine tune the choice of format 1 opcodes. On a user microprogrammable computer, one can envision tuning the format 1 instruction set to match the measured characteristics of important production programs, and loading a special highly optimized microprogram before beginning program execution. Alternately, a whole collection of single chip microprocessors could be kept in house, each with a read only microprogram tuned to a different application.

6. Discussion of the Machine Architecture

Our major point in this whole discussion is to illustrate that 1 byte instructions in this design can often do the work of 4 byte or longer instructions in conventional machines. To illustrate the savings of EM-1, Table XI gives some examples of the size of the EM-1 code compared to DEC PDP-11 code and CDC Cyber code, as examples of mini and mainframe computers. The PDP-11 and Cyber code sequences used for comparison are those a good compiler might reasonably expect to generate in order to minimize object program size. It is assumed that these are fragments from a block structured language that permits recursion and requires subscript checking. All local variables are assumed to be on the stack, not in registers (except loop indices) and EM-1 is assumed to be able to use the shortest instruction format. Both the PDP-11 and Cyber make use of calls to run-time subroutines whose size is not counted here.

As a second test, 4 programs were carefully coded in assembly language for EM-1, the PDP-11 and the Cyber. In contrast to the above examples, these were complete programs, and the ground rules permitted the use of registers. There was no run time system (i.e. everything was coded in-line) and subscripts were not checked. The results are given in Table XII. It should be noted that the PDP-11 and Cyber test programs were carefully hand coded by an experienced assembly language programmer. Few compilers could ever generate object code this compact, whereas it would be easy to have a compiler generate the EM-1 code used in the examples due to the close match between the EM-1 instruction set and reverse Polish. This means that EM-1 is actually much better than the above data might at first indicate.

It is important to realize that in an environment consisting of many short procedures, the register sets provided by a third generation machine are of little value. They can be used for temporary results during expression evaluation, but from our data, that of Alexander and Wortman, and also Knuth's, one register is usually enough. The registers cannot be used effectively to hold local variables, because they must be constantly saved and restored upon procedure calls. This save-restore overhead will be very severe if, as our data shows, one out of every four statements is a procedure call.

Although we have not emphasized execution speed, a microprogrammed EM-1 machine is potentially very

Table XI. A Comparison of EM-1, PDP-11, and Cyber Object Code Size (in Bits).

| | | | | Ratios | |
| | | | | PDP-11/ | Cyber/ |
Statements	EM-1	PDP-11	Cyber	EM-1	EM-1
I := 0	8	32	45	4.0	5.6
I := 3	16	48	60	3.0	3.8
I := J	16	48	75	3.0	4.7
I := I + 1	8	16	60	2.0	7.5
I := I + J	32	48	90	1.5	2.8
I := J + K	32	96	105	3.0	3.3
I := J + 1	24	80	75	3.3	3.1
I := A[J]	32	128	120	4.0	3.8
A[I] := 0	32	112	105	3.5	3.3
A[I] := B[J]	48	192	180	4.0	3.8
A[I] := B[J] + C[K]	80	304	285	3.8	3.6
A[I, J, K] := 0	48	176	165	3.7	3.4
IF I = J THEN . . .	24	64	105	2.7	4.4
IF I = 0 THEN . . .	16	48	60	3.0	3.8
IF I = J + K THEN . . .	40	112	150	2.8	3.8
IF FLAG THEN . . .	16	48	60	3.0	3.8
CALL P	16	64	60	4.0	3.8
CALL P1(I) (by value)	24	96	90	4.0	3.8
CALL P2(I, J) (by value)	32	128	120	4.0	3.8
CALL P3(I) (by reference)	32	112	90	3.5	2.8
FOR I FROM 1 TO N DO A [I] := 0 OD	88	176	225	2.0	2.6

fast. The microprogram would fetch the opcode and then execute a 256-way branch. Since each of the format 1 instructions is relatively simple, each instruction could be handled by a small number of microinstructions. In contrast microprograms for machines like the PDP-11 and IBM 370 must do considerable extraction and manipulation of short fields within the target instruction. This is avoided in EM-1. By having a distinct microroutine for each of the twelve instructions that push a local variable onto the stack, none of these microroutines would have to do any decoding or bit extraction, providing for very fast execution. The other format 1 instructions would also be fast for the same reason. Alternately, to reduce the size of the microprogram at the expense of execution speed, all the target instructions of a given type could share one microroutine.

At first it may appear that producing code for EM-1 would give compiler writers nightmares, due to the multiple instruction formats. This problem can be easily solved by first writing an optimizing assembler that has a single mnemonic for "load local variable onto the stack" (e.g. LODLOC SYM), etc. The assembler, and not the compilers, chooses the shortest feasible instruction format. The assembler should also recognize sequences such as PUSH 0; POP X and PUSH X; PUSH 1; ADD; POP X and replace them by ZERO X and INCR X respectively. Compilers might also leave the task of sorting the local variables on number of occurrences, and assigning the most heavily used ones lower offsets to the assembler. Once such an assembler was written, it could be used as the last

Table XII. A Comparison of EM-1, PDP-11 and Cyber Object Code Size (in Bits)

Program	EM/1	PDP-11	Cyber	Ratios PDP-11/ EM-1	Cyber/ EM-1
Towers of Hanoi	352	992	2205	2.8	6.3
sort integer array	562	1248	1260	2.2	2.2
dot product	552	832	1140	1.5	2.0
find primes	306	704	1020	2.3	3.3

pass of all compilers, allowing them to produce straightforward reverse Polish, and still get locally optimal code.

7. Summary

There is a certain analogy between a Huffman code used to encode text in a minimal number of bits, and our proposal for a machine language with a compact instruction set. In both cases it is necessary to determine the frequencies of occurrence of the data to be encoded (letters and instructions, respectively) by empirical measurements. We have done this and reported the results in Section 3. Then an encoding scheme must be devised in which the most commonly occurring cases are assigned the shortest bit patterns, and the least commonly occurring cases are assigned the longest bit patterns. This is in contrast to a scheme in which all cases are assigned the same length bit pattern. In EM-1 the most frequently occurring instructions are encoded in a single byte, which is both efficient in storage and avoids the problems associated with variable length bit strings produced by true Huffman coding. This leads to object programs that require little memory and are capable of being executed very easily (i.e. fast).

Received February 1976; revised January 1977

References
1. Alexander, W.G., and Wortman, D.B. Static and dynamic characteristics of XPL programs. *Computer 8* (1975), 41–46.
2. Denning, P.J. Is it not time to define 'structured programming'? *Operating Syst. Rev. 8* (Jan. 1974), 6–7.
3. Foster, C.C., and Gonter, R.H. Conditional interpretation of operation codes. *IEEE Trans. Comptrs. C-20*, 1 (1971), 108–111.
4. Huffman, D. A method for the construction of minimum redundancy codes. *Proc. IRE 40* (1952), 1098–1101.
5. Jensen, K., and Wirth, N. *PASCAL User Manual and Report*. Springer-Verlag, New York, 1974.
6. Knuth, D.E. An empirical study of FORTRAN programs. *Software – Practice and Experience 1* (1971), 105–133.
7. Knuth, D.E. Structured programming with go to statements, *Computing Surveys 6* (1974), 261–301.
8. Richards, M. BCPL: A tool for compiler writing and system programming. Proc. AFIPS SJCC, Vol. 34, AFIPS Press, Montvale, N.J., 1969, pp. 557–566.
9. Salvadori, A., Gordon, J., and Capstick, C. Static profile of COBOL programs. Sigplan Notices (ACM) 10 (1975), 20–33.
10. Tanenbaum, A.S. A programming language for writing operating systems. Rep. IR-3, Wiskundig Seminarium, Vrije U., Amsterdam, 1974.
11. Tanenbaum, A.S. A general purpose macro processor as a poor man's compiler. *IEEE Trans. Software Eng. SE-2* (1976), 121–125.
12. van Wijngaarden, A., Mailloux, B., Peck, J.E.L., and Koster, C.H.A. Report on the algorithmic language ALGOL 68, Num. Math. *14* (1969), 79–218.
13. Wilner, W.T. Design of the Burroughs B1700. Proc. AFIPS FJCC, Vol. 41, 497, AFIPS Press, Montvale, N.J., 1972, pp. 489–497.
14. Wilner, W.T. Burroughs B1700 Memory Utilization. Proc. AFIPS FJCC, Vol. 41, AFIPS Press, Montvale, N.J., 1972, 579–586.
15. Wortman, D.B. A study of language directed computer design. CSRG-20, U. of Toronto, Toronto, Ont. (1972).
16. Wulf, W.A., Russell, D.B., and Habermann, A.N. BLISS: A language for systems programming. *Comm. ACM 14* (1971), 780–790.

Section 2: RISC Overview

2.1 Background

While RISC systems have been defined and designed in a variety of ways by different groups, the key elements shared by most (not all) designs are these

- A limited and simple instruction set;
- A large number of general-purpose registers;
- An emphasis on optimizing the instruction pipeline.

The proponents of the RISC architecture cite two main advantages to this approach: improved performance and optimized use of VLSI. With respect to performance

- A simplified instruction set reduces or eliminates the need for microcode, which is slower than a hardwired implementation.
- A simplified instruction set makes it possible to exploit more effectively instruction pipelining.
- The use of a large number of registers makes it possible to reduce the rate of memory access, thus increasing speed.

The second area of benefit relates to the use of VLSI to implement an entire processor on a single chip. A RISC architecture is simpler and therefore easier to design and implement. Furthermore, the scarce resource of chip surface area can be optimized, since the RISC design does not require a complex control unit and lots of ROM to store the microcode.

2.2 Article Summary

The first article provides a comprehensive overview of the subject and is intended to provide a context for the remainder of the text.

The second article, "RISC: Back to the Future?," is by the chief architect of one of the most complex of CISCs, the VAX. Bell places RISC technology in the historical context of computer development since 1948, and shows that the roots of RISC can be traced to the CDC 6600.

Reprinted from *Proceedings of the IEEE*, Volume 76, Number 1, January 1988, pages 38–55. Copyright © 1988 by The Institute of Electrical and Electronics Engineers, Inc.

Reduced Instruction Set Computer Architecture

WILLIAM STALLINGS, SENIOR MEMBER, IEEE

Since the earliest days of the computer era, the general trend in computer architecture and organization has been toward increasing CPU complexity: larger instruction sets, more addressing modes, more specialized registers, and the like. However, in the past several years, there has been increasing interest in an innovative approach to computer architecture: the reduced instruction set computer (RISC). The intended performance benefits of RISC, compared to a more conventional approach, include more effective compilers, no use of microcode, more effective pipelining, and improved response to interrupts. Key characteristics of the RISC approach include: a limited and simple instruction set; the use of either a large number of registers (hundreds) or an optimizing compiler, to maximize the use of registers and minimize references to main memory; an emphasis on optimizing the instruction execution pipeline.

This paper presents a tutorial on the RISC approach and highlights the key design issues involved in RISC architecture. We begin by looking at the results of a number of studies on the instruction execution characteristics of compiled high-level language programs. The results of these studies inspired the RISC movement. The paper then summarizes approaches to three key RISC design issues: optimized register usage, reduced instruction sets, and pipelining. As examples, an experimental system, the Berkeley RISC, and a commercial system, the MIPS R2000, are presented. The paper closes with a discussion of the RISC versus CISC (complex instruction set computer) controversy.

I. INTRODUCTION

Since the development of the stored-program computer around 1950, there have been remarkably few true innovations in the areas of computer organization and architecture. One of the most interesting and, potentially, one of the most important innovations is the reduced instruction set computer (RISC). The RISC architecture is a dramatic departure from the historical trend in CPU architecture and challenges the conventional wisdom expressed in words and deeds by most computer architects. An analysis of the RISC architecture brings into focus many of the important issues in computer organization and architecture.

Most of the work has been on experimental systems, but commercial RISC systems have begun to appear [1]–[12].

Manuscript received December 3, 1986; revised August 21, 1987. The submission of this paper was encouraged after review of an advance proposal.

The author is at 5 Chesterford Gardens, London NW3 7DD, England.

IEEE Log Number 8717881.

Recently, both IBM (with its RT PC) and Hewlett-Packard (with its 900 series) have introduced machines that have both RISC and conventional characteristics [13], [14]. Although RISC systems have been defined and designed in a variety of ways by different groups, the key elements shared by most (not all) designs are these:

- a limited and simple instruction set;
- the use of either a hardware or compiler strategy to maximize the use of registers and minimize references to main memory;
- am emphasis on optimizing the instruction execution pipeline.

This paper surveys key design issues relating to RISC architecture. To begin, we present a brief survey of some results on instruction sets that inspired much of the RISC work.

II. INSTRUCTION EXECUTION CHARACTERISTICS

One of the most visible forms of evolution associated with computers is that of programming languages. As the cost of hardware has dropped, the relative cost of software has risen. Along with that, a chronic shortage of programmers has driven up software costs in absolute terms. Thus the major cost in the life cycle of a system is software, not hardware. Adding to the cost, and to the inconvenience, is the element of unreliability: It is common for programs, both system and application, to continue to exhibit new bugs after years of operation.

The response from researchers and industry has been to develop ever more powerful and complex high-level programming languages (compare Fortran to Ada). These high-level languages (HLL) allow the programmer to express algorithms more concisely, take care of much of the detail, and often support naturally the use of structured programming.

Alas, this solution gave rise to another problem, known as the *semantic gap*, the difference between the operations provided in HLLs and those provided in computer architecture. Symptoms of this gap are alleged to include execution inefficiency, excessive program size, and compiler complexity. Designers responded with architectures intended to close this gap. Key features include large instruction sets, dozens of addressing modes, and various HLL statements implemented in hardware. An example of the latter is the CASE machine instruction on the VAX-11. Such complex instruction sets are intended to

- ease the task of the compiler writer;
- improve execution efficiency, since complex sequences of operations can be implemented in microcode;
- provide support for even more complex and sophisticated HLLs.

Meanwhile, a number of studies have been done over the years to determine the characteristics and patterns of execution of machine instructions generated from HLL programs. The results of these studies inspired some researchers to look for an altogether different approach: namely, to make the architecture that supports the HLL simpler, rather than more complex.

So, to understand the line of reasoning of the RISC advocates, we begin with a brief review of instruction execution characteristics. The aspects of computation of interest are

- *Operations Performed:* These determine the functions to be performed by the CPU and its interaction with memory.
- *Operands Used:* The types of operands and the frequency of their use determine the memory organization for storing them and the addressing modes for accessing them.
- *Execution Sequencing:* This determines the control and pipeline organization.

In the remainder of this section, we summarize the results of a number of studies of high-level language programs. All of the results are based on dynamic measurements [15]. That is, measurements are collected by executing the program and counting the number of times some feature has appeared or a particular property has held true. In contrast, static measurements merely perform these counts on the source text of a program. They give no useful information on performance, because they are not weighted relative to the number of times each statement is executed.

A. Operations

A variety of studies have been made to analyze the behavior of HLL programs. Table 1 includes key results from the following studies. The earliest study of programming language, performed by Knuth [16] examined a collection of Fortran programs used as student exercises. Dynamic measurements showed that two-thirds of all statements were assignment and, of these one-third were of the type $A = B$.

The remainder seldom had more than one operator. Tanenbaum [17] published measurements of HLL constructs, collected from over 300 procedures used in operating-system programs and written in a language that supports structured programming (SAL). Patterson and Sequin [18], two of the key figures in the Berkeley RISC project, analyzed a set of measurements taken in the early stages of the RISC effort. Measurements were collected from compilers and from programs for typesetting, CAD, sorting, and file comparison. The programming languages C and Pascal were studied. Huck [19] analyzed four programs intended to represent a mix of general-purpose and scientific computing, including fast Fourier transform and integration of systems of differential equations.

There is quite good agreement in the results of this mixture of languages and applications. Assignment statements predominate, suggesting that the simple movement of data is of high importance. There is also a preponderance of conditional statements (IF, LOOP). These statements are implemented in machine language with some sort of compare and branch instruction. This suggests that the sequence control mechanism of the instruction set is important.

These results are instructive to the machine instruction set designer, indicating which types of statements occur most often and therefore should be supported in an "optimal" fashion. However, these results do not reveal which statements use the most time in the execution of a typical program. That is, given a compiled machine language program, which statements in the source language cause the execution of the most machine-language instructions?

To get at this underlying phenomenon, the Patterson programs [18] were compiled on the VAX, PDP-11, and Motorola 68000 to determine the average number of machine instructions and memory references per statement type. By multiplying the frequency of occurrence of each statement type by these averages, Table 2 is obtained. Columns 2 and

Table 2 Weighted Relative Dynamic Frequency of all Operations

	Dynamic Occurence		Machine-Instruction Weighted		Memory Reference Weighted	
	Pascal	C	Pascal	C	Pascal	C
ASSIGN	45	38	13	13	14	15
LOOP	5	3	42	32	33	26
CALL	15	12	31	33	44	45
IF	29	43	11	21	7	13
GOTO		3				
Other	6	1	3	1	2	1

Source: [18]

3 provide surrogate measures of the actual time spent executing the various statement types. The results suggest that the procedure call/return is the most time-consuming operation in typical HLL programs.

The reader should be clear on the significance of Table 2. This table indicates the relative significance of various statement types in an HLL, when that HLL is compiled for a typical contemporary instruction set architecture. Some other architecture could conceivably produce different results. However, this study produces results that are representative for contemporary complex instruction set com-

Table 1 Relative Dynamic Frequency of High-Level Language Operations

Study	[19]	[16]	[18]	[18]	[17]
Language	Pascal	Fortran	Pascal	C	SAL
Workload	Scientific	Student	System	System	System
ASSIGN	74	67	45	38	42
LOOP	4	3	5	3	4
CALL	1	3	15	12	12
IF	20	11	29	43	36
GOTO	2	9		3	
Other		7	6	1	6

puter (CISC) architectures. Thus they can provide guidance to those looking for more efficient ways to support HLLs.

B. Operands

Much less work has been done on the occurrence of types of operands, despite the importance of this topic. There are several aspects that are significant.

The Patterson study already referenced [18] also looked at the dynamic frequency of occurrence of classes of variables (Table 3). The results, consistent between Pascal and

Table 3 Dynamic Percentage of Operands

	Pascal	C	Average
Integer constant	16	23	20
Scalar Variable	58	53	55
Array/structure	26	24	25

C programs, show that the majority of references are to simple scalar variables. Further, over 80 percent of the scalars were local (to the procedure) variables. In addition, references to arrays/structures require a previous reference to their index or pointer, which again is usually a local scalar. Thus there is a preponderance of references to scalars, and these are highly localized.

The Patterson study examined the dynamic behavior of HLL programs, independent of the underlying architecture. As discussed earlier, it is necessary to deal with actual architectures to examine program behavior more deeply. One study, [20], examined DEC-10 instructions dynamically and found that each instruction on the average references 0.5 operands in memory and 1.4 registers. Similar results are reported in [19] for C, Pascal, and Fortran programs on S/370, PDP-11, and VAX-11. Of course, these figures depend highly on both the architecture and the compiler, but they do illustrate the frequency of operand accessing.

These latter studies suggest the importance of an architecture that lends itself to fast operand accessing, since this operation is performed so frequently. The Patterson study suggests that a prime candidate for optimization is the mechanism for storing and accessing local scalar variables.

C. Procedure Calls

We have seen that procedure calls and returns are an important aspect of HLL programs. The evidence (Table 2)

suggests that these are the most time-consuming operations in the compiled HLL programs. Thus it will be profitable to consider ways of implementing these operations efficiently. Two aspects are significant: the number of parameters and variables that a procedure deals with, and the depth of nesting.

In Tanenbaum's study [17], he found that 98 percent of dynamically called procedures were passed fewer than six arguments, and that 92 percent of them used fewer than six local scalar variables. Similar results were reported by the Berkeley RISC team [21], as shown in Table 4. These results

Table 4 Procedure Arguments and Local Scalar Variables

Percentage of Executed Procedure Calls with	Compiler, Interpreter and Typesetter (percent)	Small Nonnumeric Programs (percent)
> 3 arguments	0–7	0–5
> 5 arguments	0–3	0
> 8 words of arguments and local scalars		0–6
> 12 words of arguments and local scalars	1–20	0–3
	1–6	

show that the number of words required per procedure activation is not large. The studies reported earlier indicated that a high proportion of operand references are to local scalar variables. The studies just mentioned show that those references are, in fact, confined to relatively few variables.

The same Berkeley group also looked at the pattern of procedure calls and returns in HLL programs. They found that it is rare to have a long uninterrupted sequence of procedure calls followed by the corresponding sequence of returns. Rather, they found that a program remains confined to a rather narrow window of procedure-invocation depth. This is illustrated in Fig. 1 [22]. The graph illustrates call–return behavior. Each call is represented by the line moving down to the right, and each return by the line moving up and to the right. In the figure, a *window* with depth equal to 5 is defined. Only a sequence of calls and returns with a net movement of 6 in either direction causes the window to move. As can be seen, the executing program can remain within this window for quite long periods of time. The Berkeley results (for C and Pascal) showed that a window of depth 8 will need to shift only on less than 1 percent

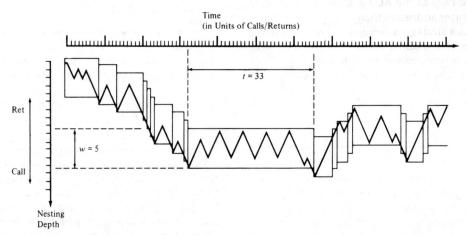

Fig. 1. The call-return behavior of programs.

of the calls or returns [23]. These results also suggest that operand references are highly localized.

D. Implications

A number of groups have looked at results such as those just reported and have concluded that the attempt to make the instruction set architecture close to HLLs is not the most effective design strategy. Rather, the HLLs can best be supported by optimizing performance of the most time-consuming features of typical HLL programs.

Generalizing from the work of a number of researchers, three elements emerge that, by and large, characterized RISC architectures. First, use a large number of registers. This is intended to optimize operand referencing. The studies just discussed show that there are several references per HLL instruction, and that there is a high proportion of move (assignment) statements. This, coupled with the locality and predominance of scalar references, suggests that performance can be improved by reducing memory references at the expense of more register references. Because of the locality of these references, an expanded register set seems practical.

Second, careful attention needs to be paid to the design of instruction pipelines. Because of the high proportion of conditional branch and procedure call instructions, a straightforward instruction pipeline will be inefficient. This manifests itself as a high proportion of instructions that are pre-fetched but never executed.

Finally, a simplified (reduced) instruction set is indicated. This point is not as obvious as the others, but should become clearer in the ensuing discussion. In addition, we will see that the desire to implement an entire CPU on a single chip leads to a reduced instruction set solution.

III. Optimized Register Usage

The results summarized above point out the desirability of quick access to operands that are referenced frequently. We have seen that there is a large proportion of assignment statements in HLL programs, and many of these are of the simple form $A = B$. Also, there are a significant number of operand accesses per HLL statement. If we couple these results with the fact that most accesses are to local scalars, heavy reliance on register storage is suggested.

The reason that register storage is indicated is that it is the fastest available storage device, faster than both main memory and cache. The register file is physically small, generally on the same chip as the ALU and control unit, and employs much shorter addresses than addresses for cache and memory. Thus a strategy is needed that will allow the most frequently accessed operands to be kept in registers and to minimize register-memory operations.

Two basic approaches are possible, one based on software and the other on hardware. The software approach is to rely on the compiler to maximize register usage. The compiler will attempt to allocate registers to those variables that will be used the most in a given time period. This approach requires the use of sophisticated program-analysis algorithms. The hardware approach is simply to use more registers so that more variables can be held in registers for longer periods of time. This section presents both approaches.

To provide some context for this section, the following subsections discuss design issues related to CPU registers.

A. Registers

To understand the role of registers in the CPU, let us consider the requirements placed on the CPU, the things that it must do:

• *Fetch instructions:* The CPU must read instructions from memory.

• *Interpret instructions:* The instruction must be decoded to determine what action is required.

• *Fetch data:* The execution of an instruction may require reading data from memory or an I/O module.

• *Process data:* The execution of an instruction may require performing some arithmetic or logical operation on data.

• *Write data:* The results of an execution may require writing data to memory or an I/O module.

To be able to do these things, it should be clear that the CPU needs to temporarily store some data. The CPU must remember the location of the last instruction so that it can know where to get the next instruction. It needs to store instructions and data temporarily while an instruction is being executed. In other words, the CPU needs a small internal memory. This memory consists of a set of high-speed registers. The registers in the CPU serve two functions:

• *User-visible registers:* These enable the machine- or assembly-language programmer to minimize main-memory references by optimizing use of registers.

• *Control and status registers:* These are used by the control unit to control the operation of the CPU and by privileged, operating system programs to control the execution of programs.

There is no clean separation of registers into these two categories. For example, on some machines the program counter is user-visible (e.g., VAX-11 architecture), but on many it is not. For purposes of the following discussion, however, we will use these categories.

B. User-Visible Registers

A user-visible register is one which may be referenced by means of the machine language that the CPU executes. Virtually all contemporary CPU designs provide for a number of user-visible registers, as opposed to a single accumulator. We can characterize these in the following categories:

• General Purpose
• Data
• Address
• Condition Codes.

General-purpose registers can be assigned to a variety of functions by the programmer. Sometimes, their use within the instruction set is orthogonal to the operation; that is, any general-purpose register can contain the operand for any opcode. This provides true general-purpose register use. Often, however, there are restrictions. For example, there may be dedicated registers for floating-point operations.

In some cases, general-purpose registers can be used for addressing functions (e.g., register indirect, displacement). In other cases, there is a partial or clean separation between data registers and address registers. *Data registers* may only be used to hold data and cannot be employed in the calculation of an operand address. *Address registers* may themselves be somewhat general-purpose, or they may be devoted to a particular addressing mode. Examples of registers are as follows:

• *Segment pointers:* In a machine with segmented addressing, a segment register holds the address of the base of the segment. There may be multiple registers, for example, one for the operating system and one for the current process.

• *Index registers:* These are used for indexed addressing, and may be autoindexed.

• *Stack pointer:* If there is user-visible stack addressing, then typically the stack is in memory and there is a dedicated register that points to the top of the stack. This allows implicit addressing; that is, push, pop, and other stack instructions need not contain an explicit stack operand.

There are several design issues to be addressed here. An important one is whether to use completely general-purpose registers or to specialize their use. With the use of specialized registers, it can generally be implicit in the opcode which type of register a certain operand specifier refers to. The operand specifier must only identify one of a set of specialized registers rather than one out of all the registers, thus saving bits. On the other hand, this specialization limits the programmer's flexibility. There is no final and best solution to this design issue, but, the trend seems to be toward the use of specialized registers.

Another design issue is the number of registers, either general-purpose or data-plus-address, to be provided. Again, this affects instruction set design since more registers require more operand specifier bits. Somewhere between 8 and 32 registers appears optimum [20]. Fewer registers result in more memory references; more registers do not noticeably reduce memory references. However, a new approach, which finds advantage in the use of hundreds of registers, is exhibited in some RISC systems.

Finally, there is the issue of register length. Registers that must hold addresses obviously must be at least long enough to hold the largest address. Data registers should be able to hold values of most data types. Some machines allow two contiguous registers to be used as one for holding double-length values.

A final category of registers, which is at least partially visible to the user, holds *condition codes* (also referred to as flags). Condition codes are bits set by the CPU hardware as the result of operations. For example, an arithmetic operation may produce a positive, negative, zero, or overflow result. In addition to the result itself being stored in a register or memory, a condition code is also set. The code may subsequently be tested as part of a conditional branch operation.

Condition code bits are collected into one or more registers. Usually, they form part of a control register. Generally, machine instructions allow these bits to be read by implicit reference, but they cannot be altered by the programmer.

In some machines, a subroutine call will result in the automatic saving of all user-visible registers, which are to be restored on return. The saving and restoring is performed by the CPU as part of the execution of call-and-return instructions. This allows each subroutine to use the user-visible registers independently. On other machines, it is the responsibility of the programmer to save the contents of the relevant user-visible registers prior to a subroutine call by including instructions for this purpose in the program.

C. The Hardware Approach

The hardware approach has been pioneered by the Berkeley RISC group [18] and is used in the first commercial RISC product, the Pyramid [24].

Register Windows: On the face of it, the use of a large set of registers should decrease the need to access memory. The design task is to organize the registers in such a fashion that this goal is realized.

Since most operand references are to local scalars, the obvious approach is to store these in registers, with perhaps a few registers reserved for global variables. The problem is that the definition of *local* changes with each procedure call and return, operations that occur frequently. On every call, local variables must be saved from the registers into memory, so that the registers can be reused by the called program. Furthermore, parameters must be passed. On return, the variables of the parent program must be restored (loaded back into registers) and results must be passed back to the parent program.

The solution is based on two other results reported above. First, a typical procedure employs only a few passed parameters and local variables. Second, the depth of procedure activation fluctuates within a relatively narrow range (Fig. 1). To exploit these properties, multiple small sets of registers are used, each assigned to a different procedure. A procedure call automatically switches the CPU to use a different fixed-size window of registers, rather than saving registers in memory. Windows for adjacent procedures are overlapped to allow parameter passing.

The concept is illustrated in Fig. 2. At any time, only one window of registers is visible and is addressable as if it were the only set of registers (e.g., address 0 through $N - 1$). The window is divided into three fixed-size areas. Parameter registers hold parameters passed down from the procedure that called the current procedure and results to be passed back up. Local registers are used for local variables, as assigned by the compiler. Temporary registers are used to

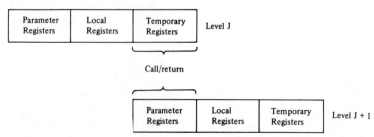

Fig. 2. Overlapping register windows.

exchange parameters and results with the next lower level (procedure called by current procedure). The temporary registers at one level are physically the same as the parameter registers at the next lower level. This overlap permits parameters to be passed without the actual movement of data.

To handle any possible pattern of calls and returns, the number of register windows would have to be unbounded. Instead, the register windows can be used to hold the few most recent procedure activations. Older activations must be saved in memory and later restored when the nesting depth decreases. Thus the actual organization of the register file is as a circular buffer of overlapping windows.

This organization is shown in Fig. 3 [21], which depicts a circular buffer of six windows. The buffer is filled to a depth

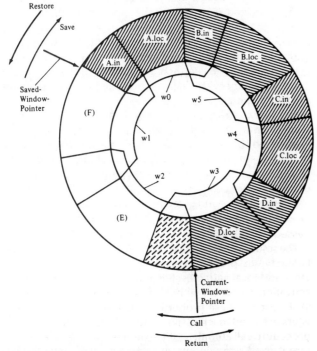

Fig. 3. Circular buffer organization of overlapped windows.

of 4 (A called B; B called C; C called D) with procedure D active. The current-window pointer (CWP) points to the window of the currently active procedure. Register references by a machine instruction are offset by this pointer to determine the actual physical register. The saved-window pointer identifies the window most recently saved in memory. If procedure D now calls procedure E, arguments for E are placed in D's temporary registers (the overlap between w3 and w4) and the CWP is advanced by one window.

If procedure E then makes a call to procedure F, the call cannot be made with the current status of the buffer. This is because F's window overlaps A's window. If F begins to load its temporary registers, preparatory to a call, it will overwrite the parameter registers of A (A.param). Thus when CWP is incremented (modulo 6) so that it becomes equal to SWP, an interrupt occurs and A's window is saved. Only the first two portions (A.param and A.loc) need be saved. Then the SWP is incremented and the call to F proceeds. A similar interrrupt can occur on returns. For example, sub-

sequent to the activation of F, when B returns to A, CWP is decremented and becomes equal to SWP. This causes an interrupt that results in the restoral of A's window.

From the preceding, it can be seen that an N-window register file can hold only N − 1 procedure activations. The value of N need not be large. As was mentioned earlier, one study [23] found that, with eight windows, a save or restore is needed on only 1 percent of the calls or returns. The Berkeley RISC computers use 8 windows of 16 registers each. The Pyramid computer employs 16 windows of 32 registers each.

Global Variables: The window scheme just described provides an efficient organization for storing local scalar variables in registers. However, this scheme does not address the need to store global variables, those accessed by more than one procedure (e.g., COMMON variables in Fortran). Two options suggest themselves. First, variables declared as global in an HLL can be assigned memory locations by the compiler, and all machine instructions that reference these variables will use memory-reference operands. This is straightforward, from both the hardware and software (compiler) points of view. However, for frequently accessed global variables, this scheme is inefficient.

An alternative is to incorporate a set of global registers in the CPU. These registers would be fixed in number and available to all procedures. A unified numbering scheme can be used to simplify the instruction format. For example, references to registers 0 through 7 could refer to unique global registers, and references to registers 8 through 31 could be offset to refer to physical registers in the current window. Thus there is an increased hardware burden to accommodate the split in register addressing. In addition, the compiler must decide which global variables should be assigned to registers.

Large Register File versus Cache: The register file, organized into windows, acts as a small, fast buffer for holding a subset of all variables that are likely to be used most heavily. From this point of view, the register file acts much like a cache memory. The question therefore arises as to whether it would be simpler and better to use a cache and a small traditional register file.

Table 5 compares characteristics of the two approaches. The window-based register file holds all of the local scalar variables (except in the rare case of window overflow) of the most recent N − 1 procedure activations. The cache holds a selection of recently used scalar variables. The register files should save time, since all local scalar variables are retained. On the other hand, the cache may make more efficient use of space, since it is reacting to the situation dynamically. Furthermore, caches generally treat all memory references alike, including instructions and other types

Table 5 Characteristics of Large Register File and Cache Organizations

Large Register File	Cache
All Local Scalars	Recently Used Local Scalars
Individual Variables	Blocks of Memory
Compiler-Assigned Global Variables	Recently Used Global Variables
Save/Restore Based on Procedure Nesting Depth	Save/Restore Based on Cache Replacement Algorithm
Register Addressing	Memory Addressing

of data. Thus savings in these other areas are possible with a cache and not a register file.

A register file may make inefficient use of space, since not all procedures will need the full window space allotted to them. On the other hand, the cache suffers from another sort of inefficiency: Data are read in blocks. Whereas the register file contains only those variables in use, the cache reads in a block of data, some or much of which will not be used.

The cache is capable of handling global as well as local variables. There are usually many global scalars, but only a few of them are heavily used [21]. A cache will dynamically discover these variables and hold them. If the window-based register file is supplemented with global registers, it too can hold some global scalars. However, it is difficult for a compiler to determine which globals will be heavily used.

With the register file, the movement of data between registers and memory is determined by the procedure nesting depth. Since this depth usually fluctuates within a narrow range, the use of memory is relatively infrequent. Most cache memories are set-associative with a small set size. Thus there is the danger that other data or instructions will displace, in the cache, frequently used variables.

Based on the discussion so far, the choice between a large window-based register file and a cache is not clear cut. There is one characteristic, however, in which the register approach is clearly superior and which suggests that a cache-based system will be noticeably slower. This distinction shows up in the amount of addressing overhead experienced by the two approaches.

Fig. 4 [25] illustrates the difference. To reference a local scalar in a window-based register file, a "virtual" register number and a window number are used. These can pass through a relatively simple decoder to select one of the physical registers. To reference a memory location in cache, a full-width memory address must be generated. The complexity of this operation depends on the addressing mode. In a set-associative cache, a portion of the address is used to read a number of words and tags equal to the set size. Another portion of the address is compared to the tags, and one of the words that was read is selected. It should be clear that even if the cache is as fast as the register file, the access time will be considerably longer. Thus from the point of view of performance, the window-based register file is superior for local scalars. Further performance improvement could be achieved by the addition of a cache for instructions only.

D. The Compiler Approach

Let us assume now that only a small number (e.g., 16–32) of registers is available on the target RISC machine. In this case, optimized register usage is the responsibility of the compiler. A program written in a high-level language has, of course, no explicit references to register. Rather, program quantities are referred to symbolically. The objective of the compiler is to keep as many computations as possible in registers rather than main memory, and to minimize load-and-store operations.

In general, the approach taken is as follows. Each program quantity that is a candidate for residing in a register is assigned to a symbolic or virtual register. The compiler then maps the unlimited number of symbolic registers into a fixed number of real registers. Symbolic registers whose usage does not overlap can share the same real register. If, in a particular portion of the program, there are more quantities to deal with than real registers, then some of the quantities are assigned to memory locations. Load-and-store instructions are used to temporarily position quantities in registers for computational operations.

The essence of the optimization task is to decide which quantities are to be assigned to registers at any given point in the program. The technique most commonly used in RISC compilers is known as graph coloring, which is a technique borrowed from the discipline of topology [26]–[28].

The graph coloring problem is this. Given a graph consisting of nodes and edges, assign colors to nodes such that adjacent nodes have different colors, and do this in such a way as to minimize the number of different colors. This problem is adapted to the compiler problem in the following way. First, the program is analyzed to build a register interference graph. The nodes of the graph are the symbolic registers. If two symbolic registers are "live" during the same program fragment, then they are joined by an edge to depict interference. An attempt is then made to color the graph with N colors, where N is the number of registers. If this fails, then nodes that cannot be colored must be placed in memory, and loads and stores must be used to make space for the affected quantities when they are needed.

Fig. 5 is a simple example of the process. Assume a program with six symbolic registers to be compiled onto a machine with three active registers. Fig. 5(a) shows the time sequence of active use of each symbolic register, and Fig. 5(b) shows the register interference graph. A possible coloring with three colors is indicated. One symbolic register, F, is left uncolored and must be dealt with using loads and stores.

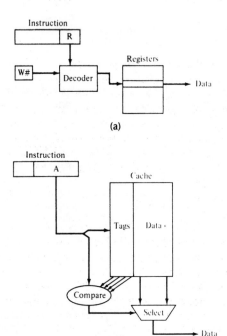

Fig. 4. Referencing a local scalar. (a) Window-based register file. (b) cache.

I = Size of executed instructions
D = Size of executed data
M = I + D = Total memory traffic

Fig. 6. (a) $A \leftarrow B + C$. (b) $A \leftarrow B + C$; $B \leftarrow A + C$; $D \leftarrow D - B$.

The second motivating factor for increasingly complex instruction sets was that instruction execution would be faster. It seems to make sense that a complex HLL operation will execute more quickly as a single machine instruction rather than as a series of more-primitive instructions. However, because of the bias towards the use of those simpler instructions, this may not be so. The entire control unit must be made more complex, and/or the microprogram control store must be made larger, to accommodate a richer instruction set. Either factor increases the execution time of the simple instructions.

In fact, some researchers have found that the speedup in the execution of complex functions is due not so much to the power of the complex machine instructions as to their residence in high-speed control store [30]. In effect, the control store acts as an instruction cache. Thus the hardware architecture is in the position of trying to determine which subroutines or functions will be used most frequently and assigning those to the control store by implementing them in microcode. The results have been less than encouraging. Thus on S/370 systems, instructions such as Translate and Extended-Precision-Floating-Point-Divide reside in high-speed storage, while the sequence involved in setting up procedure calls or initiating an interrupt handler are in slower main memory.

Thus it is far from clear that the trend to increasingly complex instruction sets is appropriate. This has led a number of groups to pursue the opposite path.

B. Characteristics of Reduced Instruction Set Architecture

Although a variety of different approaches to reduced instruction set architecture have been taken, certain characteristics are common to all of them. These characteristics are listed in Table 7 and described here. Specific examples are explored later in this section.

Table 7 Characteristics of Reduced Instruction Set Architectures

One Instruction Per Cycle
Register-to-Register Operations
Simple Address Modes
Simple Instruction Formats

The first characteristic listed in Table 7 is that one machine instruction is executed per machine cycle. A *machine cycle* is defined to be the time it takes to fetch two operands from registers, perform as ALU operation, and store the result in a register. Thus RISC machine instructions should be no more complicated, than, and execute about as fast as, microinstructions on CISC machines. With simple, one-cycle instructions, there is little or no need for microcode; the machine instructions can be hardwired. Such instructions should execute faster than comparable machine instructions on other machines, since it is not necessary to access a microprogram control store during instruction execution.

A second characteristic is that most operations should be register-to-register, with only simple LOAD and STORE operations accessing memory. This design feature simplifies the instruction set and therefore the control unit. For example, a RISC instruction set may include only one or two ADD instructions (e.g., integer add, add with carry); the VAX-11 has 25 different ADD instructions. Another benefit is that such an architecture encourages the optimization of register use, so that frequently accessed operands remain in high-speed storage.

This emphasis on register-to-register operations is unique to RISC designs. Other contemporary machines provide such instructions but also include memory-to-memory and mixed register/memory operations. Attempts to compare these approaches were made in the 1970s, before the appearance of RISCs. Fig. 6(a) illustrates the approach taken [22]. Hypothetical architectures were evaluated on program size and the number of bits of memory traffic. Results such as this one led one researcher to suggest that future architectures should contain no registers at all [32]. One wonders what he would have thought, at the time, of the RISC machine marketed by Pyramid, which contains no less than 528 registers!

What was missing from these studies was a recognition of the frequent access to a small number of local scalars and that, with a large bank of registers or an optimizing compiler, most operands could be kept in registers for long periods of time. Thus Fig. 6(b) may be a fairer comparison.

Returning to Table 7, a third characteristic is the use of simple addressing modes. Almost all instructions use simple register addressing. Several additional modes, such as displacement and PC-relative, may be included. Other, more-complex modes can be synthesized in software from the simple ones. Again, this design feature simplifies the instruction set and the control unit.

A final common characteristic is the use of simple instruction formats. Generally, only one or a few formats are used. Instruction length is fixed and aligned on word boundaries. Field locations, especially the opcode, are fixed. This design feature has a number of benefits. With fixed fields, opcode decoding and register operand accessing can occur simultaneously. Simplified formats simplify the control unit. Instruction fetching is optimized since word-length units are fetched. This also means that a single instruction does not cross page boundaries.

Taken together, these characteristics can be assessed to determine the potential benefits of the RISC approach. These benefits fall into two main categories: those related to performance and those related to VLSI implementation.

With respect to performance, a certain amount of "circumstantial evidence" can be presented. First, more-effective optimizing compilers can be developed. With more-primitive instructions, there are more opportunities for moving functions out of the loops, reorganizing code for efficiency, maximizing register utilization, and so forth. It is even possible to compute parts of complex instructions at compile time. For example, the S/370 Move Characters (MVC) instruction moves a string of characters from one location to another. Each time it is executed, the move will depend on the length of the string, whether and in which direction the locations overlap, and what the alignment characteristics are. In most cases, these will all be known at compile time. Thus the compiler could produce an optimized sequence of primitive instructions for this function.

A second point, already noted, is that most instructions generated by a compiler are relatively simple anyway. It would seem reasonable that a control unit built specifically for those instructions and using little or no microcode could execute them faster than a comparable CISC.

A third point relates to the use of instruction pipelining. RISC researchers feel that the instruction pipelining technique can be applied much more effectively with a reduced instruction set. We examine this point in some detail presently.

A final, and somewhat less significant point, is that RISC programs should be more responsive to interrupts since interrupts are checked between rather elementary operations. Architectures with complex instructions either restrict interrupts to instruction boundaries or must define specific interruptable points and implement mechanisms for restarting an instruction.

The case for improved performance for a reduced instruction set architecture is far from proven. A number of studies have been done but not on machines of comparable technology and power. Further, most studies have not attempted to separate the effects of a reduced instruction set and the effects of a large register file. The "circumstantial evidence" however, has been sufficient to encourage the RISC proponents.

The second area of potential benefit, which is more clearcut, relates to VLSI implementation. When VLSI is used, the design and implementation of the CPU are fundamentally changed. Traditional CPUs, such as the IBM S/370 and the VAX-11, consist of one or more printed circuit boards containing standardized SSI and MSI packages. With the advent of LSI and VLSI, it is possible to put an entire CPU on a single chip. For a single-chip CPU, there are two motivations for following a RISC strategy. First, there is the issue of performance. On-chip delays are of much shorter duration than inter-chip delays. Thus it makes sense to devote scarce chip real estate to those activities that occur frequently. We have seen that simple instructions and access to local scalars are, in fact, the most frequent activities. The Berkeley RISC chips were designed with this consideration in mind. Whereas a typical single-chip microprocessor dedicates about half of its area to the microcode control store, the RISC I chip devotes only about 6 percent of its area to the control unit [33].

A second VLSI-related issue is design-and-implementation time. A VLSI processor is difficult to develop. Instead of relying on available SSI/MSI parts, the designer must perform circuit design, layout, and modeling at the device level. With a reduced instruction set architecture, this process is far easier, as evidenced by Table 8 [34]. If, in addition, the

Table 8 Design and Layout Effort for Some Microprocessors

CPU	Transistors	Design (Person-Months)	Layout (Person-Months)
RISC I	44	15	12
RISC II	41	18	12
M68000	68	100	70
Z8000	18	60	70
Intel iAPx-432	110	170	90

performance of the RISC chip is equivalent to comparable CISC microprocessors, then the advantages of the RISC approach become evident.

V. RISC PIPELINING

One of the traditional methods of enhancing processor performance is instruction pipelining. The use of a reduced instruction set architecture opens up new opportunities for the effective use of pipelining. To illustrate the significance of pipelining on a RISC machine, we begin with a general discussion.

A. Pipelining Strategy

Instruction pipelining is similar to the use of an assembly line in a manufacturing plant. An assembly line takes advantage of the fact that a product goes through various stages of production. By laying the production process out in an assembly line, products at various stages can be worked on simultaneously. This process is also referred to as *pipelining*, because, as in a pipeline, new inputs are accepted at one end before previously accepted inputs appear as outputs at the other end.

To apply this concept to instruction execution, we must recognize that, in fact, the execution of an instruction involves a number of stages. As a simple approach, consider subdividing instruction processing into two stages: fetch instruction and execute instruction. There are times during the execution of an instruction when main memory is not being accessed. This time could be used to fetch the next instruction in parallel with the execution of the current one. Fig. 7(a) depicts this approach. The pipeline has two independent stages. The first stage fetches an instruction

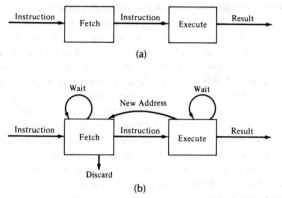

(a)

(b)

Fig. 7. Two-stage instruction pipeline. (a) Simplified view. (b) Expanded view.

and buffers it. When the second stage is free, the first stage passes the buffered instruction to the second stage. While the second stage is executing the instruction, the first stage takes advantage of any unused memory cycles to fetch and buffer the next instruction. This is called *instruction prefetch* or *fetch overlap*.

It should be clear that this process will speed up instruction execution. If the fetch and instruction stages were of equal duration, the instruction cycle time would be halved. However, if we look more closely at this pipeline (Fig. 7(b)), we will see that this doubling of execution rate is unlikely for two reasons:

1) The execution time will generally be longer than the fetch time. Execution will involve reading and storing operands and the performance of some operation. Thus the fetch stage may have to wait for some time before it can empty its buffer.

2) A conditional branch instruction makes the address of the next instruction to be fetched unknown. Thus the fetch stage must wait until it receives the next instruction address from the execute stage. The execute stage may then have to wait while the next instruction is fetched.

The time loss from the second reason can be reduced by guessing. A simple rule is the following: When a conditional branch instruction is passed on from the fetch to the execute stage, the fetch stage fetches the next instruction in memory after the branch instruction. Then, if the branch

is not taken, no time is lost. If the branch is taken, the fetched instruction must be discarded and a new instruction fetched.

While these factors reduce the potential effectiveness of the two-stage pipeline, some speedup occurs. To gain further speedup, the pipeline must have more stages. Let us consider the following decomposition of the instruction processing.

• *Fetch Instruction (FI):* Read the next expected instruction into a buffer.

• *Decode Instruction (DI):* Determine the opcode and the operand specifiers.

• *Calculate Operands (CO):* Calculate the effective address of each source operand. This may involve displacement, register indirect, indirect, or other forms of address calculation.

• *Fetch Operands (FO):* Fetch each operand from memory. Operands in registers need not be fetched.

• *Execute Instruction (EI):* Perform the indicated operation and store the result, if any, in the specified destination operand location.

With this decomposition, the various stages will be of more nearly equal duration. For the sake of illustration, let us assume equal duration and assume that only one stage that accesses memory may be active at a time. Then, Fig. 8 illustrates that a five-stage pipeline can reduce the execution time for four instructions from 20 time units to 13 time units. Note that the FI stage always involves a memory access. The FO and EI stages may or may not involve memory access, but the diagram is based on the assumption that they do.

Again, several factors serve to reduce the performance enhancement. If the five stages are not of equal length, there will be some waiting involved at various pipeline stages, as discussed before. A conditional branch instruction can invalidate several instruction fetches. A similar unpredictable event is an interrupt. Fig. 9 indicates the logic needed for pipelining to account for branches and interrupts.

Other problems arise that did not appear in our simple two-stage organization. The CO stage may depend on the contents of a register that could be altered by a previous instruction still in the pipeline. Other such register and memory conflicts could occur. The system must contain logic to account for this type of conflict.

The system should also contain additional logic to improve pipeline efficiency. For example, if an EI stage is not going to access memory, then another memory-accessing stage in another instruction can be performed in parallel.

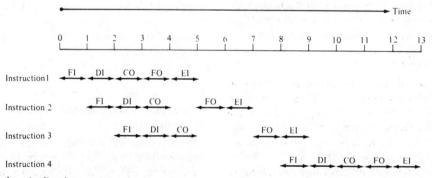

Fig. 8. Timing diagram for pipelined operation.

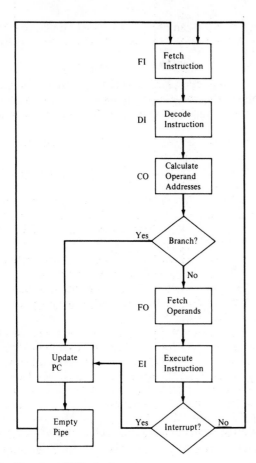

Fig. 9. Five-stage CPU pipeline.

From the preceding discussion, it might appear that the greater the number of stages in the pipeline, the faster the execution rate. However, two factors work against this conclusion:

1) At each stage of the pipeline, there is some overhead involved in moving data from buffer to buffer and in performing various preparation and delivery functions. This overhead can appreciably lengthen the total execution time of a single instruction, which can produce significant delays when the ideal pipeline pattern is not followed either through branching or memory access dependencies.

2) The amount of control logic required to handle memory and register dependencies and to optimize the use of the pipeline increases enormously with the number of stages. This can lead to a situation where the control logic controlling the gating between stages is more complex than the stages being controlled.

Thus instruction pipelining is a powerful technique for enhancing performance but requires careful design to achieve optimum results with reasonable complexity.

B. Dealing with Branches

One of the major problems in designing an instruction pipeline is assuring a steady flow of instructions to the initial stages of the pipeline. The primary impediment, as we have seen, is the conditional branch instruction. Until the instruction is actually executed, it is impossible to determine whether the branch will be taken or not.

In what follows, we briefly summarize some of the more common approaches to be taken for dealing with branches.

• *Multiple Streams:* A simple pipeline suffers a penalty for a branch instruction because it must choose one of two instructions to fetch next and may choose erroneously. A brute-force approach is to allow the pipeline to fetch both instructions, making use of multiple streams. One problem with this approach is that additional branch instructions may enter the pipeline (either stream) before the original branch is resolved. These instructions need their own multiple streams beyond what is supported in the hardware.

• *Prefetch Branch Target:* When a conditional branch is recognized, the target of the branch is prefetched, in addition to the instruction following the branch. This target is then saved until the branch instruction is executed. If the branch is taken, we have already prefetched the target.

• *Branch Prediction:* Various techniques can be used to predict whether a branch will be taken. These can be based on historical analysis of past executions (e.g., by opcode) or on some dynamic measure of the recent frequency of branching.

• *Delayed Branch:* It is possible to improve pipeline performance by automatically rearranging instructions within a program so that branch instructions occur later than actually desired.

The first three approaches are built into the hardware and are exercised at run time. The last approach listed above is performed at compile time and is used in most of the RISC compilers.

C. Pipelining with RISC Instructions

Let us now consider pipelining in the context of a RISC architecture. Most instructions are register-to-register, and an instruction cycle has the following two phases:

• I: Instruction fetch.
• E: Execute. Performs an ALU operation with register input and output.

For load and store operations, three phases are required:

• I: Instruction fetch.
• E: Execute. Calculates memory address.
• D: Memory. Register-to-memory or memory-to-register operation.

Fig. 10 depicts the timing of a sequence of instructions using no pipelining (Figs. 10–14 are based on [33]). Clearly,

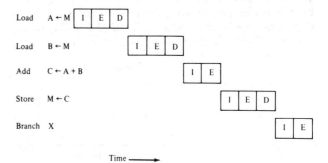

Fig. 10. Timing of sequential execution.

this is a wasteful process. Even very simple pipelining can substantially improve performance. Fig. 11 shows a two-way pipelining scheme, in which the I and E phases of two different instructions are performed simultaneously. This

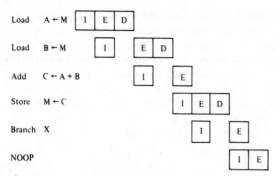

Fig. 11. Two-way pipelined timing.

scheme can yield up to twice the execution rate of a serial scheme. Two problems prevent the maximum speedup from being achieved. First, we assume that a single-port memory is used and that only one memory access is possible per phase. This requires the insertion of a wait state in some instructions. Second, a branch instruction interrupts the sequential flow of execution. To accommodate this with minimum circuitry, a NOOP instruction can be inserted into the instruction stream by the compiler or assembler.

Pipelining can be improved further by permitting two memory accesses per phase. This yields the sequence shown in Fig. 12. Now, up to three instructions can be over-

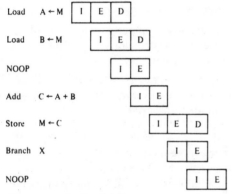

Fig. 12. Three-way pipelined timing.

lapped, and the improvement is as much as a factor of three. Again, branch instructions cause the speedup to fall short of the maximum possible. Also, note that data dependencies have an effect. If an instruction needs an operand that is altered by the preceding instruction, a delay is required. Again, this can be accomplished by a NOOP.

The pipelining discussed so far works best if the three phases are of approximately equal duration. Because the E phase usually involves an ALU operation, it may be longer.

In this case, we can divide into two subphases:

- E_1: Register file read.
- E_2: ALU operation and register write.

Because of the simplicity and regularity of the instruction set, the design of the phasing into three or four phases is easily accomplished. Fig. 13 shows the result with a four-

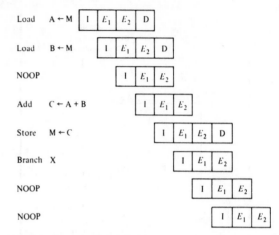

Fig. 13. Four-way pipelined timing.

way pipeline. Up to four instructions at a time can be under way, and the maximum potential speedup is a factor of four. Note again the use of NOOPs to account for data and branch delays.

D. Optimization of Pipelining

Because of the simple and regular nature of RISC instructions, pipelining schemes can be efficiently employed. There are few variations in instruction execution duration, and the pipeline can be tailored to reflect this. However, we have seen that data and branch dependencies reduce the overall execution rate.

To compensate for these dependencies, code reorganization techniques have been developed [35]. First, let us consider branching instructions. *Delayed branch*, a way of increasing the efficiency of the pipeline, makes use of a branch that does not take effect until after the following instruction. This strange procedure is illustrated in Table 9. In the first column, we see a normal symbolic instruction machine-language program. After 102 is executed, the next instruction to be executed is 105. In order to regularize the pipeline, a NOOP is inserted after this branch. However, increased performance is achieved if the instructions at 101 and 102 are interchanged. Fig. 14 shows the result. The JUMP instruction is fetched before the ADD instruction. Note,

Table 9 Normal and Delayed Branch

Address	Normal Branch		Delayed Branch		Optimized Delayed Branch	
100	LOAD	X, A	LOAD	X, A	LOAD	X, A
101	ADD	1, A	ADD	1, A	JUMP	105
102	JUMP	105	JUMP	106	ADD	1, A
103	ADD	A, B	NOOP		ADD	A, B
104	SUB	C, B	ADD	A, B	SUB	C, B
105	STORE	A, Z	SUB	C, B	STORE	A, Z
106			STORE	A, Z		

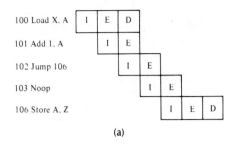

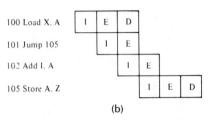

Fig. 14. Execution of delayed jump. (a) Inserted NOOP. (b) Reversed instructions.

however, that the ADD instruction is fetched before the execution of the JUMP instruction has a chance to alter the program counter. Thus the original semantics of the program are retained.

This interchange of instructions will work successfully for unconditional branches, calls, and returns. For conditional branches, this procedure cannot be blindly applied. If the condition that is tested for the branch can be altered by the immediately preceding instruction, then the compiler must refrain from doing the interchange and instead insert a NOOP. The experience of both the Berkeley RISC and IBM 801 systems is that the majority of conditional branch instructions can be optimized in this fashion [18], [30].

A similar sort of tactic, called the delayed load, can be used on LOAD instructions. On LOAD instructions, the register that is to be the target of the load is locked by the CPU. The CPU then continues execution of the instruction stream until it reaches an instruction requiring that register, at which point it idles until the load is complete. If the compiler can rearrange instructions so that useful work can be done while the load is in the pipeline, efficiency is increased.

VI. Example Systems

This section provides two concrete examples of RISC systems, the Berkeley RISC and the R2000 from MIPS Computer Systems. Unlike a number of other machines that present RISC characteristics mixed with CISC characteristics, these are both relatively "pure" RISC systems.

A. Berkeley RISC

The best documented RISC project is that conducted at the University of California at Berkeley. Two similar machines, RISC I and RISC II, were produced [18], [21]. The Berkeley RISC architecture was the inspiration for a commercially available product, the Pyramid [24].

Instruction Set: Table 10 lists the instructions for the Berkeley RISC computers.

As can be seen, most of the instructions reference only register operands. Register-to-register instructions have

three operands and can be expressed in the form

$$Rd \leftarrow R_{S1} \text{ op } S2$$

Rd and R_{S1} are register references. S2 can refer either to a register or to a 13-bit immediate operand. Register zero (R_0) is hardwired with the value 0. This form is well suited to typical programs, which have a high proportion of local scalars and constants.

The available ALU operations can be grouped as follows:

- integer addition (with or without carry)
- integer subtraction (with or without carry)
- bitwise Boolean AND, OR, XOR
- shift left logical, right logical, or right arithmetic.

All of these instructions can optionally set the four condition codes (ZERO, NEGATIVE, OVERFLOW, CARRY). Integers are represented in 32-bit 2's-complement form.

Only simple load-and-store instructions reference memory. There are separate load-and-store instructions for word (32 bits), halfword, and byte. For the latter two cases, there are instructions for loading these quantities as signed or unsigned numbers. Signed numbers are sign-extended to fill out the 32-bit destination register. Unsigned numbers are padded with 0s.

On the RISC I, the only available addressing mode, other than register, is a displacement mode. That is, the effective address of an operand consists of a displacement from an address contained in a register:

$$EA = (R_{S1}) + S2$$

or

$$EA = (R_{S1}) + (R_{S2})$$

according as the second operand is immediate or a register reference. To perform a load or store, an extra phase is added to the instruction cycle. During the second phase, the address is calculated using the ALU; the load or store occurs in a third phase. This single addressing mode is quite versatile and can be used to synthesize other addressing modes, as indicated in Table 11.

The RISC II includes an additional version of each load and store instruction using relative address:

$$EA = (PC) = S2.$$

The remaining instructions include control-transfer instructions and some miscellaneous instruction. The control-transfer instructions include conditional jump, call, and conditional return instructions. Both forms of RISC II addressing can be used.

Instruction Format: One of the major factors in the complexity of instruction processing is instruction decoding, especially the task of extracting the various instruction fields. To minimize this chore, the ideal instruction set would use a single fixed-length format with fixed field positions. The RISC instruction set comes close to this goal.

All RISC instructions are a single word (32 bits) in length (Fig. 15). The first 7 bits are the opcode, allowing up to 128 different opcodes. RISC I and RISC II use only 31 and 39 codes, respectively. The SCC bit indicates whether to set the condition codes. The DEST field usually contains a 5-bit destination register reference. For conditional branch instructions, 4 bits of the field designate which condition or conditions are to be tested.

Table 10 RISC Instruction Set

Instruction	Operands		Comments
ADD	Rs,S2,Rd	Rd←Rs + S2	integer add
ADDC	Rs,S2,Rd	Rd←Rs + S2 + carry	add with carry
SUB	Rs,S2,Rd	Rd←Rs − S2	integer subtract
SUBC	Rs,S2,Rd	Rd←Rs − S2 − carry	subtract with carry
SUBR	Rs,S2,Rd	Rd←S2 − Rs	integer subtract
SUBCR	Rs,S2,Rd	Rd←S2 − Rs − carry	subtract with carry
AND	Rs,S2,Rd	Rd←Rs | S2	logical and
OR	Rs,S2,Rd	Rd←Rs | S2	logical or
XOR	Rs,S2,Rd	Rd←Rs xor S2	logical exclusive or
SLL	Rs,S2,Rd	Rd←Rs shifted by S2	shift left
SRL	Rs,S2,Rd	Rd←Rs shifted by S2	shift right logical
SRA	Rs,S2,Rd	Rd←Rs shifted by S2	shift right arithmetic
LDXW	(Rx)S2,Rd	Rd←M[Rx + S2]	load word
LDXHU	(Rx)S2,Rd	Rd←M[Rx + S2]	load halfword unsigned
LDXHS	(Rx)S2,Rd	Rd←M[Rx + S2]	load halfword signed
LDXBU	(Rx)S2,Rd	Rd←M[Rx + S2]	load byte unsigned
LDYBS	(Rx)S2,Rd	Rd←M[Rx + S2]	load byte signed
STXW	Rm,(Rx)S2	M[Rx + S2]←Rm	store word
STXH	Rm,(Rx)S2	M[Rx + S2]←Rm	store halfword
STXB	Rm,(Rx)S2	M[Rx + S2]←Rm	store byte
LDRW	S2,Rd	Rd←M[PC + S2]	load word relative
LDRHU	S2,Rd	Rd←M[PC + S2]	load halfword unsigned relative
LDRHS	S2,Rd	Rd←M[PC + S2]	load halfword signed relative
LDRBU	S2,Rd	Rd←M[PC + S2]	load byte unsigned relative
LDRBS	S2,Rd	Rd←M[PC + S2]	load byte signed relative
STRW	Rm,S2	M[PC + S2]←Rm	store word
STRH	Rm,S2	M[PC + S2]←Rm	store halfword
STRB	Rm,S2	M[PC + S2]←Rm	store byte
JMP	COND,S2(Rx)	pc←Rx + S2	conditional jump
JMPR	COND,Y	pc←pc + Y	conditional relative
CALL	Rd,S2(Rx)	Rd←pc, next	call
		pc←Rx + S2,CWP←CWP − 1	and change window
CALLR	Rd,Y	Rd←pc, next	call relative
		pc←pc + Y,CWP←CWP − 1	and change window
RET	Rm,S2	pc←Rm + S2,CWP←CWP + 1	return and change window
CALLINT	Rd	Rd←last pc; next CWP←CWP − 1	disable interrupts
RETINT	Rm,S2	pc←Rm + S2; next CWP←CWP + 1	enable interrupts
LDHI	Rd,Y	Rd⟨31:13⟩←Y; Rd⟨12:0⟩←0	load immediate high
GTLPC	Rd	Rd←last pc	to restart delayed jump
GETPSW	Rd	Rd←PSW	load status word
PUTPSW	Rm	PSW←Rm	set status word

Table 11 Synthesizing Other Addressing Modes with RISC Addressing Modes

Mode	Algorithm	RISC Equivalent	Instruction Type
Immediate	operand = A	S2	register–register
Direct	EA = A	$R_0 + S_2$	load, store
Register	EA = R	Rs_1, Rs_2	register–register
Register indirect	EA = (R)	$Rs_1 + 0$	load, store
Displacement	EA = (R) + A	$Rs_1 + S_2$	load, store

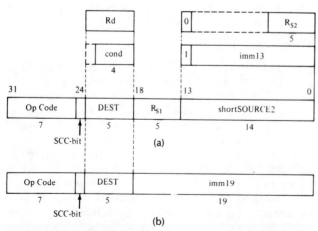

Fig. 15. RISC instruction formats. (a) Short-immediate format. (b) Long-immediate format.

The remaining 19 bits designate one or two operands, depending on opcode. A single 19-bit 2's-complement immediate operand is used for all PC-relative instructions. Otherwise, the first of the two operands is a register reference. The second operand is either a register reference or a 13-bit 2's-complement immediate operand.

Register File: The RISC register file contains 138 registers. Physical registers 0 through 9 are global registers shared by all procedures. The remaining registers are grouped into eight windows. Each process sees logical registers 0 through 31 (Fig. 16). Logical registers 26 through 31 are shared with the calling (parent) procedure, and logical registers 10 through 15 are shared with any called (child) procedure. These two portions overlap with other windows.

Pipelining: The RISC I processor uses a two-stage pipeline, dividing each instruction into fetch and execute states. RISC II uses the three stages. The second stage performs

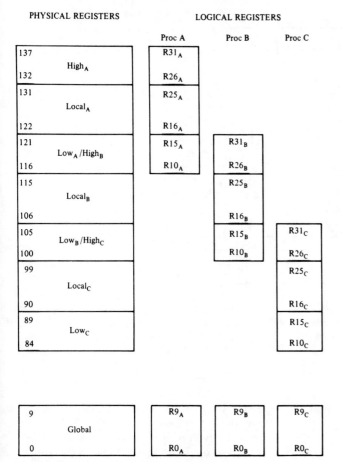

Fig. 16. Berkeley RISC register windows.

ALU operations. The third stage stores a result in Rd or accesses memory with an effective address computed in the second stage.

B. MIPS R2000

One of the first commercially available chip sets was developed by MIPS Computer Systems [36], [37]. The system was inspired by an experimental system, also using the name MIPS, developed at Stanford [38].

The RISC processor chip (called the R2000) is partitioned into two sections, one containing the CPU, and the other containing a coprocessor for memory management. The CPU has a very simple architecture. The intent was to design a system in which the instruction execution logic was as simple as possible, leaving space available for logic to enhance performance (e.g., the entire memory management unit).

The processor supports thirty-two 32-bit registers. It also provides for up to 128 kbytes of high-speed cache, half each for instructions and data. The relatively large cache (the IBM 3090 provides 128–256 kbytes of cache) enables the system to keep large sets of program code and data local to the processor, off-loading the main memory bus and avoiding the need for a large register file with the accompanying windowing logic. All processor instructions are encoded in a single 32-bit word. All data operations are register-to-register; the only memory references are pure load/store operations.

Several features found in other RISC designs are missing in the MIPS machine. As was mentioned, there are only 32

general-purpose registers, all of which are visible at all times; there are no hidden registers and no use of windowing. The optimizing compiler tailors each procedure's register usage. The 32 registers are used like a stack, with a virtual stack frame marking the top of the stack for the new procedure activation environment. By making the compiler do all the work, a procedure call or return may require as few as two instructions. In addition, the compiler uses a priority-based graph coloring algorithm to optimize register usage within and across procedures.

The R2000 makes no use of condition codes. If an instruction generates a condition, the corresponding flags are stored in a general-purpose register. This avoids the need for special logic to deal with condition codes as they affect the pipelining mechanism and the reordering of instructions by the compiler. Instead, the mechanisms already implemented to deal with register-value dependencies are employed. Further, conditions mapped onto the register file are subject to the same compile-time optimizations in allocation and reuse as other values stored in registers.

As with the Berkeley RISC, but unlike many other RISC-based machines, the MIPS uses a single instruction length. This single instruction length simplifies instruction fetch and decode, and also simplifies the interaction of instruction fetch with the virtual memory management unit (i.e., instructions do not cross word or page boundaries). The three instruction formats (Fig. 17) share common formating

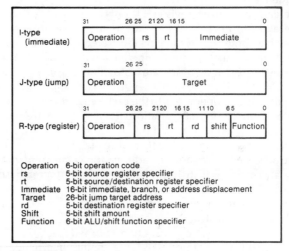

Fig. 17. MIPS instruction formats.

of opcodes and register references, simplifying instruction decode. The effect of longer instructions can be synthesized at compile time. For example, two I-type instructions can be concatenated to provide for operation on a 32-bit immediate quantity.

Only the simplest and most frequently used addressing mode is implemented in hardware. All addresses are of the form (contents of register plus immediate offset). Complex modes such as (base + index + offset) are synthesized in compile time, subject to optimizations that eliminate redundancy. This approach minimizes both hardware and pipeline latencies for loads and branches.

With its simplified instruction architecture, the MIPS can achieve very efficient pipelining. Instructions execute at a rate of almost one per cycle. The MIPS compiler is able to reorder instructions to fill delay slots with useful code 70–

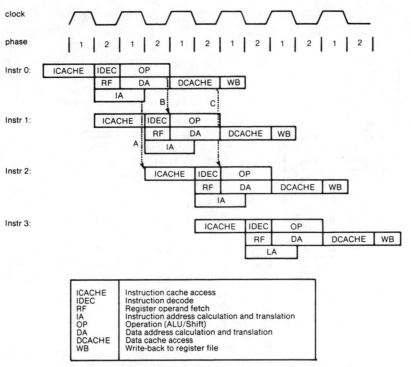

clock

phase

Instr 0:

ICACHE	IDEC	OP		
	RF	DA	DCACHE	WB
	IA			

B   C

Instr 1:

ICACHE	IDEC	OP		
	RF	DA	DCACHE	WB
A	IA			

Instr 2:

ICACHE	IDEC	OP		
	RF	DA	DCACHE	WB
	IA			

Instr 3:

ICACHE	IDEC	OP		
	RF	DA	DCACHE	WB
	LA			

ICACHE	Instruction cache access
IDEC	Instruction decode
RF	Register operand fetch
IA	Instruction address calculation and translation
OP	Operation (ALU/Shift)
DA	Data address calculation and translation
DCACHE	Data cache access
WB	Write-back to register file

Fig. 18. MIPS instruction pipeline.

90 percent of the time. All instructions follow the same sequence of five pipeline stages: instruction fetch, source operand fetch from register file, ALU operation or data operand address generation, data memory reference, and write back into register file. As illustrated in Fig. 18, there is not only parallelism due to pipelining but also parallelism within the execution of a single instruction. The clock cycle is divided into two 30-ns phases. The external instruction and data access operations to the cache each require 60 ns, as do the major internal operations (OP, DA, IA). Instruction decode is a simpler operation, requiring only a single 30-ns phase, overlapped with register fetch in the same instruction. Calculation of an address for a branch instruction also overlaps instruction decode and register fetch, so that a branch at instruction 0 in Fig. 18 can address the ICACHE access of instruction 2 (see dotted line A). Similarly, a load at instruction 0 fetches data that are immediately used by the OP of instruction 2 (dotted line C), while an ALU/shift result gets passed directly into instruction 1 with no delay (dotted line B). This tight coupling between instructions makes for a highly efficient pipeline.

VII. THE RISC VERSUS CISC CONTROVERSY

For many years, the general trend in computer architecture and organization has been toward increasing CPU complexity: more instructions, more addressing modes, more specialized registers, and so on. The RISC movement represents a fundamental break with the philosophy behind that trend. Naturally the appearance of RISC systems, and the publication of papers by its proponents extolling RISC virtues, has led to a reaction from what might be called the mainstream of computer architecture.

The work that has been done on assessing merits of the RISC approach can be grouped into two categories:

Quantitative: attempts to compare program size and execution speed of programs on RISC and CISC machines that use comparable technology.

Qualitative: examination of issues such as high-level language support and optimum use of VLSI real estate.

Most of the work on quantitative assessment has been done by those working on RISC systems [31], [39], [40], and has been, by and large, favorable to the RISC approach. Others have examined the issue and come away unconvinced [41]. There are several problems with attempting such comparisons [42]:

• There is no pair of RISC and a CISC machine that are comparable in life-cycle cost, level of technology, gate complexity, sophistication of compiler, operating-system support, and so on.

• No definitive test set of programs exists. Performance varies with the program.

• It is difficult to sort out hardware effects from effects due to skill in compiler writing.

• Most of the comparative analysis on RISC has been done on "toy" machines: not commercial products. Furthermore, most commercially available machines advertised as RISC possess a mixture of RISC and CISC characteristics [13]. Thus a fair comparison with a commercial, "pure-play" CISC machine (e.g., VAX, Intel 432), is difficult.

The qualitative assessment is, almost by definition, subjective. Several researchers have turned their attention to such an assessment [41], [43], [44], but the results are, at best, ambiguous, and certainly subject to rebuttal [45], and, of course, counter-rebuttal [46].

The success of the RISC approach in the marketplace is far from assured. As research, development, and product introduction continue, the assessment goes on.

REFERENCES

[1] W. Stallings, *Reduced Instruction Set Computers.* Washington, DC: IEEE Computer Soc. Press, 1986.

[2] R. Weiss, "RISC processors: The new wave in computer systems," *Comput. Des.*, pp. 53-73, May 15, 1987.

[3] C. Bruno and S. Brady, "The RISC factor," *Datamation*, pp. y-DD, June 1, 1986.

[4] J. Moussouris *et al.*, "A CMOS RISC processor with integrated system functions," in *Proc. Compcon Spring 86* (Mar. 1986), pp. 126-131.

[5] L. Neff, "Clipper™ microprocessor architecture overview," in *Proc. Compcon Spring 86* (Mar. 1986), pp. 191-195.

[6] F. Waters, Ed., *IBM RT Personal Computer Technology*, IBM Publ. SA23-1057, 1986.

[7] E. Basart, "RISC design streamlines high-power CPUs," *Comput. Des.*, pp. 119-122, July 1, 1985.

[8] S. Gannes, "Back-to-basics computers with sports-car speed," *Fortune*, pp. 98-101, Sept. 30, 1985.

[9] M. Miller, "Simplicity is focus in efforts to increase computer power," *The Wall Street J.*, p. 17, Aug. 23, 1985.

[10] S. Ohr, "RISC machines," *Electron. Des.*, pp. 175-190, Jan. 10, 1985.

[11] M. Seither, "Pyramid challenges DEC with RISC supermini," *Mini-Micro Syst.*, pp. 33-36, Aug. 1985.

[12] R. Bernhard, "RISCs—Reduced instruction set computers—make leap," *Syst. Software*, pp. 81-84, Dec. 1984.

[13] N. Mokhoff, "New RISC machines appear as hybrids with both RISC and CISC features," *Comput. Des.*, pp. 22-25, Apr. 1, 1986.

[14] J. Birnbaum and W. Worley, "Beyond RISC: High-precision architecture," in *Proc. Compcon Spring 86* (Mar. 1986), pp. 40-47.

[15] J. Browne, "Understanding execution behavior of software systems," *Computer*, vol. 17, pp. 83-87, July 1984.

[16] D. Knuth, "An empirical study of FORTRAN programs," *Software Practice Exper.*, vol. 1, pp. 105-133, 1971.

[17] A. Tanenbaum, "Implications of structured programming for machine architecture," *Commun. ACM*, pp. 237-246, Mar. 1978.

[18] D. Patterson and C. Sequin, "A VLSI RISC," *Computer*, pp. 8-22, Sept. 1982.

[19] T. Huck, "Comparative analysis of computer architectures," Stanford Univ. Tech. Rep. 83-243, May 1983.

[20] A. Lunde, "Empirical evaluation of some features of instruction set processor architectures," *Commun. ACM*, pp. 143-153, Mar. 1972.

[21] M. Katevenis, "Reduced instruction set computer architectures for VLSI," Ph.D. dissertation, Computer Sci. Dep., Univ. of California at Berkeley, Oct. 1983. Reprinted by MIT Press, Cambridge, MA, 1985.

[22] D. Patterson, "Reduced instruction set computers," *Commun. ACM*, pp. 8-21, Jan. 1985.

[23] Y. Tamir and C. Sequin, "Strategies for managing the register file in RISC," *IEEE Trans. Comput.*, vol. C-30, pp. 977-988, Nov. 1983.

[24] R. Ragan-Kelley and R. Clark, "Applying RISC theory to a large computer," *Comput. Des.*, pp. 191-198, Nov. 1983.

[25] W. Stallings, *Computer Organization and Architecture*. New York, NY: Macmillan, 1987.

[26] G. Chaitin, "Register allocation and spilling via graph coloring," in *Proc. SIGPLAN Symp. on Compiler Construction* (June 1982), pp. 98-105.

[27] F. Chow, M. Himelstein, E. Killian, and L. Weber, "Engineering a RISC compiler system," in *Proc. Compcon Spring 86* (Mar. 1986), pp. 132-137.

[28] D. Coutant, C. Hammond, and J. Kelley, "Compilers for the new generation of Hewlett-Packard Computers," in *Proc. Compcon Spring 86* (Mar. 1986), pp. 182-195.

[29] J. Hennessy *et al.*, "Hardware/software tradeoffs for increased performance," in *Proc. Symp. on Architectural Support for Programming Languages and Operating Systems*, pp. 2-11, Mar. 1982.

[30] G. Radin, "The 801 minicomputer," *IBM J. Res. Devel.*, pp. 237-246, May 1983.

[31] D. Patterson and R. Piepho, "Assessing RISCs in high-level language support," *IEEE Micro*, vol. 2, pp. 9-18, Nov. 1982.

[32] G. Myers, "The evaluation of expressions in a storage-to-storage architecture," *Comput. Arch. News*, June 1978.

[33] R. Sherburne, "Processor design tradeoffs in VLSI," Ph.D. dissertation, Rep. UCB/CSD 84/173, Univ. of California at Berkeley, Apr. 1984.

[34] D. Fitzpatrick *et al.*, "A RISCy approach to VLSI," *VLSI Des.*, pp. 14-20, 4th Quarter, 1981.

[35] J. Hennessy and T. Gross, "Postpass code optimization of pipeline constraints," *ACM Trans. Programming Languages Syst.*, July 1983.

[36] C. Rowen *et al.*, "RISC VLSI design for system-level performance," *VLSI Syst. Des.*, Mar. 1986.

[37] J. Moussouris *et al.*, "A CMOS RISC processor with integrated system functions," in *Proc. COMPCON Spring 86* (Mar. 1986), pp. 126-131.

[38] J. L. Hennessy, "VLSI processor architecture," *IEEE Trans. Comput.*, vol. C-33, pp. 1221-1246, Dec. 1984.

[39] J. Heath, "Re-evaluation of RISC I," *Comput. Arch. News*, Mar. 1984.

[40] D. Patterson, "RISC watch," *Comput. Arch. News*, Mar. 1984.

[41] R. P. Colwell, C. Y. Hitchcock, E. D. Jensen, H. M. B. Brinkley-Sprunt, and C. P. Kollar, "Instruction sets and beyond: Computers, complexity and controversy," *Computer*, vol. 18, pp. 8-19, Sept. 1985.

[42] O. Serlin, "MIPS, dhrystones, and other tales," *Datamation*, pp. 112-118, June 1, 1986.

[43] R. Bernhard, "More hardware means less software," *IEEE Spectrum*, December 1981.

[44] P. Wallich, "Toward simpler, faster computers." *IEEE Spectrum*, vol. 22, pp. 38-45, Aug. 1985.

[45] D. Patterson and J. Hennessy, "Comments, with reply on 'Computers, complexity, and controversy,'" by R. P. Colwell, *et al.*, *Computer*, vol. 18, pp. 142-143, Nov. 1985.

[46] R. Colwell, C. Hitchcock, E. Jensen, and H. Sprunt, "More controversy about 'computers, complexity, and controversy,'" *Computer*, p. 93, Dec. 1985.

William Stallings (Senior Member, IEEE) received the B.S. degree in electrical engineering from Notre Dame University, Notre Dame, IN, and the Ph.D. degree in computer science from the Massachusetts Institute of Technology, Cambridge, MA.

He is an independent consultant and president of Comp/Comm Consulting, London, England. He is also a frequent lecturer and the author of numerous technical papers and eleven books in the fields of data communications and computer science, including *Computer Organization and Architecture* (New York, NY: Macmillan, 1987) and *Data and Computer Communications, Second Edition* (New York, NY: Macmillan, 1988). His clients have included the Government of India, the International Monetary Fund, the National Security Agency, IBM, and Honeywell. Prior to forming his own consulting firm, he was Vice President of CSM Corp., a firm specializing in data processing and data communications for the health-care industry. He was also Director of Systems analysis and design for CTEC, Inc., a firm specializing in command, control, and communications systems.

An old idea may influence new computer designs.

RISC: BACK TO THE FUTURE?

by C. Gordon Bell

Several recent announcements indicate that computers will be changing over the next decade. The new high-speed architectures announced by Hewlett-Packard, IBM, and a startup in Sunnyvale, Calif., called MIPS Computer Systems Inc., challenge today's reliance on microprogrammed processors—a legacy of the original IBM 360.

The primary development involves the application of the so-called reduced instruction set computer (RISC) concept. RISC

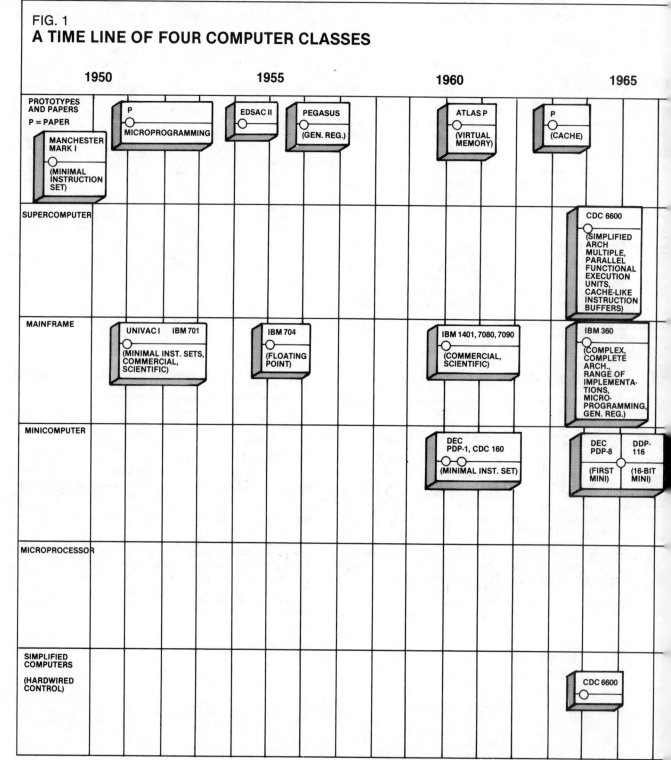

FIG. 1
A TIME LINE OF FOUR COMPUTER CLASSES

	1950	1955	1960	1965
PROTOTYPES AND PAPERS P = PAPER	MANCHESTER MARK I (MINIMAL INSTRUCTION SET); P MICROPROGRAMMING	EDSAC II; PEGASUS (GEN. REG.)	ATLAS P (VIRTUAL MEMORY)	P (CACHE)
SUPERCOMPUTER				CDC 6600 (SIMPLIFIED ARCH MULTIPLE, PARALLEL FUNCTIONAL EXECUTION UNITS, CACHE-LIKE INSTRUCTION BUFFERS)
MAINFRAME	UNIVAC I, IBM 701 (MINIMAL INST. SETS, COMMERCIAL, SCIENTIFIC)	IBM 704 (FLOATING POINT)	IBM 1401, 7080, 7090 (COMMERCIAL, SCIENTIFIC)	IBM 360 (COMPLEX, COMPLETE ARCH., RANGE OF IMPLEMENTATIONS, MICROPROGRAMMING, GEN. REG.)
MINICOMPUTER			DEC PDP-1, CDC 160 (MINIMAL INST. SET)	DEC PDP-8 (FIRST MINI); DDP-116 (16-BIT MINI)
MICROPROCESSOR				
SIMPLIFIED COMPUTERS (HARDWIRED CONTROL)				CDC 6600

Reprinted from DATAMATION, June 1, 1987 © 1986 by Cahners Publishing Company.

designs contrast with those of complex (or complete) instruction set computers (CISC), which are meant to contain a repertoire of machine instructions to handle all the data types and operations of today's high-level languages. (The CISC approach reduces the size of object programs by attempting to provide each high-level source code statement with a single machine instruction.)

The concept of RISC involves an attempt to reduce execution time by simplifying the central processor's tasks. Conventional microprogrammed architectures are predicated on relatively slow access to primary memory and read-only memories for microprograms that are five to 10 times faster. In CISC machines, which do more processing per instruction than in RISC, the processor requires five to 10 clock ticks to carry out a typical instruction.

But with continuing hardware refinements, especially in chip technology over the last decade, logic and memory speeds are now nearly identical. RISC machines exploit this development by transferring certain logical steps that are required to interpret instructions out of processor microcode and into memory as a run-time library program (see Figs. 2c and 2d). In a RISC design, all high-level language functions are constructed from simple software primitives in a fashion resembling microprogramming, except that they are stored outside the processor as regular programs.

Reducing the instruction set further reduces the work a RISC processor has to do. Since RISC has fewer types of instructions than CISC, a RISC instruction requires less processing logic to interpret than a

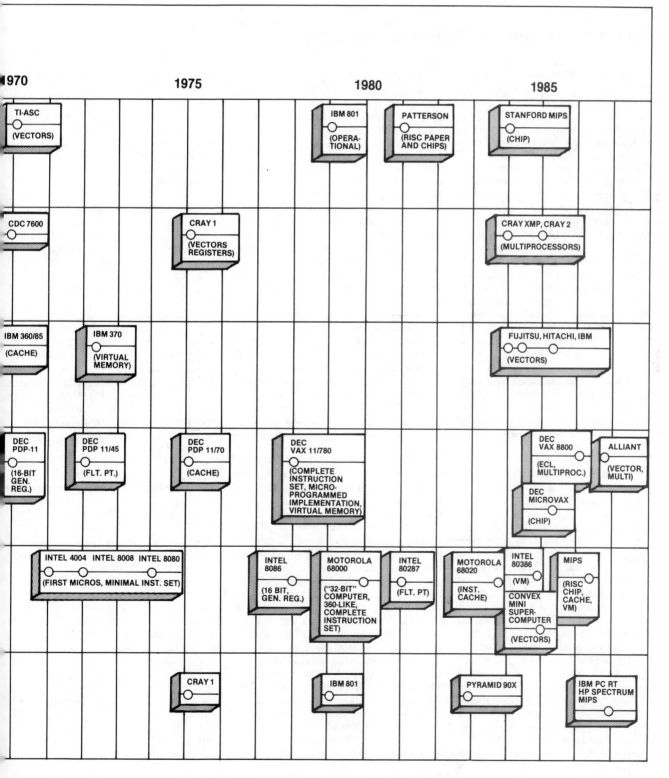

Nearly all the RISC machines resemble the simple, Cray-style architectures pioneered in the CDC 6600.

CISC instruction. The effect of such simplification is to speed up the execution rate for RISC instructions. In a RISC implementation it is theoretically possible to execute an instruction each time the computer's logic clock ticks. In practice the clock rate of a RISC processor is usually three times that of the instruction rate.

Of course, a typical instruction in a RISC machine is much less powerful than a typical CISC instruction—making comparisons of MIPS rates virtually meaningless. Benchmark tests in high-level languages are the only way to compare computers.

RISC's gains in processing time involve a cost in memory space. But since virtually all programs are implemented in high-level languages, machine-level trade-offs are scarcely noticeable to end users. If the notion of a RISC proves sound, users will see a gradual increase in performance as manufacturers go back to hard-wired control implementations and abandon the more complex microprogrammed approach used over the last two decades.

The second major development in recent architectures is the use of vector data types to speed up scientific computation. Cray Research pioneered this in 1975 with its Cray-1, and it has now been introduced in the IBM-compatible mainframes and a plethora of new minisupercomputers from Alliant Computer Systems Corp. of Acton, Mass., Convex of Dallas, and Scientific Computing Systems of Portland, Ore.

Finally, the multiprocessor approach to computing is being introduced in all computer families, from supercomputers to workstations, in order to provide the seemingly unbounded increases in performance available through parallel processing. The multiprocessor approach is independent of the architecture of the processors (i.e., whether a processor is "reduced" or "complex").

HOW RISC BEGAN

The groundwork for RISC was laid in the mid-1970s. In 1975, a team at the IBM Research Center in Yorktown Heights, N.Y., formed what was called the 801 project around a design approach credited to IBM fellow John Cocke. The goal of the project was to "achieve significantly better cost/performance for high-level language programs than that attainable by existing systems." The 801 group, which was led by George Radin, one of the primary authors of the PL/1 language, produced an operational minicomputer in 1979 (see "IBM Mini a Radical Departure," October 1979, p. 53). The IBM group acknowledged being influenced by the design simplifications—such

as hard-wired control—pioneered by Seymour Cray in his design of the first supercomputer, the CDC 6600 (c. 1964).

Professor David Patterson of the University of California at Berkeley has been the main proponent of reexamining architectures along RISC lines. His first paper on RISC, published in *Computer Architecture News* in October 1980, made the case for a simplified instruction set.

The phrase "reduced instruction set computer" was coined to describe the subsequent Berkeley effort. Berkeley researchers and engineers went on to implement operational prototypes, RISC I and RISC II, in the early '80s; a third Berkeley RISC design is oriented to multiprocessing and symbolic programming.

Pyramid Technology Corp., Mountain View, Calif., was among the first companies to build computers based on the new RISC ideas. Pyramid's 90X supermini was released in 1983.

IBM's newly introduced PC RT for scientific and engineering applications evolved from the basic 801 effort, although the machine is hardly noteworthy in terms of the initial performance or functionality. The RT chip was implemented with older generation MOS technology using a relatively slow clock of 6MHz. Performance does not appear to measure up to comparable microprocessors based on, for example, Intel's 80386 design. By using modern CMOS technology, a speedup of at least a factor of 3 is easily attainable, which would demonstrate the validity of the design approach.

The HP Spectrum series announced in February may also be related to the 801 effort. The manager of the section sponsoring the work at IBM, Joel Birnbaum, went to HP to head its research lab. As with the PC RT, Spectrum performance is uninspiring, but the series is not an adequate test of RISC since the technology used is hardly state of the art.

The chip built by MIPS Co. presents a more compelling case for RISC. MIPS Co. was formed in 1984 to build a high-performance chip based on the design ideas developed by Prof. John Hennessy and his associates at Stanford University. Initial benchmarks of the MIPS chip indicate it is five to 10 times faster than a DEC VAX-11/780 or the Motorola 68020 for the same clock speed. The MIPS Co. chip is simpler, considerably smaller, and significantly faster than any of today's microprocessors. The Defense Department's R&D arm, which sponsored the MIPS work, has adopted the architecture as a standard for high-performance implementations.

Fairchild Semiconductor Corp., Mountain View, Calif., has given further

support to the RISC approach with its recently announced microprocessor called Clipper. The leader of the Clipper development group, Howard Sachs, came from Cray Research. Clipper, implemented as three CMOS chips, is reported to be about the speed of a VAX 8600.

RISC MACHINES CRAY-LIKE

Nearly all the RISC machines unveiled so far resemble the simple, Cray-style architectures pioneered in the CDC 6600 and oriented to scientific processing (which stresses binary data types). How well a RISC design can handle the variable-length decimal and string data inherent in many commercial applications still remains to be seen. Provided the proper focus on the data types is maintained, there's no reason to believe the RISC approach will be unsuccessful.

The first operational stored program computer, the Manchester Mark I (c. 1948) was a minimal instruction set computer (MISC). The Mark I, which had a memory of 32 words (expandable to 8K words), each 32 bits long, had only six instructions: jump, load accumulator negative, subtract, store accumulator, test for zero, and stop.

Beginning with the Univac I (c. 1951), the computers that followed the Mark I in the '50s and '60s likewise had simple instruction sets, appropriately embellished with index registers to assist in the access of arrays. The design objectives of the earliest machines were that they have a minimum of registers, efficient encoding of programs (often oriented to assembly language programming), small primary memories, and processors matched to the memory's performance. The instruction sets were small and the instructions were simple and operated only on integers. Floating point hardware was introduced in the IBM 704 in 1955.

By the mid-1960s, computers had evolved to having a single set of general purpose registers combining accumulators, index and base registers, and subroutine linkage registers. The control unit for simple processors was straightforward. Each machine had a few allowable data types and instructions. Memories were slow, relative to the rate at which information could be transferred among the internal registers of the machine. By 1960, core memories had a 2μsec cycle time, with a 1μsec access time. Since internal logic operated at a 5MHz to 10MHz clock rate, five to 10 hardware operations could thus be carried out after one memory access and before the next. This ratio would change as chip technology progressed.

A simple computer of the early '60s operated at about 250,000 instructions per second since typically two memory references were required per instruction (e.g., load accumulator, add memory to accumulator, store accumulator). Performance was increased by providing overlapped memory so that a processor could access memory at a faster rate. The objective of computer design was to match the instruction processing rate of the processor to the memory. Fig. 2a shows the configuration of a hardwired processor, matched to a memory.

The second computer generation began in 1960 with many important, transistorized, core memory machines brought out by the early leaders in the minicomputer, mainframe, and supercomputer classes: DEC (PDP-1), IBM (1401 for operating on strings, 7070 for operating on decimal numbers, and 7090 for operating on scientific numbers), and Control Data (160, 604). (Seymour Cray developed the architecture for Control Data's first supercomputer in the 1960s. He later left CDC and, in 1972, founded Cray Research, the leader in the supercomputer class.)

By the mid-1960s, a second round of significant computers from these vendors established their three respective classes: DEC PDP-5 (1964), the forerunner of the PDP-8, the first minicomputer; IBM 360 (April 1964), the mainframe; and Cray's CDC 6600 (1964), the first supercomputer. Fig. 1 depicts the evolution of the "mainline" computer classes—micros, as we shall see, came with the 1970s—demonstrating how prototype ideas that first appeared on high-priced machines later spread to wide-scale use.

The IBM 360, introduced in 1964, was one of the earliest computer families to span a range of price and performance. Along with the 360, IBM introduced the word architecture to refer to the various processing characteristics of a machine as seen by the programmer and his programs. In the initial 360 product family, the model 91 exceeded the model 20 in performance by a factor of 300, in memory size by a factor of 512, and in price by a factor of 100.

360 LINE SET NEW STANDARD

The enormously successful 360 product line set an important new standard for CISC design. By virtually all measures, the instruction set was more complete and complex than any previous design, and included instructions to handle data in both the commercial and scientific environments: integers, floating point, decimal, and character strings.

The primary goal for the product line was to merge IBM's scientific and com-

FIG. 2
FOUR MAINLINE COMPUTER ARCHITECTURES

2a. Early, hardwired simple computers (c. 1950-60) and conventional microprocessors (c. 1971-)

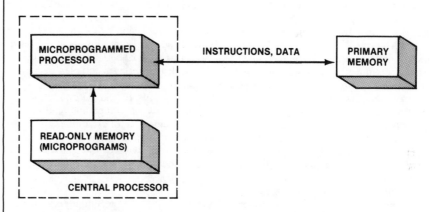

2b. Microprogrammed processor to interpret instruction set (c. 1964)

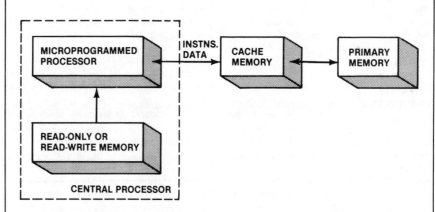

2c. Microprogrammed processor with cache (c. 1968)

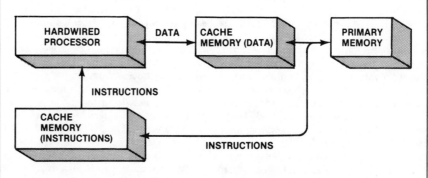

2d. Hardwired, pipelined processor with separate caches for instructions and data (c. 1985)

The goal of these early architectures was to provide processors that operated at the memory rate.

mercial computer families into a single product line in order to have a single architecture and to maximize the compatibility of the peripherals and operating systems. Since the memory sizes were small, a complex architecture was adopted in order to most efficiently encode programs of the various languages. The benefits to users were configuration flexibility and compatibility across the range.

Microprogramming, first described in a 1951 paper by the English computer pioneer Maurice Wilkes, was the technique used to implement most of the 360 line. A microprogrammed processor carries out its functions with a program, stored in a read-only memory, that interprets the larger instruction set. In effect, it is a computer within the central processor (see Fig. 2b). The microprogrammed processor is also useful for implementing the complex I/O processors that were part of the 360 architecture.

Since the 360 included a range of computers, the specific models were separate and distinct. A few of the early 360s were developed using hard-wired (non-microprogram) implementations. These were the highest-priced, high-performance models. The model 44, introduced in the late '60s, used hard-wired control, and provided an exceptionally high price/performance ratio.

CDC 6600 WAS MODEL FOR RISC

The goal behind the CDC 6600 was simply to build the largest, fastest scientific computer of the day. Hard-wired control, radical packaging (heat exchangers, for example), and an emphasis on parallelism were among the innovations of the first supercomputer.

The 6600 architecture was radically simplified compared with contemporary architectures of 1964, especially the 360's. The 6600 is now recognized as something of a RISC prototype because it used a relatively small set of general registers; only register-load and register-store instructions were used to access memory, and a minimum number of instructions were defined to operate on integer, boolean vector, and floating point data. More complex operations such as character string operations were coded from the basic operations.

The processor was completely hard-wired, with a great amount of control capabilities, so that several different instructions could be executed in parallel, through pipelining. In the 6600, a large instruction buffer, which is almost identical to today's instruction caches, was used to hold instructions without having to access the slower core memory.

By 1975, Cray had extended the 6600 architectural concept in the Cray 1 to include a small register array as a set of "vector" registers in order to maximize the performance of the computer for inherently pipelined operations.

With vector operations, a single instruction may specify a list of numbers, such as a column of a matrix, to be operated on at a given time. With the extension of vectors, it is very hard to characterize such an architecture as either simple or RISC-based. A vector processor, however, maintains the goal of delivering a result every clock tick, using a complex data type, namely a vector.

Roughly 10 years later, IBM and the Japanese 360/370-compatible vendors used the same concepts for extending the 360 architecture for high-performance scientific computation. By 1985, IBM had also introduced the vector processor in the 3090, model 200/VF.

MINIS APE LARGER COMPUTERS

Minicomputers followed the same evolutionary path taken by computers in the mainframe and supercomputer classes. Developers of the PDP-8, the first minicomputer, sought to build the smallest computer possible that would still be both widely useful and widely affordable ($18,000 in 1966).

The design of the PDP-8 followed that of its predecessor, the PDP-5, which had been implemented as the smallest (MISC) computer the design team could think of. As in the original Manchester Mark I, only two registers were included in the PDP-5 (and the original PDP-8) architecture: the accumulator and the program counter—which meant that subroutines were required for multiply/divide and floating point operations.

Registers were so expensive when the PDP-5 was built that the program counter was stored in memory location 0. The original architecture had only eight basic instructions. Subsequent additions to the architecture provided arithmetic, including floating point. The PDP-8 continued this pattern of adding complexity within the processor design.

By the early '70s, the 360 had evolved to include virtual memory, a concept first realized a decade earlier in Manchester's Atlas. The 360/85 (c. 1968) was the first computer to use the cache memory, described by computer pioneer Wilkes in 1965 as a small storage area used to hold recent fetches from primary memory (see Fig. 2c). The 370 (c. 1972) represented a high-end introduction of integrated circuits, which were used for, among other

things, both primary and cache memories. The gap between memory and logic speed had begun to close.

The advent of low-cost logic using integrated circuits led to the explosive growth of the the minicomputer industry in the 1970s. The evolution of minis followed "mainline" development, including a family of compatible computers, floating point arithmetic, virtual memory, cache memory, multiprocessors, and a complex instruction set (commercial and scientific) as pioneered by the 360.

The introduction of DEC's VAX-11/780 in 1978, which evolved from the PDP-11, marked the emergence of a high-performance or superminicomputer class that combined the design concepts of mainframes with relatively lower-cost technology.

By all accounts, VAX has about the most complete architecture, with separate sets of basic operations for each of the scientific and commercial data types and primitives to assist the operating system, including the management of virtual memory. The architecture also includes single instructions for procedure calls, DO loop control, and case statements. The initial microprogram size, in words or bits, was roughly double that of the first 360s.

MICRO ALSO APES LARGE COMPUTERS

The development of the micro has followed the evolution pattern of the mainframe and minicomputer. The first micro, the Intel 4004, was a minimal instruction set computer. Intel's subsequent microprocessors evolved from an 8-bit data orientation and small (16-bit) address to include floating point arithmetic, provide for memory management, and eventually support a large virtual address space (the 80386). The technology for implementing micros favors the microprogrammed approach in order to simplify the design whereby read-only memory arrays occupy a large area of the chip.

Motorola followed a similarly evolutionary path based on a near-360 architecture. After about 10 years of evolution, the 68020 chip set provides for floating point, a large virtual memory, and an on-chip instruction cache. National Semiconductor adopted a near look-alike to the VAX architecture.

Unlike either mainframes or minis, microprocessors are not fixed architectures. Rather, microprocessors approach a complete architecture as each new model extends the architecture of its predecessor. The chip technology determines the architecture of each implementation, which embellishes the architecture of its predecessor by adding capabilities. All the "standard" chips by Intel, Motorola, and National have followed the traditional path of evolutionary complexity: all of the chips are substantially larger and more complex (by a factor of 2 to 4) than their RISC counterparts. They require a relatively long design time and operate at a comparatively slower processing rate.

The academic and commercial interest in RISC, implemented with a simple hard-wired control unit, is motivated by trends in memory and logic technology. When memory rates were considerably slower than logic rates, microprogramming improved performance by reducing the time spent outside the processor in memory fetches. Although the microprogrammed idea originated in 1951, IBM pioneered this style of design with the 360 family.

By the early '70s, the cache memory was introduced (in the 360/85), providing in effect a substantially faster memory. New semiconductor memories also offered reduced access and cycle times. Further, the speed of small read-write memories used for registers and caches began to approach that of logic. The result was that cache-based computers underscored CISC performance limitations because no faster memory could be used for the microprogram. It was after the introduction of cache memory that the IBM research project leading to the 801 was established.

Today's large IBM mainframes require about three clock ticks per instruction, which makes the question of whether CISC is a performance limitation almost academic.

RISC GOAL IS MORE FUNCTIONS

The goal of a reduced instruction set is to make a simple hard-wired processor and to carry out as many functions as possible with software. (Fig. 2d shows the essential RISC scheme derived from the 801. Fig. 3 summarizes the two approaches.)

RISC focuses on reducing the number of instructions that operate on a conventional register array, and separating them into two classes: simple load/store of the registers, including use of the registers as base and/or index registers; and operations among the registers utilizing a three-register address format. In effect, this separation into instruction types means that a statement is compiled into the parts that access the data, and the part that performs the arithmetic of the statement.

In contrast, CISC schemes have a range of instruction formats that effectively combine memory access with the operations. The essential goal of the VAX, for ex-

FIG. 3

TWO APPROACHES TO COMPUTER DESIGN

	COMPLEX	REDUCED
Registers	8-16 gen. reg. floating pt.	16-32 gen. reg., + opt. floating pt.
Data types	bytes...double precision fl. pt. decimal, byte strings, page tables, queues, etc.	bytes...integers, fl. pt. (opt.), ? decimal, ? byte strings (software processing of O/S data)
Instructions	correspond to data types, instructions assist O/S and run-time utilities	load/store general registers, operations on data types in registers
Inst. formats	variable length, many types: load/store, R := R op R, R := Mem. op R, M: = M, M := Mem op Mem	fixed length, two main types: load/store, R := R op R
Encoding	1 instruction = 1 statement	1 inst. = 1 operand or 1 operation
Design objective	min. program length, max. work per instruction	trade-off program length, minimize time to execute instruction
Implementation	microprogrammed processor; slow, primary memory and fast clock; instructions take var. time; pipeline is complex; larger implementation may result in longer design time	hard-wired processor and software; fast processor and fast cache for instructions; instructions take one clocktime; simple pipeline
Caching	useful	essential for instructions
Compiler Design	should stress finding right instructions	should stress best ordering
Philosophy	move any useful software function into hardware, incl. diagnostics, hardware changes	move all functions to software

ample, is to provide a separate microcoded machine instruction for every statement that could be written in a high-level language, e.g., a single VAX instruction is C[i] = A[j] + B[k] and would correspond to at least four RISC instructions:

1. load accumulator 1 with A[j];
2. load accumulator 2 with B[k];
3. add accumulator 1 to accumulator 2;
4. store contents of accumulator 2 in C[i].

Because they are simple, one or more RISC instructions are usually held in a word (typically 32 bits), as in the early, word-oriented RISC machines.

The second way that a RISC scheme simplifies processing (besides having only load/stores and arithmetic operations) is by eliminating the complex data types such as floating point, decimal, and byte strings. In RISC, the necessary "primitive" operations (e.g., decimal add) are best considered part of the architecture. In the case of floating point, separate execution units are used for a completely hard-wired and parallel

implementation.

The processor is controlled by a hard-wired logic unit, not a microprogrammed processor. The goal of an implementation is to be able to carry out one operation every clock tick or every memory cycle, using a pipeline of, say, four stages, just as in early processors that matched the memory bandwidth. The single best test for a RISC architecture is to observe whether the instruction rate is within a factor of 2 of the clock rate of the processor.

Here is the basic equation governing the execution rate of a simple, scalar computer:

#P × (clock rate) × (1/ticks/instruction) × (operations + operands)/instruction × (statements/ (operations + operands)) × (compiler efficiency)

(The number of central processors is represented by P.) This general structure using multiprocessors is likely to be the basis of mainline computing in the next decade because of the negligible cost of incremental microprocessors based on CMOS technology. For scientific processors, a vector pro-

The efficiency of the compiler is a major factor that may favor the RISC approach.

cessing unit operating in parallel with the conventional processor is the surest way to increase performance by a factor of 3 to 20, depending on the problem.

PROCESSOR NUMBER IS CRUCIAL The number of processors potentially has the greatest effect, because it can quite possibly be increased indefinitely, with relatively little extra cost, depending on the amount of parallelism inherent in the problem. Companies such as Alliant, Encore, and Sequent are using multiple microprocessors (i.e., a multi) to increase performance in a radical fashion and provide substantially greater performance in the superminicomputer market. Cray is using the multiprocessor to increase performance in exactly the same fashion.

The efficiency of the compiler is a major factor that may favor the RISC approach, since there is usually only one way to carry out a given function. In the case of a complex architecture, the difficulty is finding the best way to carry out a statement, including the use of temporary general registers. There is little understanding or data that indicate that the compiler is substantially different in either case. We simply must wait for some competitive studies.

This review of the evolution of computer architecture has demonstrated the ultimate appeal of simple designs. For example, the advantages of complex microprogramming diminish directly as access time to memory is reduced. Given a relatively constant or smaller amount of a given technology, it now appears that a pipelined RISC computer could outperform a microprogrammed machine by a factor of 2 or 3. Based on the rate at which such slowly evolving technologies as TTL or ECL have been registering performance gains (i.e., 15% yearly), RISC would thus represent an immediate five- to seven-year advance over CISC. For rapidly advancing technology like CMOS, the performance of which has been improving at up to 40% per year, the switch to RISC is equivalent to a two- to three-year advance in the state of the art.

Many factors determine a computer's performance. The number of processors will have the greatest long-term effect, regardless of the number or type of instructions they execute. For the scientific market, the introduction of vectors is essential, which hardly makes the architecture very simple. For a simple instruction set, including vector operations and now multiprocessors, the best advice for today's architect is simply, "Follow Cray." If the computer is to process decimal and string data for the commercial environment, care must be taken to provide the primitive operations for the languages in the architecture. ◉

C. Gordon Bell is the assistant director of the newly formed computer and information science and engineering directorate of the National Science Foundation. He is also the chief scientist for the DANA Group, Sunnyvale, Calif., which is designing a personal supercomputer using a RISC chip. He was a vice president for engineering at DEC from 1960 to 1983, and the chief architect for the PDP-8, the System/20, the PDP-11, and the VAX-11/780. He has taught at Carnegie-Mellon University and is an IEEE fellow.

Section 3: Optimized Register Usage

3.1 Background

The results summarized in section 1 point out the desirability of quick access to operands. There is a large proportion of assignment statements in HLL programs, and many of these are of the simple form A = B. Also, there are a significant number of operand accesses per HLL statement. Finally, most accesses are to local scalars. On the basis of these results, heavy reliance on register storage is suggested. Register storage is the fastest available storage, faster than both main memory and cache. The register file is physically small, generally on the same chip as the ALU and control unit, and employs much shorter addresses than for cache and memory. Thus a strategy is needed that will allow the most frequently accessed operands to be kept in registers and to minimize register-memory operations.

Two basic approaches are possible, one based on software and the other on hardware. The software approach is to rely on the compiler to maximize register usage. The compiler will attempt to allocate registers to those variables that will be used the most in a given time period. This approach requires the use of sophisticated program-analysis algorithms. The hardware approach is simply to use more registers so that more variables can be held in registers for longer periods of time. This section presents both approaches.

To provide some context for this section, the following subsections discuss design issues related to CPU registers.

3.2 Registers

To understand the role of registers in the CPU, let us consider the requirements placed on the CPU, the things that it must do

- *Fetch instructions:* The CPU must read instructions from memory.
- *Interpret instructions:* The instruction must be decoded to determine what action is required.
- *Fetch data:* The execution of an instruction may require reading data from memory or an I/O module.
- *Process data:* The execution of an instruction may require performing some arithmetic or logical operation on data.
- *Write data:* The results of an execution may require writing data to memory or an I/O module.

To be able to do these things, it should be clear that the CPU needs to temporarily store some data. The CPU must

remember the location of the last instruction so that it can know where to get the next instruction. It needs to store instructions and data temporarily while an instruction is being executed. In other words, the CPU needs a small internal memory. This memory consists of a set of high-speed registers. The registers in the CPU serve two functions

- *User-visible registers:* These enable the machine- or assembly-language programmer to minimize main-memory references by optimizing use of registers.
- *Control and status registers:* These are used by the control unit to control the operation of the CPU and by privileged, operating system programs to control the execution of programs.

There is not a clean separation of registers into these two categories. For example, on some machines the program counter is user visible (e.g., VAX), but on many it is not. For purposes of the following discussion, however, we will use these categories.

3.3 User-Visible Registers

A user-visible register is one which may be referenced by means of the machine language that the CPU executes. Virtually all contemporary CPU designs provide for a number of user-visible registers, as opposed to a single accumulator. We can characterize these in the following categories

- General purpose
- Data
- Address
- Condition codes

General-purpose registers can be assigned to a variety of functions by the programmer. Sometimes, their use within the instruction set is orthogonal to the operation; that is, any general-purpose register can contain the operand for any opcode. This provides true general-purpose register use. Often, however, there are restrictions. For example, there may be dedicated registers for floating-point operations.

In some cases, general-purpose registers can be used for addressing functions (e.g., register indirect, displacement). In other cases, there is a partial or clean separation between data registers and address registers. *Data registers* may only be used to hold data and cannot be employed in the calculation of an operand address. *Address registers* may themselves be somewhat general purpose, or they may be devoted to a particular addressing mode. Examples are

- *Segment pointers:* In a machine with segmented addressing, a segment register holds the address of the base of the segment. There may be multiple registers, for example, one for the operating system and one for the current process.

- *Index registers:* These are used for indexed addressing, and may be autoindexed.

- *Stack pointer:* If there is user-visible stack addressing, then typically the stack is in memory and there is a dedicated register that points to the top of the stack. This allows implicit addressing; that is, push, pop, and other stack instructions need not contain an explicit stack operand.

There are several design issues to be addressed here. An important one is whether to use completely general-purpose registers or to specialize their use. We have already touched on this issue in section 1, since it affects instruction set design. With the use of specialized registers, it can generally be implicit in the opcode which type of register a certain operand specifier refers to. The operand specifier must only identify one of a set of specialized registers rather than one out of all the registers, thus saving bits. On the other hand, this specialization limits the programmer's flexibility. There is no final and best solution to this design issue, but, as was mentioned, the trend seems to be toward the use of specialized registers.

Another design issue is the number of registers, either general-purpose or data plus address, to be provided. Again, this affects instruction set design since more registers require more operand specifier bits. As we previously discussed, somewhere between 8 and 32 registers appears optimum. Fewer registers result in more memory references; more registers do not noticeably reduce memory references. However, a new approach, which finds advantage in the use of hundreds of registers, is exhibited in some RISC systems.

Finally, there is the issue of register length. Registers that must hold addresses obviously must be at least long enough to hold the largest address. Data registers should be able to hold values of most data types. Some machines allow two contiguous registers to be used as one for holding double-length values.

A final category of registers, which is at least partially visible to the user, holds *condition codes* (also referred to as flags). Condition codes are bits set by the CPU hardware as the result of operations. For example, an arithmetic operation may produce a positive, negative, zero, or overflow result. In addition to the result itself being stored in a register or memory, a condition code is also set. The code may subsequently be tested as part of a conditional branch operation.

Condition code bits are collected into one or more registers. Usually, they form part of a control register. Generally, machine instructions allow these bits to be read by implicit reference, but they can not be altered by the programmer.

In some machines a subroutine call will result in the automatic saving of all user-visible registers, which are to be restored on return. The saving and restoring is performed by the CPU as part of the execution of call and return instructions. This allows each subroutine to use the user-visible registers independently. On other machines, it is the responsibility of the programmer to save the contents of the relevant user-visible registers prior to a subroutine call by including instructions for this purpose in the program.

3.4 Control and Status Registers

There are a variety of CPU registers employed to control the operation of the CPU. Most of these, on most machines, are not visible to the user. Some of them may be visible to machine instructions executed in a control or operating-system mode.

Of course, different machines will have different register organizations and use different terminology. We list here a reasonably complete list of register types, with a brief description.

Four registers are essential to instruction execution

- *Program counter (PC):* contains the address of an instruction to be fetched.

- *Instruction register (IR):* contains the instruction most recently fetched.

- *Memory address register (MAR):* contains the address of a location in memory.

- *Memory buffer register (MBR):* contains a word of data to be written to memory or the word most recently read.

The program counter contains an instruction address. Typically, the program counter is updated by the CPU after each instruction fetch so that it always points to the next instruction to be executed. A branch or skip instruction will also modify the contents of the PC. The fetched instruction is loaded into an instruction register, where the opcode and operand specifiers are analyzed. Data are exchanged with memory by using the MAR and MBR. In a bus organized system, the MAR connects directly to the address bus, and the MBR connects directly to the data bus. User-visible registers, in turn, exchange data with the MBR.

The four registers just mentioned are used for the movement of data between the CPU and memory. Within the CPU, data must be presented to the ALU for processing. The ALU may have direct access to the MBR and user-visible registers. Alternatively, there may be additional buffering registers at the boundary to the ALU; these registers serve as input and output registers for the ALU and exchange data with the MBR and user-visible registers.

All CPU designs include a register or set of registers containing status information, often known as the *program status word* (PSW). The PSW typically contains condition codes plus other status information. Common fields or flags include the following

- *Sign:* Contains the sign bit of the result of the last arithmetic operation.
- *Zero:* Set when the result is zero.
- *Carry:* Set if an operation resulted in a carry (addition) or borrow (subtraction) out of a high-order bit. Used for multiword arithmetic operations.
- *Equal:* Set if a logical compare result is equality.
- *Overflow:* Used to indicate arithmetic overflow.
- *Interrupt Enable/Disable:* Used to enable or disable interrupts.
- *Supervisor:* Indicates whether CPU is executing in supervisor or user mode. Certain privileged instructions can only be executed in supervisor mode, and certain areas of memory can only be accessed in supervisor mode.

There are a number of other registers related to status and control that might be found in a particular CPU design. In addition to the PSW, there may be a pointer to a block of memory containing additional status information (e.g., process control blocks). In machines using vectored interrupts, an interrupt vector register may be provided. If a stack is used to implement certain functions (e.g., subroutine call), then a system stack pointer is needed. A page table pointer is used with a virtual memory system. Finally, registers may be used in the control of I/O operations.

A number of factors go in to the design of the control and status register organization. One key issue is operating system support. Certain types of control information are of specific utility to the operating system. If the CPU designer were to have a functional understanding of the operating system to be used, then the register organization could to some extent be tailored to the operating system.

Another key design decision is the allocation of control information between registers and memory. It is common to dedicate the first (lowest) few hundred or thousand words of memory for control purposes. The designer must decide how much control information should be in registers and how much in memory. The usual tradeoff of cost versus speed arises.

3.5 Example Microprocessor Register Organizations

It is instructive to examine and compare the register organization of comparable systems. In this section, we look at three 16-bit microprocessors that were designed at about the same time: the Zilog Z8000, the Intel 8086, and the Motorola MC68000. Figure 3-1 depicts the register organization of each; purely internal registers, such as a memory address register, are not shown.

The Z8000 makes use of sixteen 16-bit general-purpose registers, which can be used for data, addresses, and indexing. The designers felt that it was more important to provide a regularized, general set of registers than to save instruction bits by using special-purpose registers. Further, they preferred to leave it to the programmer to assign functions to registers, assuming that there might be a different functional breakdown for different applications. The registers can also be used for 8-bit and 32-bit operations. A segmented address space is used (7-bit segment number, 16-bit offset), and two registers are needed to hold a single address. Two of the registers are also used as implied stack pointers for system mode and normal mode.

The Z8000 also includes five registers related to program status. Two registers hold the program counter and two hold the address of a Program Status Area in memory. A 16-bit flag register holds various status and control bits.

The Intel 8086 takes a different approach to register organization. Every register is special-purpose, although some registers are also usable as general-purpose. The 8086 contains four 16-bit data registers addressable on a byte or 16-bit basis, and four 16-bit pointer and index registers. The data registers can be used as general-purpose in some instructions. In others, the registers are used implicitly. For example, a multiply instruction always uses the accumulator. The four pointer registers are also used implicitly in a number of operations; each contains a segment offset. There are also four 16-bit segment registers. Three of the four segment registers are used in a dedicated, implicit fashion to point to the segment of the current instruction (useful for branch instructions), a segment containing data, and a segment containing a stack, respectively. These dedicated and implicit uses provide for compact encoding at the cost of reduced flexibility. The 8086 also includes an instruction pointer and a set of 1-bit status and control flags.

The Motorola MC68000 falls somewhere between the design philosophies of the Zilog and Intel microprocessors. Although the MC68000 is considered a 16-bit processor because of its use of 16-bit internal and external data paths and a 16-bit ALU, it provides 32-bit registers. The MC68000 partitions its 32-bit registers into eight data registers and nine address registers. The eight data registers are used primarily for data manipulation, and are used in addressing only as index registers. The width of the registers allow 8-, 16-, and 32-bit data operations, determined by opcode. The address registers contain 32-bit (no segmentation) addresses; two of these registers are also used as stack pointers, one for users and one for the operating system, depending on the current execution mode. Both registers are numbered 7, since only one can be used at a time.

Like the Zilog designers, the Motorola team wanted a very regular instruction set, with no special-purpose registers. A concern for code efficiency led them to divide the

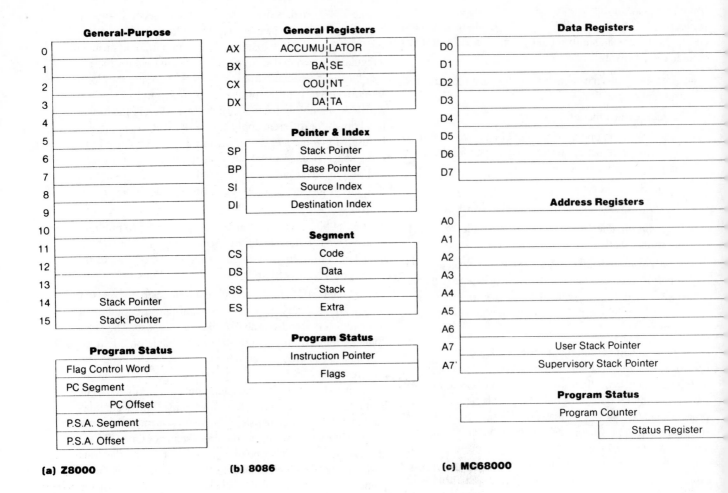

Figure 3.1: Microprocessor Register Organizations

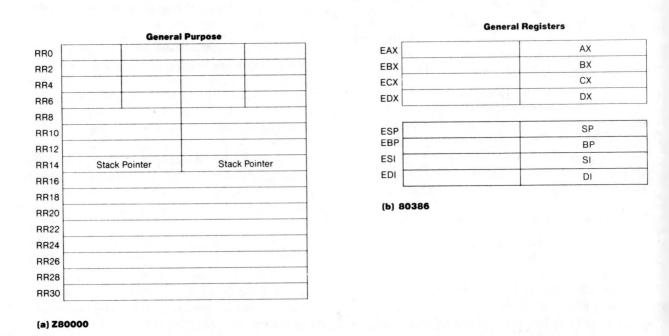

Figure 3.2: Register Organization Extensions for 32-Bit Microprocessors.

registers into two functional components, saving one bit on each register specifier. This seems a reasonable compromise between complete generality and code compaction. The point of this comparison should be clear. There is, as yet, no universally accepted philosophy concerning the best way to organize CPU registers. As with overall instruction set design and so many other CPU design issues, it is still a matter of judgment and taste.

A second instructive point concerning register organization design is illustrated in Figure 3.2. This figure shows the user-visible register organization for the Zilog Z80000 and Intel 80386, which are 32-bit microprocessors designed as extensions of the Z8000 and 8086, respectively. (Since the MC68000 already uses 32-bit registers, the MC68020, which is a full 32-bit extension, uses the same register organization.) Both of these new processors use 32-bit registers. However, to provide upward compatibility for programs written on the earlier machines, both of the new processors retain the original register organization embedded in the new organization. Given this design constraint, the architects of the new 32-bit processors had limited flexibility in designing the register organization. Virtually all of the RISC designs are free of this constraint, since they are not extensions of previous systems.

3.6 Article Summary

In "Register Allocation via Graph Coloring," it is observed that the register-allocation problem is equivalent to the graphcoloring problem in topology. From this observation, a technique is developed that was used on the IBM 801 RISC machine and is used on the IBM PC RT. A similar approach, used in the machine from MIPS Computer Systems, is described in the next paper, by Chow and Hennessy.

Next, "Strategies for Managing the Register File in RISC" explains the multiple-window approach used on the Berkeley RISC machine and analyzes alternative techniques for optimizing register use.

Finally, "Analyzing Multiple Register Sets" reports results that attempt to separate the effects of a large register file from a reduced instruction set in RISC systems.

REGISTER ALLOCATION VIA COLORING

Computer Languages 6 (1981), pp. 47-57.

Gregory J. Chaitin, Marc A. Auslander, Ashok K. Chandra, John Cocke,
Martin E. Hopkins and Peter W. Markstein

IBM T. J. Watson Research Center, Yorktown Heights, NY 10598, U.S.A.

(Received 9 October 1980)

Abstract

Register allocation may be viewed as a graph coloring problem. Each node in the graph stands for a computed quantity that resides in a machine register, and two nodes are connected by an edge if the quantities interfere with each other, that is, if they are simultaneously live at some point in the object program. This approach, though mentioned in the literature, was never implemented before. Preliminary results of an experimental implementation in a PL/I optimizing compiler suggest that global register allocation approaching that of hand-coded assembly language may be attainable.

Key Words and Phrases

register allocation, optimizing compilers, graph coloring

1. Overview of Register Allocation

In this paper we describe the Register Allocation Phase of an experimental PL/I compiler for the IBM System/370. (For an overview of the entire compiler see Cocke and Markstein [1], for background information on optimization, see Refs. [1] and [2].) It is the responsibility of this phase to map the unlimited number of symbolic registers assumed in the intermediate language into the 17 real machine registers, namely the 16 general-purpose registers ($R0$-$R15$), and the condition-code (CC).

The essence of our approach is that it is uniform and systematic. Compiler back-ends must deal with the idiosyncrasies of the machine instructions; for example, register pairs, the fact that register $R0$ is an invalid base register, and that the contents of some machine registers are destroyed as a side-effect of particular instructions. In our approach all these idiosyncrasies are entered in a uniform manner in our data structure, the interference graph. Afterwards this data structure is manipulated in a very systematic way.

Also, our approach has a rather different personality than traditional ones because we do *global* register allocation across entire procedures. Furthermore, except for the register which always contains the address of the DSA ("dynamic storage area," i.e. current stack frame) and is the anchor for all addressability, all other registers are considered to be part of a uniform pool and all computations compete on an equal basis for these registers. Most compilers reserve subsets of the registers for specific purposes; we do the exact opposite.

In our compiler a deliberate effort is made to make things as hard as possible for register allocation, i.e. to keep as many computations as possible in registers rather than in storage. For example, automatic scalars are usually kept in registers rather than in the DSA, and subroutine linkage also attempts to pass as much information as possible through registers. It is the responsibility of code generation and optimization to take advantage of the unlimited number of registers allowed in the intermediate language in order to minimize the number of loads and stores in the program, since these are much more expensive than register to register instructions. Then hopefully register allocation will map all these registers into the 17 that are actually available in the hardware. If not, it is register allocation's responsibility to put back into the object program the minimum amount of spill code, i.e. of stores and reloads of registers, that is needed.

As long as no spill code need be introduced, we feel that our approach to register allocation does a better job than can be done by hand-coders. For example, if there is a slight change in a program, when it is recompiled the Register Allocation Phase may produce a completely different allocation to accommodate the change. A hand-coder would be irresponsible to proceed in such a fashion. We also feel that our compiler succeeds in keeping things in registers rather than in storage better than other compilers, and that this is one of the salient features of the personality of the object code we produce. Moreover the mathematical elegance of the graph coloring approach described below, its systematic and uniform way of dealing with hardware idiosyncrasies, and the fact that its algorithms are computationally highly efficient, are convincing arguments in its favor.

2. Register Allocation as a Graph Coloring Problem

Our approach to register allocation is via graph coloring. This has been suggested by Cocke [1], Yershov [3], Schwartz [4], and others, but has never been worked-out in detail nor implemented before. Recall that a coloring of a graph is an assignment of a color to each of its nodes in such a manner that if two nodes are adjacent, i.e. connected by an edge of the graph, then they have different colors. A coloring of a graph is said to be an n-coloring if it does not use more than n different colors. And the chromatic number of a graph is defined to be the minimal number of colors in any of its colorings, i.e. the least n for which there is an n-coloring of it.

It is well-known [5] that given a graph G and a natural number $n > 2$, the problem of determining whether G is n-colorable, i.e. whether or not there is an n-coloring of G, is NP-complete. This suggests that in some cases an altogether impractical amount of computation is needed to decide this, i.e. that in some cases the amount of computation must be an exponential function of the size of G.

In fact experimental evidence indicates that the NP-completeness of graph coloring is not a significant obstacle to a register allocation scheme based on graph coloring. However it should be pointed out that given an arbitrary graph it is possible to construct a program whose register allocation is formulated in terms of coloring this graph (see Appendix 2). Thus some programs must give rise to serious coloring problems.

Our approach to register allocation is to build a *register interference graph* for each procedure in the source program, and to obtain 17-colorings of these interference graphs. Roughly speaking, two computations which reside in machine registers are said to interfere with each other if they are live simultaneously at any point in the program.

For each procedure P in the source program an interference graph is constructed whose nodes stand for the 17 machine registers and for all computations in the procedure P which reside in machine registers, and whose edges stand for register interferences. If the chromatic number of this graph is 17, then a register allocation has been achieved, and the register assigned to a computation is that one of the 17 machine registers which has the same color that it does. Thus computations which interfere cannot be assigned to the same machine register. On the other hand, if the chromatic number is greater than 17, then spill code must be introduced to store and reload registers in order to obtain a program whose chromatic number is 17.

3. The Concept of Interference

If a program has two loops of the form $DO\ J = 1\ TO\ 100$, J could be kept in a different register in each of the loops. In order to make this possible, each symbolic register is split into the connected components of its def-use (definition-use) chains, and it is these components, called names, which are the nodes of our interference graph. This is especially important because we always do global register allocation for entire procedures. Much additional freedom in coloring is obtained by uncoupling distant regions of the procedure by using names instead of symbolic registers as the nodes of the interference graph. However, as we explain below, some of these names are later coalesced, at which point the mapping from symbolic registers to names becomes many-many rather than one-many.

Our notion of liveness is not quite the same as that used in optimization. We consider a name X to be live at a point L in a program P if there is a control flow path from the entry point of P to a definition of X and then through L to a use of X at point U, which has the property that there is no redefinition of X on the path between L and the use of X at U. I.e. a computation is live if it has been computed and will be used before being recomputed.

Above it was stated that two names interfere if they are ever live simultaneously. Thus if at a point in the program there are k live names N_i, it is necessary to add $k(k-1)/2$ edges to the interference graph. However, we do not actually do this. If k names N_i are live at the definition point of another name N', we add the k interferences (N', N_i) to the graph. In other words, the notion of interference that we actually use is that two names interfere if one of them is live at a definition point of the other. This interference concept is better than the previous one for two reasons: it is less work to build the interference graph (k edges added vs $k(k+1)/2$), and there are programs for which the resulting interference graph has a smaller chromatic number. Here is an example of such a program:

```
P: PROC(MODE);

  DCL
    MODE            BIT(1),
    (A1,A2,A3,A4,A5,A6,A7,A8,A9,A10,
     B1,B2,B3,B4,B5,B6,B7,B8,B9,B10,
     SUM)           FIXED BIN(15) AUTO,
    (U(10),V(10)) FIXED BIN(15) STATIC EXT;

  IF MODE
    THEN DO;
      A1=U(1); A2=U(2); A3=U(3); A4=U(4); A5=U(5);
      A6=U(6); A7=U(7); A8=U(8); A9=U(9); A10=U(10);
    END;
    ELSE DO;
      B1=V(1); B2=V(2); B3=V(3); B4=V(4); B5=V(5);
      B6=V(6); B7=V(7); B8=V(8); B9=V(9); B10=V(10);
    END;

  LABEL: ;

  IF MODE
    THEN SUM = A1+A2+A3+A4+A5+A6+A7+A8+A9+A10;
    ELSE SUM = B1+B2+B3+B4+B5+B6+B7+B8+B9+B10;

  RETURN (SUM);

END P;
```

At the point in the program P marked *LABEL* the ten A_i and the ten B_i are simultaneously live, and so is *MODE*. Thus with the first method of building the interference graph there is a 21-clique and the chromatic number of the graph is 21. [Recall that an n-clique is an n-node graph with all possible $n(n-1)/2$ edges.] With the second method, however, none of the ten A variables interferes with any of the ten B variables, and the chromatic number of the interference graph is only 11. (A technical point: we have ignored the fact that all of our interference graphs contain the 17-clique of machine registers as a subgraph. Thus the chromatic number is actually 17 instead of 11.)

4. Manipulating the Interferences

There are 3 stages in processing the interference graph of a procedure. The first stage is building the graph in the manner described above. This is done by the routine C_ITF. The second stage is coalescing nodes in this graph in order to force them to get the same color and be assigned to the same machine register. This is done by the routine C_LR. The third and final stage is attempting to construct a 17-coloring of the resulting graph. This is done by a fast routine called C_CLR, or by a slower routine C_NP which uses backtracking and is guaranteed to find a 17-coloring if there is one.

Of course, backtracking is dangerous; in some unusual circumstances C_NP uses exponential amounts of time.

We now make a few general remarks about the preprocessing of the interference graph which is done for the purpose of assuring that separate nodes in the graph must get the same color. This is done by coalescing nodes, i.e. taking two nodes which do not interfere and combining them in a single node which interferes with any node which either of them interfered with before. Note that coalescing nodes in the graph before coloring it is also a way of doing some pre-coloring, for any node which is coalesced with one of the 17 machine registers has in fact been assigned to that register. Of course, such pre-colorings are a strong constraint on the final coloring, and should be avoided if possible, preferably replaced by coalesces not involving real machine registers. It should be pointed out that preprocessing the graph in this manner gives much better results than warping the coloring algorithms to try to give certain nodes the same color.

Here is an example of a typical situation in which one might wish to coalesce nodes. If there is a LR T,S (load register T from S) in the object program, it is desirable to give the names S and T the same color so that it isn't actually necessary to copy the contents of register S into register T and thus the Final Assembly Phase needn't emit any code for this intermediate language instruction. (This optimization is traditionally referred to as subsumption.) C_LR achieves this by checking the source S and target T of each LR instruction in the object program to see whether or not they interfere. If they don't, then C_LR alters the graph by combining or coalescing the nodes for S and T. Thus any coloring of the graph will necessarily give them the same color.

However, in order to make this work well, the definition of interference presented above must be altered yet again! The refinement is that the target of an LR doesn't necessarily have to be allocated to a different register than its source. Thus a LR T,S at a point at which S and the k names N_i are live only yields the k interferences of the form (T, N_i), but not the interference (T, S). (See Appendix 1 for a consistent philosophy of the "ultimate" notion of interference and approximations to it.)

Subsumption is a very useful optimization, because intermediate language typically contains many LR's. Some of these are produced for assignments of one scalar to another. But even more are generated for subroutine linkages and are introduced by value numbering and by reduction in strength. Besides eliminating LR's by coalescing sources and targets, C_LR also attempts to coalesce computations with the condition code, and to coalesce the first operand and the result of instructions like subtract which are actually two-address (to avoid the need for the Final Assembly Phase to emit code to copy the operand). C_LR also attempts to coalesce the operands of certain instructions with real registers in order to assign them to register pairs.

How is the interference graph actually colored? This is done by using the following idea, which is surprisingly powerful. If one wishes to obtain a 17-coloring of a graph G, and if a node N has less then 17 neighbors, then no matter how they are colored there will have to be a color left over for N. Thus node N can be thrown out of the graph G. The problem of obtaining a 17-coloring of G has therefore been recursively reduced to that of obtaining a 17-coloring of a graph G' with one node (and usually several edges) less than G. Proceeding in this manner, it is often the case that the entire graph is thrown away, i.e. the problem of 17-coloring the original graph is reduced to that of 17-coloring the empty graph. In fact, C_CLR gives up if the original graph cannot be reduced to the empty graph, and so spill code has to be introduced.

On the other hand, C_NP won't give up until it proves that the graph is not 17-colorable; it uses an urgency criterion to select nodes for which to guess colors, and backtracks if guesses fail. The urgency of a node is defined to be (the current number of uncolored neighbors that it has) divided by (the number of possible colors that are currently left for it). C_CLR runs in time linear in the size of the graph, while C_NP in the worst case is exponential, although this doesn't seem to happen often. The usual situation is that C_NP quickly confirms that graphs for which C_CLR gave up indeed have no 17-coloring. In fact, up to now in our experiments running actual PL/I source programs through the experimental compiler, in the handful of cases in which C_NP found a 17-coloring and C_CLR didn't, C_NP has achieved this by guessing without having to backtrack. In view of this situation, we have disabled the dangerous backtracking feature of C_NP. Furthermore, C_NP is only invoked when C_CLR fails and the user of the compiler has requested a very high level of optimization.

5. Representation of the Interference Graph

One of the most important problems in doing register allocation via graph coloring is to find a representation for the interference graph, i.e. a data structure, for which doing the 3 different kinds of operations which are performed on it – namely building the graph, coalescing nodes, and coloring it – can be done with a reasonable investment of CPU time and storage. In order to do these three different kinds of manipulations efficiently, it is necessary to be able to access the interference graph both at random and sequentially. In other words, it is necessary to be able to quickly determine whether or not two given names interfere, and to also be able to quickly run through the list of all names that interfere with a given name.

While building the graph one accesses it at random in order to determine whether an edge is already in the graph or must be added to it. While coloring the graph one accesses it sequentially, in order, for example, to count the number of neighbors that a node has (so that if this number is less than 17 the node can be deleted). And while coalescing nodes one accesses the graph both in a random and in a sequential fashion. For each LR T,S in the object code one must first check whether or not T and S interfere, which is a random access. If T and S don't interfere, one must then make all interferences of the form (S, X) into ones of the form (T, X). To do this requires sequential access to all names that interfere with S, and random access to see which interferences (T, X) are new and necessitate adding an edge to the graph.

Our solution to the problem of satisfying both of these requirements – fast random and sequential access – is to simultaneously represent the interference graph in two different data structures, one of which is efficient for random access, and the other for sequential access.

For random access operations we use an area $ITFS$ in which the interference graph is represented in the form of a bit matrix. We take advantage of the fact that the adjacency matrix of the interference graph is symmetrical to halve the storage needed. The precise addressing rule is as follows. Consider two nodes numbered i and j, where without loss of generality we assume that i is less than or equal to j. Then these are adjacent nodes in the interference graph if the $i + j^2/2$ th bit of the area $ITFS$ is a 1, and if this bit is a 0 they are not adjacent. (Here the result of the division is truncated to an integer.)

Since the adjacency matrix is usually quite sparse, and the number of bytes in the $ITFS$ area grows roughly as a quadratic function $f(n) = n^2/16$ of the number n of nodes in the interference graph, for large programs it would be better if hashing were used instead of direct addressing into a bit matrix (somewhat more CPU time would be traded for much less main memory). Since the coefficient $1/16$ of n^2 is small, if the program is not too large our bit matrix approach is ideal since it uses a small amount of storage and provides immediate access to the desired information.

For sequential access operations we keep in an area $LSTS$ lists of all the nodes which are adjacent to a given one, in the form of linked 32-byte segments. Each segment begins with a 4-byte forward pointer which is either 0 or is the offset in $LSTS$ of the first byte after the next segment of the list. This forward pointer is followed in the segment by fourteen 2-byte fields for the adjacent nodes. For any given node J, and Jth element of the vector NXT is either 0, or gives the offset in $LSTS$ of the first empty adjacent-node field in the latest segment of the list of nodes which are adjacent to J, or, if the latest segment is full, it gives the offset of the first byte after the latest segment. All segments in a list are full (give all 14 adjacent nodes), except possibly the latest one.

6. Deleting Interferences and Propagating Coalesces

Consider a LR T,S at a point in the object program where besides S the names $L_1, L_2, \ldots$ are also live. Furthermore, suppose S was subsumed with L_i. We carefully avoided making T and S interfere, but it turns out that we erroneously made T and L_i interfere. This may have blocked our subsuming T and L_i, which in turn may have blocked other subsumptions. Our solution to this problem is as follows: After C_LR does all possible desirable coalesces, the entire interference graph is rebuilt from scratch, and typically there will be fewer interferences than before. We then run C_LR again to see if any of the coalesces which were impossible before have now become possible. This entire process is repeated either a fixed number of times (usually twice will do), or until no further coalesces are obtained. It turns out that in practice this is as fast and uses much less storage than the expensive data structure (described below) which directly supports deleting interferences and propagating coalesces.

Here is a more arcane example of a situation which requires interferences to be removed: If the source and target of a LR instruction are coalesced, then the LR no longer makes its source and target interfere with the condition code, nor does it make its target interfere with all names live at that point.

As it is of some theoretical interest, we now describe the alternate representation of the interference graph mentioned above. The graph has a count associated with each edge. This is called the interference count, and it is the number of program points at which the two computations interfere. As interferences are deleted, these counts are decremented, and if they reach zero then the two computations no longer interfere with each other.

Let us be more precise. In the framework necessary to directly propagate coalesces, the interference graph is best thought of as consisting of three sparse symmetric matrices. The first one gives the interference count of any two given names. The second one gives a pointer to the list of interferences that must be deleted if these two names are coalesced, and the third sparse matrix is boolean and indicates whether it is desired to coalesce the pair of names if their interference count hits zero. In practice these three sparse matrices can be combined into a single one. Hash tables are needed to provide random access to elements of the matrix, as well as pointers in both directions to chain rows and columns together for sequential access and to permit fast deletion.

The problem with this scheme for directly deleting interferences and propagating coalesces is the large amount of memory needed to represent the interference graph.

7. Representation of the Program During Coloring

Here are some details about the way we represent the program in terms of names. In order to avoid rewriting the intermediate language text, it is actually left in terms of symbolic registers. But it is supplemented by a vector NM_MAP giving the name of the result produced by each intermediate language instruction, and also by a "ragged" array giving for each basic block in the intermediate language text a list of ordered pairs (symbolic register live at entry to the basic block, corresponding name). And the name of a computation is represented as the index into the intermediate language text of an arbitrarily chosen canonical definition point for it. It is then possible to interpret one's way down a basic block maintaining at each moment a map from the symbolic registers into the corresponding names. C_ITF does this, keeping track of which names are live at each point, in order to build the interference graph. We also take advantage of this scheme to avoid rewriting the intermediate language text to reflect coalesces – only the ragged array and the NM_MAP vector are changed.

8. Handling of Machine Idiosyncrasies

It was mentioned above that one of the important advantages of the coloring approach to register allocation is that special case considerations can be taken care of by additional interferences in the graph. For example, the fact that the base register in a load instruction cannot be assigned to the register $R0$, is handled by making all names that are used as base registers interfere with $R0$. The fact that a call to a PL/I subprogram or a library routine has the side-effect of destroying the contents of certain machine registers is handled by making all names live across the call interfere with all registers whose contents are destroyed. Thus if j computations are live across the call and k registers are destroyed by it, a total of jk interferences are added to the graph to reflect this fact.

Although subtract is a destructive 2-address instruction, in the intermediate language subtract is 3-address and non-destructive. This is done to make possible a systematic uniform optimization process. Consider the intermediate language instruction $SR\ N1,N2,N3\ (N1: = N2 - N3)$. If $N1$ and $N2$ are assigned to the same register, then code emission in the Final Assembly Phase will emit a single instruction, subtract, for this intermediate language instruction. If not, it will emit $LR\ N1,N2$

followed by SR $N1,N3$. However, if $N1$ and $N3$ are assigned to the same register, then the Final Assembly Phase is in trouble, because copying $N2$ into $N2$ destroys $N3$. In order to avoid this code-emission problem, we make $N1$ and $N3$ interfere when building the interference graph.

A large set of special-purpose interferences has to do with intermediate language instructions involving the condition code (CC). The intermediate language ignores the fact that there is actually only one CC. The way to get around this is exemplified by contrasting the compare intermediate language instruction with the actual compare instruction. The intermediate language compare is three-address: two registers are compared, and bits 2 and 3 of the result register express the result of the compare. However compare always sets the bits of the CC, not those of an arbitrary register. Code emission in the Final Assembly Phase emits machine code for the compare intermediate language instruction in the following manner. If the result of the compare intermediate language instruction is assigned to the CC, then it merely generates a compare. If the result of the compare intermediate language instruction is assigned to one of the 16 general-purpose registers, then code emission generates a compare followed by a $BALR$ which copies the contents of the CC into the indicated general-purpose register.

(A very special issue is how to deal with the fact that some instructions set the CC to reflect the sign of their result. For instance, subtract does this. In the Final Assembly Phase no code is emitted for a compare with zero of the result of a subtraction if it comes later in the same basic block as the subtract and none of the intervening instructions destroys the CC.)

9. Techniques for Inserting Spill Code

Our techniques for inserting spill code are quite heuristic and *ad hoc*. The following notion is the basis for our heuristic. At any point in the program, the *pressure on the registers* is defined to be equal to the number of live names (it might be interesting to change this to the number of live colors) plus the number of machine registers which are unavailable at that point because their contents are destroyed as a side-effect of the current instruction. Under the level two optimization compiler option, we insert spill code to immediately lower the maximum pressure on the registers in the program to 14. Under the level three optimization compiler option, successive tries are made. Spill code is inserted to bring the maximum pressure down to 20, then down to 19, etc., until a colorable program is obtained.

After inserting spill code it is necessary to recompute the def-use chains and the right number of names; there are generally more names than before. We also rerun dead code elimination, which has the side-effect of setting the operand-last-use flag bits in the intermediate language text – these flags are needed by C_ITF to keep track of which names are live at each point in the program. Note that since intermediate language text containing spill code is reanalyzed by optimization routines, and these routines only understand intermediate language written in terms of symbolic registers, the intermediate language text containing spill code must be correct in terms of symbolic registers as well as names.

How is spill code inserted to lower the register pressure? We attempt to respect the loop structure of the program and to put spill code in regions of the program which are not executed frequently. This is done in the following manner. First the decomposition of the program into flow-graphs is used bottom-up to compute the maximum register pressure in each basic block and each interval of all orders. As we do this we also obtain a bit vector of mentioned names for each basic block and interval. A *pass-through* is defined to be a computation which is live at entry to an interval but which is not mentioned (i.e. neither used nor redefined) within it. Clearly pass-throughs of high-order intervals are ideal computations to spill, i.e. to keep in storage rather than in a register throughout the interval for which they are a pass-through. We use the decomposition of the program into flow-graphs top-down in order to fix all those intervals in which the maximum pressure is too high by spilling pass-throughs.

We have explained how spill decisions are made for pass-throughs, but we have not explained how the spill code is actually inserted. This is done by using two rules. First of all, if a name is spilled anywhere, then we insert a store instruction at each of its definition points. And pass-throughs are reloaded according to the following rule: load at entry to each basic block B every name live at entry to B that is not spilled within B, but that is spilled in some basic block which is an immediate predecessor of B. These rules for inserting spill code are easy to carry out, but the other side of the coin is that they sometimes insert unnecessary code. However this unnecessary spill code is eliminated by a pass of dead code elimination which immediately follows.

Further remarks: Another idea used here is that some computations have the property that they can be redone in a single instruction whose operands are always available. We call such computations *never-killed*. An example of a never-killed computation is a load address off of the register which gives addressability to the DSA. Such computations are recalculated instead of being spilled and reloaded. Furthermore, if spilling pass-through computations doesn't lower the register pressure enough, as a last resort we traverse each basic block inserting spill code whenever the pressure gets too high.

Another approach to using recomputation instead as an alternative to spilling and reloading, is what we have called the *rematerialization* of uncoalesced LR instructions. Here the idea is to replace a LR which can't be coalesced away by a recomputation that directly leaves the result of the computation in the desired register. (Of course, this should only be done if repeating the computation at this point still gives the same result.) Rematerialization usually decreases the pressure on the registers. Furthermore, assuming that all intermediate language instructions seen at this stage of the compilation are single-cost, replacing an uncoalesced LR by a recomputation cannot increase object program path lengths, and it sometimes actually shortens them. Thus there is a sense in which rematerialization is an optimization as opposed to a spill technique.

Rematerialization is most helpful when there are LR's into real registers. Typically this occurs when parameters are passed in standard registers. The standard parameter registers are destroyed over calls so the computation to be passed cannot be kept in the standard register over the call. The adverse consequence of this is most severe in loops where many loop constant parameters may be kept in registers and are loaded into standard parameter registers before each procedure invocation. Rematerialization tends to reduce the requirement for registers to hold loop constant parameters.

An entirely different approach to spilling might be based on the following observation. It is possible to have C_CLR make the spill decisions as it colors the interference graph. Each time C_CLR is blocked because it cannot delete any more nodes (all of them have more than 16 neighbors), it simply deletes a node by deciding to always keep that computation in storage rather than in a register. By increasing the granularity in the names, one could perhaps develop this into a more global and systematic approach to spilling than the one sketched above.

10. Conclusions

We have shown that in spite of the fact that graph coloring is NP-complete, it can be developed into a practical approach to register allocation for actual programs. It is also a pleasant surprise that coalescing nodes of the graph turns out to be an important optimization technique, and that machine idiosyncrasies can be handled in a uniform manner. We believe that our approach is able to pack computations into registers globally across large programs more cleverly than a hand-coder can or should. However, when not all computations can be kept in registers across the entire program, then the spill code that we insert sometimes leaves much to be desired.

Acknowledgements

The authors wish to state that the experimental compiler described herein could not have been completed without the efforts of the remaining members of their team: Richard Goldberg, Peter H. Oden, Philip J. Owens, and Henry S. Warren Jr. Although they were not directly involved with the compiler's register allocation scheme, this enterprise was very much a team effort to which all involved made essential contributions. We also wish to thank Erich J. Neuhold for reading an earlier version of this paper and suggesting improvements in the exposition.

References

1. J. Cocke and P. W. Markstein, Measurement of program improvement algorithms. In *Information Processing 80* (Edited by S. H. Lavington), pp. 221-228. North-Holland, Amsterdam (1980).

2. F. E. Allen and J. Cocke, A program data flow analysis procedure. *Commun. ACM* 19, 137-147 (1976).

3. A. P. Yershov, *The Alpha Automatic Programming System.* Academic Press, London (1971).

4. J. T. Schwartz, *On Programming: An Interim Report on the SETL Project.* Courant Institute of Math. Sciences, New York University (1973).

5. A. V. Aho, J. E. Hopcroft and J. D. Ullman, *The Design and Analysis of Computer Algorithms.* Addison-Wesley, Reading, MA (1974).

Appendix 1. The "Ultimate" Notion of Interference

The intuitive definition of the concept of interference is that two symbolic registers (i.e. results of computations) interfere if they cannot reside in the same machine register. Similarly, a symbolic register and a machine register interfere if the symbolic register cannot be assigned to that real register. Thus two registers interfere if there exists a point in the program, and a specific possible execution of the program for which:

1. Both registers are defined (i.e. they have been assigned by previous computations in the current execution);

2. Both registers will be used (note that we are considering a specific execution. Thus we mean use, *not* potential use);

3. The values of the registers are different.

It is clear that if these conditions are met, then assigning both symbolic registers to the same real register would be incorrect for that execution. It should also be clear that if any of the three conditions is not met, then such an assignment is correct at that point in the program, for that execution.

Of course, the criteria stated above are in general undecidable properties of the program. Thus a compiler must use more restrictive conditions of interference, potentially increasing the number of registers or amount of spill code required.

One particularly simple and sufficient condition is that two symbolic interfere if they are ever simultaneously live (in the data flow sense). Consideration or experiment will show that this criterion is both expensive to compute and overly conservative. The difficulty is that application of this standard involves adding interferences for all pairs of live values at every point in the program. One could attempt to reduce this cost by observing how the liveness set changes during a linear reading of the program, so that only potentially new interferences are added. Only growth of the liveness set need be taken into account, that is to say, the fact that (a) symbolic registers become alive on assignment, and (b) the set grows by union at a control flow join. The cost of computing the simultaneously alive criterion could be reduced by applying these observations.

However, one can safely take into account (a) all by itself, and ignore (b), the effect of control flow joins. This approach, which may be called point of definition interference, is not only inexpensive to compute, but omits certain apparent interferences for which both symbolic registers can never be defined simultaneously in any symbolic registers can never be defined simultaneously in any particular execution of the program. Thus we approximate interference by reading the program, using precomputed data flow information so that the set of live values is known at every computation. At each computation, the newly defined symbolic register is made to interfere with all currently live symbolic registers which cannot be seen to have the same value as the newly defined register.

Appendix 2. Proof That All Graphs Can Arise in Register Allocation

Consider the following program. It has declarations of the variables $NODE_i$, and there are just as many of these variables as there are nodes in the desired graph. For each edge $(NODE_i, NODE_j)$ in the desired graph, the corresponding variables are summed in order to make them interfere.

```
P: PROC(EDGE,MODE) RETURNS(FIXED BIN);
    DCL (MODE,EDGE,X) FIXED BIN;
    DCL LABEL(number-of-edges) LABEL;
    ...
    DCL NODEi FIXED BIN STATIC EXT;
    ...
    GO TO LABEL(EDGE);
    ...
    /************************************/
    /* THE CALL PREVENTS OPTIMIZATION   */
    /* FROM MOVING THE LOADS OF NODEi,j. */
    /* THE ASSIGNMENT STATEMENT         */
    /* MAKES NODEi AND NODEj INTERFERE. */
    /* JOINi,j CODE FRAGMENTS MAKE      */
    /* NAMES COME OUT CORRECTLY.        */
    /************************************/
  LABEL(edge-number):
    CALL EXTERNAL_ROUTINEedge-number;
    X = NODEi + NODEj;
    IF MODE THEN GO TO JOINi;
            ELSE GO TO JOINj;
    ...
  JOINi:
    RETURN (X*NODEi);
    ...
END P;
```

"Register Allocation by Priority-Based Coloring" by F. Chow and J. Hennessy from *Proceedings of the ACM SIGPLAN '84 Symposium on Compiler Construction SIGPLAN Notices*, Volume 19, Number 6, June 1984, pages 222–232. Copyright 1984, Association for Computing Machinery, Inc., reprinted by permission.

Register Allocation by Priority-based Coloring

Frederick Chow[†] and John Hennessy

Computer Systems Laboratory
Stanford University
Stanford, CA 94305

Abstract

The classic problem of global register allocation is treated in a heuristic and practical manner by adopting the notion of priorities in node-coloring. The assignment of priorities is based on estimates of the benefits that can be derived from allocating individual quantities in registers. Using the priorities, the exponential coloring process can be made to run in linear time. Since the costs involved in register allocation are taken into account, the algorithm does not over-allocate. The algorithm can be parameterized to cater to different fetch characteristics and register configurations among machines. Measurements indicate that the register allocation scheme is effective on a number of target machines. The results confirm that, using priority-based coloring, global register allocation can be performed practically and efficiently.

1. Introduction

The view of global register allocation as a graph coloring algorithm has long been established [7]. A coloring of a graph is an assignment of a color to each node of the graph in such a manner that each two nodes connected by an edge do not have the same color. In register allocation, each node in the graph, called the interference graph, represents a program quantity that is a candidate for residing in a register.

Two nodes in the graph are connected if the quantities interfere with each other in such a way that they must reside in different registers. In coloring the interference graph, the number of colors used for coloring, r, is the number of registers available for use in register allocation. The goal is to find the best way to assign the program variables to registers so that the execution time is minimized. In global register allocation, we take into account entire procedures in deciding on the variables to be colored.

The standard coloring algorithm to determine whether a graph is r-colorable is NP-complete. It involves selecting nodes for which to guess colors, and backtracking if the guesses fail [1]. The algorithm takes only linear time when the first trial succeeds. But if the graph is not r-colorable, or is near the borderline cases, an exponential amount of computation is needed to prove that it is indeed so, since it is necessary to backtrack and attempt all possible coloring combinations before reaching the final conclusion. Thus, the standard coloring algorithm works well only when the target machines have a large number of registers. A heuristic procedure with linear running time might be best in practice, and the exponential algorithm may be made only the last resort in critical situations.

Global allocation of registers by coloring usually does not take into account the cost and saving involved in allocating variables to registers. By cost, we refer to the presence of register-memory transfer operations that put variables in registers or update their home locations to make the registers available for other uses. By saving, we refer to the gain in execution speed due to individual variables being accessed in registers. Variables occur with different frequencies and with varying degrees of clustering, so that the relative benefits of assigning registers to variables differ.

---

† Present address: Daisy Systems Corp., 139 Kifer Court, Sunnyvale, CA 94086.

The standard coloring algorithm always tries to allocate as many items in registers as possible. It does not recognize that it is sometimes non-beneficial to assign certain variables to registers over some regions in the program, possibly due to the need to save registers before procedure calls or for letting other variables use the same registers. When it is found that an r-coloring is impossible, the decision regarding which variables to be excluded in the coloring (i.e. to be spilled) is difficult to make. The spilling decisions are separate from the coloring decisions, and it is hard to predict the effect of spilling a certain variable on the outcomes of the subsequent coloring attempts. The standard coloring algorithm also does not take into account the loop structure of the program. In practice, variables occurring in frequently executed regions should be given greater preference for residing in registers.

In this paper, we present a global coloring algorithm that overcomes the above problems. The algorithm finds reasonable, though not necessarily optimal, solutions quickly, and it works for most configurations of general-purpose registers in target machines up to and including the grouping into nonintersecting register classes. It involves assigning priorities to all register-residing candidates and ordering register assignments according to this priority. The algorithm does not backtrack, and the running time is proportional to the number of registers and the number of possible live ranges to be allocated to registers.

2. Background

The algorithm we present in this paper is the register allocation algorithm used in the production optimizer UOPT [2]. UOPT is a self-contained, portable and machine-independent global optimizer on a machine-independent intermediate language called U-Code [5]. This intermediate code is output from a Pascal front-end and a Fortran front-end. The optimized versions of U-Code are translated into different target machine code by different back-end code generators.

The global optimizer UOPT performs a comprehensive set of global and local optimizations. Global register allocation is done in UOPT as the last phase

of optimization, when the final structure of the code to be emitted has been determined by earlier optimization phases and all potential register uses have been exposed. A fixed number of registers is reserved for use by the code generators. The rest are to be freely allocated by the optimizer. Since the input program is assumed executable without using the global optimizer, all program variables in the input are assumed to have been allocated in main memory. Temporaries generated by the previous phases of the optimizer are also assumed to have been allocated in home memory locations, and they are treated uniformly as variables. Due to these assumptions, it is not necessary to generate spill code for variables not allocated to registers. Instead, all objects have home memory locations and the optimizer attempts to remap memory accesses to register accesses. This contrasts with the approach used in the PL.8 compiler [1] in which the register allocation phase attempts to map the unlimited number of symbolic registers assumed during earlier compilation and optimization phases into hardware registers; if this is unsuccessful, code is added to spill computations from registers to storage and later re-load them.

The register allocation algorithm used is a combination of a local method based on usage counts and the global method based on coloring. The local phase allocates one block to a register each time. The global phase allocates one live range to a register each time. The local register allocation phase is inexpensive and near-optimal for straight-line code, but does little to contribute to the globally optimal solution. The global allocation phase is more computation-intensive. In our approach, the local allocation process is made to do as much allocation as possible so long as the allocation would not have any effect on the outcome of the global allocation phase.

3. Cost and Saving Estimates

In performing register allocation, we divide the program code into code segments, each not longer than a basic block, which represent the smallest extents of program code over which variables are allocated to registers. Assigning a variable to a register involves the loading of the variable from main memory to the assigned register prior to referencing the variable in a register in the subsequent code. If the value of the variable is changed in the intervening code where it resides in register, the home memory location of the variable has to be updated with the register content at the end of the code segment unless it is dead on exit. These extra move operations between registers and memory represent the execution time cost of the register assignment. The execution time saving of the register assignment refers to how much the code segment is rendered faster due to the variable's residing in a register. Thus, we define the following three parameters, which vary among target machines:

MOVCOST — The cost of a memory-to-register or register-to-memory move, which in practice is the execution time of the U-Code instructions RLOD (load to register) or RSTR (store from register) respectively in the target machine.

LODSAVE — The amount of execution time saved for each reference of a variable residing in register compared with the corresponding memory reference that is replaced.

STRSAVE — The amount of execution time saved for each definition of a variable residing in register compared with the corresponding store to memory being replaced.

4. Local Register Allocation

Local register allocation refers to allocation in a straight-line piece of program code, and it precedes the global allocation phase. The method of allocating registers locally using reference counts is well-established and inexpensive [3]. Locally optimal solutions to the register allocation problem do not necessarily add up to the globally optimal solution. However, it is possible to determine a portion of register allocation locally that also belongs to the global solution, so that the work load of the subsequent, more expensive global allocation phase can be made smaller.

For each variable in the local code segment being considered, the local saving that can be achieved by assigning the variable to register can be estimated by:

$$\text{NETSAVE} = \text{LODSAVE} \times u + \text{STRSAVE} \times d - \text{MOVCOST} \times n \quad (1)$$

where u is the number of uses of the variable,
d is the number of definitions and
n is either 0, 1 or 2.

n depends on whether a load of the variable to a register (RLOD) at the beginning of the code segment and a store from the register back to the variable's home location (RSTR) at the end of the code segment are to be inserted. If they are both needed, n is 2. If the first occurrence of the variable is a store, then the initial RLOD is not needed. If the variable is not altered, or if the variable is not live at the end of the code segment, then the RSTR is not necessary.

If the local code segment is considered together with its preceding and subsequent code, the term involving MOVCOST represents the uncertainty in cost with regard to NETSAVE that may or may not contribute to the final global solution. This is because if the variable is also allocated to the same register in the surrounding code, then the RLOD and RSTR at the beginning and end of the current code segment are unnecessary, and the actual value of NETSAVE is increased. Thus, for each variable in the local code, we consider two separate quantities:

$$\text{MAXSAVE} = \text{LODSAVE} \times u + \text{STRSAVE} \times d \quad (2)$$

$$\text{MINSAVE} = \text{LODSAVE} \times u + \text{STRSAVE} \times d - \text{MOVCOST} \times n \quad (3)$$

The quantity MINSAVE represents the minimum saving in the local code segment gained by allocating the variable to register. The quantity MAXSAVE is the maximum possible saving. The actual saving after all register allocation is performed will range between MINSAVE and MAXSAVE. The parameters MAXSAVE and MINSAVE also apply to variables which do not occur in the code segment, when they are both 0; in such cases, the two parameters are used only in the later global allocation process.

When the surrounding blocks are considered together with the current block, the local allocation may displace some other variable which has been assigned to the same register in the adjacent blocks and which, if allowed to occupy the same register in the current block, would enable the elimination of the RSTR's at the ends of the preceding blocks and the RLOD's at the starts of the succeeding blocks. Thus, the absolute criterion for determining the local allocation of a variable in register can be given as:

$$\text{MINSAVE} > \text{MOVCOST} \times (p + s) \quad (4)$$

where p is the number of predecessors,
s is the number of successors of the block.

When this condition is satisfied, the variable can be locally allocated in register with certainty regardless of the rest of the program. In computing the above condition, the loop nesting depths of the blocks are used as weights.

The determination of exactly which register to assign is not done in the local allocation pass. It is delayed until the global allocation phase, when the optimizer will look for opportunities to assign the same register to a variable over contiguous code segments to minimize the number of RLOD's and RSTR's.

5. Computing the Live Ranges

A live range of a variable is an isolated and contiguous group of nodes in the control flow graph in which the variable is defined and referenced. No other definition of the variable reaches a reference point inside the live range. Also, the definitions of the variable inside the live range do not reach any other reference point outside the live range. Global register allocation assigns complete live ranges to registers, and if this is not possible, parts of live ranges are assigned. Throughout a procedure, each register is occupied by live ranges or parts of live ranges that do not overlap. Computations for the separate live ranges of the program variables require processing and representation overhead. We circumvent these computations by assuming one live range for each variable in a procedure at the beginning of the global register allocation phase, even though it may have non-adjacent parts. In the course of coloring, the live ranges are broken up into smaller segments when necessary.

By virtue of the contiguity of the blocks in a live range, when the live range is assigned to a register, RLOD's are needed only at entry points to the live range and RSTR's are required only at its exit points (Fig. 1). UOPT supports both the caller-save and callee-save convention regarding registers in procedure calls. In the caller-save context, all registers need to be freed at a procedure call so that they can be used in the called procedure. Thus, live ranges are never allowed to extend over a procedure call. The register allocator is responsible for indicating which

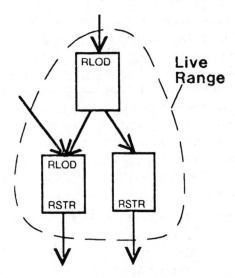

Fig. 1 A live range with associated RLOD's and RSTR's

variable home locations are to be updated from registers before a procedure call, and which variables are to be re-loaded to registers after the call. UOPT has a procedure integration pre-pass that replaces procedure calls by copying their code in-line, thus increasing non-call ranges. In the case of the callee-save convention, live ranges are allowed to extend over procedure calls, and registers are allocated across the calls.

6. The Global Coloring Algorithm

The cost and saving estimates we defined earlier, weighted by the loop-nesting depths of program points at which the variable accesses occur, play an important role in our global coloring algorithm. The coloring process is driven according to the cost and saving estimates. Each iteration assigns one live range to a register by picking the most promising live range according to the cost and saving estimates computed over each live range. By assigning the live ranges with high priorities first, it is hoped that the results of the allocation will be close to optimal. The algorithm terminates when either all live ranges or parts of live ranges have been allocated, or all registers have been used up over all code segments. Thus, the computation time does not deteriorate when r-coloring cannot be achieved. The algorithm allocates register to a live range only when the saving is higher than the cost. Thus, the over-allocation problem does not exist in our algorithm.

We assume that all variables have been assigned home locations before register allocation begins. This allows us not only to avoid the problem of having to introduce spill code. By taking into account the cost of register-memory transfer operations, we can factor the effects of not allocating in registers into the coloring decisions. Because the cost and saving estimates are weighted by loop-nesting depths, our algorithm also takes the loop structure of the program into account. Thus, variables in frequently executed regions have higher priority for residing in registers.

We assume a single live range for each variable in a procedure at the beginning of global register allocation. Apart from saving the cost of computing and representing separate live ranges prior to coloring, the interference graph is also made much simpler. The processing cost associated with accessing, manipulating and updating the interference graph during coloring is greatly reduced.

The standard coloring algorithm handles the situation of insufficient registers by spilling variables into main memory. We handle this situation by live range splitting. In the course of performing coloring, when a variable cannot be assigned the same color throughout the procedure, its live range is split into smaller live ranges. The new live ranges are treated the same way as variables as far as the coloring algorithm is concerned, and the interference graph is updated accordingly. As splitting proceeds further along, the split-out parts may not be true live ranges since the original def-use relationships may not be restricted to points inside the subranges. Splitting is repeated until all the split live ranges can be colored or until all the split live ranges consist of single code segments. If a split-out live range is left uncolored at the termination of coloring, the effect is equivalent to not allocating the variable over the region covered. Live range splitting is performed with the emphasis on not creating small live range fragments unless warranted by the situation.

As an illustration, Fig. 2(a) shows a region of code in which variables A, B and C are to be allocated in registers. Although the live range for variable A consists of two separate parts, they are initially taken as a single live range. Assume that a single register is left available to contain the three variables. Fig. 2(b)

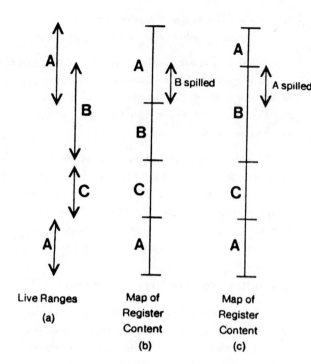

Fig. 2 Possible allocation configurations

and (c) show two possible allocation results, depending on the occurrence frequencies of the variables in the live ranges covered. To arrive at the result of Fig. 2(b), variables A and C are allocated first. The live range of variable B is then split so that one part of it is allocated and the other part spilled. In Fig. 2(c), variables B and C are allocated first. The algorithm splits the live range of A into the two naturally separate parts, and the lower live range of A is then allocated. The top live range of A is then further split so that one part is allocated and the other part that interferes with B is spilled.

In the node coloring algorithm, variables which have a number of neighbors in the interference graph less than the original number of colors available are left uncolored until the very end, since it is certain that an unused color can be found for them. These are called *unconstrained* variables or live ranges. The rest of the live ranges are assigned colors by successive iterations of Step 2 of the algorithm. Each iteration selects a live range and assigns a color to it. New live ranges are formed out of splitting during the iterations, and if any of these are unconstrained, they are added to the unconstrained pool of variables.

Algorithm *Priority-based Node Coloring.*

1. Find the live ranges whose number of neighbors in the interference graph is less than the number of colors available, and set them aside in the pool of unconstrained live ranges.

2. Repeat Steps a to c, each time assigning one color to a live range until all constrained live ranges have been assigned a color, or there is no register left that can be assigned to any live range in any code segment (taking into account registers allocated in the preceding local allocation phase).

   a. Perform Step (i) or (ii) for each live range lr until TOTALSAVE for all original or newly formed live ranges are computed:

      (i). If lr has a number of colored neighbors less than the total number of colors available, assume a color is assigned to it covering all its live blocks. Then compute and record TOTALSAVE for the variable lr as follows:

      1. In each block i of the live range lr, determine whether register load and store is necessary based on whether the adjacent blocks in the flow graph belong to the same live range. Let the number of register loads and stores be n, which ranges from 0 to 2.

      2. Compute NETSAVE_i as

      $$\text{NETSAVE}_i = \text{LODSAVE} \times u + \text{STRSAVE} \times d - \text{MOVCOST} \times n$$

      where u is the number of uses, and

      d is the number of definitions of the live range variable in block i.

      3. Let w_i denotes the loop-nesting depth of block i in the flow graph. Compute TOTALSAVE for the live range lr as:

      $$\text{TOTALSAVE} = \sum_{i \in lr} (\text{NETSAVE}_i \times w_i).$$

      (ii). If the number of colored neighbors of lr is already equal to the number of colors

available, then the live range lr has to be split. A new live range lr_1 is split out from lr as follows:

A new node in the interference graph is created for lr_1. A definition block from lr, preferably one at an entry point to lr, is first added to lr_1. Blocks adjacent to lr_1 that also belong to lr are successively added to lr_1, updating the neighbors in the interference graph until the number of colored neighbors of lr_1 in the interference graph is one less than the number of available colors. The motivation of this is to produce the largest possible live range that can still be colored. This is continued until no more blocks can be added to the new live range lr_1.

If the newly formed live range lr_1 has a number of neighbors in the interference graph less than the number of colors available, set it aside in the pool of unconstrained variables. Otherwise, add it to the pool of candidates for estimation of TOTALSAVE.

As a result of the new node in the interference graph, some previously unconstrained live ranges may now become constrained. These have to be transferred from the unconstrained pool to the constrained pool.

   b. For each live range lr, compute ADJSAVE as

   $$\text{ADJSAVE} = \frac{\text{TOTALSAVE}}{\langle \text{number of nodes in } lr \rangle}.$$

   (The quantities TOTALSAVE and ADJSAVE do not have to be recomputed if the live range has not changed since the previous iteration.)

   c. Looking at the values of ADJSAVE computed for all the uncolored but constrained live ranges in Steps a and b, choose the live range with the highest value of ADJSAVE and assign a color to it.

3. Assign colors to the unconstrained live ranges, each time using a color that has not been assigned to one of their neighbors in the interference graph.

Thus, the algorithm orders the assigning of colors according to which variable currently has the highest value of ADJSAVE (Step 2c). ADJSAVE can be visualized as the total number of occurrences of the variable in the live range, weighted by loop-nesting depths and normalized by the length of the live range. The adjustment by the live range length (the number of nodes in the live range) is needed because a live range occupying a larger region of code takes up more register resource if allocated in register. In the local allocation phase, we have already taken pure occurrence frequencies into account. Thus, when entering the global allocation phase, all the variables that remain unallocated in each code segment have occurrence frequencies that do not differ widely, so the important consideration is whether the allocation enables the same register to be assigned across contiguous code segments so that register loads and stores can be minimized. The value of ADJSAVE comprises a measure of this connectedness. The more connected the code segments in the live ranges of a variable are, the more worthy is the variable to be allocated in register, and the more difficult it will be to find the same register for it throughout; so, it is important to assign a color to it before other variables. The use of the ADJSAVE criterion is justified only if the local allocation phase precedes global allocation.

The determination of n in Step 2a(i) can make use of more information than previously possible in the local allocation phase of Section 4. If the first occurrence of the variable at an entry block is a store, then the RLOD is not needed. If all the predecessors of a block also belong to the live range, then the RLOD is also not necessary, unless any of the predecessor contains a procedure call. By the same token, RSTR's at points internal to live ranges are not always necessary. An RSTR is necessary at the exit blocks of a live range only if the live range contains at least one assignment to the live range variable and the variable is not dead on exit. At blocks internal to live ranges, RSTR's are also generated if any successor node has an RLOD, or contains a procedure call.

The computation time complexity of the above algorithm can be estimated. We are mainly concerned with Step 2 of the algorithm, since this step takes a lot more time compared with Step 3 for the unconstrained live ranges. Let r be the number of

registers. Let l be the number of live ranges, and assume that this stays fixed during the course of the algorithm. Also assume that each register is assigned to one and only one live range in the procedure, though in reality this is not always the case. Then there is r iterations for Step 2 of the algorithm. For the first iteration, a live range is to be chosen out of l live ranges. For the second iteration, the choice is to be made out of the $l - 1$ live ranges remaining. Summing all the iterations, we get

$$l + (l-1) + \ldots + (l - r + 1) = \frac{r(2l - r + 1)}{2}.$$

Thus, the algorithm is $O(r(l - r))$. The time of the algorithm proportional to both the number of registers available and the number of candidates to reside in registers.

The algorithm can easily extend to the case of multiple classes of registers. The interference graph will only give interferences between variables of the same class. The algorithm is repeated once for each class of register. In each case, the number of colors corresponds to the number of registers in the class being considered.

The relative importance between the local and global phases can be varied by changing the maximum length of code segments allowed. By setting an option, a limit on the maximum number of variable appearances allowed in a basic block is imposed. If this limit is exceeded, the remaining code is made to belong to a new block. A default value for this option serves to guard against the presence of large blocks which can degrade the output of the register allocator. When blocks are small, the local phase will not be able to allocate as many items to registers based on its allocation criteria, and more work is left to the more expensive global phase. As the limit on block lengths becomes smaller and smaller, the overall allocation also approaches the optimal solution since registers can now be allocated across shorter segments to cater to any irregular clustering of accesses. The processing cost also increases correspondingly because of the larger number of blocks involved and the greater amount of work being performed by the global phase. Thus, the register allocation algorithm has a large amount of built-in flexibility with respect to processing cost and quality of results. In practice, basic

Program	Perm	Tower	Queen	Intmm	Mm	Puzzle	Quick
% of var. references in registers	.65	.40	.76	.95	.95	.94	.67
% of var. assignments in registers	.70	.23	.72	.96	.96	.77	.77

Program	Bubble	Tree	Fft	Sieve	Quick2	Inverse	Average
% of var. references in registers	.91	.78	.87	.87	.62	.71	.77
% of var. assignments in registers	.92	.74	.80	.89	.62	.75	.76

Table 1(a). Static register allocation statistics in the DEC 10

Program	Perm	Tower	Queen	Intmm	Mm	Puzzle	Quick
% of var. references in registers	.94	.69	.87	.96	.96	.95	.80
% of var. assignments in registers	.95	.54	.88	.95	.95	.78	.80

Program	Bubble	Tree	Fft	Sieve	Quick2	Inverse	Average
% of var. references in registers	.90	.77	.86	.86	.79	.80	.86
% of var. assignments in registers	.91	.76	.81	.83	.75	.91	.84

Table 1(b). Static register allocation statistics in the 68000

blocks are usually short, and most of the work is done by the global phase.

7. Measurements

The priority-based register allocation algorithm has been implemented in the production optimizer UOPT and tested on a number of target machines. The results have shown that it is effective on a wide range of machines. We now present measurements that give us some ideas about the performance and effectiveness of our register allocation algorithm. The measurements are based on running and optimizing a set of benchmarks consisting of 13 Pascal and Fortran programs. These benchmark programs are standard, compute-bound application programs, with minimal calls to un-optimizable external routines and runtimes.

7.1. Statistical counts

Table 1(a) and Table 1(b) display the register allocation statistics for the benchmark programs in the DEC 10 and 68000 respectively. It shows the percentages of variable references and the percentages of variable assignments that are in the global registers. The table does not include register usage by the code generators for code generating purposes. The data are obtained by static counts in the optimized programs. The dynamic counts are expected to be much better, since the register allocator in UOPT takes loop-nesting depths into account.

The percentages of allocation displayed in the two tables are not 100% because both of the two machines are not load/store machines, and infrequently accessed variables will not be allocated. The two machines also have a good set of memory addressing modes, so that a variable will not be allocated unless a payoff is obtained.

The DEC 10 uses the caller-save linkage convention, and the DEC 10 code generator allows UOPT to allocate up to 9 registers out of the 14 available. Programs that have many procedure calls (e.g. Tower)

Program	Perm	Tower	Queen	Intmm	Mm	Puzzle	Quick
0. No optimization	9.62 (1.0)	1.68 (1.0)	3.95 (1.0)	1.29 (1.0)	1.42 (1.0)	5.22 (1.0)	1.60 (1.0)
1. Only local optimizations	10.92 (1.14)	1.68 (1.0)	4.22 (1.07)	1.10 (.85)	1.23 (.87)	5.24 (1.0)	1.42 (.89)
2. Only local optimizations and reg. alloc.	8.46 (.88)	1.39 (.83)	3.99 (1.01)	1.05 (.81)	1.19 (.84)	4.85 (.93)	1.25 (.78)
3. All except register alloc.	8.87 (.92)	1.36 (.81)	3.76 (.95)	.65 (.50)	.78 (.55)	3.74 (.72)	1.60 (1.0)
4. Full global optimization	7.44 (.77)	1.27 (.75)	2.67 (.68)	.42 (.33)	.55 (.38)	2.47 (.47)	1.30 (.70)

Program	Bubble	Tree	Fft	Sieve	Quick2	Inverse	Average
0. No optimization	3.69 (1.0)	1.01 (1.0)	2.85 (1.0)	5.09 (1.0)	.719 (1.0)	4.71 (1.0)	(1.0)
1. Only local optimizations	3.79 (1.03)	1.05 (1.04)	1.82 (.64)	5.22 (1.03)	.703 (.98)	3.89 (.83)	(.95)
2. Only local optimizations and reg. alloc.	2.04 (.55)	.91 (.90)	1.68 (.59)	3.30 (.65)	.487 (.68)	3.67 (.78)	(.79)
3. All except register alloc.	4.60 (1.25)	1.08 (1.07)	1.40 (.59)	5.86 (1.15)	.807 (1.12)	3.17 (.67)	(.87)
4. Full global optimization	2.33 (.63)	.93 (.93)	1.07 (.37)	3.52 (.69)	.572 (.80)	2.36 (.50)	(.61)

Running times in Seconds
(Ratio to un-optimized running times in parentheses)

Table 2. Running times to show effects of register allocation on the DEC 10

Program	Perm	Tower	Queen	Intmm	Mm	Puzzle	Quick
0 registers	8.87 (1.0)	1.36 (1.0)	3.76 (1.0)	.65 (1.0)	.78 (1.0)	3.74 (1.0)	1.60 (1.0)
2 registers	8.25 (.93)	1.28 (.94)	3.62 (.96)	.64 (.98)	.78 (.99)	2.56 (.68)	1.48 (.93)
4 registers	7.44 (.84)	1.28 (.94)	3.29 (.88)	.58 (.89)	.71 (.91)	2.54 (.68)	1.42 (.89)
6 registers	7.44 (.84)	1.27 (.93)	2.68 (.71)	.43 (.66)	.56 (.72)	2.54 (.68)	1.42 (.89)
All 9 registers	7.44 (.84)	1.26 (.92)	2.68 (.71)	.42 (.65)	.55 (.71)	2.47 (.68)	1.30 (.81)

Program	Bubble	Tree	Fft	Sieve	Quick2	Inverse	Average
0 registers	4.60 (1.0)	1.08 (1.0)	1.40 (1.0)	5.86 (1.0)	.807 (1.0)	3.17 (1.0)	(1.0)
2 registers	3.71 (.81)	.96 (.89)	1.24 (.89)	4.02 (.69)	.724 (.90)	2.89 (.91)	(.88)
4 registers	3.84 (.83)	.93 (.86)	1.14 (.81)	3.99 (.68)	.669 (.83)	2.75 (.87)	(.84)
6 registers	2.33 (.51)	.93 (.86)	1.09 (.78)	3.53 (.60)	.621 (.77)	2.40 (.76)	(.75)
All 9 registers	2.33 (.51)	.93 (.86)	1.05 (.75)	3.25 (.55)	.572 (.71)	2.35 (.74)	(.73)

Running times in Seconds
(Normalized running times in parentheses)

Table 3. Effects of the number of registers available for register allocation (DEC 10)

tend to diminish the percentage allocated because the numerous instances of register saves and re-loads around procedure calls tend to increase the cost of the allocations.

The 68000 code generator allows UOPT to use up to 6 data registers and 4 address registers, out of the 8 data registers and 8 address registers available. The register allocation statistics for the 68000 is markedly different from that for the DEC 10, which is due to the use of the callee-save linkage convention in the 68000. The percentages of variable accesses allocated in registers in the 68000 are always greater than those in the DEC 10, since register saves and re-loads do not occur around procedure calls unless there are side effects. Tables 1(a) and (b) show that the linkage convention concerning the handling of registers does affect register allocation.

7.2. Selective application

Another method to study the effectiveness of our register allocation is by comparing the running times of the benchmarks with and without register allocation. Table 2 displays the running times of the benchmarks on the DEC 10 for different extents of optimization. Rows 1 and 2 show between them the effects of adding the register allocation phase if the optimizer performs only the minimal local optimizations. Rows 3 and 4 show between them the effects of leaving out the register allocation phase when the optimizer performs its full set of optimization. The data show that the register allocation is very effective, especially when the optimizer performs other global optimizations. Without register allocation, the benefits of the other global optimizations cannot be fully exposed, because the cost of saving intermediate quantities in main memory is high enough in some cases to cancel out the benefits that can be derived from the optimizations.

7.3. Varying the number of registers

In Table 3, we investigate the effects of allowing different numbers of registers to be allocated by UOPT out of the 14 available in the DEC 10. The results displayed in Table 3 show that the optimized running times always improve when a larger number of registers are available to UOPT. The 5 registers normally used by the code generator is enough

for most practical purposes, and increasing the number used by the code generator (i.e. decreasing the number used by UOPT) does not cause appreciable improvement in execution speed.

As expected, different programs require different numbers of registers for optimal register allocation. In the programs Perm, Tower and Tree, 4 registers seem to be all that are needed; for others, increasing the number further yields better execution speeds. In the programs Puzzle and Sieve, just 2 registers can dramatically improve the program running time. Different programs have different cut-off points regarding the number of registers they need for optimal register allocation. The cut-off number of registers required is related to the *chromatic numbers* of the interference graphs — the numbers of colors needed to color the graphs.

8. Concluding Remarks

In this paper, we have shown that, by using a priority-based coloring algorithm, the traditional register allocation problem can be approached practically and efficiently. Moreover, it can be performed in the machine-independent context using a few machine parameters. Among the parameters we use are characterizations of the benefits of register accesses over memory accesses. The performance and efficiency of the algorithm are not affected by the number of registers available in the target machines.

There are possibilities for further enhancement to the register allocation scheme we have presented. In the global coloring phase, register allocation priorities are computed by assuming that the register-memory move instructions are at fixed positions. The results can be improved if the priority ordering takes into account the possibility of moving the register-memory transfer instructions to positions that can minimize execution time cost.

The problem of allocating overlapping registers of different sizes have not been considered in this paper. It would be interesting to see to what extent the priority-based coloring scheme can be adapted to such situations.

Acknowledgement

This work represents part of the research performed for the S-1 project, under Contract 2213801 from the Lawrence Livermore National Laboratory. The development of the S-1 computer is funded by the Office of Naval Research of the U. S. Navy and the Department of Energy.

References

[1] G.J. Chaitin, "Register Allocation and Spilling via Graph Coloring," *ACM SIGPLAN Notices, 17,* 6 (June 1982), *(Proceedings of the SIGPLAN 82 Symposium on Compiler Construction),* pp. 201 – 207.

[2] F. Chow, "A Portable Machine-independent Global Optimizer — Design and Measurements," Ph.D. Thesis and Technical Report 83-254, Computer System Lab, Stanford University, Dec. 1983.

[3] R.A. Freiburghouse, "Register Allocation Via Usage Counts," *Comm. ACM 17,* 11, Nov. 74.

[4] B. W. Leverett, "Register Allocation in Optimizing Compilers," Ph.D. Thesis and Technical Report CMU CS-81-103, Carnegie-Mellon University, February 1981.

[5] D. Perkins and R. Sites, "Machine-independent Pascal Code Optimization," *ACM SIGPLAN Notices, 14,* 8 (August 1979), *(Proceedings of the SIGPLAN 79 Symposium on Compiler Construction),* pp. 201–207.

[6] R.L. Sites and D.R. Perkins, "Machine-independent Register Allocation," *ACM SIGPLAN Notices, Vol. 14, Number 8 (August 1979), (Proceedings of the SIGPLAN 79 Symposium on Compiler Construction),* pp. 221–225.

[7] J.T. Schwartz, "On Programming: An Interim Report on the SETL Project," Courant Institute of Math. Sciences, New York University, 1973.

Reprinted from IEEE *Transactions on Computers*, Volume C-32, Number 11, November 1983. Copyright © 1983 by The Institute of Electrical and Electronics Engineers, Inc.

Strategies for Managing the Register File in RISC

YUVAL TAMIR, STUDENT MEMBER, IEEE, AND CARLO H. SÉQUIN, FELLOW, IEEE

Abstract—The RISC (reduced instruction set computer) architecture attempts to achieve high performance without resorting to complex instructions and irregular pipelining schemes. One of the novel features of this architecture is a large register file which is used to minimize the overhead involved in procedure calls and returns. This paper investigates several strategies for managing this register file. The costs of practical strategies are compared with a lower bound on this management overhead, obtained from a theoretical *optimal strategy*, for several register file sizes.

While the results concern specifically the RISC processor recently built at U.C. Berkeley, they are generally applicable to other processors with multiple register banks.

Index Terms—Cache fetch strategies, computer architecture, procedure calls, register file management, RISC, VLSI processor.

I. INTRODUCTION

INVESTIGATIONS of the use of high-level languages show that procedure call/return is the most time-consuming operation in typical high-level language programs [8], [9] due to the related overhead of passing parameters and saving and restoring of registers. The RISC architecture [8], [9] includes a novel scheme that results in highly efficient execution of this operation.

In conventional, register-oriented computers, the procedure call/return mechanism is based on a LIFO stack of variable size *invocation frames* (activation records). When a procedure is called, an area on top of the stack is used for storing the input arguments, saving the return address and register values, allocating local variables and temporaries, and, if the procedure calls another procedure, storing output arguments. A procedure's invocation frame denotes this area on the stack. At any point in time, the number of invocation frames in the stack is the current *nesting depth*. The invocation frame of the calling procedure overlaps that of the called procedure so that the memory locations containing the parameters passed from the calling procedure to the called procedure are part of both frames.

In most computers, register/register operations can be performed faster than the corresponding memory/memory operations. Therefore, the most heavily used local variables and temporaries are placed in registers. When a procedure is called, it must save the value of all the registers it will use and restore these values before returning control to the calling

Manuscript received July 14, 1982; revised January 3, 1983. This work was supported by the Defense Advanced Research Projects Agency under ARPA Order 3803, and monitored by Naval Electronic System Command under Contract N00039-81-K-0251.

The authors are with the Computer Science Division, Department of Electrical Engineering and Computer Sciences, University of California, Berkeley, CA 94720.

procedure. Analysis of the dynamic behavior of Pascal and C programs, executing on a VAX 11/780, has shown [8], [9] that saving and restoring register values and writing and reading of parameters from the common area of the caller and the callee are responsible for more than 40 percent of the data memory references.

In RISC, the call/return mechanism is based on *two* LIFO stacks. One of the stacks (henceforth "STACK1") contains *fixed size* frames which hold scalar quantities of the invocation frame (i.e., scalar input arguments, the return address, scalar output parameters, and scalar local variables and temporaries). The second stack (henceforth "STACK2") contains variable size frames, some of which may be empty (i.e., their size is zero). This stack is used for all nonscalar variables which are normally placed on the single stack in conventional computers. It is also used for scalars in case there is not enough space in the fixed size frame on STACK1.

The size of the STACK1 frame in RISC was determined based on a study by Halbert and Kessler [5]. The dynamic behavior of nine noninteractive UNIX™ C programs was analyzed. These programs included the main part of the C compiler *ccom*, the Pascal interpreter *pi*, the UNIX copy command *cp*, the *troff* text formatter, and the UNIX *sort* program. This study showed that a fixed frame size of 22 "words" (22 registers), with an overlap of six "words" between adjacent frames, is sufficient for all the scalar variables and arguments in over 95 percent of the procedure calls.

The implementation of STACK2 in RISC is identical to the implementation of the single LIFO stack in conventional computers: the stack itself resides in memory, there is a processor register that serves as a stack pointer, and there is another register that serves as the frame pointer [4]. There is no special hardware support for operations on STACK2 but, due to STACK1, such operations are far less frequent than operations on the LIFO stack of conventional computers. Since the implementation and operation of STACK2 is identical to those of the stack in conventional computers, STACK2 will not be discussed any further in this paper.

In conventional computers, registers are used for storing part of the invocation frame of the currently executing procedure (i.e., the top frame on the stack). In RISC, there is a large register file that is divided into several fixed size "register banks," each of which can hold one STACK1 frame. Since each STACK1 frame partially overlaps the previous STACK1 frame and the next STACK1 frame, each register bank shares some of its registers with the two neighboring register banks.

The STACK1 frame used by the currently executing procedure, is always in one of the register banks. At each point in time, the contents of one of the register banks are addressable as registers, thus providing a "window" into the register file. This register bank is always the one containing the STACK1 frame of the currently executing procedure. A procedure call modifies a hardware pointer and "moves" the window to the next register bank in the register file, where the STACK1 frame of the called procedure resides. Thus, for example, register 15 (R15) in the calling procedure is in a different physical position in the register file from R15 in the called procedure, although the operand specifier for R15 is identical in the two procedures.

A return instruction restores the previous value of the above mentioned hardware pointer so the previous values of all the registers are "restored" without any data movement. Furthermore, no memory references are required for passing arguments since they are passed in registers which are in the region of overlap between the register banks containing the STACK1 frames of the caller and the callee.

By using this scheme, a procedure call in RISC can be made as fast as a jump and with fewer accesses to data memory than are required in conventional computers.

Since the size of the register file is limited, there is a need for a mechanism which will handle the case when the procedure nesting depth exceeds the number of STACK1 frames which fit in the register file. When a procedure call is executed, a new "empty" register bank is needed. If all the register banks in the register file are in use, an "overflow" occurs. This overflow causes a trap which is handled by operating system software. The operating system must free one or more register banks to make room for the new frame. Since the STACK1 frames in the register banks which are "freed" must be preserved, the software copies the frames to a conventional LIFO stack which is kept in memory and contains only STACK1 frames.

When a return instruction is executed, the window must be moved to a register bank containing the previous frame (i.e., the frame of the calling procedure). If all the register banks are free (i.e., the calling frame is not resident), an "underflow" occurs. This underflow causes a trap, upon which the operating system software loads one or more frames from memory where they were stored when an overflow occurred.

The register file is simply a write-back cache of STACK1. The cache blocks are the STACK1 frames. The top few frames of STACK1 are in the register file while the rest are in memory. When an underflow occurs, one or more occupied STACK1 frames are *fetched* from memory. When an overflow occurs, one or more register banks are "freed." This can be interpreted as "fetching" empty STACK1 frames from memory. Since in both cases the "fetching" is done by software, there is great flexibility in defining the cache *fetch strategy* (algorithm) [10]. This strategy determines the number of frames to be moved to/from memory when an overflow/ underflow occurs.

In this paper, several fetch strategies are considered. A theoretical "optimal strategy" is developed and is used as a

reference point for evaluating the performance of several practical strategies. In addition, the effect of register file size on the performance of different strategies is investigated.

II. The Optimal Strategy

In this section an *optimal strategy* for managing the register file will be discussed. This strategy requires unbounded lookahead (possibly to the end of the call/return trace) and is therefore only useful as a lower bound on the cost of practical strategies. A proof that the proposed strategy is, in fact, "optimal" is presented.

A. Definitions

In order to facilitate further discussion, some formal definitions are required.

When a program is executing, its nesting depth constantly changes: every procedure call increases the nesting depth by one and every return decreases the nesting depth by one. Hence, for every execution of a program, there is a corresponding sequence of nesting depths. This sequence will be called a *procedure nesting depth sequence* (PNDS).

Definition 1: A *procedure nesting depth sequence* (PNDS) is a sequence of integers $D = (d_1, d_2, \cdots, d_n)$ where $d_1 = 1$, $d_i > 0$ for $1 \leq i \leq n$ and $|d_i - d_{i-1}| = 1$ for $2 \leq i \leq n$.

The integer i is an index into the PNDS; d_1 is the nesting depth at the beginning of the program. For each $i, 2 \leq i \leq n$, d_i is the nesting depth after $i - 1$ calls and returns are executed (i.e., after $i - 1$ changes in the nesting depth). Henceforth, an index into the PNDS will be called a *location*. An example of a PNDS is shown in Fig. 1.

The frames of STACK1 are numbered from 1 to m (with m being the current nesting depth, i.e., the number of the frame of the currently executing procedure). The top (i.e., highest numbered) few frames of the stack are always in the register file while the rest are in memory.

Definition 2: The *register file position* (RFP) is the number of the lowest numbered frame which is in the register file.

When an overflow occurs, the lowest number frame(s) in the register file are copied to memory and the register banks they occupy in the register file are "freed." This increases the register file position. Similarly, when an underflow occurs the RFP is decreased. Thus, the number of times the RFP is changed during the execution of the program is equal to the sum of the number of overflows and the number of underflows which occur.

Definition 3: A *register file move* (RFM) denotes an increase or decrease in the register file position.

Definition 4: The *size* of the register file move is the absolute value of the difference between the RFP before the move and the RFP after the move.

If the current nesting depth is d, the STACK1 frame being used by the currently executing procedure, is the one labeled d. The register file position must be such that this frame is contained in the register file. Hence, if the register file can hold w frames and if the RFP is p, then $p \leq d < p + w$. Before execution begins, the RFP is some positive integer p_0. During the execution of a program with a PNDS $D = (d_1, d_2, \cdots, d_n)$, for each nesting depth d_i, the corresponding RFP p_i must be such that the above condition is satisfied, i.e., $p_i \leq d_i < p_i + w$.

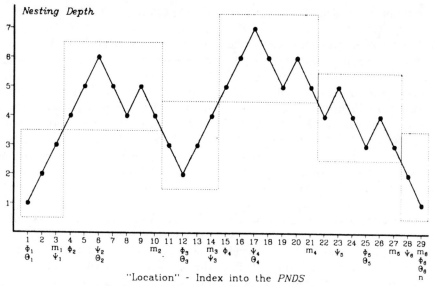

"Location" - Index into the *PNDS*

Fig. 1.   PNDS and optimal RFP's.

Definition 5: Given a PNDS $D = (d_1, d_2, \cdots, d_n)$ and a register file that can hold w frames, a valid *register file position sequence* (RFPS) is a sequence of RFP's: $P = (p_0, p_1, p_2, \cdots, p_n)$ such that the p_i's are positive integers and for all i, $1 \leq i \leq n$, $p_i \leq d_i < p_i + w$.

There is a one-to-one correspondence between nesting depths in the PNDS and RFP's in the RFPS. Successive RFP's, p_{j-1} and p_j, in the RFPS may be unequal or equal depending on whether the register file position is modified between the $j - 2$ and $j - 1$ change in the nesting depth.

Definition 6: If $P = (p_0, p_1, p_2, \cdots, p_n)$ is an RFPS, an RFM is said to occur in *location* j $(1 \leq j \leq n)$ of P, if and only if $p_j \neq p_{j-1}$.

The number of RFM's which occur during some interval in which the program is executing is of interest in this paper. The interval is defined as a subsequence of the RFPS (which corresponds to a subsequence of the PNDS).

Definition 7: If $P = (p_0, p_1, p_2, \cdots, p_n)$ is an RFPS, the number of RFM's occurring in location range $[i, j]$ of P, where $1 \leq i \leq j \leq n$, is the number of unique integers k, such that $i \leq k \leq j$ and $p_k \neq p_{k-1}$. This number will be denoted by $\text{RFM}_P[i, j]$.

Definition 8: If $P = (p_0, p_1, p_2, \cdots, pn)$, is an RFPS, the *memory traffic* occurring in location range $[i, j]$ of P, where $1 \leq i \leq j \leq n$, is the total number of STACK1 frames moved to/from memory as the RFP is set to $p_i, p_{i+1}, \cdots, p_j$ successively. This number is denoted by $\text{MT}_P[i, j]$:

$$\text{MT}_P[i, j] = \sum_{k=i}^{j} \left| p_k - p_{k-1} \right|$$

B. What is an "Optimal Strategy"?

There is some overhead involved in handling overflow/underflow traps: saving the current state, determining the cause of the trap, activating the proper trap handling routine, restoring state, and returning to normal execution. Hence, it is desirable to minimize the number of register file overflows and underflows. In addition, there is the direct *cost* involved in actually moving the data to/from memory. For each register

file move, this cost is proportional to the number of frames moved (i.e., to the size of the register file move). Hence, it is desirable to minimize the number of frames moved for each overflow/underflow, i.e., the memory traffic which is the result of overflows and underflows.

The problem of finding the "best" RFPS is similar to finding optimal strategies for handling page faults in virtual memory systems. In virtual memory systems it is also desirable to minimize both the number of page faults (since there is overhead involved in handling such faults) and the I/O involved in moving memory pages to/from disk or drum. For the virtual memory problem, Belady [1] developed an "optimal" page replacement algorithm which causes the fewest possible page faults for a program which executes in a fixed number of main memory page frames. Belady's algorithm is not realizable since it requires knowledge of the future portion of the page trace.

In the next sections it is shown that if the entire call return trace of the program (i.e., the PNDS) is known, there exists a RFPS which achieves *both* the minimum number of overflow/underflow traps and the minimum memory traffic resulting from register file moves. It is further shown that knowledge of the entire PNDS is *necessary* for achieving an optimum RFPS.

C. The Existence of an Optimal RFPS

In order to prove the existence of an optimal RFPS, an algorithm for deriving such an RFPS from a given PNDS, is presented. The optimality of the RFPS produced by the algorithm is shown by proving that no other valid RFPS can have fewer register file moves or result in less memory traffic.

An optimal RFPS can be obtained as follows. We start with the RFP at 1 and keep it there until the nesting depth exceeds the number (w) of register banks in the register file. Now the RFP must be changed, i.e., an RFM must occur. In order to determine the *optimal size* of the RFM, we must look ahead in the call/return trace (i.e., in the PNDS). Starting from the current location, we determine the longest subsequence of the PNDS for which a constant RFP is possible (i.e., in which the difference between the maximum nesting depth and the minimum nesting depth does not exceed $w - 1$). The new RFP is chosen so that it is valid for this entire subsequence. From the end of this subsequence we repeat the procedure until the entire PNDS is covered.

Special handling is required when determining the RFP for the last subsequence in the PNDS. In this case the difference between the maximum and minimum nesting depth within the subsequence may be less than $w - 1$. Hence, there is some freedom in setting the RFP. In order to minimize the memory traffic, the new RFP is chosen so that it is valid for the entire subsequence *and* the absolute value of the difference between the new RFP and the previous RFP is minimized. An example of a PNDS and the corresponding optimal RFPS is shown in Fig. 1.

More formally, the procedure can be stated as follows. Given an arbitrary PNDS $D = (d_1, d_2, \cdots, d_n)$, an optimal RFPS $P = (p_0, p_1, p_2, \cdots, p_n)$, for a register file that can hold w frames, can be obtained as follows:

[1] **let** $i = 1, p_0 = 1$
[2] **repeat**
[3]   **let** $E = (d_i, d_{i+1}, \cdots, d_m)$
        where m is the maximum integer such that
        $i \leq m \leq n$ and $\max(E) - \min(E) < w$
[4]   **if** $(m < n)$ **or** $(p_{i-1} > \min(E))$ **then**
[5]   **for** $j = i$ **to** m
            let $p_j = \min(E)$
[6]   **else**
[7]   **for** $j = i$ **to** m
            let $p_j = \max(E) - w + 1$
[8]   **let** $i = m + 1$
[9] **until** $i > n$

First, it must be shown that the algorithm generates a valid RFPS for the given PNDS. Proof of the validity of the algorithm and of the generated RFPS requires proving the following lemmas.

Lemma 1: The **repeat** and **for** loops terminate after a finite number of iterations, i.e., the algorithm always terminates.

Proof: Since n is finite and i is incremented by at least 1 during each iteration of the **repeat** loop, n is an upper bound on the number of iterations through the **repeat** loop.

It is always true that $i \geq 1$ and $m \leq n$. Hence, n is an upper bound on the number of iteration through the **for** loop (either one) each time it is entered. ∎

Lemma 2: For all i, $1 \leq i \leq n, p_i \leq d_i < p_i + w$, i.e., the RFP's generated by the algorithm are valid.

Proof: From the algorithm, if p_i is set in step 5, then $p_i \leq d_i$ [since $p_i = \min(E)$] and $d_i - p_i < w$ (since $\max(E) - \min(E) < w$). Hence, $p_i \leq d_i < p_i + w$.

If p_i is set in step 7, then $p_i \geq d_i - w + 1$ (since $p_i = \max(E) - w + 1$) and $p_i + w - 1 - d_i < w$ (since $\max(E) = p_i + w - 1$ and $\max(E) - \min(E) < w$). From the first inequality, $d_i \leq p_i + w - 1$ and from the second inequality $p_i < d_i + 1$. Hence, $p_i \leq d_i < p_i + w$. ∎

The proof of the optimality of the generated RFPS requires some additional notation. The subsequence E which is defined during the kth iteration of the **repeat** loop will be denoted E_k

(it corresponds to the kth setting of the RFP). The corresponding integer m will be denoted m_k. For convenience in notation, we define $m_0 = 0$. The number of iterations that the **repeat** loop executes before terminating will be denoted by K (it corresponds to the number of times that the RFP is adjusted). Note that $1 \leq m_1 < m_2 < \cdots < m_K = n$.

For each location range, $[m_{k-1} + 1, m_k]$, the RFP's in the RFPS generated by the algorithm are constant. Within this location range, Φ_k and Ψ_k are the locations of the first occurrence of the minimum and maximum nesting depths, respectively. More formally, see the following.

Definition 9: Φ_k and Ψ_k are the smallest integers, such that for each k ($1 \leq k \leq K$), both are in the location range $[m_{k-1} + 1, m_k]$, where $d_{\Phi_k} = \min(E_k)$ and $d_{\Psi_k} = \max(E_k)$.

In order to prove the optimality of the RFPS generated by the algorithm, it must be shown that this RFPS results in the lowest possible memory traffic. This will be done by using induction on the K boundaries of $K - 1$ location ranges. These boundaries are defined below and are denoted by Θ_k, for all k such that $1 \leq k \leq K$. The boundary point Θ_k is the location of the first minimum or maximum nesting depth within the location range $[m_{k-1} + 1, m_k]$. If the RFP in the RFPS generated by the algorithm for location range $[m_{k-1} + 1, m_k]$ is less than the RFP for location range $[m_{k-2} + 1, m_{k-1}]$, then $\Theta_k = \Phi_k$, otherwise $\Theta_k = \Psi_k$. More formally:

Definition 10: Θ_k is an integer such that for each $k, 2 \leq k \leq K, \Theta_k = \Phi_k$ if $d_{\Phi_k} < d_{\Phi_{k-1}}$, and $\Theta_k = \Psi_k$ otherwise. For convenience in notation, we define $\Theta_1 = 1$.

Fig. 1 shows the PNDS from the execution of Ackerman's function with arguments $(2, 1)$. The dotted squares show the "optimal" RFP's for a register file that can hold three frames. In this example, five RFM's are necessary (RFM$_P[1, 29]$ = 5, $K = 6$) and the memory traffic resulting from those RFM's is 12 frames (MT$_P[1, 29] = 12$).

Let $Q = (q_0, q_1, q_2, \cdots, q_n)$ be an arbitrary valid RFPS for D.

The rest of this section contains a formal proof that the number of RFM's in P and the memory traffic resulting from those RFM's are at most equal to the number of RFM's in Q and the memory traffic resulting from those RFM's, respectively.

Lemma 3: If $K > 1$, then for all k, $1 \leq k < K$, RFM$_Q[1, m_k + 1] \geq k$.

Proof: See the Appendix.

From the algorithm, for all k, $1 \leq k \leq K, d_{\Psi_k} - d_{\Phi_k} \leq w - 1$. It is now shown that for $1 \leq k \leq K - 1, d_{\Psi_k} - d_{\Phi_k} = w - 1$.

Lemma 4: If $K > 1$, then for all k, $1 \leq k \leq K - 1, d_{\Psi_k} - d_{\Phi_k} = w - 1$.

Proof: See the Appendix.

It should be noted that Lemma 4 makes no claims about the value of $(d_{\Psi_K} - d_{\Phi_K})$, i.e., it makes no claims about the case $k = K$. From the algorithm it is clear that $d_{\Psi_K} - d_{\Phi_K} < w$. So it is quite possible that $d_{\Psi_K} - d_{\Phi_K} < w - 1$.

Lemma 5: If $K > 1$, for all k, $1 \leq k \leq K - 1$, for all i, $m_{k-1} + 1 \leq i \leq m_k, p_i = d_{\Phi_k} = d_{\Psi_k} - w + 1$. For the last subsequence, i.e., $k = K$: if $\Theta_k = \Phi_k$, then $p_i = d_{\Phi_k}$, else $p_i = d_{\Psi_k} - w + 1$.

Proof: See the Appendix.

Lemma 6: If $K > 1$, then for all k, $1 \leq k \leq K$, $\mathrm{MT}_Q[1, \Theta_k]$ $\geq \mathrm{MT}_P[1, \Theta_k] + |q_{\Theta_k} - p_{\Theta_k}|$.

Proof: See the Appendix.

Using the above lemmas, we can formally prove the "optimality" of the RFPS generated by the algorithm.

Theorem 1: The RFPS P generated by the algorithm for the PNDS D is an *optimal* RFPS for D, i.e., if Q is an arbitrary valid RFPS for D, then

$$\mathrm{RFM}_P[1, n] \leq \mathrm{RFM}_Q[1, n]$$

and

$$\mathrm{MT}_P[1, n] \leq \mathrm{MT}_Q[1, n].$$

Proof: If $K = 1$, then there are no RFM's in P so $\mathrm{RFM}_P[1, n] = 0$, $\mathrm{MT}_P[1, n] = 0$, and the theorem holds.

Assume $K > 1$. In the algorithm, all the RFP's, corresponding to the same subsequence, are set to the same value (step 5 or step 7). Hence, the only way that $p_i \neq p_{i+1}$ can occur is if $i = m_k$ for some k, $1 \leq k \leq K - 1$. Thus, $\mathrm{RFM}_P[1, n] \leq K - 1$.

From Lemma 3, $K - 1 \leq \mathrm{RFM}_Q[1, m_{K-1} + 1]$. Since $m_{K-1} + 1 \leq n$, $\mathrm{RFM}_Q[1, m_{K-1} + 1] \leq \mathrm{RFM}_Q[1, n]$. Hence, $K - 1 \leq \mathrm{RFM}_Q[1, n]$. Thus, $\mathrm{RFM}_P[1, n] \leq \mathrm{RFM}_Q[1, n]$.

From Lemma 6, $\mathrm{MT}_Q[1, \Theta_K] \geq \mathrm{MT}_P[1, \Theta_K] + |q_{\Theta_K} - p_{\Theta_K}|$. Since $|q_{\Theta_K} - p_{\Theta_K}| \geq 0$, $\mathrm{MT}_Q[1, \Theta_K] \geq \mathrm{MT}_P[1, \Theta_K]$. Since $\Theta_K \leq n$, $\mathrm{MT}_Q[1, n] \geq \mathrm{MT}_Q[1, \Theta_K]$. Since $d_{\Theta_K} \in E_K$ and $d_n \in E_K$, $p_{\Theta_K} = p_{\Theta_K+1} = \cdots = p_n$. Thus, $\mathrm{MT}_P[\Theta_K + 1, n] = 0$, so $\mathrm{MT}_P[1, \Theta_K] = \mathrm{MT}_P[1, n]$. Hence, $\mathrm{MT}_P[1, n] \leq \mathrm{MT}_Q[1, n]$.

Q.E.D.

D. The Unrealizability of an Optimal Strategy

When a computer is executing a program, the entire call/return trace is not known ahead of time. In fact, it is unlikely that there is any look-ahead possible. In this section it is shown that knowledge of the entire PNDS is necessary for finding an optimal RFPS.

First, it should be noted that no simplifying assumptions about the properties of the call/return trace of "real" programs can be made. In other words, for every given sequence of integers which satisfies the definition of a PNDS (Definition 1), it is possible to construct a real program whose sequence of nesting depths is the given sequence. This is demonstrated by the program in Fig. 2 (which is written in the C language [7]). When this program is executed, its sequence of nesting depths is identical to the sequence of integers in the array *depthlist* (assuming that the sequence of integers in *depthlist* is a valid PNDS).

To show that unbounded look-ahead on the call/return trace is necessary for achieving an optimal RFPS, consider a system where there is a bounded (or nonexistent) look-ahead; more specifically, a system where at each point in time only the next t calls and returns are known in advance. (Note that in most systems $t = 0$.) Assume that the register file of the system can hold w frames and that there are two programs to be executed: PROG1 and PROG2. These programs have identical call/return traces for the first s calls and returns, where $w + t < s$. At some point, before $s - t$ calls/returns are executed, the nesting depth (in both programs) reaches $w + 1$. The nesting

```
int depthlist[] = {  /* This is the PNDS, 0 terminated */
  1, 2, 3, 2, 3, 4, 3, 2, 1, 0 } ;
int depthind = 1 ;
main()
{
  while (depthlist[depthind] > 1) {
    deeper(2) ;
    depthind = depthind + 1 ;
  }
}

deeper(curdep)
  int curdep ;  /* The current nesting depth */
{
  depthind = depthind + 1 ;
  while (depthlist[depthind] > curdep) {
    deeper(curdep+1) ;
    depthind = depthind + 1 ;
  }
  if (depthlist[depthind] == 0)
    exit(0) ;
}
```

Fig. 2. A program whose "behavior" follows an arbitrary PNDS.

depth stays between 2 and $w + 1$ until a total of s calls/returns are executed. After that, in PROG1 the nesting depth decreases and the program terminates at nesting depth 1. In PROG2, on the other hand, the nesting depth increases to $w + 2$ and then decreases until the program terminates at nesting depth 1.

In both programs, when the nesting depth first reaches $w + 1$, the same information about the call/return trace is available, and therefore any strategy for managing the register file will result in the same action being taken for both programs. This action is clearly *not* optimal for at least one of the programs. For PROG1, the optimal action is to move one frame to memory. This action is not optimal for PROG2 since another overflow will occur when a nesting depth of $w + 2$ is reached. The optimal action for PROG2 is to move two frames to memory so that only one overflow will occur during the execution of the program. Moving two frames to memory is *not* the optimal action for PROG1 since it results in unnecessary memory traffic: moving two frames to and from memory instead of one.

The fact that an optimal strategy is not realizable does not imply that all practical strategies for managing the register file are equally bad. As seen in the next section, simple changes in the strategy for managing the register file may significantly affect the cost of handling calls and returns.

III. PRACTICAL STRATEGIES FOR MANAGING THE REGISTER FILE

In most real systems, no look-ahead at the call/return trace is possible. Thus, the decision as to how many frames should be moved to/from memory when an overflow/underflow occurs must be based on the previous behavior of the executing program or be completely independent of the PNDS of the executing program.

As indicated above, two factors contribute to the *cost* (execution time) of handling register file overflows and underflows: the handling of the interrupt/trap that is initiated by the overflow/underflow and the actual transfer of the STACK1 frames to/from memory. If the number of frames which are moved when an interrupt occurs is not fixed, some computation may be required in order to calculate this number. The cost of this calculation is included in the cost of handling the interrupt. In order to evaluate the effectiveness of different strategies for managing the register file, these strategies can be tried out on the call/return trace of benchmark programs. The number of overflows/underflows and transfers of STACK1 frames which result from each strategy can thus be determined. These numbers can then be related to the *cost* of the overflow/underflow handler using the following formula:

$$cost = \alpha \times (\text{number overflows} + \text{number underflows})$$
$$+ \beta \times (\text{number frames moved})$$

where α and β are constants: α is the cost of responding to the interrupt and calculating the number of frames to be moved, and β is the cost of moving one STACK1 frame to or from memory.

A. Measurement Technique

The method used for obtaining the call/return trace of the benchmark programs used in this paper relies on the fact that the call/return trace of a program executing on a RISC computer is identical to the call/return trace of the same program executing on any similar computer. In this case, the benchmark programs are all written in the C language [7], and their call/return trace is obtained from their execution on a VAX 11/780. The assembly code produced by the C compiler is processed by an editor script which inserts calls to special procedures before and after each procedure call instruction. When the program is executed, in addition to producing its normal output, it creates a file containing a string of bits. The ith bit in the string corresponds to the ith call/return executed by the program. This bit is 1 if a call was executed, 0 if a return was executed. The bit string is the call/return trace of the program. Routines which simulate different strategies for managing the register file use this string to obtain the number of overflows/underflows and the resulting memory traffic which will occur if the benchmark program is executed using the simulated strategy.

For this study, three benchmark programs were used:

rcc   The RISC C compiler [2] which is based on Johnson's portable C compiler [6]. The call/return trace used was generated by the compiler compiling the UNIX file concatenation utility *cat*. 88 606 calls and returns were executed and a nesting depth of 26 was reached.

puzzle   This is a bin-packing program which solves a three-dimensional puzzle. It was developed by Forest Baskett. During the execution of the program, 42 710 calls and returns were executed and a nesting depth of 20 was reached.

tower   This is a Tower of Hanoi program. The call/return trace used, was obtained for the program moving 18 disks. 1 048 574 calls and returns were executed and a nesting depth of 20 was reached.

In this paper, the cost of handling register file overflows and underflows is assumed to be directly proportional to the number of RISC instructions they require. If no calculation is needed in order to determine the number of frames to be moved, the cost of responding to the interrupt is approximately 30 instructions ($\alpha = 30$ in the above discussion). The cost of moving one STACK1 frame is 16 instructions ($\beta = 16$ in the above discussion).

B. The Cost of "Fixed" Strategies

The simplest strategy for managing the register file is to always move the same number of frames (say i) *to* memory, when an overflow occurs, and always move the same number of frames (say j) *from* memory, when an underflow occurs. For a register file that can hold w frames, such a strategy will be denoted *fixed*(i, j) where i and j are integers such that $1 \leq i \leq w$ and $1 \leq j \leq w$.

When a *fixed* strategy is used, no computation is required in order to determine the number of frames to be moved. Hence, the equation

$$cost = 30 \times (\text{number overflows} + \text{number underflows})$$
$$+ 16 \times (\text{number frames moved})$$

is used to evaluate the cost of managing the register file. This equation is also used in evaluating the cost of the optimal strategy, which serves as a lower bound on the cost of other strategies.

1) Measurement Results: The actual "performance" of the optimal strategy and *fixed* strategies is presented in this section. All possible fixed strategies for register files containing 3, 5, 7, 9, 13, and 17 register banks have been tried with the three benchmark programs.

Tables I–III summarize the results for each one of the three benchmark programs with six different register file sizes and for seven different strategies. The results include the number of overflows, number of underflows, memory traffic, and cost. For the optimal strategy, the "raw" numbers are presented. For the other six strategies, the figures shown are normalized with respect to the corresponding entries for the optimal strategy with the same register file size. In the three tables w denotes the number of register banks in the register file.

The *fixed* strategies included in the tables are: the best of all *fixed* strategies (i.e., the strategy resulting in the least cost) for the particular program and register file size, the worst of all *fixed* strategies (i.e., the strategy resulting in the greatest cost) for the particular program and register file size, *fixed*$(w, 1)$ which guarantees the minimum number of overflows, *fixed*$(1, w)$ which guarantees the minimum number of underflows, *fixed*$(1, 1)$ which guarantees the minimum memory traffic, and *fixed*$(\lceil w/2 \rceil, \lceil w/2 \rceil)$ which is "symmetrical."

2) Discussion of Measurement Results: Although the three benchmark programs used are quite different, the results show many common characteristics in their behavior, as far as the management of the register file is concerned. In addition, the results for the *fixed*$(w, 1)$, *fixed*$(1, w)$, and *fixed*$(1, 1)$ strategies provide an experimental verification to the fact that the "optimal strategy," presented in Section II, does indeed minimize the number of overflows/underflows and memory traffic simultaneously.

The register file size and the way that the register file is managed can significantly affect the cost of procedure calls. Table IV shows the average number of instructions per procedure call required for managing the register file. For every

114

TABLE I
FIXED STRATEGIES WITH *rcc*

Reg File Size (w)		3	5	7	9	13	17
Best Fixed Strategy		(1,1)	(1,1)	(2,2)	(2,2)	(2,2)	(2,2)
Worst Fixed Strategy		(3,3)	(5,5)	(7,7)	(9,9)	(13,13)	(17,17)
Optimal Strategy (raw)	#Overflows	5828	1483	548	236	83	18
	#Underflows	6200	1232	474	171	71	14
	Mem. Traffic	19006	5554	2482	1376	458	74
	Cost	664936	170314	70372	34226	11948	2084
Best Fixed Strategy (normalized)	#Overflows	1.83	1.87	1.65	1.87	1.67	1.56
	#Underflows	1.53	2.25	1.91	2.58	1.96	1.79
	Mem. Traffic	1.00	1.00	1.46	1.28	1.21	1.35
	Cost	1.31	1.50	1.59	1.60	1.44	1.49
Worst Fixed Strategy (normalized)	#Overflows	2.30	7.06	9.49	10.64	43.40	79.31
	#Underflows	2.16	8.50	10.97	14.69	50.73	90.64
	Mem. Traffic	4.24	18.85	29.33	32.86	204.48	583.05
	Cost	3.15	13.53	20.99	25.54	143.50	367.79
fixed(w,1) (normalized)	#Overflows	1.00	1.00	1.00	1.00	1.00	1.00
	#Underflows	2.82	6.02	8.09	12.42	15.20	19.43
	Mem. Traffic	1.84	2.67	3.09	3.09	4.71	7.35
	Cost	1.89	2.96	3.61	4.05	5.81	8.32
fixed(1,w) (normalized)	#Overflows	3.19	3.88	5.44	5.66	4.83	3.94
	#Underflows	1.00	1.00	1.00	1.00	1.00	1.00
	Mem. Traffic	1.96	2.07	2.40	1.94	1.75	1.70
	Cost	2.01	2.31	2.83	2.57	2.26	2.08
fixed(1,1) (normalized)	#Overflows	1.63	1.87	2.26	2.92	2.76	2.31
	#Underflows	1.53	2.25	2.82	4.02	3.23	2.64
	Mem. Traffic	1.00	1.00	1.00	1.00	1.00	1.00
	Cost	1.31	1.50	1.62	1.85	1.76	1.63
$fixed(\lfloor \frac{w}{2} \rfloor, \lfloor \frac{w}{2} \rfloor)$ (normalized)	#Overflows	1.65	2.73	2.38	2.51	1.48	4.19
	#Underflows	1.55	3.29	2.76	3.46	1.70	4.79
	Mem. Traffic	2.02	4.38	4.21	4.30	3.70	16.30
	Cost	1.79	3.71	3.49	3.81	2.88	11.19

TABLE II
FIXED STRATEGIES WITH *puzzle*

Reg File Size (w)		3	5	7	9	13	17
Best Fixed Strategy		(1,1)	(1,1)	(1,1)	(2,2)	(7,7)	(3,3)
Worst Fixed Strategy		(3,3)	(5,5)	(7,7)	(9,9)	(13,13)	(17,17)
Optimal Strategy (raw)	#Overflows	736	159	26	8	1	1
	#Underflows	747	159	30	5	1	1
	Mem. Traffic	2056	514	94	30	14	8
	Cost	77386	17764	3184	810	284	158
Best Fixed Strategy (normalized)	#Overflows	1.40	1.62	1.81	1.67	1.00	1.00
	#Underflows	1.38	1.62	1.57	2.00	1.00	1.00
	Mem. Traffic	1.00	1.00	1.00	1.33	1.00	1.00
	Cost	1.22	1.33	1.36	1.53	1.00	1.00
Worst Fixed Strategy (normalized)	#Overflows	9.80	39.50	130.58	70.83	1462.00	2791.00
	#Underflows	9.85	39.50	113.17	85.00	1462.00	2791.00
	Mem. Traffic	21.05	122.20	505.64	255.00	2715.14	15815.67
	Cost	14.54	77.79	302.82	182.59	2450.39	10806.18
fixed(w,1) (normalized)	#Overflows	1.00	1.00	1.00	1.00	1.00	1.00
	#Underflows	2.96	5.00	6.07	10.80	13.00	17.00
	Mem. Traffic	2.15	3.09	3.87	3.80	1.86	5.67
	Cost	2.05	3.04	3.79	4.36	2.94	6.95
fixed(1,w) (normalized)	#Overflows	3.04	4.99	7.85	6.50	7.00	3.00
	#Underflows	1.00	1.00	1.00	1.00	1.00	1.00
	Mem. Traffic	2.18	3.09	4.34	2.60	1.00	1.00
	Cost	2.08	3.04	4.26	3.17	1.63	1.38
fixed(1,1) (normalized)	#Overflows	1.40	1.62	1.81	2.50	7.00	3.00
	#Underflows	1.38	1.62	1.57	3.00	7.00	3.00
	Mem. Traffic	1.00	1.00	1.00	1.00	1.00	1.00
	Cost	1.22	1.33	1.36	1.70	2.27	1.77
$fixed(\lfloor \frac{w}{2} \rfloor, \lfloor \frac{w}{2} \rfloor)$ (normalized)	#Overflows	1.30	2.38	2.38	1.17	1.00	2.00
	#Underflows	1.28	2.38	2.07	1.40	1.00	2.00
	Mem. Traffic	1.86	4.42	5.28	2.33	1.00	6.00
	Cost	1.53	3.33	3.66	1.90	1.00	4.46

TABLE III
FIXED STRATEGIES WITH *tower*

Reg File Size (w)		3	5	7	9	13	17
Best Fixed Strategy		(1,1)	(3,3)	(1,1)	(1,1)	(1,1)	(3,3)
Worst Fixed Strategy		(3,3)	(4,5)	(6,6)	(9,9)	(13,13)	(17,17)
Optimal Strategy (raw)	#Overflows	74898	16912	4128	1026	64	4
	#Underflows	74898	16912	4128	1026	64	4
	Mem. Traffic	262142	65534	16382	4094	254	14
	Cost	8688152	2063264	509792	127064	7904	464
Best Fixed Strategy (normalized)	#Overflows	1.75	1.11	1.98	2.00	1.98	1.00
	#Underflows	1.75	1.11	1.98	2.00	1.98	1.00
	Mem. Traffic	1.00	1.71	1.00	1.00	1.00	1.71
	Cost	1.39	1.42	1.48	1.48	1.48	1.34
Worst Fixed Strategy (normalized)	#Overflows	2.00	4.84	32.26	128.00	64.00	16384.00
	#Underflows	2.00	3.86	32.26	128.00	64.00	16384.00
	Mem. Traffic	3.43	10.00	97.54	577.41	419.28	159158.86
	Cost	2.69	7.23	65.82	359.68	246.87	85309.80
fixed(w,1) (normalized)	#Overflows	1.00	1.00	1.00	1.00	1.00	1.00
	#Underflows	3.00	5.00	7.00	9.00	13.00	17.00
	Mem. Traffic	1.71	2.58	3.53	4.51	6.55	9.71
	Cost	1.86	2.79	3.78	4.75	6.77	9.34
fixed(1,w) (normalized)	#Overflows	3.00	5.00	8.99	8.99	7.00	3.00
	#Underflows	1.00	1.00	1.00	1.00	1.00	1.00
	Mem. Traffic	1.71	2.58	3.52	4.50	3.53	1.71
	Cost	1.86	2.79	3.75	4.74	3.76	1.86
fixed(1,1) (normalized)	#Overflows	1.75	1.94	1.98	2.00	1.98	1.75
	#Underflows	1.75	1.94	1.98	2.00	1.98	1.75
	Mem. Traffic	1.00	1.00	1.00	1.00	1.00	1.00
	Cost	1.39	1.48	1.48	1.48	1.48	1.39
$fixed(\lfloor \frac{w}{2} \rfloor, \lfloor \frac{w}{2} \rfloor)$ (normalized)	#Overflows	2.33	1.11	8.47	16.48	1.00	64.00
	#Underflows	2.33	1.11	8.47	16.48	1.00	64.00
	Mem. Traffic	2.67	1.71	17.07	41.31	3.53	329.14
	Cost	2.49	1.42	12.89	29.28	2.30	192.00

TABLE IV
COST OF REGISTER FILE MANAGEMENT PER PROCEDURE CALL

Reg File Size (w)		3	5	7	9	13	17
Optimal Strategy	rcc	15.01	3.84	1.59	0.77	0.27	0.05
	puzzle	3.62	0.83	0.15	0.04	0.01	0.01
	tower	16.57	3.94	0.97	0.24	0.02	0.00*
Best Fixed Strategy	rcc	19.73	5.77	2.53	1.23	0.39	0.07
	puzzle	4.43	1.11	0.20	0.06	0.01	0.01
	tower	23.00	5.57	1.44	0.36	0.02	0.00*
Worst Fixed Strategy	rcc	47.24	52.00	33.33	19.73	38.70	17.30
	puzzle	52.68	84.71	45.15	6.93	32.59	78.94
	tower	44.57	28.44	64.00	87.17	3.72	75.50

call there is a corresponding *return*. Hence, in this context, "procedure call" includes returning from the procedure as well as invoking it.

The data indicate that, even with the optimal strategy, the cost of managing the register file may become prohibitive if the register file is too small (three register banks). In this case, for two out of the three programs (*rcc* and *tower*), it is likely that a conventional stack mechanism for handling procedure calls would have resulted in better performance. If a larger register file is used, the cost of managing the register file drops sharply. The results indicate that, for a register file of five or more register banks, this scheme compares favorably with the conventional stack mechanism.

Invoking a high-level language procedure and returning from it requires several RISC instructions in addition to those used for managing the register file. Specifically, arguments have to be copied to the area of overlap between the current STACK1 frame and the next STACK1 frame; if the procedure returns a value, it may have to be copied from this overlap area; the stack pointer and frame pointer for STACK2 may need to be updated; the actual RISC *call* and *ret* instructions must be executed. C procedures typically have less than four arguments [5]. Hence, in addition to the RISC instructions that manage the register file, between three and seven instructions will be executed for each procedure call/return pair.

If an efficient strategy (such as the "best fixed strategy") is used, the cost of managing the register file decreases as the number of register banks in the register file increases. Once this cost reaches approximately one RISC instruction per procedure call/return pair (e.g., using the "best fixed strategy" with a register file containing nine register banks), it no longer dominates the total number of instructions required for each procedure call/return. In a single chip VLSI microprocessor, chip area is a precious resource. Rather than adding more register banks (e.g., beyond nine), the limited chip area can be used more effectively for other purposes, such as an on-chip cache or hardware support for multiply, that are likely to make a greater contribution to overall processor performance. Even for the benchmarks used here, which reach a relatively high nesting depth [5], a register file with between five and nine register banks seems optimal.

Choosing a "good" strategy is critical to the success of the register file scheme. Tables II and III show that choosing the "wrong" strategy can result in more than four orders of magnitude increase in the cost of managing the register file. Furthermore, if an inefficient strategy is used, an increase in the register file size can result in an *increase* in the cost of managing the register file (since there is an opportunity to generate more useless memory traffic). In most cases, the best fixed strategy is to minimize the memory traffic (i.e., use the $fixed(1, 1)$ strategy). This can be explained by the fact that the cost of moving one frame to memory and then from memory back to the register file is about the same as the cost of handling the trap when an overflow or underflow occurs. Hence, the immediate cost of unnecessarily moving a frame (which results in one frame's worth of traffic to memory and later back to the register file) is about equal to the cost of not moving a frame when it should have been moved (an extra overflow or underflow trap). In addition, if an unnecessary move is made, the cost may include the cost of an extra overflow or underflow which will occur later. Hence, the "penalty" for moving one more frame than necessary, when an overflow or underflow occurs, is greater than the "penalty" for moving one fewer frame than necessary. Thus, if the call/return sequence is random, the best fixed strategies are likely to be those that require the movement of only one or two frames when an overflow or underflow occurs. The use of such strategies is further supported by the fact that with the optimal strategy, in cases where there are more than ten overflows/underflows throughout the execution of the program, the average number of frames moved when an overflow or underflow occurs is between 1.4 and 3 and in most cases is approximately 2.

C. Taking the Past into Account

The *fixed* strategies do not attempt to take into account the previous behavior of the executing program. It is conceivable that a strategy that does take past behavior into account would result in a lower cost, closer to that of the optimal strategy.

One way of "taking the past into account" involves keeping track of which register banks have been used since the last overflow or underflow. If two or more STACK1 frames are moved whenever an overflow or underflow occurs, it is clear that, in some cases, it will turn out that too many frames will be moved, resulting in unnecessary memory traffic. When an

overflow occurs, register banks are "freed" by copying their contents to memory. If some of the freed register banks remain unused until the next underflow, their contents remain intact and need not be copied from memory to the register file. Similarly, if too many register banks are loaded when an underflow occurs, the contents of those that are unused until the next overflow need not be copied to memory since their contents are already in the appropriate memory locations.

Many practical strategies result in unnecessary memory traffic, i.e., more memory traffic than is required by the optimal strategy. The above technique reduces the memory traffic resulting from any such strategy. Our measurements indicate that with the useless "worst fixed strategy," which produces an exorbitant number of unnecessary moves of STACK1 frames, keeping track of which register banks are used can reduce this memory traffic by up to an order of magnitude. However, with "reasonable" strategies, the gains are less impressive. If the "best fixed strategy" is $fixed(1, 1)$ then clearly no gain is possible. With the $fixed(2, 2)$ strategy, the decrease in memory traffic is less than ten percent. The above technique requires some extra hardware and a few more instructions in the trap handling routine. When the overhead of these extra instructions is taken into account, the total cost of managing the register file for the $fixed(2, 2)$ strategy is about the same as without this extra mechanism. For the $fixed(1, 1)$ strategy, the extra instructions will simply add to the cost of managing the register file without any saving in memory traffic.

We have investigated two other methods for "taking the past into account." They both involve determining the number of frames to be moved when an overflow or underflow occurs based on the previous behavior of the program. The first method (henceforth denoted C/R) is to use the call/return trace immediately preceding the overflow or underflow. The second method (henceforth denoted O/U) is to use the trace of overflows and underflows which preceded the trap being handled.

The C/R method can be implemented by adding a special shift register to the processor. Every call instruction shifts a 1 into the register and every return shifts a 0. The routine which handles the overflow/underflow trap examines the contents of this register and determines the immediately preceding call/return trace of the program. This pattern is used to access a table containing the "optimal" number of frames that should be moved, given a particular call/return pattern. This scheme adds very few instructions to the cost of handling the overflow/underflow trap.

The O/U method does not require any additional hardware. The "overflow/underflow trace" is kept in a fixed memory location and is updated each time an overflow or underflow occurs by the routine that handles these traps. The pattern in this memory location is used in the same way as the contents of the shift register for the C/R method.

Both the C/R method and O/U method require finding a mapping between "call/return patterns" or "overflow/underflow patterns" and "number of frames to be moved" so that the total cost is reduced. In order to find such a mapping (for either one of the methods) we tabulated the optimal number of frames to be moved (which can be found given unbounded look-ahead) following various call/return or overflow/underflow patterns for the three benchmark programs. We attempted to use these tables to determine which patterns indicate that a single frame should be moved and in which cases moving more than one frame would be preferable. However, we could not find a single mapping which worked better than the $fixed(1, 1)$ strategy for all three programs!

For the three benchmark programs used in this work, it appears that the optimal number of frames to be moved is, for all practical purposes, independent of the immediately preceding call/return pattern of length ten or less. The O/U method shows more promise but the results are inconclusive. Following a suggestion by Denning [3], we tested an O/U method which involved moving two frames after two consecutive overflows or underflows and moving one frame otherwise. For register file sizes of interest (between five and nine frames), the cost of managing the register file using this method was compared to the cost using the $fixed(1, 1)$ strategy. Reductions of up to 28 percent in the number of overflows and underflows and increases of up to 59 percent in the memory traffic were measured. When the extra instructions in the trap handling routines are taken into account, the overall cost was either equal to or greater than the cost of the $fixed(1, 1)$ strategy in all but one case.

IV. CONCLUSIONS

The success of the RISC architecture is due, in part, to the reduction in the number of memory accesses which is possible through the use of the register file [11]. We have shown that the effectiveness of the register file is dependent on choosing the "right" size for the register file and an efficient strategy for deciding how many frames should be moved to/from memory when an overflow/underflow occurs.

Our measurements indicate that with the simple $fixed$ strategy, $fixed(1, 1)$, the cost of managing the register file is within a factor of two of the cost of the optimal strategy (which requires unbounded look-ahead). For a register file containing more than eight register banks, the $fixed(2, 2)$ strategy yields slightly better performance.

If a "reasonable" strategy is used, the cost of managing the register file is inversely proportional to its size. If the register file is too small, the number of overflows and underflows becomes prohibitively large. Since the STACK1 frames have a fixed size, the large number of overflows and underflows results in a lot of memory traffic even when the number of registers actually used (for arguments and local variables) is small. Hence, if the register file is too small, the overall cost of procedure calls may be greater than if a conventional stack mechanism is used. Our measurements indicate that if the register file contains five or more frames, the use of the register file scheme rather than a conventional stack mechanism is worthwhile.

We have attempted to use past behavior of the program in order to predict the future behavior and reduce the cost of managing the register file. So far, our attempts have not succeeded.

The first method (keeping track of which register banks have been used since the last overflow or underflow), reduces the cost of managing the register file only for inefficient strategies.

For efficient strategies, such as $fixed(1, 1)$ or $fixed(2, 2)$, the extra overhead in the trap handling routine was greater than the savings from the reduced memory traffic.

The two other methods attempt to determine the "optimal" number of frames to be moved from the immediately preceding pattern of calls/returns or overflows/underflows. These methods appear ineffective since we could not find a single mapping between either type of patterns and number frames to be moved, which reduces the cost for all three programs. These results, while preliminary, raise serious doubts that a mapping which reduces the cost of managing the register file for a majority of programs could be found. Even in this context, the simplest solution appears to also be the best.

APPENDIX
PROOF OF LEMMAS 3–6

Lemma 3: If $K > 1$, then for all k, $1 \leq k < K$,

$$\text{RFM}_Q[1, m_k + 1] \geq k.$$

Proof: By induction on k.

Basis: $k = 1$. It is shown that $\text{RFM}_Q[1, m_1 + 1] \geq 1$. From the algorithm,

$$\max(E_1) - \min(E_1) < w$$

while

$$\max(E_1 \cup \{d_{m_1+1}\}) - \min(E_1 \cup \{d_{m_1+1}\}) \geq w.$$

Hence, either

$$d_{m_1+1} < \min(E_1)$$

or

$$d_{m_1+1} > \max(E_1).$$

By Definition 1, $d_1 = 1$ and $d_i \geq 1$ for all i, $1 \leq i \leq n$. Hence,

$$d_1 = \min(E_1 \cup \{d_{m_1+1}\}) = \min(E_1)$$

and

$$d_{m_1+1} = \max(E_1 \cup \{d_{m_1+1}\}).$$

Thus,

$$d_{m_1+1} - d_1 \geq w.$$

Since Q is a valid RFPS for D, $q_1 \leq d_1 < q_1 + w$ and $q_{m_1+1} \leq d_{m_1+1} < q_{m_1+1} + w$. $d_{m_1+1} \geq d_1 + w$ and $d_1 \geq q_1$ imply that $d_{m_1+1} \geq q_1 + w$. But $q_{m_1+1} + w > d_{m_1+1}$. Hence,

$$q_{m_1+1} + w \geq q_1 + w,$$

i.e., $q_{m_1+1} > q_1$. The fact that $q_{m_1+1} \neq q_1$ implies that at least one RFM occurs in the location range $[2, m_1 + 1]$, so $\text{RFM}_Q[1, m_1 + 1] \geq 1$.

Induction Step: Assuming that this lemma holds for $k = \alpha - 1$, where $2 \leq \alpha < K$, it is now proven that it holds for $k = \alpha$. In other words, assuming $\text{RFM}_Q[1, m_{\alpha-1} + 1] \geq \alpha - 1$, it is proven that $\text{RFM}_Q[1, m_\alpha + 1] \geq \alpha$:

If $\text{RFM}_Q[1, m_{\alpha-1} + 1] \geq \alpha - 1$, then either

$$\text{RFM}_Q[1, m_{\alpha-1} + 1] \geq \alpha$$

or

$$\text{RFM}_Q[1, m_{\alpha-1} + 1] = \alpha - 1.$$

The former case implies that $\text{RFM}_Q[1, m_\alpha + 1] \geq \alpha$ (since $m_\alpha + 1 \geq m_{\alpha-1} + 1$) and the lemma is proved. Hence, we can assume $\text{RFM}_Q[1, m_{\alpha-1} + 1] = \alpha - 1$.

The rest of the proof is similar to the proof of the *basis*: From the algorithm,

$$\max(E_\alpha) - \min(E_\alpha) < w$$

while

$$\max(E_\alpha \cup \{d_{m_\alpha+1}\}) - \min(E_\alpha \cup \{d_{m_\alpha+1}\}) \geq w.$$

Hence, either $d_{m_\alpha+1} < \min(E_\alpha)$ or $d_{m_\alpha+1} > \max(E_\alpha)$.

Assume $d_{m_\alpha+1} < \min(E_\alpha)$:

From the algorithm and the definition of Ψ, $d_{\Psi_\alpha} - d_{m_\alpha+1} \geq w$. Since Q is a valid RFPS for D,

$$q_{\Psi_\alpha} \leq d_{\Psi_\alpha} < q_{\Psi_\alpha} + w$$

and

$$q_{m_\alpha+1} \leq d_{m_\alpha+1} < q_{m_\alpha+1} + w.$$

Hence,

$$q_{\Psi_\alpha} + w > d_{\Psi_\alpha} \geq d_{m_\alpha+1} + w \geq q_{m_\alpha+1} + w,$$

i.e., $q_{\Psi_\alpha} > q_{m_\alpha+1}$.

Assume $d_{m_\alpha+1} > \max(E_\alpha)$:

From the algorithm and the definition of Φ,

$$d_{m_\alpha+1} - d_{\Phi_\alpha} \geq w.$$

Since Q is a valid RFPS for D,

$$q_{\Phi_\alpha} \leq d_{\Phi_\alpha} < q_{\Phi_\alpha} + w$$

and

$$q_{m_\alpha+1} \leq d_{m_\alpha+1} < q_{m_\alpha+1} + w.$$

Hence,

$$q_{m_\alpha+1} + w > d_{m_\alpha+1} \geq d_{\Phi_\alpha} + w \geq q_{\Phi_\alpha} + w,$$

i.e., $q_{m_\alpha+1} > q_{\Phi_\alpha}$.

The fact that $q_{\Psi_\alpha} \neq q_{m_\alpha+1}$ ($q_{\Phi_\alpha} \neq q_{m_\alpha+1}$) implies that there is at least one RFM in the location range $[\Psi_\alpha + 1, m_\alpha + 1]$ ($[\Phi_\alpha + 1, m_\alpha + 1]$). But $\Psi_\alpha \geq m_{\alpha-1} + 1$ ($\Phi_\alpha \geq m_{\alpha-1} + 1$). Hence, there is at least one RFM in the location range $[m_{\alpha-1} + 2, m_\alpha + 1]$, i.e., $\text{RFM}_Q[m_{\alpha-1} + 2, m_\alpha + 1] \geq 1$. But by assumption $\text{RFM}_Q[1, m_{\alpha-1} + 1] = \alpha - 1$. Hence, $\text{RFM}_Q[1, m_\alpha + 1] \geq \alpha$. ∎

Lemma 4: If $K > 1$, then for all k, $1 \leq k \leq K - 1$,

$$d_{\Psi_k} - d_{\Phi_k} = w - 1.$$

Proof: From the algorithm,

$$\max(E_k) - \min(E_k) < w$$

while

$$\max(E_k \cup \{d_{m_k+1}\}) - \min(E_k \cup \{d_{m_k+1}\}) \geq w.$$

Hence, either $d_{m_k+1} < \min(E_k)$ or $d_{m_k+1} > \max(E_k)$.

By Definition 1, $|d_{m_k+1} - d_{m_k}| = 1$. Since $d_{m_k} \in E_k$, either $d_{m_k+1} = \min(E_k) - 1$ or $d_{m+1} = \max(E_k) + 1$. Hence,

$$\max(E_k \cup \{d_{m_k+1}\}) - \min(E_k \cup \{d_{m_k+1}\})$$
$$= \max(E_k) - \min(E_k) + 1.$$

Thus, $\max(E_k) - \min(E_k) \geq w - 1$. But from the algorithm, $\max(E_k) - \min(E_k) \leq w - 1$. Hence,

$$\max(E_k) - \min(E_k) = w - 1,$$

i.e., $d_{\Psi_k} - d_{\Phi_k} = w - 1$. ∎

Lemma 5: If $K > 1$, for all k, $1 \leq k \leq K - 1$, for all i,

$$m_{k-1} + 1 \leq i \leq m_k, p_i = d_{\Phi_k} = d_{\Psi_k} - w + 1.$$

For the last subsequence, i.e., $k = K$: if $\Theta_k = \Phi_k$, then $p_i = d_{\Phi_k}$, else $p_i = d_{\Psi_k} - w + 1$.

Proof: For all i, $1 \leq i \leq n$, the value of p_i is set in step 5 or in step 7 of the algorithm.

If $1 \leq k \leq K - 1$, then by Lemma 4,

$$d_{\Psi_k} - d_{\Phi_k} = w - 1.$$

Hence,

$$d_{\Phi_k} = d_{\Psi_k} - w + 1,$$

and the same value (d_{Φ_k}) will be assigned to p_i in step 5 or step 7 of the algorithm.

If $k = K$, then it may be the case that $d_{\Psi_k} - d_{\Phi_k} < w - 1$. Hence, it may make a difference whether the value of p_i is assigned in step 5 or in step 7. This is controlled by the value of Θ_k.

If $\Theta_k = \Phi_k$, then, by the definition of Θ,

$$d_{\Phi_k} < d_{\Phi_{k-1}}.$$

Since $k - 1 < K$,

$$p_{m_{k-1}} = p_{\Phi_{k-1}} = d_{\Phi_{k-1}}.$$

Hence,

$$\min(E_k) < p_{m_{k-1}},$$

and the second clause in step 4 of the algorithm is satisfied. Thus, p_i ($m_{k-1} + 1 \leq i \leq m_k$) is assigned a value in step 5 of the algorithm. So

$$p_i = d_{\Phi_k}.$$

If $\Theta_k = \Psi_k$, then, by the definition of Θ,

$$d_{\Phi_k} \geq d_{\Phi_{k-1}}.$$

Since $k - 1 < K$,

$$p_{m_{k-1}} = p_{\Phi_{k-1}} = d_{\Phi_{k-1}}.$$

Hence,

$$\min(E_k) \geq p_{m_{k-1}},$$

and the second clause in step 4 of the algorithm is *not* satisfied. Since $k = K$, $m_k = n$, and the first clause in step 4 of the algorithm is also *not* satisfied. Thus, p_i ($m_{k-1} + 1 \leq i \leq m_k$) is assigned a value of step 7 of the algorithm. So

$$p_i = d_{\Psi_k} - w + 1.$$

Lemma 6: If $K > 1$, then for all k, $1 \le k \le K$,

$$\mathrm{MT}_Q[1, O_k] \ge \mathrm{MT}_P[1, O_k] + |q_{O_k} - p_{O_k}|.$$

Proof: By induction on k.

Basis: $k = 1$. It is shown that $\mathrm{MT}_Q[1, O_1] \ge \mathrm{MT}_P[1, O_1] + |q_{O_1} - p_{O_1}|$.

By the definition of O, $O_1 = 1$. Hence,

$$\mathrm{MT}_Q[1, O_1] = \mathrm{MT}_Q[1, 1] = |q_1 - q_0|$$

and

$$\begin{aligned}
\mathrm{MT}_P[1, O_1] + |q_{O_1} - p_{O_1}| &= \mathrm{MT}_P[1, 1] + |q_1 - p_1| \\
&= |p_1 - p_0| + |q_1 - p_1|.
\end{aligned}$$

By Definitions 2 and 5, for all i, $1 \le i \le n$,

$$1 \le q_i \le d_i < q_i + w$$

and

$$1 \le p_i \le d_i < p_i + w.$$

By Definition 1, $d_1 = 1$. Hence, $q_1 = p_1 = 1$. From the algorithm, $p_0 = 1$. Hence,

$$\mathrm{MT}_P[1, O_1] + |q_{O_1} - p_{O_1}| = |p_1 - p_0| + |q_1 - p_1| = 0.$$

Since $|q_1 - q_0| \ge 0$,

$$\mathrm{MT}_Q[1, O_1] \ge 0.$$

Thus,

$$\mathrm{MT}_Q[1, O_1] \ge \mathrm{MT}_P[1, O_1] + |q_{O_1} - p_{O_1}|.$$

Induction Step: Assuming that this lemma holds for $k = \alpha - 1$, where $2 \le \alpha \le K$, it is now proven that it holds for $k = \alpha$. In other words, assuming

$$\mathrm{MT}_Q[1, O_{\alpha-1}] \ge \mathrm{MT}_P[1, O_{\alpha-1}] + |q_{O_{\alpha-1}} - p_{O_{\alpha-1}}|,$$

it is proven that

$$\mathrm{MT}_Q[1, O_\alpha] \ge \mathrm{MT}_P[1, O_\alpha] + |q_{O_\alpha} - p_{O_\alpha}|.$$

From Definition 8,

$$\mathrm{MT}_Q[1, O_\alpha] = \mathrm{MT}_Q[1, O_{\alpha-1}] + \mathrm{MT}_Q[O_{\alpha-1} + 1, O_\alpha]$$

and

$$\mathrm{MT}_P[1, O_\alpha] = \mathrm{MT}_P[1, O_{\alpha-1}] + \mathrm{MT}_P[O_{\alpha-1} + 1, O_\alpha].$$

Using the induction hypothesis,

$$\begin{aligned}
\mathrm{MT}_Q[1, O_\alpha] \ge{}& \mathrm{MT}_P[1, O_{\alpha-1}] + |q_{O_{\alpha-1}} - p_{O_{\alpha-1}}| \\
&+ \mathrm{MT}_Q[O_{\alpha-1} + 1, O_\alpha].
\end{aligned}$$

$\mathrm{MT}_Q[O_{\alpha-1} + 1, O_\alpha]$ is the number of STACK1 frames transferred to/from memory in location range $[O_{\alpha-1} + 1, O_\alpha]$. A change by one in the RFP indicates that one STACK1 frame is transferred to or from memory. Hence, the memory traffic in location range $[O_{\alpha-1} + 1, O_\alpha]$ is at least the difference between the RFP at the beginning of the range and the RFP at the end of the range, i.e.,

$$\mathrm{MT}_Q[O_{\alpha-1} + 1, O_\alpha] \ge |q_{O_\alpha} - q_{O_{\alpha-1}}|.$$

Hence,

$$\begin{aligned}
\mathrm{MT}_Q[1, O_\alpha] \ge{}& \mathrm{MT}_P[1, O_{\alpha-1}] + |q_{O_{\alpha-1}} - p_{O_{\alpha-1}}| \\
&+ |q_{O_\alpha} - q_{O_{\alpha-1}}|.
\end{aligned}$$

From Definition 8 and the algorithm,

$$\begin{aligned}
\mathrm{MT}_P[O_{\alpha-1} + 1, O_\alpha] &= \sum_{\beta = O_{\alpha-1}+1}^{O_\alpha} |p_\beta - p_{\beta-1}| \\
&= \sum_{\beta = O_{\alpha-1}+1}^{m_{\alpha-1}} |p_\beta - p_{\beta-1}| + |p_{m_{\alpha-1}+1} - p_{m_{\alpha-1}}| \\
&\quad + \sum_{\beta = m_{\alpha-1}+2}^{O_\alpha} |p_\beta - p_{\beta-1}| = |p_{m_{\alpha-1}+1} - p_{m_{\alpha-1}}|.
\end{aligned}$$

Since $\alpha - 1 < K$, by Lemma 5, $p_{m_{\alpha-1}} = d_{\Phi_{\alpha-1}}$. From the algorithm, $p_{m_{\alpha-1}+1} = p_{m_\alpha}$. Hence,

$$\mathrm{MT}_P[O_{\alpha-1} + 1, O_\alpha] = |p_{m_\alpha} - d_{\Phi_{\alpha-1}}|.$$

Thus,

$$\mathrm{MT}_P[1, O_\alpha] = \mathrm{MT}_P[1, O_{\alpha-1}] + |p_{m_\alpha} - d_{\Phi_{\alpha-1}}|.$$

In the rest of the proof, the following four cases will be handled separately:

Case A: $O_\alpha = \Phi_\alpha$ and $O_{\alpha-1} = \Phi_{\alpha-1}$
Case B: $O_\alpha = \Phi_\alpha$ and $O_{\alpha-1} = \Psi_{\alpha-1}$
Case C: $O_\alpha = \Psi_\alpha$ and $O_{\alpha-1} = \Phi_{\alpha-1}$
Case D: $O_\alpha = \Psi_\alpha$ and $O_{\alpha-1} = \Psi_{\alpha-1}$.

Case A: $O_\alpha = \Phi_\alpha$ and $O_{\alpha-1} = \Phi_{\alpha-1}$:

$$\begin{aligned}
|q_{O_{\alpha-1}} - p_{O_{\alpha-1}}| + |q_{O_\alpha} - q_{O_{\alpha-1}}| \\
= |q_{\Phi_{\alpha-1}} - p_{\Phi_{\alpha-1}}| + |q_{\Phi_\alpha} - q_{\Phi_{\alpha-1}}| \\
= |p_{\Phi_{\alpha-1}} - q_{\Phi_{\alpha-1}}| + |q_{\Phi_{\alpha-1}} - q_{\Phi_\alpha}| \ge p_{\Phi_{\alpha-1}} - q_{\Phi_{\alpha-1}} \\
+ q_{\Phi_{\alpha-1}} - q_{\Phi_\alpha} = p_{\Phi_{\alpha-1}} - q_{\Phi_\alpha} \\
= (p_{\Phi_{\alpha-1}} - p_{\Phi_\alpha}) + (p_{\Phi_\alpha} - q_{\Phi_\alpha}).
\end{aligned}$$

By Lemma 5, since $O_\alpha = \Phi_\alpha$ and $\alpha - 1 < K$, $p_{\Phi_\alpha} = d_{\Phi_\alpha}$ and $p_{\Phi_{\alpha-1}} = d_{\Phi_{\alpha-1}}$. Hence,

$$\begin{aligned}
|q_{O_{\alpha-1}} - p_{O_{\alpha-1}}| + |q_{O_\alpha} - q_{O_{\alpha-1}}| \\
\ge (d_{\Phi_{\alpha-1}} - d_{\Phi_\alpha}) + (d_{\Phi_\alpha} - q_{\Phi_\alpha}).
\end{aligned}$$

Since Q is a valid RFPS for D,

$$q_{\Phi_\alpha} \le d_{\Phi_\alpha} < q_{\Phi_\alpha} + w.$$

Hence, $(d_{\Phi_\alpha} - q_{\Phi_\alpha}) \ge 0$. Thus,

$$|q_{O_{\alpha-1}} - p_{O_{\alpha-1}}| + |q_{O_\alpha} - q_{O_{\alpha-1}}| \ge d_{\Phi_{\alpha-1}} - d_{\Phi_\alpha}.$$

From the definition of O, since $O_\alpha = \Phi_\alpha$, $d_{\Phi_{\alpha-1}} > d_{\Phi_\alpha}$. Hence,

$$d_{\Phi_{\alpha-1}} - d_{\Phi_\alpha} = |d_{\Phi_{\alpha-1}} - d_{\Phi_\alpha}|.$$

Thus,

$$|q_{O_{\alpha-1}} - p_{O_{\alpha-1}}| + |q_{O_\alpha} - q_{O_{\alpha-1}}| \ge |d_{\Phi_{\alpha-1}} - d_{\Phi_\alpha}|.$$

Therefore,

$$\mathrm{MT}_Q[1, O_\alpha] \ge \mathrm{MT}_P[1, O_{\alpha-1}] + |d_{\Phi_{\alpha-1}} - d_{\Phi_\alpha}|.$$

By Lemma 5, since $O_\alpha = \Phi_\alpha$, $p_{m_\alpha} = d_{\Phi_\alpha}$. Hence,

$$\mathrm{MT}_P[1, O_\alpha] = \mathrm{MT}_P[1, O_{\alpha-1}] + |d_{\Phi_\alpha} - d_{\Phi_{\alpha-1}}|.$$

Thus,

$$MT_Q[1, \Theta_\alpha] \geq MT_P[1, \Theta_\alpha].$$

Case B: $\Theta_\alpha = \Phi_\alpha$ and $\Theta_{\alpha-1} = \Psi_{\alpha-1}$:

$$|q_{\Theta_{\alpha-1}} - p_{\Theta_{\alpha-1}}| + |q_{\Theta_\alpha} - q_{\Theta_{\alpha-1}}|$$
$$= |q_{\Psi_{\alpha-1}} - p_{\Psi_{\alpha-1}}| + |q_{\Phi_\alpha} - q_{\Psi_{\alpha-1}}|$$
$$= |p_{\Psi_{\alpha-1}} - q_{\Psi_{\alpha-1}}| + |q_{\Psi_{\alpha-1}} - q_{\Phi_\alpha}| \geq p_{\Psi_{\alpha-1}}$$
$$- q_{\Psi_{\alpha-1}} + q_{\Psi_{\alpha-1}} - q_{\Phi_\alpha} = p_{\Psi_{\alpha-1}} - q_{\Phi_\alpha}.$$

From the algorithm, $p_{\Psi_{\alpha-1}} = p_{\Phi_{\alpha-1}}$. Hence,

$$|q_{\Theta_{\alpha-1}} - p_{\Theta_{\alpha-1}}| + |q_{\Theta_\alpha} - q_{\Theta_{\alpha-1}}| \geq p_{\Phi_{\alpha-1}} - q_{\Phi_\alpha}.$$

The rest of the proof for this case is identical to the proof of Case A.

Case C: $\Theta_\alpha = \Psi_\alpha$ and $\Theta_{\alpha-1} = \Phi_{\alpha-1}$:

$$|q_{\Theta_{\alpha-1}} - p_{\Theta_{\alpha-1}}| + |q_{\Theta_\alpha} - q_{\Theta_{\alpha-1}}|$$
$$= |q_{\Phi_{\alpha-1}} - p_{\Phi_{\alpha-1}}| + |q_{\Psi_\alpha} - q_{\Phi_{\alpha-1}}|$$
$$\geq q_{\Phi_{\alpha-1}} - p_{\Phi_{\alpha-1}} + q_{\Psi_\alpha} - q_{\Phi_{\alpha-1}} = q_{\Psi_\alpha} - p_{\Phi_{\alpha-1}}$$
$$= (q_{\Psi_\alpha} - p_{\Phi_\alpha}) + (p_{\Phi_\alpha} - p_{\Phi_{\alpha-1}}).$$

By Lemma 5, since $\Theta_\alpha = \Psi_\alpha$ and $\alpha - 1 < K, p_{\Phi_\alpha} = d_{\Psi_\alpha} - w + 1$ and $p_{\Phi_{\alpha-1}} = d_{\Phi_{\alpha-1}}$. Hence,

$$|q_{\Theta_{\alpha-1}} - p_{\Theta_{\alpha-1}}| + |q_{\Theta_\alpha} - q_{\Theta_{\alpha-1}}| \geq (q_{\Psi_\alpha} - d_{\Psi_\alpha} + w - 1)$$
$$+ (d_{\Psi_\alpha} - w + 1 - d_{\Phi_{\alpha-1}}).$$

Since Q is a valid RFPS for D,

$$q_{\Psi_\alpha} \leq d_{\Psi_\alpha} < q_{\Psi_\alpha} + w.$$

Hence, $q_{\Psi_\alpha} - d_{\Psi_\alpha} + w > 0$, so

$$q_{\Psi_\alpha} - d_{\Psi_\alpha} + w - 1 \geq 0.$$

Thus,

$$|q_{\Theta_{\alpha-1}} - p_{\Theta_{\alpha-1}}| + |q_{\Theta_\alpha} - q_{\Theta_{\alpha-1}}| \geq d_{\Psi_\alpha} - w + 1 - d_{\Phi_{\alpha-1}}.$$

From the definition of Θ, since $\Theta_\alpha = \Psi_\alpha, d_{\Phi_\alpha} > d_{\Phi_{\alpha-1}}$. From the algorithm,

$$\max(E_{\alpha-1}) - \min(E_{\alpha-1}) < w$$

while

$$\max(E_{\alpha-1} \cup \{d_{m_{\alpha-1}+1}\}) - \min(E_{\alpha-1} \cup \{d_{m_{\alpha-1}+1}\}) \geq w.$$

Hence, either $d_{m_{\alpha-1}+1} < d_{\Phi_{\alpha-1}}$ or $d_{m_{\alpha-1}+1} > d_{\Psi_{\alpha-1}}$. In this case, since $d_{\Phi_\alpha} > d_{\Phi_{\alpha-1}}$ and $d_{m_{\alpha-1}+1} \geq d_{\Phi_\alpha}$, it must be true that $d_{m_{\alpha-1}+1} > d_{\Psi_{\alpha-1}}$. By the definition of Ψ, $d_{\Psi_\alpha} \geq d_{m_{\alpha-1}+1}$. Hence,

$$d_{\Psi_\alpha} > d_{\Psi_{\alpha-1}}.$$

By Lemma 4, since $\alpha - 1 < K, d_{\Psi_{\alpha-1}} = d_{\Phi_{\alpha-1}} + w - 1$. Hence, $d_{\Psi_\alpha} > d_{\Phi_{\alpha-1}} + w - 1$, so

$$d_{\Psi_\alpha} - w + 1 - d_{\Phi_{\alpha-1}} > 0.$$

Thus,

$$d_{\Psi_\alpha} - w + 1 - d_{\Phi_{\alpha-1}} = |d_{\Psi_\alpha} - w + 1 - d_{\Phi_{\alpha-1}}|.$$

By Lemma 5, since $\Theta_\alpha = \Psi_\alpha, p_{m_\alpha} = d_{\Psi_\alpha} - w + 1$. Hence,

$$|q_{\Theta_{\alpha-1}} - p_{\Theta_{\alpha-1}}| + |q_{\Theta_\alpha} - q_{\Theta_{\alpha-1}}| \geq |p_{m_\alpha} - d_{\Phi_{\alpha-1}}|.$$

Therefore,

$$MT_Q[1, \Theta_\alpha] \geq MT_P[1, \Theta_{\alpha-1}] + |p_{m_\alpha} - d_{\Phi_{\alpha-1}}|.$$

It has been shown above that $MT_P[1, \Theta_\alpha] = MT_P[1, \Theta_{\alpha-1}] + |p_{m_\alpha} - d_{\Phi_{\alpha-1}}|$. Hence,

$$MT_Q[1, \Theta_\alpha] \geq MT_P[1, \Theta_\alpha].$$

Case D: $\Theta_\alpha = \Psi_\alpha$ and $\Theta_{\alpha-1} = \Psi_{\alpha-1}$:

$$|q_{\Theta_{\alpha-1}} - p_{\Theta_{\alpha-1}}| + |q_{\Theta_\alpha} - q_{\Theta_{\alpha-1}}|$$
$$= |q_{\Psi_{\alpha-1}} - p_{\Psi_{\alpha-1}}| + |q_{\Psi_\alpha} - q_{\Psi_{\alpha-1}}|$$
$$\geq q_{\Psi_{\alpha-1}} - p_{\Psi_{\alpha-1}} + q_{\Psi_\alpha} - q_{\Psi_{\alpha-1}} = q_{\Psi_\alpha} - p_{\Psi_{\alpha-1}}.$$

From the algorithm, $p_{\Psi_{\alpha-1}} = p_{\Phi_{\alpha-1}}$. Hence,

$$|q_{\Theta_{\alpha-1}} - p_{\Theta_{\alpha-1}}| + |q_{\Theta_\alpha} - q_{\Theta_{\alpha-1}}| \geq q_{\Psi_\alpha} - p_{\Phi_{\alpha-1}}.$$

The rest of the proof for this case is identical to the proof of Case C.

∎

ACKNOWLEDGMENT

We would like to thank P. Denning, D. Ferrari, M. Katevenis, J. Ousterhout, R. Sherburne, and A. Smith for their useful suggestions on improving this paper and D. Patterson for his help with the development of some of the initial RISC analysis tools.

REFERENCES

[1] L. A. Belady, "A study of replacement algorithms for a virtual storage computer," *IBM Syst. J.*, vol. 5, no. 2, pp. 78–101, 1966.
[2] R. Campbell, "A C compiler for RISC," M.S. rep., Univ. California, Berkeley, Dec. 1980.
[3] P. J. Denning, private communication, May 1982.
[4] *VAX11 Architecture Handbook*, Digital Equipment Corp., 1979.
[5] D. Halbert and P. Kessler, "Windows of overlapping register frames," in *CS292R Final Project Reports* (unpublished), Univ. California, Berkeley, June 1980, pp. 82–100.
[6] S. C. Johnson, "A portable compiler: Theory and practice," in *Proc. 5th ACM Symp. Principles of Programming Languages*, Jan. 1978, pp. 97–104.
[7] B. W. Kernighan and D. M. Ritchie, *The C Programming Language.* Englewood Cliffs, NJ: Prentice-Hall, 1978.
[8] D. A. Patterson and C. H. Séquin, "RISC I: A reduced instruction set VLSI computer," in *Proc. 8th Annu. Symp. Comput. Architecture*, Minneapolis, MN, May 1981, pp. 443–457.
[9] ——, "A VLSI RISC," *Computer*, vol. 15, pp. 8–21, Sept. 1982.
[10] A. J. Smith, "Cache memories," *Comput. Surveys*, vol. 14, pp. 473–530, Sept. 1982.
[11] Y. Tamir, "Simulation and performance evaluation of the RISC architecture," Electron. Res. Lab., Univ. California, Berkeley, Memo. UCB/ERL, M81/17, Mar. 1981.

Yuval Tamir (S'78) received the B.S.E.E. degree ("with highest distinction") from the University of Iowa, Iowa City, in 1979 and the M.S. degree in electrical engineering and computer science from the University of California, Berkeley, in 1981.

Since 1979 he has been a Research Assistant in the Electronics Research Laboratory at U.C. Berkeley where he is currently working on his Ph.D. dissertation. His research interests are fault-tolerant computing, computer architecture, and distributed systems.

Mr. Tamir is a student member of the IEEE Computer Society and the Association for Computing Machinery.

Carlo H. Séquin (M'71-SM'80-F'82) received the Ph.D. degree in experimental physics from the University of Basel, Basel, Switzerland, in 1969.

In 1969-1970 he performed postdoctoral work at the Institute of Applied Physics, University of Basel, which concerned interface physics of MOS transistors and problems of applied electronics in the field of cybernetic models. From 1970 to 1976 he worked at Bell Laboratories, Murray Hill, NJ, in the MOS Integrated Circuit Laboratory on the design and investigation of charge-coupled devices for imaging and signal processing applications. He spent 1976-1977 on leave of absence with the University of California, Berkeley, where he lectured on integrated circuits, logic design, and microprocessors. In 1977 he joined the faculty in the Department of Electrical Engineering and Computer Sciences, where he is Professor of Computer Science. Since 1980 he has headed the CS Division as Associate Chairman for Computer Sciences. His research interests lie in the field of computer architecture and design tools for very large scale integrated systems. In particular, his research concerns multimicroprocessor computer networks, the mutual influence of advanced computer architectures and modern VLSI technology, and the implementation of special functions in silicon. Since 1977 he has been teaching courses in structured MOS-LSI design. He is an author of the first book on charge-transfer devices, and has written many papers in that field.

Dr. Séquin is a member of the Association for Computing Machinery and the Swiss Physical Society.

Analyzing Multiple Register Sets

Charles Y. Hitchcock III and H. M. Brinkley Sprunt

Department of Electrical and Computer Engineering

Carnegie-Mellon University

Pittsburgh, PA 15213

Abstract

This paper summarizes results from recent experiments which quantify the performance effects of multiple register sets on computer architectures[1]. These experiments started with the simulation of procedure-intensive benchmarks on three different computer architectures which had various register set schemes added to them. The results from these simulations were dramatic, yet they were difficult to interpret since many interacting factors were involved. This led to a more focussed study to characterize the parameter passing and procedure context switching costs of various register set schemes. The basic hypothesis behind this work, that the performance gains from multiple register sets are independent of instruction set complexity, is supported by the results. Also of interest is the perspective this study gives on the interactions between parameter passing, procedure state saving, and machine architecture.

Introduction

As members of the Archons project [6] at CMU, we are interested in decentralized resource management and are considering computer architectures to "support" such a system. The RISC (Reduced Instruction Set Computer) advocates are prescribing minimalist architectures tied to single-cycle implementations to obtain the high performance that we desire. This stands in stark contrast to our CISC (Complex Instruction Set Computer) tendency to migrate complex functions, ones that might perform interprocess communication or resource allocation, into an architecture. Naturally, we examined the RISC literature to see what we might gain from such an approach.

The many papers about the RISC I[2] project at Berkeley have claimed impressive performance for this single-chip processor. In spite of these attractive results, we were unable to see the RISC I as constituting proof that RISC machines are superior. The results were inconclusive because the RISC I's performance is not solely determined by its instruction set, but is also aided by a powerful scheme of multiple register sets (MRSs).

Most computer architectures that employ general purpose registers have their single logical register set implemented as a single physical register set (SRS). Yet for many years designers have made computers that physically contain multiple register sets (MRSs). These MRSs were usually used to retain the state of multiple processes. For example, up to 32 processes' states could be maintained in the SDS Sigma 7 computer (circa 1966). Such an MRS scheme can, however, be used to cache the procedure state of a single process. Rather than having to save the local variables, temporary values, and parameters contained in the register set during a procedure call, a new, empty register set is provided. Procedure calls and returns become largely a matter of changing a pointer which determines the active physical register set. Furthermore, these register sets can overlap so that parameters can be passed between procedures without the cost of moving them to and from memory. Such overlapping was done on the BELLMAC-8, although its "registers" are mapped into main memory. A detailed description of an overlapping register set (ORS) scheme is found in [7], with a designer's overview in [4].

It was impossible to draw conclusions about the effects of the RISC I's "reduced" nature since its ORS performance was not factored out of its reported results. This lack of differentiation moved us to do our own experiments to calibrate the effects that ORS and MRS schemes can have on a computer architecture. It was believed that such effects would be completely orthogonal to an architecture's instruction set complexity. A previous paper [1] outlined the goals of this study, along with those of a complementary set of experiments. [2] The results from this MRS exploration [5] are summarized here.

---

[1]This research is sponsored in part by the Department of the Army under contract DAA B07-82-C-J164

[2]In this paper, the term *RISC* always refers to a computer design philosophy, while *RISC I* refers to a particular research project.

Ideally, the goal of this study would have been to answer the question "What are the effects and costs involved in incorporating multiple register sets in a computer architecture?" This question could be broken down into these five issues:

1. In what ways is an architecture's performance changed by incorporating multiple register sets?

2. What changes are necessary to a machine's instruction set and internal structures to support such register sets?

3. How do multiple register sets affect the task of writing a compiler for an architecture?

4. What is the impact of multiple register sets on a machine which needs quick context swaps?

5. How does the choice of high-level language or application affect the usefulness of multiple register sets?

While we hoped to explore these and other considerations, our focus was on gauging the effects that MRSs can have on an architecture's performance experimentally, the first issue listed above. In implementing our experiments, we were forced to think about and make decisions involving the other four issues.

Experimental Methodology

To establish the performance effects of MRSs, we decided to run a series of simulations. First, we would simulate benchmarks on an existing machine that has a single set of general purpose registers. We would then alter its architecture to include eight register sets and repeat the simulations. Any difference observed would be attributable to the MRSs. Similarly, we could alter the architecture to include an ORS scheme and again observe the effects.

The key metric used in this study is processor-memory traffic, a metric indicative of an architecture's performance and independent of any particular implementation. Processor-memory traffic is an especially good metric for studying MRSs. This is because the use of MRS is predicated on reducing the amount of data traffic produced by procedure calls, which is often the most costly high-level language operation in terms of memory

references. [7] It is also worth noting that processor-memory traffic does accurately characterize the performance of machines that saturate their memory busses, as does the RISC I.

Note that this study only claims to make valid intra-machine comparisons. These experiments were designed to vary only register structures within an architecture so as to expose the effects of MRSs. We believe that the performance differences produced by altered register structures can largely be characterized by our chosen metrics. The differences between architectures cannot be expressed so simply. As such, drawing conclusions by comparing results from different architectures is not valid. We added eight register sets to the CISC machines since the RISC I had eight register sets. This was done only to allow the *trends* between machines to be comparable, not to make cross-architecture comparisons valid.

Three variations of simulators were created for three different architectures. MRSs and ORSs were "added" to the DEC VAX/11 and the Motorola 68000, both originally SRS machines. The third architecture, RISC I, already had these features. Two additional RISC I's were created, one with multiple non-overlapping register sets and one with only a single register set. These three architectures were chosen because they all use general-purpose registers, both RISC and CISC were represented, and reasonable software support was available for each. Furthermore, the two CISCs are commercial successes and were the subjects of previous RISC studies.

Of course, programs were needed to exercise these simulators. The obvious source for such programs was Berkeley. They had gathered a number of C benchmarks for their RISC I studies and some of these were purposefully procedure-intensive so as to demonstrate the power of ORSs. Since ORS, MRS, and SRS variations of the same machine should perform identically when not executing procedure calls, we concentrated on highly-recursive benchmarks hoping that these would expose the effects of MRSs most dramatically. If so, then they would provide a good means of testing the hypothesis that MRS performance benefits are orthogonal to instruction set complexity. It should be emphasized, however, that the benchmarks we used are not necessarily representative of any "real" computing environment but are merely used to examine the effects of MRSs.

Most of the modifications necessary to conduct our experiments were hardware changes; however, it was also necessary in some cases to modify the software. The SRS and MRS variations of the architectures examined in this study can run the same code. The actual operations performed during the call and return instruction sequences of the MRS machines do change to make use of the MRSs, but the instruction sequence itself is unaltered. The code for the ORS machines, however, does need to be modified. This is because the parameters are passed by a different mechanism, via overlapped registers instead of a memory stack. While reworking a compiler could produce the desired result, it was much easier for us to change the assembly code by hand. Altering it in a rote fashion was simple since only the parameter-passing code had to be changed. Care was taken not to introduce any special optimizations in the process. If an aspect of the alteration was in doubt, the result was modelled as closely as possible to the RISC I code, which was compiled and optimized by software.

Results and Interpretation

The results from these experiments support the hypothesis that the performance effects of multiple register sets are orthogonal to the complexity of an architecture's instruction set. The MRS and ORS versions of the VAX and the 68000 both show decreases in processor-memory traffic when compared to the standard versions of these architectures, as seen in Figures 1 and 2. Similarly, the SRS version of RISC I requires many more memory reads and writes than does the standard RISC I with overlapped register sets (see Figure 3). The procedure intensive benchmarks Towers of Hanoi, Fibonnacci, and Ackermann probably do not represent any typical application environment, but they do show the effects of the multiple and overlapped register set mechanisms.

Though each of these architectures exhibits a decrease in processor-memory traffic from the SRS to ORS versions, the average decrease is greatest for RISC I (68% as compared to 53% for the 68000 and 45% for the VAX). The RISC I shows a large decrease partly because the same overflow/underflow scheme used by the standard ORS RISC I is also used for both the MRS and SRS versions. This scheme always saves/restores 16 registers (10 local and 6 overlap) on every overflow/underflow regardless of whether these

registers are being used or not. The reason for using this scheme was to make the MRS and SRS versions as close to the original architecture as possible. The scheme's effect is most dramatic when only one register set is available since every call or return must save or restore 16 registers, as in the SRS version. A more reasonable save/restore scheme is used by both the 68000 and the VAX in which each procedure has a mask specifying the registers that the procedure will modify. Only the specified registers are saved and restored on procedure boundaries. Though the mask register scheme is not optimal, it is much more efficient for procedures which do not use many registers.

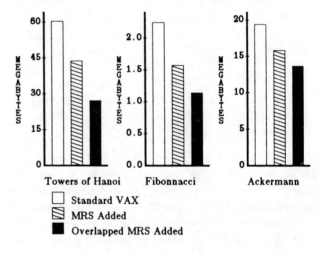

Figure 1: Total processor-memory traffic for benchmarks on the standard VAX and two modified VAXes, one with multiple register sets and one with overlapping multiple register sets.

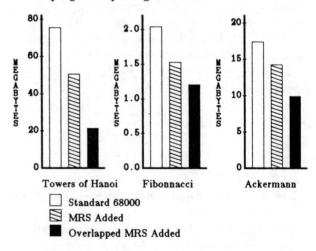

Figure 2: Total processor-memory traffic for benchmarks on the standard 68000 and two modified 68000's, one with multiple register sets and one with overlapping multiple register sets.

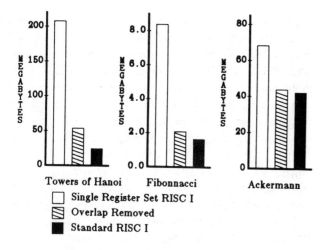

Single Register Set RISC I
Overlap Removed
Standard RISC I

Figure 3: Total processor-memory traffic for benchmarks on the standard RISC I and two modified RISC I's, one with no overlap between register sets and one with only one register set.

To examine further the effect of the register saving/restoring scheme a register mask scheme similar to those of the VAX and 68000 was added to the SRS version of the RISC I. This addition does increase the complexity of the RISC I but it is a reasonable change since the required chip area would be made available by reducing the number of register sets from eight to one. The results from this new simulator are presented in Figure 4. As expected, the amount of processor-memory traffic for the register mask SRS versions dropped significantly. The most interesting result is that the register mask SRS RISC I performs <u>better</u> than the standard ORS RISC I on Ackerman's function. This behavior is counter-intuitive for three reasons:

1. SRS versions of an architecture typically do not perform better than ORS versions.

2. Ackermann's function performs better on the register mask SRS version of RISC I while Hanoi and Fibonnacci do not.

3. The VAX and the 68000 do not show similar behavior even though they use register mask schemes.

A better understanding of these benchmarks and the multiple register set mechanisms is needed to explain this seemingly anomalous behavior.

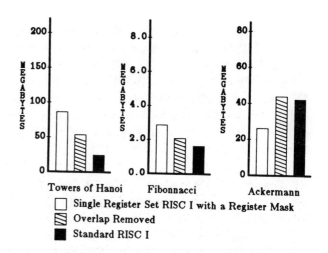

Single Register Set RISC I with a Register Mask
Overlap Removed
Standard RISC I

Figure 4: Total processor-memory traffic for benchmarks on the standard RISC I and two modified RISC I's, one with no overlap between register sets and one with a single register set which makes use of a register mask to indicate which registers should be saved and restored on procedure calls and returns.

Each of these benchmarks are similar in that they perform a lot of procedure calls but they are very different in the number of procedure calls per overflow of the register file. For the standard ORS RISC I with eight overlapping register sets, the number of calls per overflow is 2 for Ackermann, 22 for Fibonnacci, and 65 for Hanoi. RISC I's register file overflows very often while executing Ackermann's function whereas overflows are rare for Fibonnacci and Hanoi. It is this difference in the number of calls per overflow that accounts for the apparent discrepancy in the performance of the register mask SRS RISC I on these benchmarks.

The register mask SRS RISC I performs better than the standard ORS RISC I on Ackermann's function because the register mask SRS version saves and restores less state than the standard ORS version does. The difference between the SRS versions of RISC I in Figures 3 and 4 is solely attributable to the processor-memory traffic overhead due state saving and restoring on register file overflows. Using the standard state saving/restoring scheme for the SRS RISC I is very wasteful since overflows occur on every procedure call. The register mask scheme for the SRS RISC I is not as wasteful; it decreases the processor memory traffic for each benchmark by better than 50%.

This explanation of the seemingly anomalous be- havior reminds us that two performance issues are being tested here: parameter passing efficiency and state saving and restoring efficiency. To properly evaluate test these MRS mechanisms, these perfor- mance factors should not be mixed together as they are in these benchmarks. Doing so made interpret- ing our benchmark results difficult for several reasons:

- While the benchmarks were picked to dis- play the effects of MRSs, it is difficult to attribute performance differences to actual mechanism differences. Determining when an observed difference is due to parameter passing changes or to a new overflow- handling strategy requires detailed ex- amination of instruction count summaries and memory traffic counts. The amount of non-procedure call activity that these benchmarks perform further obfuscates the results.

- Performance predictions are difficult to generalize or adapt for a specific applica- tion. If a particular application generally uses many more parameters or exhibits a fairly unusual call/return profile, then it is not obvious how the performance of any of these schemes would change. The benchmark results are not helpful in this regard. While they might show perfor- mance trends, they can not be used to analyze performance for a real workload.

- Even small changes made to the parameter passing or call instruction mechanisms can dramatically affect the benchmark results. Trying a whole spectrum of mechanism variations would be appealing if it were not for the limited result interpretation due to the factors mentioned.

- The benchmarks do not represent any realistic computing environment. Ackermann's function was used only to show procedure call performance since this operation dominates this program's execu- tion. Yet, its worth for showing the per- formance of an MRS architecture is dubious since its call per overflow rate is so low.

In considering these factors, a more narrow analysis of the mechanisms involved provides more easily in- terpreted results. Similarly, determining memory traffic as a function of the architecture and environment-related factors, such as the average number of parameters to be passed, yields more general results.

The original interest of this study was the perfor- mance of various parameter passing schemes and the efficiency of using MRSs. By coding the call/return sequences of hypothetical or real ar- chitectures, it is possible to generate equations that describe the performance of various parameter pass- ing schemes in terms of instruction and data traffic. By properly parameterizing these equations, a general gauge of performance is obtained. The next section examines the creation and use of equations to compare parameter passing schemes, while the one following it evaluates different state saving strategies.

Call Sequence Costs

In order to analyze the costs involved in a call/return sequence, we first list the operations that are involved. The actions that characterize a call/return sequence are:

1. Prepare any parameters for passing: This code, if necessary, would move any parameters into position, onto a parameter passing stack for instance. Often these moves can be optimized away since some parameters are calculated into position be- fore the call.

2. Call the procedure: This instruction places the processor in a new procedure context. We are not concerned with the method of creating a new (empty) procedure context here. (Explicit calculations that compare mechanisms that prepare a new procedure context are developed in the next section.) The saving of registers in use, and similar state preserving functions, are presumed to be free.

3. Prepare parameters for use by procedure: Sometimes parameters are moved into the CPU before they are used in a calculation. If this movement is done as part of a cal- culation which uses the parameter (i.e., is not done in a separate instruction), then this code is not explicitly present and, hence, does not add to the procedure call's overhead.

4. Prepare any result for return: This code is analogous to that for preparing a parameter to be passed.

5. Return from procedure: This instruction returns the processor to the caller's procedure context. As with the call instruction, the restoration of procedure state is assumed to be free.

6. Prepare the result for use: This code is analogous to that for preparing parameters for use.

We will examine an example of such code, and the equation that derives from it. The code that characterizes the RISC I's call/return sequence is:

```
a.   add r0, rParam, rOverlap
b.   call r15, destination
c.   nop
** change to the called procedure context **
d.   add r0, rOverlap, rUse
** body of called procedure is executed **
e.   add r0, rResult, rOverlap
f.   ret  r31
g.   nop
** change back to calling procedure context **
h.   add rOverlap, r0, rUse
```

Each of the above operations is described below:

a. Move parameter to an overlap register, repeat as necessary for multiple parameters.

b. Branch to a new procedure, saving the old PC in register 15.

c. Insert a NOP if necessary (RISC I branching is delayed and often another instruction is placed here).

d. Move parameter into a register to be used, repeat for multiple parameters.

e. Move result to overlap register.

f. Return to calling the procedure, restoring the PC with register 31's value (the calling procedure's register 15).

g. Insert a NOP if necessary (RISC I branching is delayed and often another instruction is here).

h. Move result out of the overlap area.

Note that (a.) (d.) (e.) and (h.) can sometimes be optimized away.

By counting the instruction bytes for the above code, we calculate the call/return overhead for a highly unoptimized call with a single parameter which receives a single result. By generating equations which characterize number of parameters, whether there is a result, and the likelihood of optimizations, a far more general result is produced.

Total Memory Bytes Transferred:
$$= \text{Sum of instruction bytes from (a.) to (h.)}$$
$$= 4[N(PP + TP) + R(PR + TR) + CN + RN + 2]$$

where

N - number of parameters
PP - fraction of prepare parameter moves (a.)
CN - fraction of nop's following calls (c.)
TP - fraction of take parameter moves (d.)
R - fraction of returns that produce a result
PR - fraction of prepare result moves (e.)
RN - fraction of nop's following returns (g.)
TR - fraction of take result moves (h.)

To be of any specific use, actual values for these variables need to be found for the application code of interest. For this study, values were borrowed from existing analyses where possible (see [3] for a good summary). If unavailable, they were estimated based on samples of code. This was often the case since many code characteristics which are of interest when analyzing MRS machines, such as calls per overflow, have not commonly been measured. It should be stressed here that the values we used and the results from our equations are not meant to be definitive. They do, however, result from a process that can be adapted to known applications.

When analyzing the RISC I in this way, the considerations leading to its call/return overhead equation are few. This is largely due to its load/store ORS architecture and its 32 bit implementation. For a 68000 using a memory stack to pass parameters, many more complications arise:

• Traffic created by data reads and writes needs to be counted.

• Different addressing modes can be used which vary the instruction size.

• Parameters can vary in size (byte, halfword, word).

• The sources and destinations of the parameters are not always registers, as is almost always the case with the RISC I.

This can lead to an unmanageable proliferation of variables. Rather than attempt to deal with this wealth of information for the general case, we constrained our call/return example to the passing of 32-bit values which are found in registers.

Equations and values were generated for four styles of RISC I. The first was the standard ORS RISC I which passes its parameters in its overlapping registers. Since the MRS and SRS versions of the RISC I execute the same call/return sequence, passing parameters on a stack in memory, one equation characterizes both of them. Two other variations of parameter passing were tried. One added push and pop instructions to the RISC I architecture and used these for passing parameters on a memory stack. Where the SRS RISC I required two instructions to perform a push (a subtract followed by a store), this version was assumed to require only one. The last version passed parameters in the RISC I's global registers. These physical registers exist in the logical register address space of every procedure. A parameter can be placed into a global register, a call instruction executed, and the parameter will be found in the same global register unchanged. This eliminates the need to move a parameter on and off a stack in memory.

Equations and values were also generated for three 68000 versions (ORS, SRS using global registers, and SRS using a memory stack) as well as three VAX versions (ORS, SRS using global registers, and SRS using a memory stack). The cost of each of these call/return sequences, in terms of total memory bytes transferred, are plotted in Figures 5, 6, and 7. Since all three architectures use the same code for both SRS and non-overlapping MRS versions, the SRS results presented also apply to MRS machines.

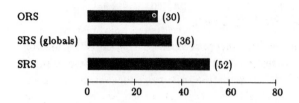

Figure 6: Total memory bytes transferred for a call/return sequence on three variations of 68000.

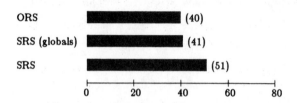

Figure 7: Total memory bytes transferred for a call/return sequence on three variations of VAX.

The bar graphs above show a much greater variation among the RISC I machines than among the VAX machines, with the 68000 variations somewhere in between. This is due to three factors.

1. The VAX has very compact push and pop register instructions which account for only 6 bytes of traffic apiece. This is not much more than the register-to-register moves that they replace (which create 3 bytes of traffic apiece) and is half the size of RISC I's synthesized push and pop.

2. The procedure calling convention used by our VAX C compiler returns results in register 0. This feature was retained, and as such register 0 acts as a global register for return values. This means that the ORS and SRS versions are identical for their return sequences.

3. The VAX architecture maintains an elaborate stack structure. In keeping with our goal of changing an architecture as little as possible for these experiments, this stack mechanism was kept. The processor-memory traffic overhead imposed as a result constitute roughly half of the totals in Figure 7.

The 68000, in fact, shares the first two factors with

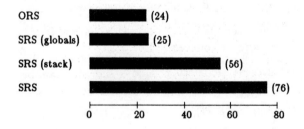

Figure 5: Total memory bytes transferred for a call/return sequence on four variations of RISC I.

the VAX, accounting in part for its intermediate role.

State Saving Costs

This section discusses the costs involved in saving and restoring procedure state when an overflow or underflow of a processor's register file occurs. As with analyzing the costs involved to pass parameters between procedures, a general analysis of the costs associated with procedure state saving could be quite complex. The actual operations involved are simple: save the previous procedure state on an overflow and restore state on an underflow. However, the methods used can be very elaborate.

The factors that affect the cost of procedure state saving and restoring are:

- Frequency of state saving: This varies with the number of register sets available and the call/return profile of the application program. More register sets reduce the frequency of state saving. A call/return profile which exhibits a high degree of call locality will overflow the register file less often than a profile with frequent large changes in call depth.

- Amount of state to be saved: This depends on the number of registers available in each register set, how the application program uses those registers, and how the state to be saved is specified (whether the entire state is always saved, or whether a mask feature is provided to save only the state that might be changed).

- Complexity of the instructions used to save and restore state: This ranges from having no special state saving mechanisms to very elaborate and complex mechanisms. Processors without special instructions to handle state saving (like RISC I) must perform this function using other primitive instructions. A microcoded mechanism, like the VAX's, is very complex but eliminates the need for multiple state saving instructions.

Though many things affect the efficiency of state saving and restoring, some distinct methods exist to reduce the amount of state that must be saved.

- Provide multiple register sets which reduce the frequency of register file overflows.

- Provide special instructions to save and restore state. This reduces the processor-memory traffic cost by eliminating the need for many primitive instructions to do the same jobs.

- Provide methods to specify which state should not be lost (using register masks, for example).

- Use smart register allocation strategies and other optimization strategies to avoid the necessity of saving some state.

We have already seen an example of the difference a smart state saving algorithm can make with the two versions of the SRS RISC I. The cost in terms of processor-memory traffic of an overflow on the original ORS RISC I is approximately 188 bytes (31 instructions, 16 of which are stores). This figure is independent of the number of registers that actually need to be saved. The RISC I saves 16 registers whenever it overflows. A more elaborate scheme which stores the subset of registers that are actually being used would involve iterative testing. Such testing, with the RISC I's primitive instruction set, would greatly increase the cost of an overflow.

The register mask RISC I machine, however, is assumed to be microcoded. As such it requires no instruction bytes and it has a processor-memory traffic cost of 4 bytes times the number of registers saved (a total of 24 bytes for Ackermann and Fibonnacci and 32 bytes for Hanoi). This much lower cost accounts for its superior performance on Ackermann which has a very high overflow rate.

Other Issues

We have discussed, in this paper, the performance gains due to MRSs, the machine changes required to support MRSs, and how MRSs affect compiled code. This discussion leaves points 4 and 5, as outlined earlier, unexplored. An examination of these remaining points, context swap performance and suitability to various high-level languages, can be found in [5] as well as further detail on all issues described in this paper.

Conclusion

The results presented in this paper support the hypothesis that performance gains due to multiple register sets are independent of instruction set complexity. The magnitude of such gains is determined by the register structure implemented, the mechanisms used to manage that structure, and the calls per overflow rate which is dependent on the usage environment of the machine. All three of these factors were explored and discussed in this paper. The results from this paper do not relieve a computer designer from running his own simulations, or creating his own equations, but they do provide insight into what may be expected from incorporating multiple register sets.

Acknowledgements

We would like to thank Prof. E. Douglas Jensen and Robert P. Colwell for sharing with us their insights on this topic. We would also like to that the RISC I creators at the University of California at Berkeley for sharing their RISC I software with us.

References

1. Robert P. Colwell, Charles Y. Hitchcock III, and E. Douglas Jensen. "Peering Through the RISC/CISC Fog: An Outline of Research". *Computer Architecture News 11*, 1 (March 1983), 44-50.

2. Robert P. Colwell. The Performance Effects of Functional Migration and Architectural Complexity in Object-Oriented Systems. PhD thesis, Carnegie-Mellon University. Expected completion in May, 1985.

3. Reinhold P. Weicker. "Dhrystone: A Synthetic Systems Programming Benchmark". *Communications of the ACM 27*, 10 (October 1984), 1013-1030.

4. Daniel C. Halbert and Peter B. Kessler. Windows of Overlapping Register Frames. CS292R Final Reports, University of California, Berkeley, June 9, 1980.

5. Charles Y. Hitchcock III and H. M. Brinkley Sprunt. An Evaluation of Multiple Register Sets. Carnegie-Mellon University, May, 1985. To be published.

6. E. Douglas Jensen. The Archons Project: An Overview. Proceedings of the International Symposium on Synchronization, Control, and Communication in Distributed Systems, 1983. Academic Press.

7. David A. Patterson and Carlo H. Sequin. "A VLSI RISC". *Computer 15*, 9 (September 1982), 8-21.

Section 4: RISC Compilers

4.1 Background

One of the major goals of the RISC approach is to achieve high performance. Success depends not only on the organization and architecture of the processor but on the effectiveness of the compiler. In most cases, programmers (even systems programmers) use high-level languages. Thus the performance of a program will depend critically on how well it has been compiled into the target machine language.

The importance of the compiler for performance is true on any machine, but is especially significant on RISC machines. Most of the RISC designers on the various projects report that (1) they expect that more effective compilers can be built for RISC as opposed to CISC machines and (2) the success of their design depends on the development of a good RISC compiler.

The reasoning behind the first point above is this: Because RISC instructions are primitive, a compiler can use them more efficiently to generate optimized code. In contrast, CISC instructions are difficult to use effectively because the compiler is limited to dealing with more aggregated, less primitive building blocks. This hinders the compiler in performing such tasks as efficient register allocation.

The evidence to date suggests that RISC compilers, on average, will expend more compile-time effort than CISC compilers in an attempt to optimize the target code. The expected payoff, of course, is enhanced run-time performance.

The articles in this section discuss the RISC compilers used on four commercially available machines. It can be seen that two concerns are of major importance in all of these efforts: optimized register usage and efficient exploitation of pipelining. The topic of register usage was examined in detail in Section 3. To provide some context for this section, the concept of instruction pipelining is discussed next.

4.2 Article Summary

The first article, by Coutant et al., presents the family of compilers developed for the new RISC-based Hewlett-Packard computers. The paper provides considerable detail on the optimization techniques employed. It also examines RISC-related design issues and explains how these have been addressed by the compiling system.

The article by Hopkins describes the compiler for the IBM PC RT. The most important optimizations performed by this compiler are moving code out of loops, elimination of redundant computations, and register allocation. Examples of each are given.

Next, "Engineering a RISC Compiler System" examines the compiler suite for the product from MIPS Computer Systems, which is based on the Stanford MIPS project. Pipeline-optimization and register-allocation techniques are described.

Finally, "Optimizing Compilers for the SPARC Architecture: An Overview" describes how the compilers use the SPARC RISC architecture and discusses the design of the compilers. The article looks at addressing, synthesized instructions, and tagged data support.

COMPILERS FOR THE NEW GENERATION OF HEWLETT-PACKARD COMPUTERS

Deborah S. Coutant, Carol L. Hammond, and Jon W. Kelly
Hewlett-Packard
1501 Page Mill Road
Palo Alto, CA 94304

WITH THE ADVENT of any new architecture, compilers must be developed to provide high-level language interfaces to the new machine. Compilers are particularly important to the reduced-complexity, high-precision architecture currently being developed at Hewlett-Packard in the program that has been code-named Spectrum. The Spectrum program is implementing an architecture that is similar in philosophy to the class of architectures called RISCs (reduced instruction set computers).[1] The importance of compilers to the Spectrum program was recognized at its inception. From the early stages of the new architecture's development, software design engineers were involved in its specification.

The design process began with a set of objectives for the new architecture.[2] These included the following:

- It must support high-level language development of systems and applications software.
- It must be scalable across technologies and implementations.
- It must provide compatibility with previous systems.

These objectives were addressed with an architectural design that goes beyond RISC. The new architecture has the following features:

- There are many simple instructions, each of which executes in a single cycle.
- There are 32 high-speed general-purpose registers.
- There are separate data and instruction caches, which are exposed and can be managed explicitly by the operating system kernel.
- The pipeline has been made visible to allow the software to use cycles normally lost following branch and load instructions.
- Performance can be tuned to specific applications by adding specialized processors that interface with the central processor at the general-register, cache, or main memory levels.

The compiling system developed for this high-precision architecture* enables high-level language programs to use these features. This paper describes the compiling system design and shows how it addresses the specific requirements of the new architecture. First, the impact of high-level language issues on the early architectural design decisions is described. Next, the low-level structure of the compiling system is explained, with particular emphasis on areas that have received special attention for this architecture: program analysis, code generation, and optimization. The paper closes with a discussion of RISC-related issues and how they have been addressed in this compiling system.

Designing an Architecture for High-Level Languages

The design of the new architecture was undertaken by a team made up of design engineers specializing in hardware, computer architecture, operating systems, performance analysis, and compilers. It began with studies of computational behavior, leading to an initial design that provided efficient execution of frequently used instructions, and addressed the trade-offs involved in achieving additional functionality. The architectural design was scrutinized by software engineers as it was being developed, and their feedback helped to ensure that compilers and operating systems would be able to make effective use of the proposed features.

A primary objective in specifying the instruction set was to achieve a uniform execution time for all instructions. All instructions other than loads and branches were to be realizable in a single cycle. No instruction would be included that required a significantly longer cycle or significant additional hardware complexity. Restricting all instructions by these constraints simplifies the control of execution. In conventional microcoded architectures, many instructions pay an overhead because of the complexity of control required to execute the microcode. In reduced-complexity computers, no instruction pays a penalty for a more complicated operation. Functionality that is not available in a single-cycle instruction is achieved through multiple-instruction sequences or, optionally, with an additional processor.

As the hardware designers began their work on an early implementation of the new architecture, they were able to discover which instructions were costly to implement, required additional complexity not required by other instructions, or required long execution paths, which would increase the cycle time of the machine. These instructions were either removed, if the need for them was not great, or replaced with simpler instructions that provided the needed functionality. As the hardware engineers provided feedback about which instructions were too costly to include, the software engineers investigated alternate ways of achieving the same functionality.

For example, a proposed instruction that provided hardware support for a 2-bit Booth multiplication was not included because the additional performance it provided was not justified by its cost. Architecture and compiler engineers worked together to propose an alternative to this instruction. Similarly, several instructions that could be

---

*The term "high-precision architecture" is used because the instruction set for the new architecture was chosen on the basis of execution frequency as determined by extensive measurements across a variety of workloads.

used directly to generate Boolean conditions were deleted when they were discovered to require a significantly longer cycle time. The same functionality was available with a more general two-instruction sequence, enabling all other operations to be executed faster.

The philosophy of reduced-complexity computers includes the notion that the frequent operations should be fast, possibly at the expense of less frequent operations. However, the cost of an infrequent operation should not be so great as to counterbalance the efficient execution of the simple operations. Each proposed change to the architectural specification was analyzed by the entire group to assess its impact on both software and hardware implementations. Hardware engineers analyzed the instruction set to ensure that no single instruction or set of instructions was causing performance and/or cost penalties for the entire architecture, and software engineers worked to ensure that all required functionality would be provided within performance goals. Compiler writers helped to define conditions for arithmetic, logical, and extract/deposit instructions, and to specify where carry/borrow bits would be used in arithmetic instructions.

As an example of such interaction, compiler writers helped to tune a conditional branch nullification scheme to provide for the most efficient execution of the most common branches. Branches are implemented such that an instruction immediately following the branch can be executed before the branch takes effect.[1] This allows the program to avoid losing a cycle if useful work is possible at that point. For conditional branches, the compiler may or may not be able to schedule an instruction in this slot that can be executed in both the taken-branch and non-taken-branch cases. For these branches, a nullification scheme was devised which allows an instruction to be executed only in the case of a taken branch for backward branches, and only in the case of a non-taken branch for forward branches. This scheme was chosen to enable all available cycles to be used in the most common cases. Backward conditional branches are most often used in a loop, and such branches will most often be taken, branching backwards a number of times before falling through at the end of the iteration. Thus, a nullification scheme that allows this extra cycle to be used in the taken-branch case causes this cycle to be used most often. Conversely, for forward branches, the nullification scheme was tuned to the non-taken-branch case. Fig. 1 shows the code generated for a simple code sequence, illustrating the conditional branch nullification scheme.

Very early in the development of the architectural specification, work was begun on a simulator for the new computer architecture and a prototype C compiler. Before the design was frozen, feedback was available about the ease with which high-level language constructs could be translated to the new instruction set. The early existence of a prototype compiler and simulator allowed operating system designers to begin their development early, and enabled them to provide better early feedback about their needs, from the architecture as well as the compiler.

At the same time, work was begun on optimization techniques for the new architecture. Segments of compiled code were hand-analyzed to uncover opportunities for optimization. These hand-optimized programs were used as a guideline for implementation and to provide a performance goal. Soon after the first prototype compiler was developed, a prototype register allocator and instruction scheduler

were also implemented, providing valuable data for the optimizer and compiler designers.

Compiling to a Reduced Instruction Set

Compiling for a reduced-complexity computer is simplified in some aspects. With a limited set of instructions from which to choose, code generation can be straightforward. However, optimization is necessary to realize the full advantage of the architectural features. The new HP compiling system is designed to allow multiple languages to be implemented with language-specific compiler front ends. An optimization phase, common to all of the languages, provides efficient register use and pipeline scheduling, and eliminates unnecessary computations. With the elimination of complex instructions found in many architectures, the responsibility for generating the proper sequence of instructions for high-level language constructs falls to the compiler. Using the primitive instructions, the compiler can construct precisely the sequence required for the application.

For this class of computer, the software architecture plays a strong role in the performance of compiled code. There is no procedure call instruction, so the procedure calling sequence is tuned to handle simple cases, such as *leaf routines* (procedures that do not call any other procedures), without fixed expense, while still allowing the complexities of nested and recursive procedures. The saving of registers at procedure call and procedure entry is dependent on the register use of the individual procedure. A special calling convention has been adopted to allow some complex operations to be implemented in low-level routines known as *millicode*, which incur little overhead for saving registers and status.

Compiling to a reduced instruction set can be simplified because the compiler need not make complicated choices among a number of instructions that have similar effects. In the new architecture, all arithmetic, logical, or conditional instructions are register-based. All memory access is done through explicit loads and stores. Thus the compiler need not choose among instructions with a multitude of addressing modes. The compiler's task is further simplified by the fact that the instruction set has been constructed in

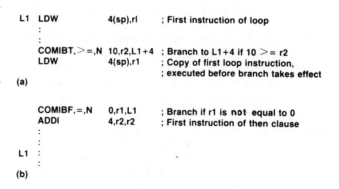

Fig. 1. *An illustration of the conditional branch nullification scheme. (a) The conditional branch at the end of a loop will often be followed by a copy of the first instruction of the loop. This instruction will only be executed if the branch is taken. (b) The forward conditional branch implementing an if statement will often be followed by the first instruction of the then clause, allowing use of this cycle without rearrangement of code. This instruction will only be executed if the branch is not taken.*

a very symmetrical manner. All instructions are the same length, and there are a limited number of instruction formats. In addition to simplifying the task of code generation, this makes the task of optimization easier as well. The optimizer need not handle transformations between instructions that have widely varying formats and addressing modes. The symmetry of the instruction set makes the tasks of replacing or deleting one or more instructions much easier.

Of course, the reduced instruction set computer, though simplifying some aspects of the compilation, requires more of the compilers in other areas. Having a large number of registers places the burden on the compilers to generate code that can use these registers efficiently. Other aspects of this new architecture also require the compilers to be more intelligent about code generation. For example, the instruction pipeline has become more exposed and, as mentioned earlier, the instruction following a branch may be executed before the branch takes effect. The compiler therefore needs to schedule such instructions effectively. In addition, loads from memory, which also require more than a single cycle, will interlock with the following instruction if the target register is used immediately. The compiler can increase execution speed by scheduling instructions to avoid these interlocks. The optimizer can also improve the effectiveness of a floating-point coprocessor by eliminating unnecessary coprocessor memory accesses and by reordering the floating-point instructions.

In addition to such optimizations, which are designed to exploit specific architectural features, conventional optimizations such as common subexpression elimination, loop invariant code motion, induction variable elaboration, and local constant propagation were also implemented.[3] These have a major impact on the performance of any computer. Such optimizations reduce the frequency of loads, stores, and multiplies, and allow the processor to be used with greater efficiency. However, the favorable cost/performance of the new HP architecture can be realized even without optimization.

The Compiler System

All of the compilers for the new architecture share a common overall design structure. This allows easy integration of common functional components including a symbolic debugger, a code generator, an optimizer, and a linker. This integration was achieved through detailed planning, which involved the participation of engineers across many language products. Of the new compilers, the Fortran/77, Pascal, and COBOL compilers will appear very familiar to some of our customers, since they were developed from existing products available on the HP 3000 family of computers. All of these compilers conform to HP standard specifications for their respective languages, and thus will provide smooth migration from the HP 1000, HP 3000, and HP 9000 product lines. The C compiler is a new product, and as mentioned earlier, was the compiler used to prototype the instruction set from its earliest design phase. The C compiler conforms to recognized industry standard language specifications. Other compilers under development will be integrated into this compiler system.

To achieve successful integration of compilers into a homogeneous compiling system it was necessary to define distinct processing phases and their exact interfaces in terms of data and control transfer. Each compiler begins execution through the front end. This includes the lexical,

syntactic, and semantic analysis prescribed by each language standard. The front ends generate intermediate codes from the source program, and pass these codes to the code generators. The intermediate codes are at a higher level than the machine code generated by a later phase, and allow a certain degree of machine abstraction within the front ends.

Two distinct code generators are used. They provide varying degrees of independence from the front ends. Each interfaces to the front ends through an intermediate code. One of these code generation techniques has already been used in two compiler products for the HP 3000. Fig. 2 shows the overall design of the compilers. Each phase of the compilation process is pictured as it relates to the other phases. The front ends are also responsible for generating data to be used later in the compilation process. For example, the front end generates data concerning source statements and the types, scopes and locations of procedure/function and variable names for later use by the symbolic debugger. In addition, the front end is responsible for the collection of data to be used by the optimizer.

These compilers can be supported by multiple operating systems. The object file format is compatible across operating systems.

Code Generation

The code generators emit machine code into a data structure called SLLIC (Spectrum low-level intermediate code). SLLIC also contains information regarding branches and their targets, and thus provides the foundation for the building of a control flow graph by the optimizer. The SLLIC data structure contains the machine instructions and the

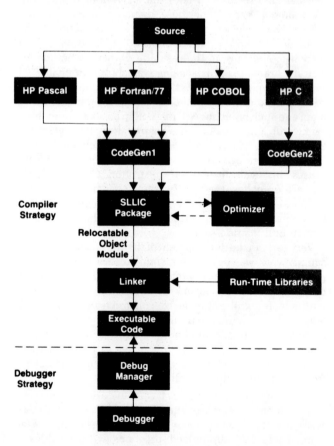

Fig. 2. *The compiler system for HP's new generation of high-precision-architecture computers.*

specifications for the run-time environment, including the program data space, the literal pool, and data initialization. SLLIC also holds the symbolic debug information generated by the front end, is the medium for later optimization, and is used to create the object file.

The reduced instruction set places some extra burden on the code generators when emitting code for high-level language constructs such as byte moves, decimal operations, and procedure calls. Since the instruction set contains no complex instructions to aid in the implementation of these constructs, the code generators are forced to use combinations of the simpler instructions to achieve the same functionality. However, even in complex instruction set architectures, complex case analysis is usually required to use the complex instructions correctly. Since there is little redundancy in the reduced instruction set, most often no choice of alternative instruction sequences exists. The optimizer is the best place for these code sequences to be streamlined, and because of this the overall compiler design is driven by optimization considerations. In particular, the optimizer places restrictions upon the code generators.

The first class of such restrictions involves the presentation of branch instructions. The optimizer requires that all branches initially be followed by a NOP (no operation) instruction. This restriction allows the optimizer to schedule instructions easily to minimize interlocks caused by data and register access. These NOPs are subsequently replaced with useful instructions, or eliminated.

The second class of restrictions concerns register use. Register allocation is performed within the optimizer. Rather than use the actual machine registers, the code generators use symbolic registers chosen from an infinite register set. These symbolic registers are mapped to the set of actual machine registers by the register allocator. Although register *allocation* is the traditional name for such an activity, register *assignment* is more accurate in this context. The code generators are also required to associate every syntactically equivalent expression in each procedure with a unique symbolic register number. The symbolic register number is used by the optimizer to associate each expression with a value number (each run-time *value* has a unique *number*). Value numbering the symbolic registers aids in the detection of common subexpressions within the optimizer. For example, every time the local variable i is loaded it is loaded into the same symbolic register, and every time the same two symbolic registers are added together the result is placed into a symbolic register dedicated to hold that value.

Although the optimizer performs transformations at the machine instruction level, there are occasions where it could benefit from the existence of slightly modified and/or additional instructions. *Pseudoinstructions* are instructions that map to one or more machine instructions and are only valid within the SLLIC data structure as a software convention recognized between the code generators and the optimizer. For example, the NOP instruction mentioned above is actually a pseudoinstruction. No such instruction exists on the machine, although there are many instruction/ operand combinations whose net effect would be null. The NOP pseudoinstruction saves the optimizer from having to recognize all those sequences. Another group of pseudoinstructions has been defined to allow the optimizer to view all the actual machine instructions in the same canonical form, without being restricted by the register use prescribed by the instructions. For example, some instructions use the same register as both a source and a target. This makes optimization very difficult for that instruction. The solution involves the definition of a set of pseudoinstructions, each of which maps to a two-instruction sequence, first to copy the source register to a new symbolic register, and then to perform the operation on that new register. The copy instruction will usually be eliminated by a later phase of the optimizer.

Another class of perhaps more important pseudoinstructions involves the encapsulation of common operations that are traditionally supported directly by hardware, but in a reduced instruction set are only supported through the generation of code sequences. Examples include multiplication, division, and remainder. Rather than have each code generator contain the logic to emit some correct sequence of instructions to perform multiplication, a set of pseudoinstructions has been defined that makes it appear as if a high-level multiplication instruction exists in the architecture. Each of the pseudoinstructions is defined in terms of one register target and either two register operands or one register operand and one immediate. The use of these pseudoinstructions also aids the optimizer in the detection of common subexpressions, loop invariants, and induction variables by reducing the complexity of the code sequences the optimizer must recognize.

Control flow restrictions are also placed on generated code. A *basic block* is defined as a straight-line sequence of code that contains no transfer of control out of or into its midst. If the code generator wishes to set the carry/borrow bit in the status register, it must use that result within the same basic block. Otherwise, the optimizer cannot guarantee its validity. Also, all argument registers for a procedure/function call must be loaded in the same basic block that contains the procedure call. This restriction helps the register allocator by limiting the instances where hard-coded (actual) machine registers can be *live* (active) across basic block boundaries.

Optimization

After the SLLIC data structure has been generated by the code generator, a call is made to the optimizer so that it can begin its processing. The optimizer performs intraprocedural local and global optimizations, and can be turned on and off on a procedure-by-procedure basis by the programmer through the use of compiler options and directives specific to each compiler. Three levels of optimization are supported and can also be selected at the procedural level.

Optimization is implemented at the machine instruction level for two reasons. First, since the throughput of the processor is most affected by the requests made of the memory unit and cache, optimizations that reduce the number of requests made, and optimizations that rearrange these requests to suit the memory unit best, are of the most value. It is only at the machine level that all memory accesses become exposed, and are available candidates for such optimizations. Second, the machine level is the common denominator for all the compilers, and will continue to be for future compilers for the architecture. This allows the implementation of one optimizer for the entire family of compilers. In addition to very machine specific optimizations, a number of theoretically machine independent optimizations (for example, loop optimizations) are also included. These also benefit from their low-level implementation, since all potential candidates are exposed. For example, performing loop optimizations at the machine level allows the optimizer to move constants outside the loop, since the machine has many registers to hold them. In summary, no optimization has been adversely affected by this strategy; instead, there have been only benefits.

Level 0 optimization is intended to be used during program development. It is difficult to support symbolic debugging in the presence of all optimizations, since many optimizations reorder or delete instruction sequences. Nonsymbolic debugging is available for fully optimized programs, but users will still find it easier to debug nonoptimized code since the relationship between the source and object code is clearer. No code transformations are made at level 0 that would preclude the use of a symbolic debugger. In particular, level 0 optimizations include some copy and NOP elimination, and limited branch scheduling. In addition, the components that physically exist as part of the optimizer, but are required to produce an executable program, are invoked. These include register allocation and branch fixing (replacing short branches with long branches where necessary).

After program correctness has been demonstrated using only level 0 optimizations, the programmer can use the more extensive optimization levels. There are two additional levels of optimization, either of which results in code reordering. The level any particular optimization component falls into is dependent upon the type of information it requires to perform correct program transformations. The calculation of data flow information gives the optimizer information regarding all the resources in the program. These resources include general registers, dedicated and status registers, and memory locations (variables). The information gleaned includes where each resource is defined and used within the procedure, and is critical for some optimization algorithms. Level 1 optimizations require no data flow information, therefore adding only a few additional optimizations over level 0. Invoking the optimizer at level 2 will cause all optimizations to be performed. This requires data flow information to be calculated.

Level 1 optimization introduces three new optimizations: peephole and branch optimizations and full instruction scheduling. Peephole optimizations are performed by pattern matching short instruction sequences in the code to corresponding templates in the peephole optimizer. An example of a transformation is seen in the C source expression

```
if (flag & 0x8)
```

which tests to see that the fourth bit from the right is set in the integer flag. The unoptimized code is

```
LDO      8(0), 19      ; load immediate 8 into r19
AND      31,19,20      ; intersect r31 (flag) with r19 into r20
COMIBT, = 0,20,label   ; compare result against 0 and branch
```

Peephole optimization replaces these three instructions with the one instruction

```
BB,> =   31,28,label   ; branch on bit
```

which will branch if bit 28 (numbered left to right from 0) in r31 (the register containing flag) is equal to 0.

Level 1 optimization also includes a branch optimizer whose task is to eliminate unnecessary branches and some unreachable code. Among other tasks, it replaces branch chains with a single branch, and changes conditional branches whose targets are unconditional branches to a single conditional branch.

The limited instruction scheduling algorithm of level 0 is replaced with a much more thorough component in level 1. Level 0 scheduling is restricted to replacing or removing the NOPs following branches where possible, since code sequence ordering must be preserved for the symbolic debugger. In addition to this, level 1 instructions are scheduled with the goal of minimizing memory interlocks. The following typify the types of transformations made:

- Separate a load from the instruction that uses the loaded register
- Separate store and load instruction sequences
- Separate floating-point instructions from each other to improve throughput of the floating-point unit.

Instruction scheduling is accomplished by first constructing a dependency graph that details data dependencies between instructions. Targeted instructions are separated by data independent instructions discovered in the graph.

The same register allocator is used in level 0 and level 1 optimization. It makes one backwards pass over each procedure to determine where the registers are defined and used and whether or not they are live across a call. It uses this information as a basis for replacing the symbolic registers with actual machine registers. Some copy elimination is also performed by this allocator.

Level 2 optimizations include all level 1 optimizations as well as local constant propagation, local peephole transformations, local redundant definition elimination, common subexpression and redundant load/store elimination, loop invariant code motion, induction variable elaboration and strength reduction, and another register allocator. The register allocator used in level 2 is partially based on graph coloring technology.[4] Fully optimized code contains many more live registers than partially optimized or nonoptimized code. This register allocator handles many live registers better than the register allocator of levels 0 and 1. It has access to the data flow information calculated for the symbolic registers and information regarding the frequency of execution for each basic block.

Control Flow and Data Flow Analysis

All of the optimizations introduced in level 2 require data flow information. In addition, a certain amount of control flow information is required to do loop-based optimizations. Data flow analysis provides information to the optimizer about the pattern of definition and use of each resource. For each basic block in the program, data flow information indicates what definitions may reach the block (reaching definitions) and what later uses may be affected by local definitions (exposed uses). Control flow information in the optimizer is contained in the basic block and interval structures. *Basic block analysis* identifies blocks of code that have no internal branching. *Interval analysis* identifies patterns of control flow such as if-then-else and loop constructs.[5] Intervals simplify data flow calculations, identify loops for the loop-based optimizations, and enable partial update of data flow information.

In the optimizer, control flow analysis and data flow analysis are performed in concert. First, basic blocks are identified. Second, local data flow information is calculated for each basic block. Third, interval analysis exposes the structure of the program. Finally, using the interval structure as a basis for its calculation rules, global data flow analysis calculates the reaching definitions and exposed uses.

Basic block analysis of the SLLIC data structure results in a graph structure where each basic block identifies a sequence of instructions, along with the predecessor and successor basic blocks. The interval structure is built on top of this, with the smallest interval being a basic block. Intervals other than basic blocks contain subintervals which may themselves be any type of interval. Interval types include basic block, sequential block (the subintervals follow each other in sequential order), if-then, if-then-else, self loop, while loop, repeat loop, and switch (case statement). When no such interval is recognized, a set of subintervals may be contained in either a *proper interval* (if the control flow is well-behaved) or an *improper interval* (if it contains multiple-entry cycles or targets of unknown branches). An entire procedure will be represented by a single interval with multiple descendants. Fig. 3 shows the interval structure for a simple Pascal program.

Calculation of data flow information begins with an analysis of what resources are used and defined by each basic block. Each use or definition of a resource is identified by a unique *sequence number*. Associated with each sequence number is information regarding what resource is

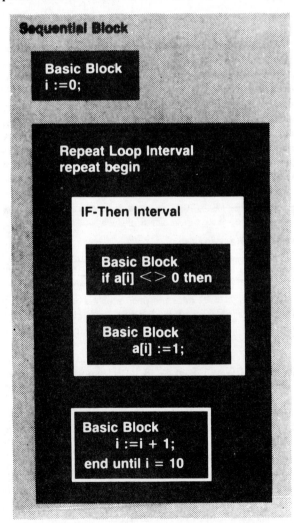

Fig. 3. *This figure illustrates the interval structure of a simple sequence of Pascal code. The nested boxes represent the interval hierarchy.*

being referenced, and whether it is a use or a definition. Each SLLIC instruction entry contains sequence numbers for all of the resources defined or used by that instruction. The local data flow analysis determines what local uses are exposed at the top of the basic block (i.e., there is a use of a resource with no preceding definition in that block) and what local definitions will reach the end of the block (i.e., they define a resource that is not redefined later in the block). The local data flow analysis makes a forward and backward pass through the instructions in a basic block to determine this information.

Local data flow information is propagated out from the basic blocks to the outermost interval. Then, information about reaching definitions and exposed uses is propagated inward to the basic block level. For known interval types, this involves a straightforward calculation for each subinterval. For proper intervals, this calculation must be performed twice for each subinterval, and for improper intervals, the number of passes is limited by the number of subintervals.

As each component of the optimizer makes transformations to the SLLIC graph, the data flow information becomes inaccurate. Two strategies are employed to bring this information up-to-date: *patching* of the existing data flow information and partial recalculation. For all optimizations except induction variable elimination, the data flow information can be patched by using information about the nature of the transformation to determine exactly how the data flow information must be changed. All transformations take place within the loop interval in induction variable elimination. The update of data flow information within the loop is performed by recalculating the local data flow information where a change has been made, and then by propagating that change out to the loop interval. The effect of induction variable elimination on intervals external to the loop is limited, and this update is performed by patching the data flow information for these intervals.

Aliasing

The concept of resources has already been presented in the earlier discussion of data flow analysis. The optimizer provides a component called the *resource manager* for use throughout the compiler phases. The resource manager is responsible for the maintenance of information regarding the numbers and types of resources within each procedure. For example, when the code generator needs a new symbolic register, it asks the resource manager for one. The front ends also allocate resources corresponding to memory locations for every variable in each procedure. The resources allocated by the resource manager are called *resource numbers*. The role of the resource manager is especially important in this family of compilers. It provides a way for the front end, which deals with memory resources in terms of programmer variable names, and the optimizer, which deals with memory resources in terms of actual memory locations, to communicate the relationship between the two.

The most basic use of the resource numbers obtained through the resource manager is the identification of unique programmer variables. The SLLIC instructions are decorated with information that associates resource numbers with each operand. This allows the optimizer to recognize uses of the same variable without having to compare addresses. The necessity for communication between the front ends and the optimizer is demonstrated by the following simplified example of C source code:

```
proc() {
 int i, j, k, *p;
 .
 .
 .
 i = j + k;
 *p = 1;
 i = j + k;
 .
 .
 .
}
```

At first glance it might seem that the second calculation of j + k is redundant, and in fact it is a common subexpression that need only be calculated once. However, if the pointer p has been set previously to point to either j or k, then the statement *p = 1 might change the value of either j or k. If p has been assigned to point to j, then we say that *p and j are *aliased* to each other. Every front end includes a component called a *gatherer*[6] whose responsibility it is to collect information concerning the ways in which memory resources in each procedure relate to each other. This information is cast in terms of resource numbers, and is collected in a similar manner by each front end. Each gatherer applies a set of language specific alias rules to the source. A later component of the optimizer called the aliaser reorganizes this information in terms more suitable for use by the local data flow component of the optimizer.

Each gatherer had to solve aliasing problems specific to its particular target language. For example, the Pascal gatherer was able to use Pascal's strong typing to aid in building sets of resources that a pointer of some particular type can point to. Since C does not have strong typing, the C gatherer could make no such assumptions. The COBOL compiler had to solve the aliasing problems that are introduced with the REDEFINE statement, which can make data items look like arrays. Fig. 4 shows the structure of the new compilers from an aliasing perspective. It details data

and control dependencies. Once the aliasing data has been incorporated into the data flow information, every component in the optimizer has access to the information, and incorrect program transformations are prevented.

The aliaser also finishes the calculation of the aliasing relationships by calculating the transitive closure* on the aliasing information collected by the gatherers. The need for this calculation is seen in the following skeleton Pascal example:

```
procedure p;
 begin
 p : ^integer;
 q : ^integer;
 .
 .
 .
 p := q;
 .
 .
 .
 q := p;
 .
 .
 .
 end;
```

The aliasing information concerning q must be transferred to p, and vice versa, because of the effects of the two assignment statments shown. The aliaser is an optimizer component used by all the front ends, and requires no language specific data. Another type of memory aliasing occurs when two or more programmer variables can overlap with one another in memory. This happens within C unions and Fortran equivalence statements. Each gatherer must also deal with this issue, as well as collecting information concerning the side effects of procedure and function calls and the use of arrays.

The SLLIC Package

The SLLIC data structure is allocated, maintained, and manipulated by a collection of routines called the *SLLIC package*. Each code generator is required to use these routines. The SLLIC package produces an object file from the SLLIC graph it is presented with, which is either optimized or unoptimized. During implementation it was relatively easy to experiment with the design of the object file, since its creation is only implemented in one place. The object file is designed to be transportable between multiple operating systems running on the same architecture.

The SLLIC graph also contains the symbolic debug information produced by the front end. This information is placed into the object file by the SLLIC package. The last step in the compilation process is the link phase. The linker is designed to support multiple operating systems. As much as possible, our goal has been for the new compilers to remain unchanged across operating systems, an invaluable characteristic for application development.

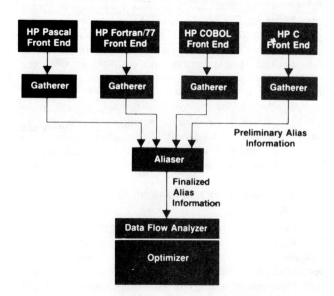

Fig. 4. *Scheme for the collection of alias information.*

*Transitive closure: For a given resource, the set of resources that can be shown to be aliased to the given resource by any sequence of aliasing relationships.

Addressing RISC Myths

The new compiling system provides a language development system that is consistent across languages. However, each language presents unique requirements to this system. Mapping high-level language constructs to a reduced-complexity computer requires the development of new implementation strategies. Procedure calls, multiplication, and other complex operations often implemented in microcode or supported in the hardware can be addressed with code sequences tuned to the specific need. The following discussion is presented in terms of several misconceptions, or myths, that have appeared in speculative discussions concerning code generation for reduced-complexity architectures. Each myth is followed by a description of the approach adopted for the new HP compilers.

Myth: An architected procedure call instruction is necessary for efficient procedure calls.

Modern programming technique encourages programmers to write small, well-structured procedures rather than large monolithic routines. This tends to increase the frequency of procedure calls, thus making procedure call efficiency crucial to overall system performance.

Many machines, like the HP 3000, provide instructions to perform most of the steps that make up a procedure call. The new HP high-precision architecture does not. The mechanism of a procedure call is not architected, but instead is accomplished by a software convention using the simple hardwired instructions. This provides more flexibility in procedure calls and ultimately a more efficient call mechanism.

Procedure calls are more than just a branch and return in the flow of control. The procedure call mechanism must also provide for the passing of parameters, the saving of the caller's environment, and the establishment of an environment for the called procedure. The procedure return mechanism must provide for the restoration of the calling procedure's environment and the saving of return values.

The new HP machines are register-based machines, but by convention a stack is provided for data storage. The most straightforward approach to procedure calls on these machines assumes that the calling procedure acquires the responsibility for preserving its state. This approach employs the following steps:

- Save all registers whose contents must be preserved across the procedure call. This prevents the called procedure, which will also use and modify registers, from affecting the calling procedure's state. On return, those register values are restored.
- Evaluate parameters in order and push them onto the stack. This makes them available to the called procedure which, by convention, knows how to access them.
- Push a *frame marker*. This is a fixed-size area containing several pieces of information. Among these is the *static link*, which provides information needed by the called procedure to address the local variables and parameters of the calling procedure. The return address of the calling procedure is also found in the stack marker.
- Branch to the entry point of the called procedure.

To return from the call, the called procedure extracts the return address from the stack marker and branches to it. The calling procedure then removes the parameters from the stack and restores all saved registers before program flow continues.

This simple model correctly implements the steps needed to execute a procedure call, but is relatively expensive. The model forces the caller to assume all responsibility for preserving its state. This is a safe approach, but causes too many register saves to occur. To optimize the program's execution, the compiler makes extensive use of registers to hold local variables and temporary values. These registers must be saved at a procedure call and restored at the return. The model also has a high overhead incurred by the loading and storing of parameters and linkage information. The ultimate goal of the procedure call convention is to reduce the cost of a call by reducing memory accesses.

The new compilers minimize this problem by introducing a procedure call convention that includes a register partition. The registers are partitioned into *caller-saves* (the calling procedure is responsible for saving and restoring them), *callee-saves* (the called procedure must save them at entry and restore them at exit), and *linkage* registers. Thirteen of the 32 registers are in the caller-saves partition and 16 are in the callee-saves partition. This spreads the responsibility for saving registers between the calling and called procedures and leaves some registers available for linkage.

The register allocator avoids unnecessary register saves by using caller-saves registers for values that need not be preserved. Values that must be saved are placed into registers from the callee-saves partition. At procedure entry, only those callee-saves registers used in the procedure are saved. This minimizes the number of loads and stores of registers during the course of a call. The partition of registers is not inflexible; if more registers are needed from a particular partition than are available, registers can be borrowed from the other partition. The penalty for using these additional registers is that they must be saved and restored, but this overhead is incurred only when many registers are needed, not for all calls.

In the simple model, all parameters are passed by being placed on the stack. This is expensive because memory references are made to push each parameter and as a consequence the stack size is constantly altered. The new compilers allocate a permanent parameter area large enough to hold the parameters for all calls performed by the procedure. They also minimize memory references when storing parameters by using a combination of registers and memory to pass parameters. Four registers from the callee-saves partition are used to pass user parameters; each holds a single 32-bit value or half of a 64-bit value. Since procedures frequently have few parameters, the four registers are usually enough to contain them all. This removes the necessity of storing parameter values in the parameter area before the call. If more than four 32-bit parameters are passed, the additional ones are stored in the preallocated parameter area. If a parameter is larger than 64 bits, its address is passed and the called procedure copies it to a temporary area.

Additional savings on stores and loads occur when the called procedure is a leaf routine. As mentioned previously, the optimizer attempts to maximize the use of registers to hold variable values. When a procedure is a leaf, the register allocator uses the caller-saves registers for this purpose, thus eliminating register saves for both the calling and called procedures. It is never necessary to store the return address or parameter registers of a leaf routine since they will not be modified by subsequent calls.

Leaf routines do not need to build a stack frame, since they make no procedure calls. Also, if the allocator succeeds in representing all local variables as registers, it is not necessary to build the local variable area at entry to the leaf procedure.

The convention prescribes other uses of registers to eliminate other loads and stores at procedure calls. The return address is always stored in a particular register, as is the static link if it is needed.

To summarize, the procedure call convention used in the new HP computers streamlines the overhead of procedure calls by minimizing the number of memory references. Maximal use of registers is made to limit the number of memory accesses needed to handle parameters and linkage. Similarly, the convention minimizes the need to store values contained in registers and does not interfere with attempts at optimization.

Myth: The simple instructions available in RISC result in significant code expansion.

Many applications, especially commercial applications, assume the existence of complex high-level instructions typically implemented by the system architecture in microcode or hardware. Detractors of RISC argue that significant code expansion is unavoidable since the architecture lacks these instructions. Early results do not substantiate this argument.[7,8] The new HP architecture does not provide complex instructions because of their impact on overall system performance and cost, but their functionality is available through other means.

As described in an earlier article,[2] the new HP machines do not have a microcoded architecture and all of the instructions are implemented in hardware. The instructions on microcoded machines are implemented in two ways. At the basic level, instructions are realized in hardware. More complex instructions are then produced by writing subroutines of these hardware instructions. Collectively, these constitute the microcode of the machine. Which instructions are in hardware and which are in microcode are determined by the performance and cost goals for the system. Since HP's reduced instruction set is implemented solely at the hardware level, subroutines of instructions are equivalent to the microcode in conventional architectures.

To provide the functionality of the complex instructions usually found in the architecture of conventional machines, the design team developed the alternative concept of *millicode instructions* or routines. Millicode is HP's implementation of complex instructions using the simple hardware instructions packaged into subroutines. Millicode serves the same purpose as traditional microcode, but is common across all machines of the family rather than specific to each.

The advantages of implementing functionality as millicode are many. Microcoded machines may contain hidden performance penalties on all instructions to support multiple levels of instruction implementation. This is not the case for millicode. From an architectural viewpoint, millicode is just a collection of subroutines indistinguishable from other subroutines. A millicode instruction is executed by calling the appropriate millicode subroutine. Thus, the expense of executing a millicode instruction is only present when the instruction is used. The addition of

millicode instructions has no hardware cost and hence no direct influence on system cost. It is relatively easy and inexpensive to upgrade or modify millicode in the field, and it can continue to be improved, extended, and tuned over time.

Unlike most microcode, millicode can be written in the same high-level languages as other applications, reducing development costs yet still allowing for optimization of the resultant code. Severely performance-critical millicode can still be assembly level coded in instances where the performance gain over compiled code is justified. The size of millicode instructions and the number of such instructions are not constrained by considerations of the size of available control store. Millicode resides in the system as subroutines in normally managed memory, either in virtual memory where it can be paged into and out of the system as needed, or in resident memory as performance considerations dictate. A consequence of not being bound by restrictive space considerations is that compiler writers are free to create many more specialized instructions in millicode than would be possible in a microcoded architecture, and thus are able to create more optimal solutions for specific situations.

Most fixed instruction sets contain complex instructions that are overly general. This is necessary since it is costly to architect many variations of an instruction. Examples of this are the MVB (move bytes) and MVW (move words) instructions on the HP 3000. They are capable of moving any number of items from any arbitrary source location to any target location. Yet, the compiler's code generators frequently have more information available about the operands of these instructions that could be used to advantage if other instructions were available. The code generators frequently know whether the operands overlap, whether the operands are aligned favorably, and the number of items to be moved. On microcoded machines, this information is lost after code generation and must be recreated by the microcode during each execution of the instruction. On the new HP computers, the code generators can apply such information to select a specialized millicode instruction that will produce a faster run-time execution of the operation than would be possible for a generalized routine.

Access to millicode instructions is through a mechanism similar to a procedure call. However, additional restrictions placed on the implementation of millicode routines prevent the introduction of any barriers to optimization. Millicode routines must be leaf routines and must have no effect on any registers or memory locations other than the operands and a few scratch registers. Since millicode calls are represented in SLLIC as pseudoinstructions, the optimizer can readily distinguish millicode calls from procedure calls. Millicode calls also use different linkage registers from procedure calls, so there is no necessity of preserving the procedure's linkage registers before invoking millicode instructions.

The only disadvantage of the millicode approach over microcode is that the initiation of a millicode instruction involves an overhead of at least two instructions. Even so, it is important to realize that for most applications, millicode instructions are infrequently needed, and their overhead is incurred only when they are used. The high-precision architecture provides the frequently needed instructions directly in hardware.

Myth: RISC machines must implement integer multiplication as successive additions.

Integer multiplication is frequently an architected instruction. The new architecture has no such instruction but provides others that support an effective implementation of multiplication. It also provides for inclusion of a high-speed hardware multiplier in a special function unit.[2]

Our measurements reveal that most multiplication operations generated by user programs involve multiplications by small constants. Many of these occurrences are explicitly in the source code, but many more are introduced by the compiler for address and array reference evaluation. The new compilers have available a trio of instructions that perform shift and add functions in a single cycle. These instructions, SH1ADD (shift left once and add), SH2ADD (shift left twice and add) and SH3ADD (shift left three times and add) can be combined in sequences to perform multiplication by constants in very few instructions. Multiplications by most constants with absolute values less than 1040 can be accomplished in fewer than five cycles. Negatively signed constants require an additional instruction to apply the sign to the result. Multiplication by all constants that are exact powers of 2 can be performed with a single shift instruction unless overflow conditions are to be detected. Additionally, multiplications by 4 or 2 for indexed addressing can be avoided entirely. The LDWX (load word indexed) and LDHX (load half-word indexed) instructions optionally perform unit indexing, which combines multiplication of the index value with the address computation in the hardware.

The following examples illustrate multiplication by various small constants.

Source code:
    4*k
Assembly code:
    SH2ADD   8,0,9   ; shift r8 (k) left 2 places,
                              add to r0 (zero) into r9
Source code:
    −163*k
Assembly code:
    SH3ADD   8,8,1   ; shift r8 (k) left 3 places, add
                              to itself into r1
    SH3ADD   1,1,1   ; shift r1 left 3 places, add to
                              itself into r1
    SH1ADD   1,8,1   ; shift r1 left 1 place, add to
                              k into r1
    SUB   0,1,1   ; subtract result from 0 to
                              negate; back into r1
Source code:
    A(k)
Assembly code:
    LDO   −404(30),9   ; load array base address
                              into r9
    LDW   −56(0,30),7 ; load unit index value into r7
    LDWX,S   7(0,9),5   ; multiply index by 4 and
                              load element into r5

When neither operand is constant or if the constant is such that the in-line code sequence would be too large, integer multiplication is accomplished with a millicode instruction. The multiply millicode instruction operates under the premise that even when the operands are un-

known at compile time, one of them is still likely to be a small value. Application of this to the multiplication algorithm yields an average multiplication time of 20 cycles, which is comparable to an iterative hardware implementation.

Myth: RISC machines cannot support commercial applications languages.

A popular myth about RISC architectures is that they cannot effectively support languages like COBOL. This belief is based on the premise that RISC architectures cannot provide hardware support for the constructs and data types of COBOL-like languages while maintaining the one-instruction-one-cycle advantages of RISC. As a consequence, some feel that the code expansion resulting from performing COBOL operations using only the simple architected instructions would be prohibitive. The significance of this is often overstated. Instruction traces of COBOL programs measured on the HP 3000 indicate that the frequency of decimal arithmetic instructions is very low. This is because much of the COBOL program's execution time is spent in the operating system and other subsystems.

COBOL does place demands on machine architects and compiler designers that are different from those of languages like C, Fortran, and Pascal. The data items provided in the latter languages are represented in binary and hence are native to the host machine. COBOL data types also include packed and unpacked decimal, which are not commonly native and must be supported in ways other than directly in hardware.

The usual solution on conventional machines is to provide a commercial instruction set in microcode. These additional instructions include those that perform COBOL field (variable) moves, arithmetic for packed decimal values, alignment, and conversions between the various arithmetic types.

In the new HP machines, millicode instructions are used to provide the functionality of a microcoded commercial instruction set. This allows the encapsulation of COBOL operations while removing the possibility of runaway code expansion. Many COBOL millicode instructions are available to do each class of operation. The compiler expends considerable effort to select the optimal millicode operation based on compile-time information about the operation and its operands. For example, to generate code to perform a COBOL field move, the compiler may consider the operand's relative and absolute field sizes and whether blank or zero padding is needed before selecting the appropriate millicode instruction.

Hardware instructions that assist in the performance of some COBOL operations are architected. These instructions execute in one cycle but perform operations that would otherwise require several instructions. They are emitted by the compiler in in-line code where appropriate and are also used to implement some of the millicode instructions. For example, the DCOR (decimal correct) and UADDCM (unit add complement) instructions allow packed decimal addition to be performed using the binary ADD instruction. UADDCM prepares an operand for addition and the DCOR restores the result to packed decimal form after the addition. For example:

```
r1 and r2 contain packed decimal operands
r3 contains the constant X'99999999'

    UADDCM 1,3,31   ; pre-bias operand into r31
    ADD     2,31,31 ; perform binary add
    DCOR    31,31   ; correct result
```

Millicode instructions support arithmetic for both packed and unpacked decimal data. This is a departure from the HP 3000, since on that machine unpacked arithmetic is performed by first converting the operand to packed format, performing the arithmetic operation on the packed data, and then converting the result back to unpacked representation. Operations occur frequently enough on unpacked data to justify the implementation of unpacked arithmetic routines. The additional cost to implement them is minimal and avoids the overhead of converting operands between the two types. An example of the code to perform an unpacked decimal add is:

```
r1 and r2 contain unpacked decimal operands
r3 contains the constant X'96969696'
r4 contains the constant X'0f0f0f0f'
r5 contains the constant X'30303030'

    ADD   3,1,31    ; pre-bias operand into r31
    ADD   31,2,31   ; binary add into r31
    DCOR  31,31     ; correct result
    AND   4,31,31   ; mask result
    OR    5,31,31   ; restore sum to unpacked decimal
```

In summary, COBOL is supported with a blend of hardware assist instructions and millicode instructions. The compiled code is compact and meets the run-time execution performance goals.

Conclusions

The Spectrum program began as a joint effort of hardware and software engineers. This early communication allowed high-level language issues to be addressed in the architectural design.

The new HP compiling system was designed with a reduced-complexity machine in mind. Register allocation, instruction scheduling, and traditional optimizations allow compiled programs to make efficient use of registers and low-level instructions.

Early measurements have shown that this compiler technology has been successful in exploiting the capabilities of the new architecture. The run-time performance of compiled code consistently meets performance objectives. Compiled code sizes for high-level languages implemented in this low-level instruction set are comparable to those for more conventional architectures. Use of millicode instructions helped achieve this result. Complex high-level language operations such as procedure calls, multiplication, and COBOL constructs have been implemented efficiently with the low-level instructions provided by the high-precision architecture. A later paper will present performance measurements.

Acknowledgments

The ideas and results presented in this paper are the culmination of the work of many talented engineers involved with the Spectrum compiler program. We would like to acknowledge the individuals who made significant technical contributions to the work presented in this paper in the following areas: early compiler development and optimizer investigation at HP Laboratories, optimizer development, aliasing design and implementation in the compiler front ends, code generator design and implementation, procedure call convention design, and object module specification.

Megan Adams	Tom Lee
Robert Ballance	Steve Lilker
Bruce Blinn	Daniel Magenheimer
William Buzbee	Tom McNeal
Don Cameron	Sue Meloy
Peter Canning	Terrence Miller
Paul Chan	Angela Morgan
Cary Coutant	Steve Muchnick
Erik Eidt	Karl Pettis
Phil Gibbons	David Rickel
Adiel Gorel	Michelle Ruscetta
Richard Holman	Steven Saunders
Mike Huey	Carolyn Sims
Audrey Ishizaki	Ron Smith
Suneel Jain	Kevin Wallace
Mark Scott Johnson	Alexand Wu
Steven Kusmer	

We feel privileged to have the opportunity to present their work. We would like to extend special thanks to Bill Buzbee for his help in providing code examples, and to Suneel Jain for providing the description of the optimization components.

References

1. D.A. Patterson, "Reduced Instruction Set Computers," *Communications of the ACM*, Vol. 28, no. 1, January 1985, pp. 8-21.
2. J.S. Birnbaum and W.S. Worley, Jr., "Beyond RISC: High-Precision Architecture," *Hewlett-Packard Journal*, Vol. 36, no. 8, August 1985, pp. 4-10.
3. A.V. Aho and J.D. Ullman, *Principles of Compiler Design*, Addison-Wesley, 1977.
4. G.J. Chaitin, "Register Allocation and Spilling via Graph Coloring," *Proceedings of the SIGPLAN Symposium on Compiler Construction*, June 1982, pp. 98-105.
5. M. Sharir, "Structural Analysis: A New Approach To Flow Analysis in Optimizing Compilers," *Computer Languages*, Vol. 5, Pergamon Press Ltd., 1980.
6. D.S. Coutant, "Retargetable High-Level Alias Analysis," *Conference Record of the 13th ACM Symposium on Principles of Programming Languages*, January 1986.
7. J.A. Otto, "Predicting Potential COBOL Performance on Low-Level Machine Architectures," *SIGPLAN Notices*, Vol. 20, no. 10, October 1985, pp. 72-78.
8. G. Radin, "The 801 Computer," *Symposium on Architectural Support for Programming Languages and Operating Systems*, March 1982, pp. 39-47.

Components of the Optimizer

The optimizer is composed of two types of components, those that perform data flow and control flow analysis, and those that perform optimizations. The information provided by the analysis components is shared by the optimization components, and is used to determine when instructions can be deleted, moved, rearranged, or modified.

For each procedure, the control flow analysis identifies basic blocks (sequences of code that have no internal branching). These are combined into intervals, which form a hierarchy of control structures. Basic blocks are at the bottom of this hierarchy, and entire procedures are at the top. Loops and if-then constructs are examples of the intermediate structures.

Data flow information is collected for each interval. It is expressed in terms of resource numbers and sequence numbers. Each register, memory location, and intermediate expression has a unique resource number, and each use or definition of a resource has a unique sequence number. Three types of data flow information are calculated:

■ Reaching definitions: for each resource, the set of definitions that could reach the top of the interval by some path.
■ Exposed uses: for each resource, the set of uses that could be reached by a definition at the bottom of the interval.
■ UNDEF set: the set of resources that are not available at the top of the interval. A resource is available if it is defined along all paths reaching the interval, and none of its operands are later redefined along that path.

From this information, a fourth data structure is built:

■ Web: a set of sequence numbers having the property that for each use in the set, all definitions that might reach it are also in the set. Likewise, for each definition in the set, all uses it might reach are also in the set. For each resource there may be one or many webs.

Loop Optimizations

Frequently the majority of execution time in a program is spent executing instructions contained in loops. Consequently, loop-based optimizations can potentially improve execution time significantly. The following discussion describes components that perform loop optimizations.

Loop Invariant Code Motion. Computations within a loop that yield the same result for every iteration are called loop invariant computations. These computations can potentially be moved outside the loop, where they are executed less frequently.

An instruction inside the loop is invariant if it meets either of two conditions: either the reaching definitions for all its operands are outside the loop, or its operands are defined by instructions that have already themselves been identified as loop invariant. In addition, there must not be a conflicting definition of the instruction's target inside the loop. If the instruction is executed conditionally inside the loop, it can be moved out only if there are no exposed uses of the target at the loop exit.

An example is a computation involving variables that are not modified in the loop. Another is the computation of an array's base address.

Strength Reduction and Induction Variables. Strength reduction replaces multiplication operations inside a loop with iterative addition operations. Since there is no hardware instruction for integer multiplication in the architecture, converting sequences of shifts and adds to a single instruction is a performance improvement. Induction variables are variables that are defined inside the loop in terms of a simple function of the loop counter.

Once the induction variables have been determined, those that are appropriate for this optimization are selected. Any multiplications involved in the computation of these induction variables are replaced with a COPY from a temporary. This temporary holds the initial value of the function, and is initialized preceding the loop. It is updated at the point of all the reaching definitions of the induction variable with an appropriate addition instruction. Finally, the induction variable itself is eliminated if possible.

This optimization is frequently applied to the computation of array indices inside a loop, when the index is a function of the loop counter.

Common Subexpression Elimination

Common subexpression elimination is the removal of redundant computations and the reuse of the one result. A redundant computation can be deleted when its target is not in the UNDEF set for the basic block it is contained in, and all the reaching definitions of the target are the same instruction. Since the optimizer runs at the machine level, redundant loads of the same variable in addition to redundant arithmetic computations can be removed.

Store-Copy Optimization

It is possible to promote certain memory resources to registers for the scope of their definitions and uses. Only resources that satisfy aliasing restrictions can be transformed this way. If the transformation can be performed, stores are converted to copies and the loads are eliminated. This optimization is very useful for a machine that has a large number of registers, since it maximizes the use of registers and minimizes the use of memory.

For each memory resource there may be multiple webs. Each memory web is an independent candidate for promotion to a register.

Unused Definition Elimination

Definitions of memory and register resources that are never used are removed. These definitions are identified during the building of webs.

Local Constant Propagation

Constant propagation involves the folding and substitution of constant computations throughout a basic block. If the result of a computation is a constant, the instruction is deleted, and the resultant constant is used as an immediate operand in subsequent instructions that reference the original result. Also, if the operands of a conditional branch are constant, the branch can be changed to an unconditional branch or deleted.

Coloring Register Allocation

Many components introduce additional uses of registers or prolong the use of existing registers over larger portions of the procedure. Near-optimal use of the available registers becomes crucial after these optimizations have been made.

Global register allocation based on a method of graph coloring is performed. The register resources are partitioned into groups of disjoint definitions and uses called register webs. Then, using the exposed uses information, interferences between webs are computed. An interference occurs when two webs must be assigned different machine registers. Registers that are copies of each other are assigned to the same register and the copies are eliminated. The webs are sorted based on the number of interferences each contains. Then register assignment is done using this ordering. When the register allocator runs out of registers, it frees a register by saving another one to memory temporarily. A heuristic algorithm is used to choose which register to save. For example, registers used heavily within a loop will not be saved to free a register.

Peephole Optimizations

The peephole optimizer uses a dictionary of equivalent instruction patterns to simplify instruction sequences. Some of the patterns identify simplifications to addressing mode changes, bit manipulations, and data type conversions.

Branch Optimizations

The branch optimizer component traverses the instructions, transforming branch instruction sequences into more efficient instruction sequences. It converts branches over single instructions to instructions with conditional nullification. A branch whose target is the next instruction is deleted. Branch chains involving both unconditional and conditional branches are combined into shorter sequences wherever possible. For example, a conditional branch to an unconditional branch is changed to a single conditional branch.

Dead Code Elimination

Dead code is code that cannot be reached at program execution, since no branch to it or fall-through exists. This code is deleted.

Scheduler

The instruction scheduler reorders the instructions within a basic block, minimizing load/store and floating-point interlocks. It also schedules the instructions following branches.

Suneel Jain
Development Engineer
Information Technology Group

An Optimization Example

This example illustrates the code generated for the following C program for both the unoptimized and the optimized case.

```
test ( )
{
int i, j;
int a1[25], a2[25], r[25][25];

for (i = 0; i < 25; i + +) {
    for (j = 0; j < 25; j + +) {
        r [i] [j] = a1 [i] * a2 [j];
    }
  }
}
```

In the example code that follows, the following mnemonics are used:

rp	return pointer, containing the address to which control should be returned upon completion of the procedure
arg0	first parameter register
arg1	second parameter register
sp	stack pointer, pointing to the top of the current frame
mret0	millicode return register
mrp	millicode return pointer.

The value of register zero (r0) is always zero.

The following is a brief description of the instructions used:

LDO	immed(r1),r2	$r2 \leftarrow r1 +$ immed.
LDW	immed(r1),r2	$r2 \leftarrow *(r1 +$ immed)
LDWX,S	r1(r2),r3	$r3 \leftarrow *(4*r1 + r2)$
STW	r1,immed(r2)	$*(r2 +$ immed) $\leftarrow r1$
STWS	r1,immed(r2)	$*(r2 +$ immed)$\leftarrow r1$
STWM	r1,immed(r2)	$*(r2 +$ immed)$\leftarrow r1$ AND $r2 \leftarrow r2 +$ immed
COMB,< =	r1,r2,label	if $r1 < = r2$, branch to label
BL	label,r1	branch to label, and put return address into r1 (for procedure call)
BV	0(r1)	branch to address in r1 (for procedure return)

ADD	r1,r2,r3		$r3 \leftarrow r1 + r2$
SH1ADD	r1,r2,r3		$r3 \leftarrow 2*r1 + r2$
SH2ADD	r1,r2,r3		$r3 \leftarrow 4*r1 + r2$
SH3ADD	r1,r2,r3		$r3 \leftarrow 8*r1 + r2$
COPY	r1,r2		$r2 \leftarrow r1$
NOP			no effect

In the following step-by-step discussion, the unoptimized code on the left is printed in black, and the optimized code on the right is printed in color. The code appears in its entirety, and can be read from the top down in each column.

Save callee-saves registers and increment stack pointer. Unoptimized case uses no register that needs to be live across a call.

LDO	2760(sp),sp	STW	2, − 20(0,sp)
		STWM	3,2768(0,sp)
		STW	4, − 2764(0,sp)

Assign zero to i. In the optimized case, i resides in register 19.

STW	0, − 52(0,sp)	COPY	0,19

Compare i to 25. This test is eliminated in the optimized case since the value of i is known.

LDW	− 52(0,sp),1
LDO	25(0),31
COMB,< = ,N	31,1,L2

In the optimized version, a number of expressions have been moved out of the loop:

{maximum value of j}	LDO	25(0),20
{address of a1}	LDO	− 156(sp),22
{address of a2}	LDO	− 256(sp),24
{address of r}	LDO	− 2756(sp),28
{initial value of 100*i}	LDO	0(0),4
{maximum value of 100*i}	LDO	2500(0),2

Initialize j to zero, and compare j to 25. This test has also been eliminated in the optimized version, since the value of j is known. Note that j now resides in register 21.

L3
STW	0, − 56(0,sp)	COPY	0,21
LDW	− 56(0,sp),19		
LDO	25(0),20		
COMB,< = ,N	20,19,L1		

In the optimized version, the load of a1[i] is moved out of the inner loop, since the value of i is constant in the inner loop.

LDWX,S	19(0,22),23

Register 28 contains the address of r, and register 4 contains the value 100*i, which is the offset of the ith row of array r. This is constant over the inner loop, and has been moved out.

ADD	28,4,3

L6

The loop begins with the load of a1[i] into the first parameter register. This value has already been loaded in the optimized version, and need only be copied.

LDO	− 156(sp),21		
LDW	− 52(0,sp),22		
LDWX,S	22(0,21),arg0	COPY	23,arg0

The value of a2[j] is loaded into the second parameter register, and the .nultiply millicode instruction is called. In the optimized case, the address of a2[0] and the value of j are both already in registers.

```
LDO       -256(sp),1
LDW       -56(0,sp),19
BL        mull,mrp                    BL        mull,mrp
LDWX,S    19(0,1),arg1                LDWX,S    21(0,24),arg1
```

Store the result into r[i][j]. The three SHxADD instructions calculate 100*i. Note that most of the following is loop invariant, and has been moved out of the loop in the optimized case.

```
LDO       -2756(sp),19   {address of r}
LDW       -52(0,sp),20   {value of i}
SH1ADD    20,20,21       {r21 ← 3 * i}
SH3ADD    21,20,22       {r22 ← 25 * i}
SH2ADD    22,0,1         {r1 ← 100 * i}
ADD       19,1,31        {address of r + 100 * i}
LDW       -56(0,sp),19   {value of j}
SH2ADD    19,31,20       {add j*4 to address}    SH2ADD    21,3,31
STWS      mret0,0(0,20)  {store}                 STWS      mret0,0(0,31)
```

Increment j.

```
LDW       -56(0,sp),21                LDO       1(21),21
LDO       1(21),22
STW       22,-56(0,sp)
```

Compare j to the value 25 (already in register 20 in the optimized version). The position after the conditional branch contains no useful instruction in the unoptimized case. In the op-

timized version, the first instruction of the loop has been copied to this position, and the target adjusted to the following instruction. Because the branch has the nullification flag set (,N), the following instruction will not be executed when the branch is not taken.

```
LDW       -56(0,sp),1
LDO       25(0),31
COMBF,< =  31,1,L6                    COMBF,< =,N  20,21,L6 + 4
NOP                                   LDWX,S       21(0,24),25
L1
```

Increment i, and test for the end of the loop. In the optimized version, induction variable elaboration has removed the 100*i multiplication, and added a new induction variable to contain that value. This value, in register 4, is now tested against a maximum value of 2500, contained in register 2. This branch has been scheduled like the previous branch.

```
LDW       -52(0,sp),19
LDO       1(19),20                    LDO       1(19),19
STW       20,-52(0,sp)                LDO       100(4),4
LDW       -52(0,sp),21
LDO       25(0),22
COMBF,< =  22,21,L3                   COMBF,< =,N 2,4,L3 + 4
NOP                                   COPY      0,21
L2
```

Finally, the registers are restored, and control is returned to the calling procedure.

```
                                      LDW       -2788(0,sp),2
                                      LDW       -2764(0,sp),4
BV        0(rp)                       BV        0(rp)
LDO       -2760(sp),sp               LDWM      -2768(0,sp),3
```

Compiling for the RT PC ROMP

M.E. Hopkins

Introduction

The IBM RT PC ROMP architecture is relatively low level and simple. A natural consequence is that the primitive instructions should execute rapidly on most implementations. Does the choice of such a low level interface make sense given that almost all programming today is, or should be, done in a high level language? Could compiler writers do a better job if the CPU was somewhat more elaborate, with additional functions tailored to the constructs commonly found in high-level languages? Of course it is clear that code can be generated for any execution model. Examples of execution models are register transfer, stack, and storage-to-storage. Unlike human coders, compilers will tirelessly and accurately generate long sequences of code to map one model of a language onto a machine with another model. The hard task is to obtain efficient code for a particular machine.

Which style of machine is best? Our preference for a machine like the ROMP is based partly on fundamental engineering constraints and partly on our ability to use well understood compilation techniques to obtain high quality code. An example of a fundamental engineering constraint is that operations that are internal to the CPU, such as register-to-register add, run faster than instructions that reference storage, even on machines with caches. (The fact that some machines slow down basic arithmetic to memory reference speed should not concern us.) Examples of compilation techniques will be given later. We also have a certain bias to simple hardware solutions. Part of this is aesthetic, but we also have a suspicion grounded on experience that the next language just may not match the complex operation which is built into an elaborate architecture.

The discussions that follow are based on the PL.8 compiler, which accepts source programs written in C, Pascal and PL.8, a systems dialect of PL/I. A description of the compiler is given in Auslander and Hopkins[1]. PL.8 produces optimized object code for System/370 and MC68000 as well as ROMP and the 801 minicomputer [2]. The compiler largely relies on global optimization and register allocation to produce good object code. The VRM and various ROMP tools were developed using PL.8. Originally, the compiler was an experimental vehicle used to build software for the 801 minicomputer, but in recent years it has been used in a number of internal IBM projects. It is not presently available to customers.

Hardware/Software Cooperation

Both hardware and software affect system performance. The compiler writer must accept his share of the responsibility. The ROMP architecture divides the task in ways that lead to better performance without excessive burden on either hardware or software. A few examples will indicate how responsibility is shared.

One of the more expensive operations on many computers is branching. As long as instruction execution proceeds sequentially it is possible to prefetch and decode instructions ahead of their actual execution. This overlapping is usually termed pipelining. When a branch is encountered a new instruction stream must be found. Conditionality and computed branch targets complicate the decisions that must be made in hardware. Very-high-performance machines do prefetch on multiple paths and retain branch history tables to avoid "flushing the pipe." Most one-chip processors simply accept expensive branches as a fact of life. The ROMP solution is to define a family of execute branches that perform the next ("subject") instruction in parallel with the branch. Implementing this facility only complicates the hardware a little. It thus becomes the responsibility of the compiler to produce execute branches. Through most of compilation, the compiler only deals with branches in the familiar non-execute format. At one point a scheduling process is run which rearranges code between labels and branches. (This unit is termed a basic block.) One of the goals of scheduling is to place an instruction that could become the subject of an execute branch just in front of the branch. (The main constraint is that the branch cannot depend on the result of the subject instruction.) Other optimizations are unaware of the compilation of execute branches. Final assembly then looks at the instruction that precedes every branch and flips the pair if it is valid to convert a normal to an execute branch. Branches tend to constitute over 20% of all instructions executed. Even if only half of all branches can be transformed to the execute form, a modest increase in hardware and compiler complexity has resulted in the effect of a 10% reduction in the path length or number of instructions executed.

A similar situation exists with loads. Loads tend to take substantially more time than register-to-register (RR) ops, but it is possible for the hardware (in Real mode) to overlap the load with execution of the following instruction if the next instruction does not require the result of the load. The scheduling process also rearranges code to facilitate such overlap. If loads constitute 15% or 20% of all executions, it is easy to see that another 10% or greater reduction in effective path length may be achieved here. Notice that a machine that bundles the fetch of an operand from memory with a computation cannot easily overlap fetching with some other function.

Of course the object code that comes from such a compiler looks strange. In some sense, you are seeing the equivalent of the internal state of a very costly high-performance pipelined processor. Writing optimal assembly language code requires some care on the ROMP. It is rather like microcoding. However, on the ROMP the process is systematic, if tedious, making it

fortunate that most programming is done in a high-level language.

Compilation Strategies

The most important optimizations performed by the PL.8 compiler are probably moving code out of loops, the elimination of redundant computations (commoning), and register allocation. The ROMP makes these operations easier and more profitable.

Let us examine these optimizations in the light of machine models and how they evaluate expressions:

- Stack computation

- Memory-to-memory

- Memory-to-register

- Register-to-register

Consider the source code fragment:

```
x = a + b;
(a few statements, which destroy x, leaving
a and b)
y = a + b;
```

If the recomputation of a + b is to be avoided on the stack machine, an explicit copy in storage must be made and then the value must be refetched from storage when assigning to y. The trouble with this strategy is that "remembering" is very costly. On the ROMP an RR Add costs one cycle, while Loads and Stores take between three and five cycles depending on whether the machine is in real or virtual mode and whether or not it is possible to overlap another instruction with the load. Unless an operation is very expensive, it is often as efficient to recompute as to "remember" on a stack machine. On a memory-to-memory machine one must often pay for an explicit copy as in the following code for a hypothetical memory-to-memory machine:

```
temp = a + b
x = temp
    :    .
y = temp
```

The added storage references may well make commoning counterproductive. We shall say no more about the stack or memory model. Whatever their virtues for simplifying compilation, they seem to guarantee more storage references and thus worse performance than the other two models.

The storage-to-memory model is shared by 370 and MC68000. At first glance a 370-type approach seems attractive.

```
x = a + b;    L R1, a
              A R1,b
              ST R1, x

y = a + b;    ST R1, y
```

On the ROMP we get:

```
x = a + b;    L R1, a
              L R2, b
              CAS R3, R1, R2 Add
              ST R3, x

y = a + b;    ST R3,y
```

The ROMP takes one more instruction. (It does have some opportunities to obtain overlap on the Loads by inserting unrelated instructions, but let us ignore that benefit). If the example is changed slightly to:

```
x = a + b;
y = a - b;
```

We then get on 370:

```
x = a + b;    L R1, a
              A R1, b
              ST R1, b

y = a - b;    L R1, a
              S R1, b
              ST R1, y
```

After the first statement, neither a nor b are available and they are the operands of the next statement. On the ROMP, both are available and so there is no need for an expensive refetch. Of course we can turn the 370 into a ROMP-style, register-to-register machine. The problem is that the 370 Add instruction destroys one of its operands, while CAS, an Add that doesn't set the condition code on the ROMP, is three-address. The PL.8 compiler goes to considerable effort to give 370 code the benefits of both the

storage-to-register and register-to-register approaches. It is not clear that the effort is worth it. On some 370 models, two Loads and an Add Register may be as fast as Load, Add from Storage. In any case there are relatively few storage-to-register computational operations in a typical snapshot of 370 execution. One typical mix shows the following most frequently-executed storage-to-register ops.

Instruction	% of execution
C: compare	1.74
N:and	1.26
AL:add logical	1.07
CL:compare logical	.44
A:add	.39
S:subtract	.37
O:or	.36
CH:compare half	.33
AH:add half	.24
SH:subtract half	.10
MH:multiply half	.07

If all such ops are included, the percentage of executions is less than 6.5%. Modest as this figure is, it overstates the advantage to be gained from memory-to-register ops, as many of these instructions are addressing literals. On the ROMP they would be immediate ops. In light of frequency of usage, potential performance improvement, hardware requirements and compiler complexity it is hard to believe that storage-to-register ops are cost effective.

The reader may not be impressed with optimizing a + b, and would be correct if the only benefit of optimization was a rewrite of the user's program at the source level. The most potent effects of an optimizing compiler are derived from reducing the administrative code used to implement high-level constructs. Consider what it takes to implement the following code fragment in PL.8.

```
1 a                  static ext,
2 b                  integer,
2 c (0:10),
     3 d             integer,
     3 e             integer,
     3 f             char (16);
  x = e(i);
```

The reference to e(i) includes the following factors:

- The address of the structure a

- The displacement of e within a

- i times the stride of c.

In PL.8 and Pascal, subscript range testing is normally done even on production code. Thus there is also a trap to ensure that the value of i is between zero and ten. The fetch of e(i) may be commoned or moved out of a loop, but there are many other opportunities for optimization. The load of the address constant to locate the structure need not be repeated when a reference is made to b. Storing into d(i) requires no additional instructions. Programs are filled with opportunities to reuse portions of this administrative type code. The higher the level of the machine, the less chance there will be for reuse, as one factor may change.

An example of this phenomenon is in subscript computations. As the ROMP does not have a built-in multiply instruction, the compiler generates a series of shifts, adds and subtracts when the stride is a constant. Thus a multiply by 24 is implemented as:

shiftl(i, 4) + shiftl(i, 3)

If somewhere else in the program there is a multiply of i by 8 or 16, one of the shifts already used to compute i*24 will suffice. By systematically exploiting the many small opportunities for optimization that occur in real programs, the PL.8 compiler can produce programs that execute very rapidly on the ROMP.

It is now necessary to discuss register allocation. So far we have tacitly assumed that there would be enough registers to hold all the intermediate results which optimization creates. A large number of registers require, not only more hardware, but more bits in the instruction to name the particular register. Compiler studies showed that, while 32 registers were beneficial, 16 were a reasonable compromise. A PL.8-type compiler approach would probably not be very effective with substantially fewer than 16 registers. The code would tend to look like the memory-to-memory model of computation. The PL.8 compiler uses a graph coloring algorithm [3] to assign the infinite number of

symbolic registers used during optimization to the 16 available on the ROMP, but other methods can be used.

It is particularly important that a machine not restrict the register allocation by typing registers or otherwise constraining their use. Implicit usage is also undesirable. Even the ROMP has some minor problems here, but they are easily overcome. Register 0 cannot be used as a base because the CPU assumes this means the value zero. The register allocation phase of the compiler overcomes this problem by introducing an interference in the coloring graph. Each symbolic register used as a base interferes with real register zero; thus, the compiler will not assign such a symbolic register to R0. Branch and Link implicitly uses R15. This was chosen by the compiler writers to match the proposed linkage conventions. The most bothersome constraint is paired shifts. Normal shifts on the ROMP are of the form:

Shift   RA, shift amount

The value to be shifted is in RA and is returned to the same register. If only this form of instruction were available, implementing a multiply by an arbitrary constant using shifts and adds would often require intermediate copies. Rather than introduce a 4-byte nondestructive shift instruction, the paired shift was introduced. Every register has a twin whose name is obtained by complementing the low bit of the name (e.g., the twin of R2 is R3 and vice versa). The PL.8 register allocator handles this in the following manner. The internal form of the program used by optimization has shifts with separate target, source and shift count fields. Prior to register coloring an attempt is made to coalesce the source and target. If this fails, an attempt is made to coalesce the source and target onto a particular pair of real registers. Other cases, which seem to be rare, result in an extra load register.

On machines like the 370 there are a plethora of problems associated with registers:

- The 370 really has fewer than 16 registers because at least one must be reserved for program addressability.

- The fact that integer multiply destroys a

pair of registers introduces complications.

- The PL.8 compiler has never really exploited 370 instructions that use register pairs such as the loop closing BXLE op and double length shifts. (We are not alone in not using BXLE. It has a frequency of less than .01% on most execution samples.)

- The fact that some arithmetic and logical instructions work on less than a full word is a constant problem. It takes a lot of special analysis to decide when a short op can be used.

While the ROMP does have some minor irregularities in its register scheme, it is a substantial improvement on our past architectures, resulting in few problems for an optimizing compiler whose goal is to retain many available quantities in registers.

Checking and Linkage
In recent years programming languages have attempted to guard against programming errors and raise the level of the source language. The ROMP instruction set supports both.

The trap instructions provide an economic method to test for unusual or erroneous conditions during execution. Pascal and PL.8 both customarily run in production with checking enabled. However, it is possible to eliminate these checks. By having separate checking ops and then optimizing code, the compiler writer can ensure that the correctness criteria of a wide variety of languages are efficiently enforced.

The efficient implementation of a language like C, in which primitives are coded as basic functions, clearly depends on linkage. However, higher level languages which implement data abstractions also depend on the subroutine mechanisms. In implementing procedure call, the ROMP convention is to load the first four parameters into registers. The invoked procedure may then use them in place or copy them into other registers. The important point is that they seldom need to be copied into storage, an expensive operation. Longer parameter lists must be put in storage, but these are relatively infrequent. This strategy is much more efficient than the traditional 370 or UNIX type linkage, which passes parameters in storage. When invoking

a procedure, it is not normally necessary to load its address. System routines such as multiply or the primitive storage allocator are kept in low memory and the 24-bit absolute branch can be used to access them. Relative branching within a bound module, which is as large as a megabyte, is also possible with a single instruction. On entry to a procedure it is merely necessary to do a Store Multiple to save any registers that will be used and bump the stack pointer. Stack overflow is normally caught by an attempt to reference a protected page. (For procedures with large stack frames an explicit check is made.) Exit from a procedure consists of loading the return value in a register, restoring the saved registers and executing a branch register.

In practice, there are many variations on this theme, depending on the language, system conventions, and the user's program. For example, in Figure 1 we see the object code for a function that performs the typical C storage-to-storage move. Because it is able to work entirely out of registers that are, by convention, not saved over a call, it has no prologue and an epilogue that consists of a branch register. As source programs and languages become more complex, procedure call overhead will increase, but the compiler writer can always choose the minimum code sequence for the task at hand. One interesting consequence of the MMU relocate is that, given inverted page tables, many systems will want to allocate a very large contiguous stack when a process is created. There is no reason to maintain the stack in disjoint sections, as the mere existence of address space does not degrade performance as is the case with conventional page tables.

High-Level Functions
High-level functions on the ROMP are implemented with subroutines rather than microcode. The most obvious examples are

```
/* move to a byte of zeros. */
move (t, s)
char *t, *s;

while (*t + + = *s + +);
return;
```

multiply, divide and storage-to-storage move. On 370 instruction traces, move constitutes about 2% of all executions, making it, by far, the most important complex instruction. It

Object Code for ROMP

```
2: 000000                                    PDEF    move
5: 000000                          %6:
5: 000000 LCS     4003                        LCS    r0,$MEMORY+*s(r3)
5: 000002 INC     9131                        INC    r3,r3,1
5: 000004 INC     9121                        INC    r2,r2,1
5: 000006 CIS     9400                        CIS    cr,r0,0
5: 000008 BNBX    89AF FFFC                   BFX    cr,b26/eq,%6
5: 00000C STC     DE02 FFFF                   STC    r0,$MEMORY+*t-1(r2)
7: 000010 BNBR    E88F                         BFR    24,r15
```

Figure 1 Example

tends to consume close to 10% of the execution time. On large 370 machines 2 bytes are moved per cycle. (A cycle is taken to mean the time for a minimum op such as a register add.) For aligned moves, the ROMP can achieve close to this rate by means of an "unrolled" loop. For unaligned moves, a carefully handcrafted subroutine has been written. It uses ops which are of otherwise marginal utility, such as MCxx. There are even some compensations for not having the 370 MVC op. The ROMP move subroutine has been tailored to make moves of overlapped data nondestructive, thus satisfying the PL.8 rule. Once again we note that high-level instructions never quite do what they are supposed to do, but low-level ops can be specialized to the specific requirements.

The various versions of multiply on 370 constitute about .1% of all instructions executed. High-performance 370 machines tend to have a very expensive multiplier. Low-end machines implement the multiply instruction with a microcode operator that is the functional equivalent of the ROMP Multiply Step instruction. It is hard to see how the ROMP solution results in significantly worse performance. Sometimes there may be better performance. Constant multiplies can be done with adds and shifts. Some applications may not require a full 32-bit multiply. If the multiplier is only 12 bits long, then it is possible to get a product with six rather than 16 multiply step instructions. Once again the basic instruction set permits the user or compiler writer to do exactly what he wants with great efficiency rather than depending on the foresight of some computer architects. (Those of us who participated in the development of the ROMP architecture are constantly grateful that we did not enshrine our more exotic requirements in silicon.)

One of the sadder sequences of code is to

see a divide by two in a binary search or heap sort implemented with a divide rather than a shift instruction. Even on high-performance machines, divide can take almost ten times a shift. That is a big loss of performance in a loop that is likely to be very important. This doesn't occur because compiler writers are unaware that a right shift can sometimes replace a divide by a power of two. The problem is negative numbers as dividends. (− 1)/2 is 0 on 370. − 1 shifted right one bit is still − 1. The substitution of a shift for a divide only works for positive dividends. For the PL.8 language we decided to implement a true twos complement divide subroutine using the Euclidean algorithm that rounds down rather than toward 0. Thus replacing divides with shifts gives the same result. In this case a low-level instruction set gave us a new view of source language semantics. We simply implemented the divide subroutine that we wanted rather than accepting built-in semantics.

The ROMP does have Load and Store Multiple ops. It would be possible to get along without them. However, this is one case where a high-level instruction improves performance. This is because they permit the CPU to send one address to the memory subsystem and then do a series of Loads or Stores without the interference of fetching a series of instructions and sending effective addresses to the memory subsystem.

The ROMP approach to implementing high-level function frees the compiler writer and user from the tyranny of instruction sets without giving up any significant performance. Furthermore, the engineer can concentrate on making Load, Store and Branch run well. Here is the frequency of execution of the top ten instructions in a typical snapshot of 370 execution.

Instruction	% of Executions
BC:Branch Condition	20.2
L:Load	15.5
TM:Test Under Mask	6.1
ST:Store	5.9
LR:Load Register	4.7
LA:Load Address	4.0
LTR:Test Register	3.8
BCR:Branch Register	2.9
MVC:Move Characters	2.1
LH:Load Half Word	1.8

Together these constitute 67% of all instructions executed. Clearly the vast majority of the over two hundred 370 instructions occur a good deal less than 1% of the time. Most of the above have direct counterparts in the ROMP instruction set. Other than move, it is hard to think of any 370 instruction which might have improved ROMP performance if it had been implemented.

Code Size and Path Length
The 801 minicomputer was designed to have the shortest possible path length, and code size was sacrificed to achieve this. This is highly appropriate on a machine with a cache. In a machine with a storage hierarchy, most of the faults come from referencing data. Doubling the size of the code only marginally increases the number of faults. However, the ROMP does not have a cache. In order to multiplex the 32-bit memory channel with instructions and data, it helps to have short instructions.

For this reason the ROMP has short forms of many commonly occurring full-function instructions. In addition, a compromise was made such that, of the register-to-register operations, only CAS, the form of add that does not set the condition register, is fully three-address. Shifts have the paired form while subtract and the logical ops destroy one operand. This is a compromise. Add occurs so frequently that a 16-bit, three-address format has a big benefit. There are not enough code points to have all the other RR instructions in 16-bit, nondestructive format. Because the register allocator was able to coalesce operands most of the time, a 16-bit, two-operand format was chosen for the other RR ops. Similar reasoning led us to have short-form increment and decrement instructions.

All in all, the ROMP is surprisingly space efficient without undue performance loss. The average length of a ROMP instruction varies from application to application, but is usually well under 3 bytes. In some cases, the ROMP does require an added instruction but it is relatively infrequent and an easy decision for the compiler.

Details
A number of small details contribute to

making the ROMP a good target for compilers.

- Condition codes tend to be an awkward match for many systematic methods of compilation. In the ROMP, those instructions that set the relational bits of the condition register set them in the same way as a compare with zero. This permits the compiler to eliminate all compares with zero that are preceded by an instruction that sets the same register as the register comparand. It is also important to not set the condition register on Load, Store, or the basic Adds that compute addresses. This permits code to be inserted, or rearranged without worrying about the condition register. The condition register test bit provides an efficient means to move and compare arbitrary bits even when their position in a word must be computed at run time. This makes it very efficient to implement packed arrays of bits and Pascal-type sets.

- Load instructions that fetch bytes and half-words from storage either set the remainder of the register to zero or fill it with sign bits. This makes it easier to treat partial words as algebraic or logical quantities. On 370 one of the most common idioms is a subtract of a register from itself followed by an insert character. LC does the entire job on the ROMP.

- The Load and Store Multiple instructions can be used to do block moves or zero large areas in an efficient manner.

- Sometimes constant data will not fit into the ROMP 16-bit immediate field. Instructions are provided that treat the immediate field as a left-justified quantity. It is thus possible to follow either of two strategies. Use two ops if either the upper or lower form is insufficient. The alternative is to manufacture the constant in a register, which requires two instructions, but then the constant may be reused many times by short, fast RR ops.

Other Methodologies
Not all source languages will be implemented with optimizing compilers like PL.8.

Where high-quality object code is not crucial it may pay to have a very fast compiler that produces mediocre object code. A number of features make this a reasonably easy task. Even code from a very naive compiler is quite compact. The large number of general-purpose registers means it is easy to reuse values over short stretches. The large displacement means one can reserve large areas for intermediate results without fearing overflow. High-level function can be invoked via subroutines with a reasonable in-line overhead. Finally, code can be addressed and constants can always be manufactured on-the-fly without establishing or maintaining addressability to code segments and a literal pool as is required on 370.

Another method of implementation is interpretation. The ROMP is a very good interpreter. This should not surprise us as it is really a general-purpose micro engine.

Conclusion
The ROMP architecture provides the high-level language compiler writer with the right set of implementation primitives. Its strength is the ability to combine the basic operations in new ways suited to the task at hand. In Figure 1 we have an example of how a common idiom in C is efficiently implemented. It is hard to see how the most specialized instruction could improve very much on this. After all, there will have to be a fetch and store, as well as a test and bumps for each character moved. A high-level instruction would be further complicated by considerations of crossing page boundaries, running too long, etc. If we build in this instruction we are tailoring the machine to C; other languages such as Pascal, ADA, FORTRAN and COBOL that do not share the

C convention that character strings are terminated with a zero, will find the op useless. However, even C may nct find this the best strategy for character movement all the time. Large buffers should not be moved 1 byte at a time. Then there are other idioms in C, for searching tables, scanning input forward and backward, looking for other characters and an infinite number of other tasks. Is each of these to be a special op? Will the compiler have to look for complicated patterns trying to match a complex function to a complex instruction? The ROMP permits the compiler writer to combine primitives to efficiently solve the particular problem at hand for a wide variety of source languages.

As the programming community moves toward languages that are more powerful than C it becomes even more urgent to rely on basic constructs. Only the simplest languages can be based on complex, high-level messages. Thousands of hieroglyphics are much less powerful than an alphabet of twenty-odd characters. Fast, primitive operations will be required to efficiently implement the high level languages of the future.

References
1. M. Auslander and M.E. Hopkins, "An Overview of the PL.8 compiler," *Proc. of the Sigplan '82 Symposium on Compiler Writing,* Boston, MA, June 23-25, 1982.

2. George Radin, "The 801 Minicomputer," *Proc. of Symposium on Architectural Support for Programming Languages and Operating Systems,* Palo Alto, California, March 1-3, 1982.

3. Gregory J. Chaitin, Marc A. Auslander, Ashok K. Chandra, John Cocke, Martin E. Hopkins, and Peter W. Markstein, "Register Allocation via Coloring," *Computer Languages,* Vol 6, No 1, 1981, 47-57.

ENGINEERING A RISC COMPILER SYSTEM

F. Chow, M. Himelstein, E. Killian, L. Weber

MIPS Computer Systems
930 Arques Ave
Sunnyvale, CA 94086

Abstract

RISC machine compilers play a more important role in enhancing system performance than conventional compilers. In a RISC system, traditional boundaries between hardware, compiler, and operating system are modified to optimize overall system performance. Responsibility for a given function shifts to the compiler system when the compiler can do a better job, often using special techniques to accomplish its new tasks. With careful engineering, such a system can be both run-time and compile-time efficient.

Introduction

The MIPS machine, like other RISC machines, provides an interesting challenge for compiler writers. A RISC machine provides primitive hardware functions rather than bundling functionality into complex instructions, allowing the compiler to optimize below the level of other architectures. The compiler can generate optimal code for a simple machine more easily since the architecture provides fewer alternatives in performing a given function. This allows the compiler to focus its attention on other aspects of optimization, including global optimization and an efficient run-time environment.

The MIPS machine was designed according to RISC principles: maximizing performance through trade-offs between hardware and software. As such, the architectural design[1] was developed in parallel with the operating system[2] and compiler effort. Many architectural decisions were made based on special support provided by the compilers.

The MIPS compiler system was designed to satisfy a number of objectives:
- It must support a reduced instruction set by providing for functions not present in the hardware.
- It must produce code and data that achieve maximum run-time efficiency.
- It must be compile-time efficient.
- It must be tested and bootstrapped before having hardware.

This paper presents the MIPS compiler system by addressing these issues and relating them to the relevant components in the system.

Overview of the MIPS Compiler Suite

The MIPS compiler suite contains compilers for C, Pascal and FORTRAN 77. FORTRAN and Pascal adhere to the existing ANSI Standards, and C conforms to the defacto standard.[3] MIPS Pascal and FORTRAN contain common extensions. As figure 1 shows, each language has its own front-end, while common back-end phases generate and optimize code. MIPS' run-time libraries provide language-dependent functions for each language.

The front-ends translate the semantics of the different languages into an intermediate

	cpp		macro pre-processor
pc Pascal	f77 FORTRAN	cc C	
	Uload		U-code loader optional
	Umerge		procedure integrator optional
	Uopt		global optimizer optional
	Ugen		MIPS code generator
	As1		reorganizer

dbx Debugger	ld Linker	Library

Figure 1 - MIPS Compiler Structure

representation, called U-Code, used by several of the common phases. U-Code is a stack-oriented pseudo-machine language originating from the version in use at Stanford University.[4] With U-Code as the intermediate representation, the system provides uniform compilation and optimization support to C, Pascal and FORTRAN.

Each front-end produces a symbol table file that contains loader and debugger information. Each compiler phase may add to or modify the symbol table to provide information for the loader or extend debugger information. The loader uses the symbol table information for relocation and merges it into the final object module. The source-level debugger uses the symbol table to provide a robust debugging environment even in the face of optimizations.

Every compiler phase performs optimizations. An optional phase, called Uopt, performs global optimization and register allocation. The code generator, called Ugen, does local optimizations and produces MIPS assembly language output. The final assembly phase, called As1, does peep-hole optimizations and architecture-dependent pipeline scheduling and produces a MIPS machine language object module.

Supporting a Reduced Instruction Set

The MIPS machine has a simple and uniform instruction set. All instructions are 32 bits in length and execute in one cycle. The compiler synthesizes operations that require greater instruction length or cycles from sequences of instructions.[5] Close interaction between compiler design and architecture design[6] results in synthesized operations that are as efficient as their counterparts in conventional machines, and sometimes more efficient.

Accessing Data

The MIPS architecture provides only one addressing mode: the sum of a register and a 16-bit signed offset. Addressing static memory requires a 32-bit absolute address, so the assembler uses two instructions to synthesize an absolute address reference: the first loads a register with the high 16 bits of the address and the second performs the reference using the low 16 address bits as the offset from that register. This 8-byte sequence is comparable in length to an absolute address reference in other architectures (for example, it is 7 bytes on a

VAX*), and is just as fast. Other optimizations further reduce the cost of this synthesis. For example, pipeline reorganization may schedule these instructions separately to occupy idle cycles in other sequences, or peephole optimization may recognize the high 16 bits of the address as common to two references.

To reduce the cost of static memory references even further, the system dedicates one register, called the global pointer, to address 64K of static data. The code generator, assembler, and linker all participate in grouping small pieces of static data so they can be addressed by this one register in a one cycle, 4-byte reference, which is a substantial improvement in density and speed. Control over all components of the system was key in using this simple technique.

The global optimizer also plays a role in reducing the cost of accessing 32-bit constants and addresses. Since it is expensive to load such constants into registers, the optimizer analyzes their appearances and assigns them to registers in the regions where they occur. It also eliminates load redundancies by moving the loading of these constants out of loops.

Calling Procedures

Procedure call, entry, and return is another area where the compiler must synthesize the proper functionality. A good design allows effective subsetting of the complete procedure call mechanism. In our design, a procedure call, entry, and return can be as fast and simple as two instructions in two cycles. The protocol specifies only how to pass parameters and what registers to preserve across the procedure call. This allows the called procedure to organize its stack frame (if any) as appropriate.

For each procedure, the code generator allocates space for the largest parameter list used in the body. The code allocates this space once on entry to the procedure. Each point of call requires no further stack manipulation. The first four words of parameters are placed in specific registers (often the parameter computation is done directly into the appropriate register), and other parameters are placed in the stack. 95% of the calls require no memory references because they pass fewer than four words of parameters. An instruction stores the return address in a register and transfers control to the called procedure. The contract between caller and callee specifies that the callee may freely use the *unsaved* registers, but must preserve the

---

* VAX is a Trademark of Digital Equipment Corporation.

saved registers. Variables live at the point of call will be allocated to saved registers by Uopt and Ugen. The result of a function is returned in a register.

On entry to a procedure, the first four parameters and the return address appear in registers and the other parameters are on the the stack. The called procedure then allocates a stack frame by subtracting the frame size from the stack pointer, saving registers with explicit store instructions, and moves register parameters and the return address to home locations. On return, the sequence is reversed.

A procedure that does not call any other procedure is called a *leaf procedure*. Leaf procedures do not need parameter and return address registers for further calls, and the parameters and return address are assigned to their input registers. No data movement is necessary. A leaf can allocate register variables to unsaved registers, eliminating the need to save and restore registers. With no registers to save and no calls to make, a leaf often needs no stack frame because everything resides in registers. At this point the subtract and add from

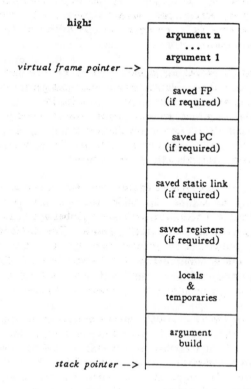

Figure 2 - MIPS Stack Frame

the stack pointer are eliminated, leaving only the call and return jumps as overhead.

A frame pointer is used in most linkage conventions to support the allocation of data on the activation stack. The frame pointer mechanism is not used in the MIPS compiler system. This is possible because the the frame pointer is usually known to the compiler to be at a fixed offset from the stack pointer, which is computed to be the maximum size of the stack frame. A compile-time fixed offset from the stack pointer is called the *virtual frame pointer*. When a procedure uses dynamic allocation, which is rare, the code generator allocates the fixed-size portion of the stack frame and then uses another register to remember this point in the stack before allocating the variable-sized data. Figure 2 illustrates the activation stack frame at the point of a call.

To support stack traces and general debugging, the compiler adds symbol table entries to specify the register and size that together represent a virtual frame pointer. The symbol table specifies the location of the return address (either in its input register or in the stack frame). We have shifted the task of maintaining a simple activation stack for debugging from procedure entry to compile and debug time.

Scheduling Instructions in Software

In the MIPS machine's pipeline, "load" and "branch" instructions cause memory delays. Rather than providing expensive scheduling and interlocking in hardware, we rely on the final assembly phase of the compiler, As1, to ensure consistency between instructions.[7] An optimization called pipeline reorganization improves performance by 20% on average, by ordering instructions to remove memory delays and to overlap floating point instruction with other instructions.

A load delay occurs when one instruction loads a value into a register and the next instruction uses that register. As1 changes the instruction order so that the instruction following the load does not depend on the load. This permits one instruction to access memory in parallel while executing another instruction.

Branches in the MIPS architecture take effect after the instruction following the branch instruction; this is called a *delayed branch*. The hardware can execute the instruction already in the pipeline while accessing the instruction determined by the branch. As1 places an instruction that logically precedes the branch instruction in the delay slot of the branch.

If As1 cannot find a suitable instruction from above the branch, it replicates the instruction at the target of the branch provided no side-effects occur if the branch falls through.

The independent floating point unit can execute its instructions in parallel with ordinary instructions and memory operations. As1 orders instructions so that the machine does useful work while the floating point unit executes its slightly slower instructions.

Reorganization presents an interesting challenge to the debugger. Source-level debuggers provide facilities to stop and examine program state on any source line. A reorganized program may have already executed instructions from lines following the desired source line and may not have executed all the instructions preceding the line.

To permit the debugging of production programs, the MIPS compiler system stores procedure-relative line number information for each instruction. The debugger uses the line number information to simulate a source-code consistent view of program execution.

Handling Complex Operations

The MIPS instruction set lacks bit field operations. The front-ends of the compiler assume responsibility for translating bit field inserts and extracts into machine primitive instructions such as shifts, bit-wise AND and bit-wise OR. The global optimizer can recognize these simpler operations and apply its optimization techniques on all or part of them. For example, optimization improves assignments to multiple bit fields in the same word.

Another example of a complex operation is multiplication. The final assembly phase of the compiler translates multiplication into optimal instruction sequences. Even though the MIPS machine has a hardware multiplication unit, it is often better to synthesize a multiplication from simpler instructions when multiplying by simple constants. For example, multiplication by 14 executes in three cycles (two shifts and a subtract), which is faster than a hardware multiply.

The MIPS machine only provides the fastest executing forms of branch instructions, which comprise the majority of branches based on dynamic frequency. More complex branch conditions are synthesized by the final assembly phase. The assembler can use the extra instruction to fill a delay slot of another instruction.

Achieving Run-time Efficiency

The MIPS machine provides an ideal target for many optimizations. Work at Stanford[8] shows that machine-independent optimizations are particularly effective on RISC machines. The global optimizer, which operates on U-code, is derived from that work. MIPS has refined the U-Code intermediate language to make it expose most MIPS machine primitives to the optimizer. In addition, most of the optimizations were specifically tailored to the MIPS environment. The global optimizations performed include: copy propagation, common subexpressions, invariant code motion, removal of redundant assignments, strength reduction, and linear function test replacements.

Uopt also provides register allocation among its optimizations. The load/store nature of RISC machines makes register allocation especially effective. By globally analyzing usage patterns, the register allocator decides which variables best reside in registers. Uopt uses a priority-based global graph-coloring algorithm,[9] which often achieves optimal results with reasonable compile-time cost. Register allocation helps realize the full benefits of the other global optimizations, since intermediate computational results are best saved in registers. The 31 general-purpose registers provided by the MIPS machine also increases the versatility of the register allocator.

The MIPS global optimizer operates on one procedure at a time. Because large procedures generally offer more opportunities for optimization, MIPS provides a procedure integrator, called Umerge, which selectively copies procedures in-line at their point of call, eliminating call overhead while increasing the global optimizer's impact.

Both Uopt and Umerge operate on a single compilation unit at a time. The MIPS compiler also provide the framework for supporting global optimizations across an entire load module. The U-Code loader, called Uload, merges separate compilation units into a single file at the U-Code level. This enables multi-module programs to achieve the same degree of optimization as single-module programs.

The code generator was designed specifically for the MIPS architecture and generates very good local code. Although attention to detail is critical, we found code selection straight-forward for the MIPS machine. To improve local code quality, Ugen recognizes and optimizes local common subexpressions, performs simplification and folding in expressions, deletes dead code, and does branch and label optimization. Ugen also allocates expression temporaries to registers in a manner which maximizes reorganization opportunities.

Assuring Compile-time Efficiency

To reduce compilation time, the MIPS compiler system uses binary forms for all interfaces, including U-Code, symbol table files and assembler code. The compilers are self compiling, and therefore self optimizing.

The MIPS compiler system employs a sophisticated symbol table. The symbol table supplies a large amount of source file information to the symbolic debugger and external symbol information to the loader. The design goals for the symbol table included minimizing disk space usage and reducing the cost to compiler passes. The symbol table also contains enough information to help debug optimized code. Due to the symbol table design, full debugging symbol tables are typically a third to a half smaller than 4.2BSD or System V COFF symbol tables, even though they contain more information.

The loader is another example of compiler efficiency. In a multi-module program, changing one module requires recompiling only that module, but requires relinking all the modules and libraries. Therefore, we have stressed efficiency in the loader design. For example, we have optimized library scanning by including a hash table in the library for externals. To process a library, the loader hashes the remaining undefined symbols into the library's hash table. This scan is efficient because a program typically contains fewer undefined symbols during a load than defined externals in the library.

Sophisticated optimizations such as those found in our compiler system can significantly lengthen compilation time. We are using execution time statistics to provide the compiler with accurate information on what areas of a program require optimization. This feedback mechanism allows the global optimizer and procedure integrator to optimize only those areas which promise the greatest gains.

Testing Strategies

The RISC approach is most effective when the hardware, compiler, and operating system are developed simultaneously. In development of the compiler, the goal has been to have a fully-tested production-quality system available at the same time as the hardware. To support operating system work with a similar goal, a well-debugged compiler

was actually needed substantially earlier. No compiler system can achieve production-quality status without extensive testing, particularly on many large programs.

Simulation is the answer, but conventional simulation is far too slow to permit extensive testing of large programs. A novel simulator, called Moxie, was developed that translates a MIPS object file to a VAX object file. Moxie translates object file formats as well as converting MIPS instructions to VAX instructions. The resulting VAX program is then run, and in effect simulates the MIPS code. Moxie also translates MIPS UNIX* system calls to VAX UNIX system calls, thus allowing the simulation of programs that do arbitrary I/O and system interaction.

This technique allows MIPS code to "run" at the rate of 600K instructions per second on a VAX 780, sufficiently fast to run numerous UNIX programs (such as yacc, grep, diff, and cpp), to bootstrap the MIPS compiler itself, and to test the compilers with C, FORTRAN, and Pascal validation suites.

Moxie also has extensive tracing facilities that provide precise instruction counting statistics and a cache simulator that models the effects of program interaction with main memory. With these tools, accurate benchmark (e.g. whetstone, linpack) results were obtained before hardware was available.

A symbolic debugger layered on top of Moxie uses both the original and translated binaries along with a Moxie-generated table mapping MIPS instruction addresses to their VAX counterparts. This environment provides both machine-level access to MIPS registers and instructions (use for compiler development) and source-level debugging (useful for applications written in C, FORTRAN, and Pascal).

Conclusion

The compiler is an integral part of a RISC-based computer system. The MIPS compiler system is responsible for providing functionality not present in the hardware. Supporting absolute address references, multiplication, and procedure call mechanism using more primitive hardware functions are a few examples of operations that the MIPS compiler system does better than an equivalent hardware-only implementation. The techniques are simple, but quite effective. The

---

* UNIX is a Trademark of AT&T.

compiler also performs important traditional optimizations. The net effect is a system that is both compile-time and run-time efficient. We believe this approach, based on careful engineering of the compiler system with respect to the underlying hardware, results in a superior compiler compared to current multi-targeted compilers.

Acknowledgement

We would like to thank the members of the compiler development group for their fine job in implementing the compiler system. We would also like to thank the MIPS architecture group for providing a very clean machine architecture. And, we especially thank all those users who found that last bug in the compiler.

1. John Moussouris, Les Crudele, Dan Freitas, Craig Hansen, Ed Hudson, Steve Przybylski, Tom Riordan, and Chris Rowen, "A CMOS RISC Processor with Integrated System Functions," *Proceedings COMPCON*, IEEE, (March 4-6, 1986).

2. Mike DeMoney, Jim Moore, and John Mashey, "Operating System Support on a RISC," *Proceedings COMPCON*, IEEE, (March 4-6, 1986).

3. Brian W. Kernighan and Dennis M. Ritchie, *The C Programming Language*, Prentice-Hall (1978).

4. Peter Nye and Fred Chow, "A Transporter's Guide to the Stanford U-Code Compiler System," *Technical Report*, Computer Systems Laboratory, Stanford University, (June 1983).

5. M. E. Hopkins, "Compiling High-Level Functions on Low-Level Machines," *Proceedings ICCD*, IEEE , (October 1983).

6. John L. Hennessy, "VLSI Processor Architecture," *IEEE Trans. on Computers* C-33(12) pp. 1221-1246 (Dec 1984).

7. Thomas Gross, "Code Optimization of Pipeline Constraints," *Technical Report No. 83-255*, Computer Systems Laboratory, Stanford University, (December 1983).

8. Fred Chow, "A Portable Machine-Independent Global Optimizer — Design and Measurements," *Ph.D. Thesis and Technical Report 83-254*, Computer Systems Laboratory, Stanford University, (Dec 1983).

9. Fred Chow and John Hennessy, "Register Allocation by Priority-based Coloring," *Proceedings SIGPLAN*, ACM, (June 17-22, 1984).

"Optimizing Compilers for SPARC" by S.S. Muchnick, *Sun Technology*, Summer 1988, pages 64–67.

WEAVING ELEGANT PROGRAMS FOR SPARC BEGINS WITH ITS HIGH-PERFORMANCE COMPILERS

SPARC (Scalable Processor ARChitecture), a new architecture for computer systems, was designed by a team of Sun hardware and software engineers. Sun provides compilers for C, FORTRAN 77 with VMS extensions, Pascal, and Modula-2 for SPARC, all based on the same code generation and optimization technology. In addition, Sun offers Common Lisp and will soon offer Ada for SPARC (derived from third-party products), with Smalltalk, Prolog, Mainsail, and other languages on the way from other vendors. We deal with support for the first set of languages in depth here and mention some of the others peripherally.

RISC Technology

As a reduced instruction set computer (RISC) architecture, SPARC achieves high performance by making the things that account for the overwhelming majority of real computing as fast as possible, while not unduly slowing down other operations. Judicious application of this principle results in an architecture that has a relatively simple set of operations and only a few addressing modes. As seen by a compiler, SPARC is in the Berkeley RISC II and SOAR tradition, with register windows, delayed branches and delayed loads with hardware interlocks, a floating-point coprocessor, and a few special instructions to support tagged data. All instructions are 32 bits long, and most take only a single machine cycle to execute in current implementations.

Because only a few choices are available (or, in many cases, only one) for the proper instructions and addressing modes to use for a given operation, compilers can generate locally optimal code for expressions with relative ease, leaving more time available for developers to address questions of the runtime environment and global code optimization.

Registers

The effective use of registers is typically among the most important resource-allocation issues for

This article is an expanded version of a paper delivered at the COMPCON '88 Conference, March 1988, San Francisco, California.

Optimizing Compilers for SPARC

a compiler. The load/store nature of RISC architectures underscores the criticality of effective register usage. Robert Garner describes SPARC's register model in some detail ("SPARC Architecture," pp 42-55). Here we provide a synopsis of the features of greatest importance to compiler writers and then describe how our compilers use the registers.

SPARC provides three sets of registers that are visible to the user program at any time:

- global integer registers
- global floating-point registers
- windowed integer registers

Global integer register g0 is special in that it reads as zero and discards values written to it. The other global integer registers are managed by software using the caller-saves protocol (that is, around a subroutine call, the caller saves and restores the registers containing live values). These registers could be used for global variables and pointers, either visible to the programmer or maintained as part of the program's execution environment. For instance, one could, by convention, address global variables by offsets from one or more global registers, allowing quick access to 2^{13} bytes of global storage per register so dedicated. The global floating-point registers are also managed entirely by software. Our compilers use them as caller-saved register variables and temporaries.

The windowed registers are further subdivided into three sets: *in*s, *out*s, and *local*s. A save instruction may be executed as part of a procedure prologue, changing the machine's interpretation of register numbers so that the calling procedure's *out*s become the called procedure's *in*s, and a new set of *local*s and *out*s is provided. In Sun's SPARC compilers, the save also allocates a new stack frame by setting the new stack pointer from the old one. Similarly, the restore instruction executed in a procedure epilogue restores the register-number interpretation to the caller's state and simultaneously cuts back the stack. The overlap of *in* and *out* registers provides a way to pass most parameters in registers. One of the *out*s receives a call's return address, and another is the caller's stack pointer, which becomes the callee's frame pointer. This leaves six registers for user parameters[1] (additional parameters are passed on the memory stack). A procedure returns a value by writing it to one or more of its *in* registers, where it is available to the caller in the corresponding *out*. Unused *in* registers and all the *local*s are available for a procedure's automatic storage and temporaries. Because an implementation can provide only a bounded set of windows, provision exists for a trap to occur when a procedure is entered if all windows are in use and when a procedure is exited from if the window being returned to does not have the proper values in it. The operating system can then spill or refill register windows, as needed.

Addressing and Stack Models

The computational instructions obtain all their data from registers and immediate fields in instructions and put their results in registers. Only load and store instructions access memory. The load and store instructions have two addressing modes—one that adds the contents of two integer registers and one that adds the contents of an integer register and a 13-bit signed immediate. The semantics of g0 also make an absolute addressing mode available.

All but one of the integer computational instructions use the same means to specify their operands and results—that is, one operand comes from a general register, and the other either comes from a register or is a sign-extended 13-bit immediate, and the result is stored in a register. The exception is the sethi instruction, which constructs 32-bit constants and addresses for access to global data. It loads an immediate 22-bit constant into the high end of a register and puts 0s in the other 10 bits. Thus, for example, the following sequence (see the box on pp 76-77 for a description of SPARC assembly language)

```
sethi      %hi(loc),%i1
ld         [%i1+%lo(loc)],%i2
```

can be used to load the word at address loc into i2. Although the need for an extra instruction to construct 32-bit constants and addresses may appear to be a disadvantage, it is fully in line with RISC design principles—it helps make the common cases fast without significantly slowing down the low-frequency ones. Constants are usu-

Figure 1. *Register names and special uses.*

Register Names			
Register numbers	Alternate numbering	Names	Windowed?
r24 to r31	i0 to i7	*in*s	yes
r16 to r23	l0 to l7	*local*s	yes
r8 to r15	o0 to o7	*out*s	yes
r0 to r7	g0 to g7	*global*s	no

Distinguished Registers	
Register	Use
g0	zero value & discard result
sp (same as o6)	stack pointer
fp (same as i6)	frame pointer
o7	return address

ally short, so sethi is rarely needed, and the address construction is frequently optimizable to a single instruction because %hi(loc) turns out to be a loop invariant.

Despite the number of registers available to programmers, many procedures still require a memory stack frame. The stack frame may contain several sorts of elements:

- parameters beyond the sixth, if any
- parameters that must be addressable are stored in the stack at entry to a procedure because registers do not have memory addresses
- a one-word hidden parameter, used when the caller is expecting to be returned a C-language *struct* by value; it gives the address of the stack space allocated by the caller to receive the value
- space for the window-overflow trap handler to store the procedure's *in* and *local* registers
- automatic variables that must be addressable, including automatic arrays and automatic records
- some compiler-generated temporaries
- space for saving floating-point registers across calls

Automatic variables on the stack are addressed relative to fp, whereas temporaries and outgoing parameters are addressed relative to sp. When a procedure is active, its stack frame appears as in Figure 2.

Synthesized Instructions

We use the term *synthesized instruction* to refer to one that generally is included in a more complex architecture, such as the DEC VAX or IBM 370, but that is replaced by a series of instructions or a special-case subroutine call in a RISC architecture. In SPARC, the most important instances of synthesized instructions are for procedure call, procedure entry, multiply, and divide.

Procedure Call and Entry

Rather than provide a complex procedure-call instruction such as the DEC VAX CALLS, which takes an argument count and list of arguments and sets up the stack frame in addition to passing control to the procedure, SPARC provides two instructions, namely call and jmpl, that can invoke a procedure. Both call and jmpl occupy a single cycle plus a delay slot. The call instruction takes a 30-bit PC-relative *word* displacement from the instruction; it branches to the target address and stores the return address in o7. Jump and link (jmpl) takes a target address that is the sum of two registers or a register and an immediate and stores the return address in a specified

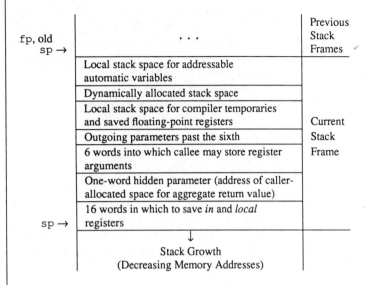

register. Additional instructions are required to pass parameters and to move from one register window to the next. The save instruction accomplishes the latter as part of the entry-point sequence of the called routine, and a corresponding restore instruction occurs on exit. The save and restore instructions also set the callee's stack pointer and reset it for the caller.

Aggregate Value Return

Some programming languages, including C, some dialects of Pascal, and Modula-2, allow a user to define functions that return an aggregate value, such as a C *struct* or a Pascal *record*. Because such a value generally does not fit into the registers, another value-returning protocol must be used to return the value in memory. Reentrancy and efficiency considerations require that the memory used to hold such a return value be allocated by the function's caller. The address of this memory area is passed as the one-word hidden parameter mentioned above. Because of the lack of type safety in the C language, a function should not assume that its caller is expecting an aggregate return value and has provided a valid memory address. Thus, some additional handshaking is required.

When a procedure expecting an aggregate function value to be returned is compiled, an unimplemented instruction (unimp) is placed at the point to which the callee would ordinarily return. The immediate field in this instruction is the low-order 12 bits of the size in bytes of the aggregate value expected. When an aggregate-

Figure 2. *Memory stack layout for an active routine.*

returning function is about to return its value in the memory allocated by its caller, it first tests for the presence of this unimp instruction in the caller's instruction stream. If it finds it and the size is appropriate, the function returns control to the location following the unimp instruction. Otherwise, no value can be returned. Conversely, if a scalar-returning function is called when an aggregate value is expected, the function returns as usual, executing the unimp instruction and causing a trap. For example, suppose we define in C a pair-of-integers type PAIR:

```
typedef struct pair
{
        int first;
        int second;
}
        PAIR;
```

and call

```
PAIR p13;
p13 = make_pair(1,3);
```

with make_pair defined by

```
PAIR make_pair(m,n)
        int m, n;
{       PAIR p;
        p.first = m;
        p.second = n;
        return p;
}
```

The call to make_pair generates the code in Figure 3. The structure is returned from the subroutine by a special leaf routine (on entry to it, i7 contains the address of the call to make_pair, o0 contains the address of the *struct* being returned, and o1 contains the number of bytes the called routine expects to return) that executes the code shown in Figure 4.

Figure 3. *Code generated for the call to* make_pair.

```
add     %sp,LP15,%o0    ! construct 1-word hidden parameter
st      %o0,[%sp+64]    ! and save it in stack frame
mov     1,%o0           ! set up first argument
call    make_pair       ! call the routine
mov     3,%o1           ! set up second argument
                        ! in delay slot of call
unimp   8
        %fp,8,%o1       ! move the returned value
ld      [%o0],%o2       ! to its destination
ld      [%o0+4],%o3
st      %o2,[%o1]
st      %o3,[%o1+4]
```

Integer Multiplication and Division

SPARC provides no integer multiply, divide, or remainder instructions, so these operations are synthesized from more elementary instructions. SPARC has a multiply step instruction mulscc,[2] but it is not used to multiply variables by constants. Instead, SPARC does multiplication by constants known at compile time by using sequences of shifts and adds (it also uses subtracts if overflow detection is not an issue). For example, multiplication by 30 in a C program is performed by the following sequence:

```
sll     %o2,1,%o2       ! 2 * x → x
sll     %o2,4,%o3       ! 16 * x → y
sub     %o3,%o2,%o2     ! y - x → x
```

SPARC does multiplication of variables by variables and all divisions and remainders other than by powers of 2 by calling special leaf routines. Based on statistics gathered from running an instrumented version of the system, the routines are biased so as to terminate quickly for the common cases—namely, either operand being short in a multiply and the operands of a divide or remainder being about the same length. For example, for multiplication the length of the smaller operand determines the cycle count in the following manner[3]:

Length (in bits)	Cycles
1 to 4	18
5 to 8	25
9 to 12	33
13 to 16	41
17 to 32	60

Our measurements show that more than 90% of var x var multiplications have at least one nonnegative operand. They also show that more than 90% of the time, one of the operands is at most 7 bits long, and 99% of the time one is at most 9 bits long. Combining existing statistics on the distribution of operands presented in Magenheimer et al., 1987, with our own measurements, we estimate that the average multiplication (including both the constant- and variable-operand cases) takes less than 6 cycles, and the average var x var subcase takes about 24 cycles.

Tagged Data Support And Explicit Trapping

In addition to the ordinary add and subtract instructions, SPARC provides versions that interpret the low-order two bits of a word as a type tag. If the tags of the two operands are not both zero (or if arithmetic overflow occurs in the add or subtract operation), the integer overflow condition code bit is set, and (optionally) an overflow trap occurs. These tagged arithmetic instructions are intended to be used in implementations of languages such as Common Lisp and Smalltalk, which allow polymorphic functions. Sun Common Lisp currently uses the tagged instructions and has never existed in a form that did not use them. They cut the time necessary to do *fixnum* (integer) addition and subtraction from six cycles to three (or five to two, if the delay slots of the branches below can be filled productively). In particular, if one tags *fixnums* with the low-order two bits 0, then adding two tagged values in registers can be done by the code shown in Figure 5 instead of by that shown in Figure 6.

ParcPlace Smalltalk does not currently use the tagged instructions (and may never do so) because of some incompatible historical choices made in its tagging mechanism. The implementors estimate that they would increase overall performance by about 2.5%, but the Sun-4/200 is already the fastest Smalltalk engine available by a large margin.

Ada provides for the raising of exceptions during expression evaluation for certain operand values but does not require an exception until the data value is actually stored. One can, for example, compute an expression with halfword data in 32-bit arithmetic and only raise an exception if the final result is too large to store in a halfword. SPARC's explicit trap-on-condition instruction, ticc, accommodates this optimization by allowing one to generate (assuming 11 contains the value of the expression and g3 has been previously set to 2^{16}) the code in Figure 7 once before the store rather than after each operation. There is no loss of efficiency in implementing Ada arithmetic compared to architectures such as the VAX, which provide halfword arithmetic.

SPARC Compilers

The SPARC compilers for C, FORTRAN with VMS extensions, Modula-2, and Pascal are based on the same technology used in the Sun-2 and Sun-3 compilers, as described in Ghodssi et al., 1986. Because that paper describes the basic technology in detail, we concentrate here on the new SPARC-oriented components and the additional optimizations that Sun has added recently for all its architectures.

The SPARC versions of the C, FORTRAN, and Pascal compilers include global optimization, and all four include a new code generator, assembler, and peephole optimizer targeted to SPARC. The compilers are structured as shown in Figure 8. The component names that may not be familiar are as follows:

• *aliaser* determines which variables may at

```
        ld      [%i7+8],%o3      ! fetch 2nd instruction beyond the call
        and     %o1,0xfff,%o4    ! extract low-order 12 bits of size
        sethi   %hi(UNIMP),%o5   ! put high-order 20 bits of unimp in o5
        or      %o4,%o5,%o5      ! combine opcode and size
        cmp     %o5,%o3          ! compare with 2nd instr. beyond call
        bne     LE12             ! branch to return if no match
        nop

. . .

! copy the struct from [%o0], using the same loop the compiler
! does for large structure assignment

. . .

        add     %i7,4,%i7        ! bump return address beyond unimp
LE12:
        jmp     %i7+8            ! return
        restore                  ! restore register window
```

Figure 4. *Leaf routine for structure return.*

```
        taddcc  %11,%12,%o1      ! add tagged & set cond. codes
        bvs     nonfixnum        ! branch on overflow or nonzero tag
        nop
```

Figure 5. *Efficient way to add two tagged values.*

```
        or      %11,%12,%o1      ! extract or of tags
        and     %o1,3,%o1
        bnz     nonfixnum        ! branch on nonzero tag
        add     %11,%12,%o2
        bvs     nonfixnum        ! branch on overflow
        nop
```

Figure 6. *Naive way to add two tagged values.*

```
        subcc   %g3,%11,%g0      ! set cond. codes & discard arith. result
        tleu    overflow         ! trap on unsigned
```

Figure 7. *Code generated for halfword-overflow checking.*

some time point to the same location
• *iropt* is the global optimizer
• *cgrdr* translates the Sun IR intermediate code used by the global optimizer into the PCC trees expected by the code generator
• *c2* is the assembly-level optimizer

The arrows in Figure 8 describe the path followed when global optimization and inlining are both enabled. When either is disabled, certain components are skipped, in some cases depend-

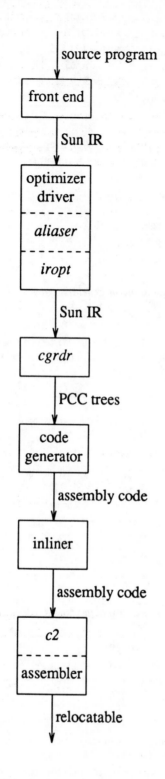

source program

↓

front end

↓ Sun IR

optimizer
driver
- - - - - -
aliaser
- - - - - -
iropt

↓ Sun IR

cgrdr

↓ PCC trees

code
generator

↓ assembly code

inliner

↓ assembly code

c2
- - - - - -
assembler

↓ relocatable

Figure 8. *Structure of the SPARC optimizing compilers.*

ing on the source language being compiled.

In contrast to our Sun-2 and Sun-3 compilers, which run *c2* as a separate pass prior to the assembler, the SPARC *c2* is integrated into the assembler and operates on an internal linked-list form of the assembly language. This technique results in nontrivial savings in compilation time because we read and write one less intermediate file.

The compilers support several levels of optimization that require various amounts of compilation time and produce various qualities of code. For example, the C compiler has four levels of optimization (in addition to the "no optimization" level):

O1   This level invokes only the peephole optimizer.

O2   This and the following levels invoke both the global and peephole optimizers. At the O2 level, expressions involving global variables and pointers are not candidates for optimization.

O3   This level optimizes expressions involving global variables but makes worst-case assumptions about pointers.

O4   This level traces, as assiduously as possible, what pointers may point to.

In general, the amount of compilation time required and the speed of the resulting code increase as the optimization level increases. It is interesting to note, however, that O3 and O4 almost always produce the same code, but that compilation with O4 tends to be slightly faster because it typically uses less virtual memory. Some examples for which O4 does produce better code than O3 are C programs that take the addresses of local variables, and then dereference them, and Pascal programs containing *with* statements.

Source-Language Compatibility
Efficient use of the SPARC architecture requires more stringent interpretation of a few points in the programming languages, particularly C. The following are a few examples.

Pointer Punning
The Sun-2 and Sun-3 architectures support access to (4-byte) words on any even-byte boundary in memory, though there is a significant performance penalty for references to data not aligned on boundaries corresponding to their sizes. In contrast, SPARC loads and stores trap if the memory address is not aligned on the corresponding boundary. For example, casting a C character-string pointer to a pointer to an integer is likely to produce a trap when it is dereferenced. Similarly, passing a pointer to a short integer as a parameter to a routine that expects a pointer to an integer may produce a trap.

Aggregate Construction
For the same reason as above, the rules for aligning and packing elements of data aggregates are different on SPARC from those on previous Sun systems. For example, a C structure containing a character item followed by a pointer item will

place the pointer item on a word boundary on SPARC but on only an even boundary for Sun-2 or Sun-3. This applies to all Sun languages.

Aggregate and Union Parameter Passing

Previous Sun architectures pass parameters in the memory stack. Because they have less stringent alignment restrictions than SPARC does, and because C does not require type checking across procedure calls, it is possible on Sun-2 and Sun-3 systems to pass a series of separate parameters to a routine expecting to receive a single structure parameter. This arrangement should always have been an error, and on SPARC systems it is. A similar mismatch occurs if an element of a union is passed to a routine expecting to receive a parameter of the *union* type.

Variable-Type Argument Lists

On previous Sun architectures it was usually possible to write routines that accepted arguments of varying types in C without using the varargs macros, though this was highly nonportable. SPARC requires use of varargs because most parameters are passed in registers by default.

Because most parameters are passed in registers on SPARC, Sun's new compilers differ from the Sun-2 and Sun-3 compilers in the order of evaluation of parameters to procedure calls. Depending on the evaluation order is, of course, highly nonportable anyway.

The conversion of Sun's compilers to SPARC was an opportunity to drop a few obsolete constructs in C—namely the so-called old-fashioned initializers and assignment operators (see Section 17 of the *C Reference Manual*, in Kernighan and Ritchie, 1978). In addition, Sun C now treats enumerated type values as integers.

The Global and Peephole Optimizers

The SPARC global optimizer *iropt* is shared with the Sun-2 and Sun-3 compilers. Tailoring it for one architecture or another involves describing the register model to the global register allocator and tuning a few other components in minor ways—for example, determining which types of common subexpressions are worth reevaluating rather than saving and the appropriate degree of loop unrolling. Note that we use the term *global optimizer* in the sense in which it is most frequently used in the compiler literature: to refer to an optimizer that works on whole procedures rather than on basic blocks. The current global optimizer does not do interprocedural optimization.

The global optimizer performs the following optimizations:

- loop-invariant code motion
- induction-variable strength reduction
- common subexpression elimination (local and global)
- copy propagation (local and global)
- register allocation (modified graph coloring)
- dead code elimination
- loop unrolling
- tail-recursion elimination

A separate pass handles inlining of language-defined (and user) routines after code generation and before peephole optimization. The peephole optimizer:

- eliminates unnecessary jumps
- eliminates redundant loads and stores
- deletes unreachable code
- does loop inversion
- utilizes machine idioms
- performs register coalescing
- handles instruction scheduling
- does leaf-routine optimization
- performs cross jumping
- handles constant propagation

See Ghodssi et al., 1986, for a discussion of most of these optimizations. Only the new ones, namely tail-recursion elimination, loop unrolling, and leaf-routine optimization, are presented here.

Tail-Recursion Elimination

Given a self-recursive procedure whose only action upon being returned to is to itself return (and to always return the same value, if any), tail-

```
void insert_node(n,l)
        int n;
        struct node *l;
{       if (n > l->value)
                if (l->next == nil) make_node(&l->next,n);
                else insert_node(n,l->next);
}
```

Figure 9. *C routine to insert a node into a linked list.*

Figure 10. *The same routine after tail-recursion elimination.*

```
void insert_node(n,l)
        int n;
        struct node *l;
{loop:
        if (n > l->value)
                if (l->next == nil) make_node(&l->next,n);
                else
                {       l = l->next;
                        goto loop;
                }
}
```

recursion elimination converts the body of the procedure into a loop. For example, the C routine in Figure 9 to insert a node into a linked list is compiled as if it were the code in Figure 10.

On SPARC, this typically saves register-window overflows and underflows, and on all Sun architectures it saves stack allocation, manipulation, and deallocation.

Call by reference (or the ability to pass the address of a local variable to another routine, as found in C) poses some tricky issues when combined with recursion. The following Pascal program illustrates the problem:

```
program tailrec(output);
var x, y: integer;
procedure f(var a, b: integer; n: integer);
        var c: integer;
        begin
                c := 0;
                if n = 0
                then begin
                            a:= 4;
                            writeln(b)
                end
                else if n = 1
                then
                            f(b,c,0)
                else
                            f(b,c,1);
        end;
begin
f(x,y,2);
end .
```

During the third recursive invocation of f( ), with n = 0, a and b point to the previous two invocations' local variables c, respectively. If tail-recursion elimination folds the c's into a single location, the program prints 4 rather than 0. Thus, it may be essential that two invocations of a tail-recursive routine have different stack areas for their local variables. The optimizer detects this situation and suppresses the tail-recursion elimination.

A trickier situation occurs in C. One can call a routine with different numbers of parameters in different calls, so that a tail-recursive call inside the routine might have more parameters than some call from outside it, resulting in different stack space requirements. Currently, the global optimizer has no way to detect this situation because we do not attempt interprocedural data-flow analysis and optimization.

Loop Unrolling and Instruction Scheduling

Loop unrolling replaces the body of a loop with several copies of the body, adjusting the loop control code accordingly. Although this optimi-zation is generally valuable for loops with constant bounds, because it reduces the overhead of looping, the optimization is particularly valuable for an architecture such as SPARC because it typically increases the effectiveness of instruction scheduling.

We apply loop unrolling to loops that satisfy four conditions. Namely, the loop must

- contain only a single basic block (that is, straight-line code)
- generate at most 40 triples of Sun IR code[4]
- contain floating-point operations
- have simple loop control

If these conditions are satisfied, the loop body is copied once. A special compiler flag makes it possible to unroll more copies in the relatively rare cases in which that is appropriate.

SPARC has branches with a one-instruction delay and with an option to annul conditionally (that is, not execute) the delay-slot instruction. The SPARC load instructions may overlap with the execution of the following instruction if that instruction does not use the value loaded. Also, SPARC allows integer instructions and one or more floating-point instructions (how many is implementation-dependent) to proceed in parallel. The Sun-4 implementation allows one floating-point additive operation and one floating-point multiplicative operation at the same time. The Sun-4 instruction scheduler must pay attention to scheduling as many as four types of operations at once:

- a branch or load
- an integer unit instruction other than a branch or load
- an additive floating-point instruction
- a multiplicative floating-point instruction

The scheduler uses the technique described in Gibbons and Muchnick, 1986, and, in general, is quite effective. For example, for the Stanford benchmark, adding instruction scheduling to the other optimizations performed at level O3 increases performance on the individual benchmark components by anywhere from 8% to 20%. Measured statically, the scheduler utilizes all but 5% of the branch delay slots in the Stanford benchmark and fills 49% of them without resorting to annulment. Statically, about 74% of loads are scheduled so that the immediately following instruction does not use the target of the load, and almost all the remaining 26% are in basic blocks that are so short that there is no possible alternative.

In-Line Expansion

In-line expansion is a way for a compiler writer or

user to specify assembly-language code sequences to replace source-language calls. A separate pass between code generation and peephole optimization accomplishes the expansion.

As an example of inlining, instead of generating a call instruction for add(j,k) in the following C routine:

```
int example(j,k)
        register int j, k;
{       int i;
        i = j - k;
        i = add(j,k);
        return i;
}
int add(a,b)
        int a, b;
{       return a + b;
}
```

one can specify that the compiler should use the in-line expansion template

```
.inline_add,8
add     %o0,%o1,%o0
.end
```

Although such expansions save execution time by replacing procedure calls by in-line code, their greatest benefit comes from introducing opportunities for further optimization in the peephole optimizer. In the above example, the peephole optimizer discovers, after inlining, that add( ) has no side effects, so the value of i computed by i = j - k is dead, and hence its computation can be removed—which it could not have determined without the inline expansion because no interprocedural analysis is done.

The SPARC architecture defines an interface for a second implementation-defined coprocessor (as well as the floating-point unit). Inlining could provide smooth, efficient access to its operations from higher-level languages.

Leaf-Routine Optimization
As mentioned above, leaf routines (routines that call no others) are comparatively common. If a leaf routine uses few registers and needs no local stack frame, one can enter and exit it with the minimum possible overhead by omitting the save and restore and adjusting the register numbers it uses. This approach reduces the number of register-window overflows and underflows incurred. For example, the trivial routine

```
int leaf(i,j)
        int i, j;
{       int k;
        return i + 3 * j;
}
```

would be naively compiled as in Figure 11. With leaf-routine optimization, though, it would be compiled as in Figure 12, saving a minimum of two cycles and possibly much more if it caused fewer register-window overflows to be incurred and if it saved a large amount of stack space. Although this optimization frequently does not make much difference, it is occasionally significant. For example, in our standard benchmark of C compiler performance (measuring the compiler itself, not the code it produces), when compiled with O3 optimization, it reduces register-window overflows by 15%.

Sun-4 vs. Sun-3 Performance
The benchmark numbers that follow provide a quick comparison of Sun-3 and Sun-4 systems. The Sun-3/100 Series is based on a 16.67-MHz Motorola MC68020 with a 16.67-MHz MC68881 floating-point processor and an optional Sun Floating Point Accelerator (FPA). The Sun-3/200 Series uses a 25-MHz Motorola MC68020 with a 20-MHz MC68881 floating-point processor and an optional Sun FPA. In both cases the Sun FPA is based on the Weitek 1164/1165 floating-point arithmetic units running at 16.67 MHz. The Sun-4/200 Series is based on the Fujitsu SPARC MB86900 Integer Unit (IU) and Floating-Point Controller (FPC) and the same Weitek 1164/1165, all running at 16.67 MHz. The measured Sun-3 and Sun-4 sys-

```
_leaf:
        save    %sp,-64,%sp     ! slide register window and stack
        sll     %i1,1,%o1       ! 2 * j --> %o1
        add     %i1,%o1,%o0     ! 3 * j --> %o0
        add     %i0,%o0,%i0     ! i + 3 * j --> value register
        jmp     %i7+8           ! return
        restore                 ! and restore register window
```

Figure 11. *Routine compiled without leaf-routine optimization.*

Figure 12. *Routine compiled with leaf-routine optimization.*

```
_leaf:
        sll     %o1,1,%o2       ! 2 * j --> %o2
        add     %o1,%o2,%o1     ! 3 * j --> %o1
        jmp     %o7+8           ! return (delayed branch)
        add     %o0,%o1,%o0     ! and put i + 3 * j --> value register
```

Dhrystone in C (Version 1.1) Dhrystone instr. per sec.	
Sun-3/100	3850
Sun-3/200	7140
Sun-4/200	19000

C compiler (in C) times in seconds	
Sun-3/100	11.7
Sun-3/200	6.4
Sun-4/200	3.2

Figure 13. *Dhrystone benchmark.*

Figure 14. *C-compiler benchmark.*

Figure 15. *Stanford (Hennessy) benchmark.*

Stanford (Hennessy) in C times in milliseconds			
	Sun-3/100 + FPA	Sun-3/200 +FPA	Sun-4/200
Perm	752	412	110
Towers	950	484	175
Queens	302	176	90
Intmm	404	248	150
Puzzle	1816	1088	553
Quick	344	200	97
Bubble	390	232	120
Tree	1242	696	203
Mm	498	376	253
FFT	840	584	461

Figure 16. *Linpack benchmark.*

100 × 100 Linpack in FORTRAN (rolled loops) MFLOPS		
	single	double
Sun-3/100 + FPA	0.62	0.40
Sun-3/200 + FPA	0.86	0.46
Sun-4/200	1.6	1.1

Figure 17. *Global vs. peephole optimizer.*

Effect of Optimization Levels Percentage improvements				
	O1	O2	O3	O4
Perm	28	62	62	62
Towers	26	54	57	57
Queens	16	58	58	58
Intmm	17	55	56	56
Puzzle	28	68	73	73
Quick	27	60	63	63
Bubble	25	64	73	73
Tree	13	77	81	81
Mm	14	45	47	47
FFT	16	28	28	28

tems ran either Sun Operating System (SunOS) Release 3.2 or Release 4.0 and, in all cases, used globally optimizing compilers at the –O3 level of optimization.

The first benchmark we consider is Weicker's Dhrystone program, Version 1.1, in C. This synthetic integer-only benchmark attempts to simulate the performance of systems code, but to a considerable extent it measures string copy and string compare (see Figure 13).

Next we consider the Sun-3 C compiler compiling a section of itself (see Figure 14). The Stanford, or Hennessy, benchmark suite consists of several routines that compute permutations, solve some puzzles (Towers of Hanoi, Eight Queens, and Forest Baskett's blocks puzzle), multiply matrices (integer and floating point), compute a floating-point fast Fourier transform, and sort in three different ways (quick, bubble, and tree). Only the components below the double line in Figure 15 involve floating point.

The Linpack benchmark is a FORTRAN program that measures the solving of linear equations. The case shown in Figure 16 is for 100 × 100 matrices with rolled loops.

Effect of Optimizations

Figure 17 compares the effects of the optimizations performed by the global and peephole optimizers in various ways, in all cases by observing their effects on the Stanford benchmark. Figure 17 compares the effect on SPARC code of the four levels of optimization provided by the C compiler: O1, O2, O3, and O4. In all figures in this section, the numbers represent percentage improvements in execution time[5] over totally unoptimized code.

For these benchmarks, O1 improves the code's execution time by an average of 21%, O2 improves it by an average of 57%, and both O3 and O4 by an average of 59%, though there is considerable variation from one benchmark component to another.

Figure 18 shows the effect of O3 optimization for SPARC with and without the peephole optimizer. On average, doing only the global optimizations in O3 improves the code by 43%, compared to full O3's 59%.

Finally, Figure 19 shows the effect of the accumulation of optimizations for SPARC. In particular, this figure shows the effect of accumulating the optimizations done at level O3, in the order in which they are ordinarily performed. Each run includes peephole optimization but only the following global optimizations:

Column 1: no global optimizations
Column 2: column 1 plus tail-recursion elimination
Column 3: column 2 plus loop-invariant

code motion

Column 4: column 3 plus induction-variable strength reduction

Column 5: column 4 plus common sub-expression elimination

Column 6: column 5 plus copy propagation

Column 7: column 6 plus global register allocation

Column 8: column 7 plus loop unrolling (that is, all global optimizations)

Note that some of the percentages are negative—in some cases the optimizations performed up to that point slow the code down. This slowdown occurs because some optimizations create opportunities for later ones, and no effort is made to clean up the code after each individual one. Note that the O1 percentages in Figure 17 and the column 1 percentages in Figure 19 are different, even though they both include only peephole optimizations. This difference results because the code produced for a C program by invoking O1 generates PCC trees directly, while the code measured in column 1 goes through the Sun IR phase, resulting in somewhat different code.

Code and Program Size

This section compares code and total program size for several large programs. It does not include the Stanford benchmark because that benchmark is too small to show a significant difference, because of UNIX's predilection for rounding sizes up to the next full page. Instead, this section shows ratios of sizes for the C compiler front end, the troff text formatter, the window-based mail handler, make, and the C and pixrect[6] libraries, compiled on the Sun-3 and Sun-4 systems with O2 optimization.

The measurements were all collected on SunOS Release 4.0 systems and hence include the effects of shared libraries. With the advent of shared libraries, most executables are built without libraries linked in and are linked to shared instances of them dynamically at runtime. The result is considerable savings of both disk space and memory space in return for a small time penalty.

Figure 20a shows sizes of the various programs after they have been linked but before libraries have been linked into them.

Figure 20b shows sizes of both static and dynamic versions of two libraries. The dynamic (that is, shared) versions are larger because of the need to generate position-independent code and code to address separate copies of global variables for each use of the library.

With O2-level optimization, SPARC code and whole programs are usually only marginally larger than Sun-3 code and whole programs, though

Global vs. Peephole Percentage improvements		
	O3, no peephole	O3
Perm	28	62
Towers	35	57
Queens	40	58
Intmm	46	56
Puzzle	54	73
Quick	40	63
Bubble	53	73
Tree	74	81
Mm	35	47
FFT	25	28

Figure 18. *O3 optimization, with and without the peephole optimizer.*

Figure 19. *Percentage differences from Figure 17.*

Effect of Individual Optimizations Percentage improvements								
	1	2	3	4	5	6	7	8
Perm	24	24	17	17	14	23	62	62
Towers	21	23	22	23	18	28	57	57
Queens	17	20	16	-16	0	3	58	58
Intmm	16	17	23	14	25	26	56	56
Puzzle	28	28	38	-6	21	20	73	73
Quick	24	29	25	4	0	4	63	63
Bubble	25	25	22	-6	1	0	73	73
Tree	11	63	61	62	59	66	81	81
Mm	16	16	22	13	20	21	47	47
FFT	12	12	12	-3	9	10	26	28

Figure 20a. *Sizes of statically linked programs.*

Programs with dynamic linking (after static linking)						
	sizes				ratios	
	Sun-3 text	Sun-4 text	Sun-3 total	Sun-4 total	text	total
ccom	188416	204800	310768	318640	1.09	1.03
troff	65536	81920	675136	691848	1.25	1.02
mailtool	65536	73728	90112	98304	1.13	1.09
make	65536	81920	88704	105648	1.25	1.19

Figure 20b. *Sizes of static and dynamic versions of two libraries.*

Static and dynamic libraries						
	sizes				ratios	
	Sun-3 text	Sun-4 text	Sun-3 total	Sun-4 total	text	total
libc (static)	206832	223656	225160	255984	1.08	1.14
libpixrect (static)	104720	168048	129520	168448	1.60	1.30
libc (dynamic)	286720	311296	311296	393216	1.09	1.26
libpixrect (dynamic)	114688	163840	122880	180224	1.43	1.47

code is occasionally as much as 60% larger, and whole programs can be as much as about 50% larger.

Conclusions

The primary design considerations for SPARC were to provide an architecture that:

1. is scalable through several technologies and performance levels
2. is well matched to available and near-future compiler technology
3. provides in its first implementation a significant performance improvement over previous Sun processors
4. could gain wide acceptance as an industry standard

The compilers' model of the SPARC architecture is general enough to cover most modern programming languages and considerably exploits SPARC's inherent performance. Optimization is much more important for realizing the full performance of RISC systems than for the more traditional CISC systems, and, consequently, Sun expects to continue adding capabilities to its global and peephole optimizers over time. ▰

Acknowledgments

The design and development of the SPARC user programming model and compilers was a joint effort involving many people; chief among them being Christopher Aoki, Vida Ghodssi, Michel Helft, Men Lee, Richard Tuck, David Weaver, and Alexand Wu

Footnotes

1. Six is more than adequate, because the overwhelming majority of procedures take fewer than six parameters. The average number of parameters, measured statically or dynamically, is no greater than 2.1.
2. The **cc** indicates that the instruction sets the integer condition codes.
3. These are for the case of a nonnegative multiplier. Negative multipliers require one more cycle for operands up to 16 bits long and up to four more cycles for longer operands.
4. This restriction is imposed in order to keep the unrolled blocks of code relatively short, so as not to unduly expand the object code.
5. For example, the number 54 at the intersection of row Towers and column O2 in Figure 17 indicates that Towers compiled with O2 optimization runs in $(100-54)\% = 46\%$ of the time a totally unoptimized version of Towers requires.
6. The pixrect library is one of the lower layers of the SunView window system.

Reading SPARC Assembly Language

SPARC assembly-language instructions are written with an optional label field terminated by a colon (:), followed by the operation code and the arguments. Comments begin with an exclamation point (!) and run to the end of the line. In all cases, source operands precede the result operand. The opcodes used in this article and their meanings are shown on the next page.

- Pseudo-operations that generate no code, such as .inline and .end, are written with a leading period.
- The registers are named as described in the article, except that in assembly language, each

is preceded by a percent sign (%). The names %sp and %fp are synonyms for the stack and frame pointers, respectively. The %hi( ) operator extracts the high-order 22 bits of its (32-bit) operand, and %lo( ) extracts the low-order 13 bits.

- The first operand of a three-operand instruction is always a register name. The second may be either a register name or a (13-bit signed) constant.
- Storage is addressed by writing a sum in square brackets. In a few other contexts, such as the target address of a jmp, the address is written as a sum but without the brackets.

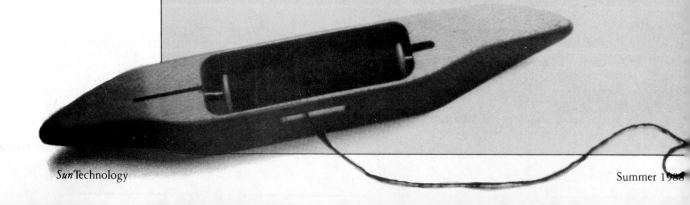

References

how, Frederick, Stephen Correll, Mark Himelstein, Earl Killian, and Lawrence Weber, "How Many Addressing Modes are Enough?" Proceedings of the Second Intl. Conf. on Arch. Support for Prog. Lang. and Oper. Sys., *SIGPLAN Notices*, vol. 22, no. 10, Oct. 1987, pp. 117-121.

hueh, R. and L.T. Quach, "CMOS Gate Array Implementation of SPARC," Proceedings of the 1988 COMPCON Conference, San Francisco, Mar. 1988.

Deutsch, L. Peter, personal communication, 22 Oct. 1987.

Garner, Robert, Anant Agrawal, Will Brown, David Hough, Bill Joy, Steve Kleiman, Steven Muchnick, Dave Patterson, Joan Pendleton, and Richard Tuck, "The Scalable Processor Architecture (SPARC)," Proc. of the 1988 COMPCON Conf., San Francisco, Mar. 1988.

Ghodssi, Vida, Steven S. Muchnick, and Alex Wu, "A Global Optimizer for Sun FORTRAN, C, and Pascal," Proceedings of the Summer 1986 USENIX Conference, June 1986, pp. 318-334.

Gibbons, Philip B., and Steven S. Muchnick, "Efficient Instruction Scheduling for a Pipelined Architecture," Proceedings of the SIGPLAN Symposium on Compiler Construction, Palo Alto, CA, June 1986.

Gingell, Robert A., Meng Lee, Xuong T. Dang, and Mary S. Weeks, "Shared Libraries in SunOS," Proc. of the Summer 1987 USENIX Conf., June 1987, Phoenix, AZ, pp. 131-146.

Goss, L., "CMOS Custom Chip Implementation of SPARC," Proc. of the 1988 COMPCON Conf., San Francisco, Mar. 1988.

Katevenis, Manolis, "Reduced Instruction Set Computer Architectures for VLSI," Ph.D. dissertation, Computer Science Division, University of California, Berkeley, 1983. Also published by MIT Press, Cambridge, MA.

Kernighan, Brian W. and Dennis M. Ritchie, *The C Programming Language*, Prentice-Hall, Englewood Cliff, NJ, 1978.

Kleiman, Steven, and Dock Williams, "SunOS on SPARC," Proc. of the 1988 COMPCON Conf., San Francisco, Mar. 1988.

Magenheimer, Daniel J., Liz Peters, Karl Pettis, and Dan Zuras, "Integer Multiplication and Division on the HP Precision Architecture," Proc. Second Intl. Conf. on Arch. Support for Prog. Lang. and Oper. Sys., Palo Alto, CA, Oct. 1987.

"Smalltalk 80 on the Sun-4—Call for Beta Testers," *Smalltalk-80 Newsletter*, no. 11, Sept. 1987, p. 5.

Soltesz, L., "A High-Performance, High-Density Bipolar Implementation of SPARC," Proc. of the 1988 COMPCON Conf., San Francisco, Mar. 1988.

Sun-4 Assembly Language Reference Manual, Sun Microsystems, Mountain View, CA, Part No. 800-1788-05, 1988.

The SPARC Architecture Manual, Sun Microsystems, Inc., Mountain View, CA, Part No. 800-1399-07, 1987.

Ungar, David, Ricki Blau, A. Dain Samples, and David Patterson, "Architecture of SOAR: Smalltalk on a RISC," Proceedings of the 11th Annual International Symposium on Computer Architecture, Ann Arbor, MI, June 1984.

Opcode	Meaning	Opcode	Meaning
add	add	or	logical or
and	logical and	restore	restore previous register window
bne	branch on not equal	save	move to next register window
bnz	branch on not zero	sethi	Set high 22 bits
bvs	branch on overflow set	sll	shift left logical
call	call subroutine	st	store word
cmp	compare (pseudo-op)	sub	subtract
jmp	jump (pseudo-op)	subcc	subtract and set condition codes
ld	load word	tadcc	tagged add and set condition codes
mov	move register to register (pseudo-op)	tleu	trap on less than or equal unsigned
nop	no operation (pseudo-op)	unimp	unimplemented instruction

Section 5: Example Systems

5.1 Background

The pioneering work on RISC has produced three experimental or prototype systems: the RISC I from Berkeley, the 801 from IBM, and MIPS from Stanford. Quite recently, commercially-available systems based on RISC principles have begun to appear. This section provides a survey of both categories of systems.

5.2 Article Summary

"A Perspective on the 801/Reduced Instruction Set Computer" reports on the seminal work on RISC done at IBM and the resulting prototype. This work inspired later efforts and marked the true beginning of the RISC movement. One of the most notable of the successors to the 801 is IBM's own product, the RT PC. This machine is an outgrowth of the experimental IBM 801 system. "The IBM RT PC ROMP Processor and Memory Management Unit Architecture" discusses RT/801 differences and provides a description of the RT processor and memory management unit chips.

"R2000 Processor Overview" describes the architecture and implementation strategy for one of the most successful commercial RISC products, the MIPS R2000.

The RISC-based product family from Hewlett-Packard is described in some detail in "Precision Architecture." Design objectives and the resulting design principles are discussed.

"Architectural Tradeoffs in the Design of MIPS-X" examines the design of a second generation VLSI RISC processor developed at Stanford. The MIPS-X is a follow-on to the MIPS project, which has been one of the most fruitful of academic research efforts (together with the RISC project at Berkeley) and has produced much of the experimental data on RISC. The original Stanford MIPS was the inspiration for the commercial MIPS product line.

The next article, "The Clipper Processor: Instruction Set Architecture and Implementation," looks at an interesting commercial product that is a mix of RISC and CISC design elements.

The final two articles survey the current status of RISC implementations. "A Survey of RISC Processors and Computers of the Mid-1980s" focuses on design and systems issues relating to a variety of commercial and academic RISC systems, and provides a comparative analysis. "Where There's RISC, There's Opportunity" is a survey of commercial RISC products with an emphasis on the direction of the marketplace.

A perspective on the 801/Reduced Instruction Set Computer

by M. E. Hopkins

From the earliest days of computers until the early 1970s, the trend in computer architecture was toward increasing complexity. This complexity revealed itself through the introduction of new instructions that matched the application areas. Microcode was an implementation technique that greatly facilitated this trend; thus, most computers were implemented using microcode. In 1975, work began at the Thomas J. Watson Research Center on an experimental minicomputer. This project, termed the 801 project, questioned the trend toward complexity in computer architecture. It was observed that most of the complex instructions were seldom used. Thus, a computer could be designed with only simple instructions without drastically increasing the path length or number of instructions required to implement an application. This made it possible to implement a machine without resorting to microcode, which improved performance. This paper described the background and evolution of these ideas in the context of the 801 experimental minicomputer project.

Computers are unlike other tools in that they are truly general-purpose instruments. The interface seen by an airline ticket agent is that of a machine that makes airline reservations. A secretary sees a text-editing machine. To the applications programmer, who uses a high-level language like FORTRAN or COBOL, the computer is a FORTRAN or COBOL machine. However, the assembly language programmer and compiler writer see the underlying machine architecture, an IBM System/370, a DEC VAX, or some other instruction set.

A *computer architecture* is an abstract description of a machine; interest in computer architectures transcends any particular machine. Thus, there can be many models of System/370 or VAX, all of which can execute the same program. Because performance is so important, computer architecture is always done with a particular set of implementation techniques in mind. Register files, buses, and adders have similar properties in a wide variety of realizations, and implementation techniques such as parallel operations have wide applicability. The details of the various realizations may also influence the architect's decisions. For example, the architect may have to specify what happens in the case of a parity error, an event that does not occur on a purely abstract machine. On the other side of the architectural interface, the architect must cater to the needs of those who construct programs. This paper examines some issues in computer architecture in the light of an experimental processor known as the 801/RISC (reduced instruction set computer).

Background. Because they lacked clear criteria, computer architects between 1946 and 1975 tended to specify ever more complex systems, as hardware capability increased and the tools used for design became more powerful. The computers acquired more instructions, more addressing modes, more data types, and more special features. The experience of IBM is not very different from that of the rest of the industry in this respect. The IBM Type 701 was introduced early in the 1950s. It was truly minimal, because any complexity would have reduced reliability. Floating-point arithmetic was done with subroutines. By the time the IBM Type 704 was intro-

Table 1   Ten most-used instructions in a typical instruction mix

Operation Code	Instruction Name	Percentage of Total Executions
BC	Branch	20.16
L	Load word	15.49
TM	Test under mask	6.06
ST	Store word	5.88
LR	Load register to register	4.70
LA	Load effective address	4.04
LTR	Load and test register	3.78
BCR	Branch on register	2.69
MVC	Move characters	2.10
LH	Load half word	1.88

duced in the mid-1950s, it had instructions that performed floating-point arithmetic. Providing floating-point arithmetic by an instruction as opposed to a subroutine offered no new function. However, performance improved in two ways: (1) The new engine had circuitry to perform efficiently floating-point functions such as normalization that required many basic cycles on a 701. (2) By performing the high-level operation entirely in the CPU, the transfer of instructions between memory and the CPU was reduced.

This notion of adding new instructions tailored to the expected application became a guiding principle of computer architecture. By the early 1960s, IBM was producing families of computers oriented to their expected application area. The IBM Type 7090 was the scientific and engineering successor to the 704. It had fixed-word binary and floating-point instructions, whereas the 7080 had variable-length decimal arithmetic and edit instructions suited to commercial work. By this time, much programming was being done in high-level languages like FORTRAN and COBOL. Both machines had FORTRAN and COBOL compilers. Unfortunately, there were no systematic methods of comparing architectures. However, anecdotal evidence suggested that the 7090 actually executed commercial applications faster than the 7080, even though both machines used the same circuit technology. Nobody examined this situation, perhaps because software and the portability of customer applications were deemed to be problems of higher priority that urgently required solutions.

The solution was System/360, a machine that coalesced all applications. The technology to implement a machine with many diverse instructions was pro-

vided by very fast read-only storage that permitted the economical implementation of microcode.[1] This ushered in a new era of machines with a great diversity of instructions. In addition, fundamental improvements were made in the treatment of the memory hierarchy. Virtual memory was introduced on the System/360 Model 67 and caches on the Model 85. The general direction of both architecture and implementation was toward greater complexity.

In 1975 the 801 project was started at the IBM Thomas J. Watson Research Center. (The project was so named because the Research Center is Building Number 801.) Our intention was to re-examine the trend toward complexity. The 801 was to be a hardware and software system. Almost all programming would be done in a high-level language. The goal was to discover how to deliver the most computing power at the lowest cost in an environment geared to programmer productivity. A prototype version of the 801 was built and system software was written. This included a compiler known as the PL.8,[2-5] which became a tool and a means of studying the effectiveness of the 801 architecture. Projects with similar goals have also been pursued at the University of California at Berkeley and at Stanford University.[6] This architectural point of view has become known as RISC, from Paterson's Berkeley Reduced Instruction Set Computer (RISC) computer.[7,8]

The term RISC nicely captures the spirit of research into the premise that less is better. The various aspects of architecture addressed in the 801 project are discussed in References 9 and 10. However, our goal was not to have the fewest possible instructions, but to simplify the machine's data flow to make the basic instructions run faster. Also, we had observed that mechanisms such as virtual memory and caches had been separately introduced on System/370, and we thought that this project might discover whether a more consistent and efficient implementation might be possible if a fresh start were taken. Adequacy to implement a broad spectrum of high-level languages efficiently was also a concern. This paper examines the reasoning that led to the experimental 801 architecture.[11] Many of the lessons learned during the project have been incorporated into Romp, the CPU for the IBM Personal Computer RT.[12]

System/360 instruction traces

An illuminating insight into computer architecture was provided by the first instruction traces on System/360. The motivation was to perform an experiment to determine an optimal geometry for the cache on what would become the Model 85. However, the determination of frequency of instruction usage was a natural by-product. It is easy to see that most instructions on a machine with about 200 instructions will be executed very infrequently. It came as a surprise, however, that load, store, branch, and a few simple register operations almost completely dominated the mix of instructions. The ten instructions that ranked highest in percentage of total instructions executed are given in Table 1.

Together these ten instructions capture two thirds of all instructions executed, a discovery that raises several questions. If storage-to-register add and add logical are not among the top ten, is it worthwhile to have instructions that combine the two relatively basic functions of fetching a value from storage and then performing an arithmetic or logical operation? System/370 has a comprehensive set of instructions that fetch one operand from storage and the other from a register and put the result of the operation back into the register. Together these instructions, which include add, subtract, compare, AND, OR, and exclusive OR, constitute less than 6.5 percent of all executions. Also consider other complicated instructions. Load multiple and store multiple together account for 2.4 percent of all executions. Integer multiply is 0.115 percent, and divide is 0.111 percent of all executions. The loop-closing operations BXLE and BXH are 0.066 percent. With the exception of the instructions pack and convert to decimal (0.008 percent), the decimal and edit instructions are not represented on this trace.

We then considered how representative of the range of actual customer environments this trace might have been. If small snapshots are taken, differences based on the application and compiler or on the human coder who wrote the program can certainly be seen. There are scientific traces for which you can almost see the code for the inner loop of matrix multiply as produced by a particular FORTRAN compiler. In general, scientific program traces look a little different from others. In extreme cases, they may have 10 percent or more floating-point instructions. There may be other differences, such as significantly fewer of the instructions associated with linkage—BAL (Branch And Link), for example. However, it is surprising how often scientific programs spend most of their time doing integer calculations. In many cases, a large proportion of their execution seems to be spent in the input/output and formatting

Table 2	Example trace results for storage-to-storage logical operations on System/370	
Operation	**Frequency of Use**
NC AND	0.050
OC OR	0.058
XC exclusive OR	0.555

routines. Knuth has an interesting discussion of this phenomenon.[13] In the late 1960s, short object code traces of code produced by the COBOL compiler sometimes showed a measurable number of decimal instructions. In recent years, this has become less true; a number of factors account for this. Commercial applications have become more diverse. Very little decimal processing is required in an inventory control application. More of the CPU cycles are now concerned with data base, network, communication, and screen formatting, all of which is systems-type code and is often performed by some subsystem. As the control program takes on more functions, it is inevitable that there will be less decimal computation. Thus, there is an overall tendency for traces of program execution to become like systems code. With the exception of floating-point, it is very difficult to identify an instruction that is potentially important, but only in a limited set of environments. The existence of trace tapes tends to inhibit the introduction of new instructions in existing architectures. For example, will any newly proposed instruction be executed more frequently than the existing Translate and Test instruction (0.001 percent)? It is also a useful exercise for those proposing a new architecture to construct hypothetical typical mixes.

We also considered execution time as opposed to frequency. Obviously, the more complex the instructions, the greater the execution time. Time taken is a function of a particular implementation, so we cannot state general rules. However, one observation has been that programmers and compilers sometimes choose a single operation that is relatively slow in preference to a sequence of faster instructions. For example, the average length of an operand of the Move Characters (MVC) instruction that performs storage-to-storage move on System/370 is less than seven bytes. Thus there must be a number of one-, two-, and four-byte moves. On virtually every System/370 implementation the Load-Store sequence is considerably faster than MVC for short align moves.

The trace tapes also provide information to those designing machines. For example, the frequency of

Figure 1   General features of the System/360 design

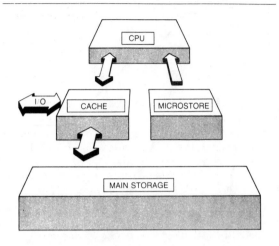

Figure 2   General features of the experimental 801 Reduced
             Instruction Set Computer

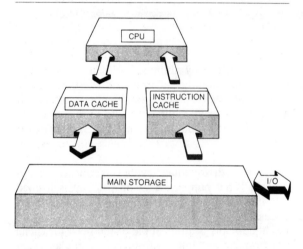

storage-to-storage logical operations in one System/370 trace is given in Table 2.

Why is the XC instruction used ten times more frequently than NC or OC? The explanation is that an exclusive OR of a variable to itself provides a means of setting storage to zero. Machine designers can and do capitalize on this fact. Thus both operands that coincide run more than twice as fast as operands that are disjoint. For those developing a new architecture, the lesson may be to provide a fast way to zero storage rather than providing storage-to-storage logical operations.

Although many insights can be gained from trace tapes, the important fact to the 801 project members

was that, in practice, the simple instructions are the most frequently used and in that sense are the most important.

Considerations leading to the 801 experiment

In 1975, when the 801 experiment project began, most System/370 machines were implemented with a cache and microstore, as shown in Figure 1. The cache had been introduced to provide faster access to main storage, that is, to bring the speed of memory more in line with that of the CPU. The CPU fetched instructions from the cache and interpreted them on the basis of a microprogram in the microstore. An average System/370 instruction might take 20 or 30 microinstructions. Neither the cache nor the microstore is part of System/370 architecture, but perhaps they provide an architectural opportunity. The cache and microstore could be, and often are, implemented in the same technology. Consider why the frequently executed first-level-interrupt handler (FLIH) and the task dispatcher are executed out of the cache, whereas decimal divide is executed out of microstore. One approach is to make key system facilities into high-level, complex machine instructions that are executed out of the microstore. This has the advantage of permitting the chosen functions to be implemented faster because the microinstructions can each be executed in a single cycle. Because the FLIH and dispatcher are implemented primarily with simple operations that have a direct counterpart in microcode, there is a potential for a 20-to-1 improvement in performance. Further gains may be realized by reducing traffic to main storage, because the microstore has a separate path to the CPU. Perhaps even more instructions might be designed to exploit this advantage. Such instructions reflect the design of the system software and the requirements of compiler writers. As more specialization is introduced, it is inevitable that the microstore will become larger. Eventually it may be necessary to make it writable and page it like the cache, using some least recently used (LRU) replacement scheme.

But why do we permit only the microcoders to access the microstore; can it be made available to all? If we do, there will be a new interface with many of the same properties of our current computer architecture. As more microcode is written, there will be a need for microcode compilers. Such questions as whether the microcode compilers have an option to do subscript range checking will have to be answered. The microcode instruction interface will have to be precisely defined to enhance portability to protect a

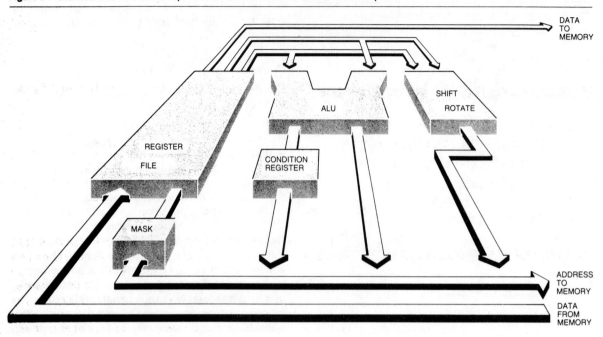

large investment in microcode. Great care will have to be taken to ensure that it is safe, easy to use, and a good target for compilers. Because good performance is obtained by using microcode, the performance problems of many users will have to be in the hands of the microcoders. The 801 group chose a different approach to a solution. An architecture was specified that would not—as System/370 does—tacitly assume an implementation in microcode.

The assumed 801 experimental system design is shown in Figure 2. In the architecture, the only built-in instructions are those that can be implemented in a single cycle, with the simple sort of CPU that was used to interpret the System/370 instruction set. The microstore has been exchanged for an instruction cache. Figure 3 gives an idealized data flow for such a machine. Such an approach provides a pervasive performance improvement for all executions of the simple instructions that the trace tapes have shown to be most frequent. The overall system design of Figure 2 also provides advantages over the micro-code implementation in Figure 1. By providing separate data and instruction caches, the bandwidth to memory is potentially doubled. One of the problems encountered with traditional cache architectures is that the I/O is run through the cache. Thus the I/O activity tends to fill up the cache. The experimental

801 architecture, by running I/O directly to memory, tends to increase the memory bandwidth even further. Notice that the chief justification for the cache and microstore in Figure 1 was to reduce memory traffic; the 801 solution is an improvement upon this.

There is a disadvantage with this split-cache approach. What happens if an instruction is fetched into the instruction cache and, while there, its main-storage reflection is copied into the data cache and modified? This is an example of the need for cache synchronization. Input-output has a similar problem. In practice, nobody modifies instructions; thus, the 801 approach is to abandon the practice. However, there are some programs that must construct programs. Loaders are the most conspicuous example. The 801 experimental architecture makes the notion of a cache explicit; those programs that construct programs must issue instructions to synchronize the caches. The vast majority of programs need never be concerned with cache synchronization, but its use is required in a few areas of the system for programs to function correctly. The 801 requires software synchronization. In the light of current software practice, this imposes a modest burden on a very few systems programs in return for a substantial improvement in the price/performance ratio.

Having specified the 801 architecture with the tacit assumption that an implementation will have a split cache, we do not believe that we have unduly restricted the freedom of implementers. Both a cache

---

A shifting of responsibility between hardware and software was recognized by the 801 experimenters.

---

and noncache implementation of an 801 must cope with the fact that storage operations and branches are inherently slower than register operations. We first describe how the 801 architecture ameliorates this and then consider why registers are faster. The basic idea with loads is to use the arithmetic and logical unit (ALU) to compute the *effective address* in one cycle. This effective address is then sent out to the memory subsystem. In order to avoid the cost of examining page tables in memory, most memory subsystems maintain a hardware look-aside that maps recently used virtual addresses to real memory. This is called a translation look-aside buffer (TLB). As TLB miss ratios of under two percent are common, we concentrated on the 98 percent of references that hit the TLB. The memory system would be given the real address by the TLB and fetches would be given the data from memory. After dispatching the address, the CPU locks the target register of the load and proceeds to execute the next instruction(s), unless they use the target register, in which case the CPU waits until the load is complete. For this strategy to be effective, compilers and assembly-language coders must arrange instructions to ensure a maximum of overlap. Notice that even instructions of very modest complexity would inhibit this process. Suppose it is desired to add X in storage to register RX, and add Y to register RY. Assuming that it takes two cycles to get to the storage data, which are presumed to be in the cache, and one cycle to do the operation, on System/370 we would have the following code:

A RX,X	2 cycles to fetch
	1 cycle to add
A RY,Y	2 cycles to fetch
	1 cycle to add

6 cycles total

On the experimental 801, the code would be the following:

L R0,X	2 cycles to fetch
L R1,Y	1 cycle not overlapped
A RX,RX,R0	0 cycles
	(overlaps previous load)
A RY,RY,R1	1

4 cycles total

Although the 801 code has more instructions, it runs faster. Of course, one can adopt similar strategies on System/370. The experimental 801 solution is simpler in hardware. It does require that the compiler writers make the effort to schedule instructions, as such local rearrangement of code is called. It is possible, at considerable cost in hardware (not microcode), to dynamically rearrange the components of the multifunction instructions during execution to achieve the 801-type overlap. The trouble with this kind of solution is that, even if one can afford the hardware, complexity has its own price, and the ultimate result of many such solutions is a slower basic cycle. If the cost of a more complex implementation is an increase to 11 levels of logic from 10 due to chip crossings or such considerations, then the machine is 10 percent slower overall and this was done for 6 percent storage to register computational operations. The requirement to schedule instructions is an example of a shifting of responsibility between hardware and software that was recognized by the 801 experimenters, even though it is never explicitly mentioned in the architecture.

It is now appropriate to examine why a cache is inherently slower than registers. Access to a cache requires two sets of translation. First, the effective virtual page must be converted to a real page by accessing the TLB. Then the memory subsystem must determine whether the cache line within the page is also within the cache. Such lookups are normally done by hashing the address and doing a comparison. (On some architectures the cache can be kept virtual, which permits the cache lookup to be done in parallel with the TLB lookup.) Further complications occur because misses and storage key violations are possible. In general, the construction of a memory subsystem is highly complex. A good summary of implementation techniques is provided in Reference 14. The complexity of accessing a cache can be contrasted with accessing a register, the name of which is in the instruction itself. In a properly architected machine, it is possible to begin fetching both register operands before the operation has been decoded. If a register operand is not needed, it can be discarded. The key architectural requirement is always to place the source register names in the same positions within the instruction format. The existence of instruction formats that permit great variability in the placement of register names is one of the major barriers to improving performance on some machines. In general, register access is so simple that it is feasible to fetch two operands out in a single cycle. In the idealized 801 in Figure 3, there are three paths out of the register file. This permits the CPU to do all its work for a store in one cycle, although the memory subsystem may consume more cycles. The quantity to be stored can be fetched as well as the base and index registers, which are added to compute the effective address. There are also two paths into the register file. The first is for normal results from the ALU. The second permits the result of a load to be returned to its target register in the same cycle as a register-to-register operation. With three outputs and two inputs, a register file can be viewed as having five times the bandwidth of a cache, and there is no need to go through a virtual-to-real translation and cache lookup.

Branches are also inherently slower than pure register operations. When instruction execution is sequential, it is relatively easy for the CPU to overlap the execution of the current instruction with the fetch of the next, but a taken branch interrupts this process. Some larger machines keep branch history tables to predict branches. However, the 801 provides an architectural alternative to assist the implementers. The basic idea is to define a companion operation for every branch instruction that executes the next (subject) instruction in parallel with the branch. These are called "execute branches" on the 801 and "delayed branches" on the Berkeley RISC. As the outcome of the branch cannot depend on the results of the subject instruction, the implementer can design hardware to overlap execution of the branch and the subject instruction.

Such hardware is not as complex as that required for branch overlap on high-performance machines, but it is far from simple. The chief complications result from cache and TLB misses on the branch itself, the

Table 3 Effect of execute branches on one hundred average instructions using two cycles

Case with No Execute Branches

Instruction Type	Number of Instructions	Cycles per Instruction	Total Cycles
Branches	20	2	40
Storage	30	2	60
Register	50	1	50
Total			150

Case with Execute Branches

Instruction Type	Number of Instructions	Cycles per Instruction	Total Cycles
Branches	5	2	10
Execute branches	15	2	30
Storage	20	2	40
Storage (subject instructions)	10	0	0
Register	45	1	45
Register (subject instructions)	5	0	0
Total			125

subject instruction, and the branch target. It is interesting to do a quick analysis to determine the potential value of this type of branch. We assume two cases: A taken branch costs (a) two cycles and (b) five cycles. This bounds the problem for high-performance cache machines and simple machines without caches. We assume the same distribution of instructions in each case. Consider the case of the two-cycle cache first in Table 3, which assumes that three quarters of all branches can be converted to execute form. Of these, two thirds cover storage operations, and the rest cover register operations. As can be seen in Table 3, this set of assumptions provides a 10 percent performance improvement. The 18 percent saving obtained on the cacheless implementation shown in Table 4 is even more dramatic. The assumptions behind these improvements can be questioned. In particular, the average storage instruction may take less time because of overlap. One can also question the mix, or whether three quarters of the branches can be converted to execute form and whether two thirds of the subject instructions will be storage operations. However, for a wide range of reasonable assumptions, execute branch seems to be very cost-effective. It is common for those designing machines to invest great effort to obtain performance improvements of less than one percent, and here we see a potential gain of 10 to 18

Table 4   Effect of execute branches on one hundred average
            instructions

Case with No Execute Branches

Instruction Type	Number of Instructions	Cycles per Instruction	Total Cycles
Branches	20	5	100
Storage	30	5	150
Register	50	1	50
Total			300

Case with Execute Branches

Instruction Type	Number of Instructions	Cycles per Instruction	Total Cycles
Branches	5	5	25
Execute branches	15	5	75
Storage	20	5	100
Storage (subject instructions)	10	0	0
Register	45	1	45
Register (subject instructions)	5	0	0
Total			245

percent. There is, however, a software price to be paid. The compiler writers will have to produce execute branches. One way to do this is as follows. In the compiler phase that rearranges code to maximize overlap on loads, an attempt is made to move a suitable instruction next to each branch. Final assembly then flips the branch with the previous instruction if there is no interdependence. In practice great care may have to be taken. Consider the code that typically closes an iterative loop:

```
AI    R1,R1,1    Bump R1
CI    R1,100     Test if limit exceeded
BLE   LOOP       Branch on low or equal
```

Given such a sequence, it may not be possible to find a suitable subject instruction.

Under the right circumstances, the code can be reordered and the loop-closing instruction altered to test for inequality as follows:

```
CI    R1,100     Test if limit reached
AI    R1,R1,1    Bump R1
BNE   LOOP       Branch not equal
```

Final assembly can then flip the AI and the BNE to produce the following sequence:

```
CI    R1,100
BNEX  LOOP
AI    R1,R1,1
```

Notice that there must be a form of add that does not set the condition code for this to work. Such details are extremely important.

This transformation is not the end. Consider the following standard loop in C that does a storage-to-storage move:

while (*t++=*s++);

For those who do not read C, this statement moves a string of characters located by the pointer s to the storage located by the pointer t, one byte at a time, terminating when a zero byte is moved. In the process, the pointers t and s are incremented on each iteration of the loop. The following is some code produced by the PL.8 compiler in Yorktown, with somewhat idealized cycle counts on the right:

```
LOOP    LCS     R0,0(RS)     5
        INC     RS,1         1
        STCS    R0,0(RT)     5
        CIS     R0,0         1
        BNZX    LOOP         5
        INC     RT,1         0
                             ——
                             17 total cycles
```

On the surface, it may seem that it is impossible to improve this code. However, the store character instruction can be made the subject of the BNZX, as follows:

```
LOOP    LCS     R0,0(RS)     5
        INC     RS,1         1
        INC     RT,1         1
        CIS     R0,0         1
        BNZX    LOOP         5
        STC     -0,-1(RT)    0
                             ——
                             13 total cycles
```

The trick is to have the compiler move instructions that modify the base address by a constant, altering the displacement field to reflect the add. This transformation provides a saving of almost 25 percent on the most common idiom in C, and it is also used in many similar situations.

The subject of execute branches provides a good example of the following range of considerations that are pertinent to architectural decisions:

- Instruction frequencies
- Hardware implementation techniques in a variety of situations

- The way in which instructions are actually used, including linguistic idioms
- Compiler design
- Details such as which instructions should set the condition code

Having these kinds of data, the architect must evaluate whether a proposal such as branch and execute is worth the inevitable hardware and software imple-

---

Except for loads, stores, and branches, all the instructions can be implemented to execute in one cycle.

---

mentation problems, given the expected usage patterns. Execute branches are a graphic example of the partnership among hardware implementation, architecture, and compiler design that took place in the experimental 801 project.

High-level function

The 801 experimental architecture provides a set of primitive instructions. Except for loads, stores, and branches, all the instructions can be implemented to execute in one cycle on a simple implementation. Now consider the function performed by more complex operations, such as those that exist on System/370.

Integer multiplication provides an example of the variety of techniques used to implement high-level function on the 801. We first assessed the extent of the problem. Typical System/370 traces show that all forms of integer multiply constitute less than 0.15 percent of all executions. Depending on the model, it takes between five and thirty times as long to do a multiply compared with a register add on System/370. Considerable hardware is required to achieve the lower number. In practice, it is often achieved by doing integer multiply in a very expensive floating-point unit. The most economical way to implement multiply is to have a 2-by-32-bit microcode multiply step instruction. The System/370 multiply

instruction is then implemented by executing 16 such operations in microcode.

The experimental 801 architecture provides a multiply step instruction in its instruction repertoire. The control program provides a multiply subroutine that is shared by all users. It consists of 16 consecutive multiply-step instructions. By software convention, the multiplier and multiplicand are passed, and the product is returned in registers. To the extent that multiply is frequently used, the code is in the cache; thus, the proportional time is roughly the same as that of the microcoded System/370 implementations, even if we include linkage costs. This should not be a surprise, because the same work is being done. An important difference is that the microstore and multiply-step instruction are only available to the microcoder, whereas on the 801 the instruction cache and multiply-step instruction are available to all. Suppose there is a problem that requires only a 12-bit multiplier. In this case, it is possible to write a 12-bit multiply subroutine, which remains in the cache to the extent that it is used. Such a routine can be further specialized to handle negative operands in special ways and to check ranges. In effect, the programmer can define his own variations on multiply, and it is difficult to see why they should perform very differently than a microcoded routine in the same technology. It is even possible to put multiply-step instructions in line, providing the effect of in-line microcode.

In practice, many multipliers are constants derived from subscript calculations. Most compilers convert multiplies by power-of-two shifts to the left. On the experimental 801-type machines, it is common practice to convert all constant multipliers to a series of shifts, adds, and subtracts. In practice, it is rare to require more than three or four instructions, so that it may be possible to exceed the performance of an expensive high-speed multiply unit for most cases.

In practice, both compilers and human coders try to reduce the number of costly instructions. One example is to have the compilers do strength reduction. This is a compiler optimization that replaces multiplies that result from subscript calculations with adds. Consider the following program fragment:

```
declare
    x(0:100)        character (50);
do i = 0 to 100;
  if x(i) = y        then
    leave;
end do i;
```

As each element of the array x takes fifty bytes, a reference to $x(i)$ requires multiplying i by fifty. The process of strength reduction introduces an auxiliary variable i', which is set to zero at the beginning of the loop and incremented by 50 on each iteration, eliminating the need for a multiply. Such optimizations apply to the experimental 801 as well as to more complex machines. Their tendency is to reduce the benefit that might be obtained by having complex operations.

Partly because of the lack of high-level instructions but also because the use of subroutines is so central to much of good programming practice, a great deal of attention has been given to providing efficient linkage on the experimental 801. There are three classes of branch and link instruction:

- Relative branching is used within a bound module. A 32-bit instruction can generally be made to accommodate 20 to 26 address bits. This establishes a maximum size for link-edited modules of 1 to 64 megabytes.
- An absolute branch is required to get to shared supervisor routines, such as multiply or storage-to-storage move. The address field of the instruction is of limited size, so such microcode routines have to be located in the first few megabytes of virtual memory.
- A branch and link can be done on the contents of a register in situations in which the invoked routine is computed at run time.

The first two forms of Branch And Link (BAL) require no load to link to a subroutine, a significant saving given that BAL constitutes between 1 and 2 percent of all instructions executed.

The number of available registers and how they are used are central to the efficiency of linkage. Because intermediate results are maintained in registers and can be retrieved rapidly, it is a good idea to have a fairly large number of registers. The number of bits required to name a register in an instruction is an architectural constraint, but there are usually also technological limitations on the number of registers. A system constraint is the necessity to save and restore registers when there is a process switch. The first experimental version of the 801 was built with 16 registers. Studies of code produced by the PL.8 compiler showed that over 50 percent of all the procedures in a large sample had some register *spill code*, which comprises the load and store instructions that would not be required if there were more regis-

ters. Because the technology made a 32-register machine possible, we decided to define the next experimental 801 with 32 registers. Because more bits were required to name the registers, this necessitated

---

Having a uniform instruction size also simplifies, and thus speeds, the process of instruction fetch.

---

going to a machine that had only 32-bit instructions. The 801 prototype had 16- and 32-bit instructions. Uniform instructions have advantages beyond permitting more registers. It is possible to define all register operations so that there is no need to destroy one of the operands. Having a uniform instruction size also simplifies, and thus speeds, the process of instruction fetch. For example, there can never be two cache misses when fetching an instruction.

Reference 12 gives a detailed description of linkage and register conventions on a 16-register computer chip known as Romp. We give a summary for a 32-register machine. Up to six parameters are passed in registers; the rest are passed in storage. Studies have shown that most procedures have very few parameters, which means that a called routine can usually use the parameters directly in the registers, and the caller need only go to storage if the value passed has to be fetched. For languages like FORTRAN, which do calls by reference, parameters are pointers to the argument. For languages like C that have value parameters, the actual values are passed in registers. These six registers and perhaps a few more will be assumed to be destroyed over a call. One register is dedicated to pointing to the stack frame, and it may be necessary to dedicate another register to a process communication area or similar region of storage. Thus, there are about 20 registers that must be preserved over each procedure call, whereas about ten may be altered. A routine that alters only the first ten registers need not save any registers. Paradoxically, having more registers in the hardware can mean fewer saves. With this approach it is possible to have very simple linkage for simple subroutines.

Figure 4 C-language loop to do a storage-to-storage move

```
    while (*t++ = *s++);
    return;

Object code for Romp

5|  000000                          %6:
5|  000000 LCS      4003                    LCS     r0,$MEMORY+*s(r3)
5|  000002 INC      9131                    INC     r3,r3,1
5|  000004 INC      9121                    INC     r2,r2,1
5|  000006 CIS      9400                    CIS     cr,r0,0
5|  000008 BNBX     89AF FFFC               BFX     cr,b26/eq,%6
5|  00000C STC      DE02 FFFF               STC     r0,$MEMORY+*t-1(r2)
7|  000010 BNBR     E88F                    BFR     24,r15
```

Figure 4 shows the PL.8 code for a subroutine that does the C storage-to-storage move on the Romp processor. There is no prologue, and the epilogue is a branch register. More complex programs and the requirements of different languages necessitate more linkage instructions, but it is important that this cost be incremental. The 801 approach, unlike the introduction of powerful complex operations, permits specialization to what is required in a particular situation. There is no need to do extra work. Note that there is a tacit assumption here that most linkage code is to be constructed by compilers. Conventions that have many options are just too hard for hand coders.

The experimental 801 does not have load-multiple or store-multiple instructions. It uses a subroutine to save and restore registers. The save routine consists of a series of stores into consecutive words and can be entered at any point so that only the required registers are saved. From a performance point of view, this is similar to the situation that exists on System/370 with store- and load-multiple instructions. Those instructions usually have a fixed overhead for start-up that is roughly proportional to the BAL and BR required in the subroutine prologue. In addition, it is possible to bundle other functions related to linkage in the register-save routine. Bumping the stack pointer and testing for stack overflow are examples.

The 801 has a simple data flow. The following two examples show that it is still possible to have pow-erful instructions by capitalizing on the available hardware.

Load and store instructions have an update or auto-increment form. The idea behind this is that once the CPU has computed the effective address of a load or a store, the updated effective address can be returned to the register file. Such instructions are particularly useful in loops that traverse arrays or strings, and no new hardware is required. On other computers, with auto-increment, pre- and post-increment forms are sometimes provided. That is, the addition is done either before or after the address is sent to the memory bus. Post-increment requires another set of wires to send the contents of the base register directly to the memory. This additional hardware does not seem to be worth the slight convenience of alternative formats.

Storage-to-storage move consumes a lot of computer time. A reasonable guess on System/370 is 2 percent of the executions and 10 percent or more of the time, if MVC and MVCL are both included. On the experimental 801, short moves are done with in-line loads and stores, but long moves require a subroutine. If both the source and target are aligned on a word boundary, which is quite common, a table consisting of a series of update loads and stores can move the data at the speed of the memory bus. Unaligned moves can be done at the same rate by exploiting the shifter-rotater. The idea is to introduce a version of the store instruction that takes the quantity to be stored and rotates it by the difference in alignment between the source and target. Bits shifted out on the right are saved in an internal CPU register for the next store; those saved from the previous store are combined with the quantity to be stored. Thus the central part of the storage-to-storage move loop consists entirely of a sequence of update load and rotate-update-store instructions, and this sequence can proceed as fast as the bus. Of course, this requires a

---

The suitability of the experimental 801 as a target for compilers was a primary consideration.

---

number of instructions to initialize the loop. The existence of shift-and-rotate-type instructions provides most of the functionality to implement this otherwise exotic instruction.

A target for compilers

The suitability of the experimental 801 as a target for compilers was a primary consideration. On the surface, one might expect that compiler writers would want a machine that was close to the high-level language. However, a machine with basic instructions is better suited to optimization techniques. The most important are code motion out of loops and the elimination of redundant computations. Suppose a program contains a reference to $x(i, j)$. If optimization is done separately on each of the addressing components, the fact that one of the components cannot be optimized need not affect the others. If the above reference occurs in a do loop on i, the load of base of the variable x as well as the load and multiply of j may be moved out of the loop. Newer languages are characterized by complex addressing paths, often involving descriptors. By producing the straightforward code to access such variables and then performing standard optimizations, the compiler can produce good object code. If instructions are complex, any variation in one of the operands inhibits the movement or elimination of the instruction. This subject is covered more fully in References 12 and 14.

A number of details make the 801 approach more effective as a target for compilers. *Condition code* has always been troublesome. To reflect the source languages, one might like to have a relational operator that produces a zero or a one in a register. The problem is that compare is basically a subtract, and construction of the boolean value has to be done very late in the cycle. There is a real danger that the materialization of zero or one in a register may lengthen the basic ALU cycle. Thus it seems best to retain the condition register, which is well suited to its primary use in branching. It also lets one avoid repeating compares—if a three-way choice is made among high, low, and equal—as in a binary search. It is especially important to restrict the instructions that set the condition code. If loads and stores set the condition code, it may be very difficult to insert register-spill code. The scheduling of loads and execute branches can also be constrained by instructions that set the condition register. Finally, it is important that it be possible to easily fetch and restore the contents of the condition register.

It is very desirable to have a set of immediate instructions that contain the operand rather than fetching it from a register. It is not necessary to provide full 32-bit versions, because most constants that actually occur can be defined in 16 bits. The CPU extends these short constants to a full 32 bits by using zeros, ones, or sign bits. If a constant cannot be represented in 32 bits, it has to be loaded from storage or manufactured at execution time. The latter is preferable, and, for this purpose, it is desirable to have a version of load address that shifts the immediate value left by 16 bits. Immediate instructions are heavily used.

The 801 has base-plus-signed-displacement and base-plus-index forms of loads and stores. Studies have shown that it is rare on System/370 to use the base, index, and displacement, all in one instruction. Thus the experimental 801 is not designed with hardware implementing a three-input adder that is rarely used.

Local program addressability should be relative. Perhaps 2 percent of System/370-executed instructions are concerned with establishing, saving, or restoring addressability to the program. An adequate set of immediate operations makes it unnecessary to have an instruction relative-addressing mode for data.

Many high-level languages have rules that can be policed only at run time. Because enforcement is normally costly, most compilers make such checking optional, and it is customary to do without checking during production. This situation has been likened to that of a sailor who uses his life vest only during drills, going without it during the hurricane. To make software checking more economical, the 801 provides instructions that compare the contents of a register with an immediate value or another register. A trap is taken if the test is satisfied. These trap operations can be subjected to the same sort of optimization as is applied to other computations. Thus the number of trap instructions can be reduced, and, when they must be executed, the cost is about the same as that of a register add. Traps are one of the ways that a low-level machine can encourage high-level languages and such good software engineering practice as run-time checks during production.

From the compiler writer's point of view, the experimental 801 is attractive because it is regular. Many decisions are simplified because it always pays to replace two register operations with one. However, it is difficult to obtain an objective measure of regularity. For example, the 801 has only three of the 16 possible boolean operations. This is an irregularity, but it is simply not worthwhile to provide them all, because most are seldom used and the compiler can construct them when they occur using, at most, two instructions. The 801 is a good target for compilers because most of the computations implied by high-level language constructs are variations on addressing code. In practice, computers spend most of their time locating data which in turn locate other data. Such computation is facilitated by full 32-bit addressing, many registers, and instructions that can leave the operands intact. The key to efficiency seems to be reuse. Efficient subroutine linkage is also of utmost importance.

Future uses of hardware

How should computer architects respond to declining hardware costs? From one point of view, the experimental 801 is an expensive machine. It has a full 32-bit single-cycle ALU and shifter. There are 32 general-purpose registers, each 32 bits wide, with three output and two input ports to the register file. Internal buses are all 32 bits wide. Externally, the 801 presents 32 address bits and data bits to the memory-management unit. These are all expensive items and many have been left out of machines with more complex instruction sets.

Because all instructions are 32 bits, the object code for an 801 program is sometimes a little larger than that of System/370. This shows up most on small

---

One of the lessons of the 801 experiment may be that the best way to implement a large system is to concentrate on the simpler instructions.

---

procedures that do not use 32 registers. An average code expansion seems to be about 20 percent more than System/370 for the same high-level language program. In most cases, this is not significant because data misses in the storage hierarchy are much more frequent than instruction misses. If misses are a problem, the size of the instruction cache can be increased, which is a good use for hardware.

In the future, the largest improvements in performance will probably come about through improving the memory hierarchy. On-chip caches and TLB are an obvious way to speed execution, because they attack the fundamental problem of the performance of the storage system. Wider data paths to memory might also improve performance. For example, the ability to load and store two registers might reduce the overhead associated with call and return, if there were a 64-bit-wide path to memory. Besides work on CPU architecture, the 801 effort at Yorktown has also explored a new memory hierarchy.[15] This is not the place to describe this work, but it is interesting to note some of its characteristics because it sheds light on the uses of hardware. Basically, it is an attempt to share files that are directly mapped into a user's virtual address space. Because the 32-bit address space is not enough, segment registers are introduced in the memory-management unit. Because sharing at the page level would result in too many deadlocks, 16 lock bits are provided for each TLB entry. This permits locking, journaling, and recovery on each 128 bytes of storage in a file. A lot of hardware is required to implement this. The Romp CPU is smaller than the memory-management unit. This cost is justified because the functions performed are very important, and a software solution would require a great deal of overhead. Notice, though, that the hardware does not have to do the entire job. It is enough to give an interrupt on reference to a locked page; systems software can do the rest, as is the case with virtual memory.

One of the lessons of the 801 experiment may be that the best way to implement a large system is to concentrate on the simpler instructions. Thus, there are proposed implementations of more complex architectures that hardwire all the simple, frequently occurring operations and trap on the rest—that is,

---

Increased parallelism is an attractive way to circumvent the constraints imposed by current technology.

---

implement them in software. The success of such an approach has not been proved and will depend partly on human coders changing their habits to treat future systems more like an 801.

Increased parallelism is an attractive way to circumvent the constraints imposed by current technology. The introduction of an asynchronous floating-point coprocessor undoubtedly speeds many scientific applications. The frequency of floating-point arithmetic in such applications, the increased performance from specially designed hardware, and the ability to execute in parallel provides ample justification. Combining many simple 801s or similar processors may prove to be an efficient way to achieve large-scale parallelism. A word of caution should be raised here, as there have been many failed or only marginally successful attempts to do this. The problem lies with the software, not the hardware.

Concluding remarks

The basic 801 approach was conceived by John Cocke; however, one can trace the notions much further back. In 1951, at the dawn of the computer age, Alan Turing suggested to Christopher Strachey,

then a mathematics teacher at Harrow School, that it would be an interesting exercise to simulate one computer on another. Strachey duly wrote a program to simulate the Manchester ACE computer on itself. After a night of debugging he was able to demonstrate that his simulator was able to execute the program that played *God Save The King* on the hooter, albeit very slowly.[16] This was an early graphic demonstration that all computers are logically equivalent. It was certainly not an accident that the problem was suggested by Turing, who had mathematically demonstrated the equivalence of all computers fifteen years earlier. If all computers are logically equivalent, on what basis can the architect make sensible choices when designing the instruction set interface that is implemented by engineers and seen by programmers?

The development of new computer architectures has been driven by many factors. Hardware cost, performance, and reliability have always been important considerations, but other factors have also been taken into account from the very beginning. In 1947, John Mauchly wrote about EDVAC, "A decision must be made as to which operations shall be built in and which are to be coded into instructions. . . . Ultimate choice must depend upon the analysis by the designer of the character of the work to be performed by the machine, the frequency of the occurrence of operations, and the ease with which the non-built-in operations can be compounded from those which are built in."[17] The 801 emphasis on simple instructions is just a restatement of this old wisdom. Programming has long been recognized as a bottleneck. After all, Turing hired Strachey on the basis of his ability to check out a large program in a single overnight session. Apart from hiring talented programmers, what can be done about programming? The issue is truly complex, because today most programming is done in high-level language. Thus, the exact nature of the computer should concern only the compiler writers, but programmers will use a high-level language only if the compiler produces object code of adequate quality. How diligently must the compiler writer work? What is "adequate?"

The 801 project experiment can be viewed as an attempt to answer these questions in the light of current technology. The microcode approach arose in IBM because it seemed necessary to produce a uniform product line. In 1963, there were many different architectures in the product line, each with exotic features geared to the perceived needs of particular users. Read-only storage provided the means to implement a compatible family of machines with a wide range of cost, while at the same time retaining the same sort of instructions. Increased reliance on high-level language programming tended to undercut the argument for high-level operations based on ease of programming. Also, the introduction of caches provided the opportunity to trade the microstore—which was available only to microcoders—for an instruction cache available to all. The existence of trace tapes showing actual instruction execution demonstrated the importance of hardwiring the simple operations and cast doubt on the economic value of complex operations.

There is no single novelty among the 801/RISC concepts. If anything, they reflect enduring values that clearly go back to the first computers, incorporating the few great ideas that have been developed since then, which include virtual memory and caches. As a research vehicle, the 801 experiment has served as a reminder that hardware is never free, that simplicity is sometimes best, and that a fresh look at existing ideas such as virtual memory and caches can repay big dividends.

Cited references

1. D. A. Paterson, "Microprogramming," *Scientific American* **243**, No. 3, 36–43 (March 1983).
2. M. Auslander and M. E. Hopkins, "An overview of the PL.8 compiler," *ACM SIGPLAN Notices* **17**, No. 26, 22–31 (June 1982); *Proceedings of the SIGPLAN '82 Symposium on Compiler Writing*, Boston, MA, June 23–25, 1982; published by the Association for Computing Machinery, 11 West 42nd Street, New York, NY 10036.
3. G. J. Chaitin, M. A. Auslander, A. K. Chandra, J. Cocke, M. E. Hopkins, and P. W. Markstein, "Register allocation via coloring," *Computer Languages* **6**, 45–57 (1981).
4. G. J. Chaitin, "Register allocation and spilling via graph coloring," *ACM SIGPLAN Notices* **17**, No. 26, 98–105 (June 1982); *Proceedings of the SIGPLAN '82 Symposium on Compiler Writing*, Boston, MA, June 23–25, 1982; published by the Association for Computing Machinery, 11 West 42nd Street, New York, NY 10036.
5. V. Markstein, J. Cocke, and P. Markstein, "Optimization of range checking," *ACM SIGPLAN Notices* **17**, No. 26, 114–119 (June 1982); *Proceedings of the SIGPLAN '82 Symposium on Compiler Writing*, Boston, MA, June 23–25, 1982; published by the Association for Computing Machinery, 11 West 42nd Street, New York, NY 10036. See also "The IBM RT PC Subroutine Linkage Conventions," *IBM RT Personal Computer Technology*, pp. 131–133; SA23-1057 (1986), available through IBM branch offices.
6. J. Hennessy, N. Jouppi, F. Basket, T. Gross, and J. Gill, "Hardware/software tradeoffs for increased performance," *Proceedings of the Symposium on Architectural Support for Programming Languages and Operating Systems*, Palo Alto, CA, March 1–3, 1982, pp. 2–11; published by the Association for Computing Machinery, 11 West 42nd Street, New York, NY 10036.
7. D. A. Paterson, "Reduced instruction set computers," *Communications of the ACM* **28**, No. 1, 8–21 (January 1985).
8. A. J. Smith, "Cache memories," *ACM Computing Surveys* **14**, No. 3, 473–530 (September 1982).
9. G. Radin, "The 801 minicomputer," *IBM Journal of Research and Development* **27**, No. 3, 237–246 (May 1983).
10. G. Radin, "The 801 minicomputer," *SIGARCH Computer Architecture News* **10**, No. 2, 39–47 (March 1982).
11. M. E. Hopkins, "A definition of RISC," *Proceedings of the International Workshop on High-Level Computer Architecture*, Los Angeles, CA, May 21–25, 1984, pp. 3.8–3.11; published by the University of Maryland, Department of Computer Science, College Park, MD 20742.
12. M. E. Hopkins, "Compiling for the RT PC Romp," *IBM RT Personal Computer Technology*, pp. 76–82; SA23-1057 (1986), available through IBM branch offices.
13. D. E. Knuth, "An empirical study of FORTRAN programs," *Software Practice*, Vol. 1, John Wiley & Sons, Inc., New York (1971), pp. 105–133.
14. M. E. Hopkins, "Compiling high level function on low level machines," *Proceedings of the IEEE International Conference on Computer Design*, Portchester, NY, October 31–November 3, 1983, pp. 617–619; published by the IEEE Computer Society Press, 1109 Spring Street, Suite 300, Silver Spring, MD 20910 (1983).
15. P. D. Hester, R. O. Simpson, and A. Chang, "The IBM RT Romp and memory management unit architecture," *IBM RT Personal Computer Technology*, pp. 48–56; SA23-1057 (1986), available through IBM branch offices.
16. A. Hodges, *Alan Turing: The Enigma*, Simon & Schuster, Inc., New York (1983), p. 447.
17. J. W. Mauchly, "Preparation of problems for EDVAC-type machines," *The Origins of Digital Computers, Selected Papers*, B. Randell, Editor, Springer-Verlag, New York (1973), pp. 365–369.

Martin E. Hopkins *IBM Research Division, Thomas J. Watson Research Center, P.O. Box 218, Yorktown Heights, New York 10598.* Martin Hopkins is manager of compilers in the Advanced Minicomputer Department. He spent ten years with the Computer Usage Company, working mainly on compiler development. Since joining the Research Division in 1969, he has worked on computer architecture as well as compiler development. In 1985, he received a corporate award for his work on the PL.8 language and compiler. He has a B.A. in philosophy from Amherst College.

Reprint Order No. G321-5289.

The IBM RT PC ROMP processor and memory management unit architecture

by R. O. Simpson
P. D. Hester

The ROMP processor is the microprocessor used in the IBM RT PC. It is a 32-bit processor with an associated memory management unit implemented on two chips. ROMP is derived from the pioneering RISC project, the 801 Minicomputer at IBM Research. This paper describes some of the trade-offs which were made to turn the research project into a product. It gives an introduction to the architecture of ROMP, including the addressing model supported by ROMP's memory management unit. Some of the unique features of the programming model are explained, with high-level language coding examples which show how they can be exploited. ROMP's architecture is extensible, and the fact that almost all programming for the RT PC has been in high-level languages means that the RT PC hardware architecture can be extended as needed to meet future requirements while preserving the investment in existing software.

At the center of the IBM RT PC™ are the IBM-designed Reduced Instruction Set Computer (RISC) processor and its memory management unit. The processor is called ROMP, an acronym for Research/OPD Micro Processor. The name tells something of the origin of the processor.

The 801 Minicomputer project at the IBM Thomas J. Watson Research Center in Yorktown Heights, New York, had defined an architecture for and built a prototype of a simple but very high-performance computer.[1,2] At about the same time (the late 1970s) the IBM Office Products Division (OPD) in Austin, Texas, was searching for a new microprocessor to be used in advanced office equipment. The ROMP project began as a joint effort between OPD and the Research Division, with the goal of adapting the architectural concepts of the 801 to an actual product.

ROMP's 801 heritage shows clearly in its architecture, and in fact the same highly optimizing compiler (PL.8)[3-6] is used for both. However, ROMP had a different set of design goals than the 801. While the 801 was an experiment in RISC architecture whose main goal was to demonstrate that a machine could be built which sustained a rate of one instruction per cycle, ROMP was to be part of a product and thus had constraints (primarily cost) that did not apply to the 801. These constraints strongly affected ROMP's design.

In this paper we first give some details of the implementation of the ROMP processor and its Memory Management Unit (MMU). The parallels between the 801 and ROMP are shown, and the differences between them are explained. ROMP's programming model is described and some examples are given of the use of its features.

Design goals

The RT PC ROMP processor was designed to

- Provide an architected address and data width of 32 bits
- Provide an efficient target for an optimizing compiler
- Support virtual memory

- Provide system integrity through separate user and supervisor states
- Provide improved error detection and reporting facilities

The first requirement dictated an architecture providing both 32-bit address and data quantities. As a result, it was decided that all registers and computations would support 32-bit quantities. However, the architecture provides for specific support of 8-bit and 16-bit quantities as well; individual 8-bit bytes and 16-bit halfwords can be loaded and stored and can be manipulated within the 32-bit registers.

The ROMP processor architecture was defined with the assumption that most software would be developed in a high-level language. A joint study between OPD and the IBM Research Division was conducted to evaluate the PL.8 optimizing compiler and the architectural requirements to take advantage of the compiler optimization techniques. The study indicated the need for a large number (16 or 32) of 32-bit general-purpose registers, and an instruction set closely matched to the compiler intermediate language.

During the architecture definition, it became clear that systems using processors of this class must provide virtual memory. ROMP saves sufficient machine state when a page fault occurs to identify the faulting instruction and address and to re-execute the load or store operation once the fault has been resolved. This virtual memory support is common on mainframes and some minicomputers, but had not appeared in a microprocessor prior to the design of the ROMP.

The need to provide protection of user programs and isolation of control program functions resulted in the definition of separate user and supervisor states. Only instructions which cannot be used to affect system integrity are valid in user state. Instructions associated with control program functions are valid in supervisor state only.

Certain requirements and facilities are provided for error detection and reporting, including parity checking on all external buses, bus time-out detection, and nonmaskable hardware error detection interrupts.

Cost constraints

The prototype 801 had been built from low-density but very high-speed circuitry. A VLSI version of the

801 in the technology available at the outset would have required many chips, would have dissipated power in excess of requirements, and would have exceeded the cost targets for a small system to be used in an office. ROMP's design was driven by the need to minimize the number of parts (VLSI chips).

Two chips. Existing technology did not allow functions as complex as the ROMP and its MMU to be

---

ROMP's 2-byte instructions reduce the bandwidth required for instruction fetching.

---

combined into a single chip, so one chip was used for the processor and one for the MMU. The split is about even; the two chips are of comparable complexity (the MMU is somewhat larger than the ROMP).

High performance with inexpensive memory. The 801 had exceptionally high performance: 15.1 MIPS at a cycle time of 63 nanoseconds. However, much of its performance depended on its two caches, which could deliver an instruction word and a data word on each CPU cycle. Since such caches were prohibitively costly for small systems, pipelining techniques normally found in larger machines were adapted to the ROMP so that useful work may be done during the (comparatively) long time needed for memory operations. The techniques include asynchronous prefetching and partial decoding of instructions, a packet-switched channel between the ROMP and the MMU, execution of instructions beyond a "load" until the loaded data are actually needed, and delayed branches which overlap the execution of another instruction with the fetching of the branch target. In addition, the fact that many of ROMP's instructions are only 2 bytes long reduces the bandwidth required for instruction fetching; this bandwidth reduction is necessary because without the 801's two independent caches, the MMU can only supply one word per cycle to ROMP.

RAM size. All of the 801's instructions were 4 bytes long. This simplified instruction fetching and decoding and allowed enough room to name three registers with 5-bit numbers in most instructions. Code density was considered more important for ROMP, which

---

The 2-byte instructions predominate in instruction mixes.

---

was to have a much smaller main memory than the high-performance 801. ROMP has both 2-byte and 4-byte instructions, with the 2-byte instructions predominating in both the static and dynamic instruction mixes.

Adapting the 801

ROMP's similarities and differences. The ROMP programming model and instruction set are derived from the 801 processor for which the PL.8 compiler was originally designed. With the implementation of the short instruction format, it is clear that it is not possible to provide three 5-bit register fields in a 16-bit instruction. To allow space for an op-code, the instructions were changed from three-address to two-address and the register field width reduced from 5 bits to 4. Thus ROMP has 16 general registers, rather than the 801's 32. Reducing the size of the register file also freed silicon area on the ROMP chip for implementing the rest of the CPU.

None of the 801's instruction set philosophy was changed, however. All storage accesses are still through "load" and "store" instructions, and all computation is done on operands in the general registers. That the ROMP instruction set is a good target for a compiler is demonstrated by the fact that the PL.8 compiler generates ROMP object code that is generally smaller than 801 object code for the same program.

The elimination of the 801's caches means that ROMP has a longer latency on memory accesses. The compiler "pipelines" the "load" operations by separating them from the use of the loaded data as far as possible. If several instructions can be placed between a load and the use of the data, the storage

access is done in parallel with useful work in the CPU, as shown in Figure 1. The short loop illustrated is executed entirely from the ROMP instruction pre-fetch buffer, so the loop-closing jump instruction takes only one cycle rather than five. The compiler schedules the load operation two instructions prior to the use of the data loaded. Five total cycles are required for the load data to become available, and the CIS (compare) must wait two cycles for the load to complete. However, this has reduced the effective load time from five to three cycles. The combination of loop-mode execution from the pre-fetch buffer and load scheduling has reduced the total number of execution cycles for this loop from 15 to 9, a 40 percent performance improvement. This loop executes at approximately 6.7 MIPS in an RT with an Advanced Processor Card, 100 nanoseconds cycle time. This pipelining was also done on the 801, but the compiler tries to move the load and use instructions farther apart on ROMP. Note that the pipelining is possible because the storage access (load) and computation instructions are separate. If an instruction such as "add storage to register" were implemented, there would be no opportunity to fetch the operand from storage in advance of its use.

ROMP does not have an instruction cache such as the 801 had. Rather, instructions are fetched ahead a word at a time into a 16-byte instruction queue (called a pre-fetch buffer on ROMP). This queue is filled asynchronously as instructions are executed; the processor does not normally have to wait for an instruction to be returned from memory before beginning execution except for branches taken. Two features are provided which utilize the time that would otherwise be wasted waiting for a branch target to be fetched.

1. 801-style delayed branches (called branch-with-execute) allow ROMP to get a head start on fetching the branch target. The instruction which physically follows the branch in memory is executed regardless of the outcome of the conditional branch test, as if it had been *before* the branch. While this instruction (the *subject* instruction) is being executed, the branch target is being fetched. The compiler is often able to find an instruction which can be moved from just before to just after the branch in this way; such instructions execute "for free," as shown in Figure 2. The final store operation of this loop places the computed value of **y** into array element **x[i]**. The execution of the STS (store) instruction is completely overlapped with the fetching of the branch target, the first

Figure 1   A typical memory-to-memory move in C programming language

```
/* C character string move -- Copy character string s to
   string t until a zero character is found in s          */
move (t,s)
char *t,*s;
{
    while (*t++ = *s++);
}
```

ROMP object code, from the PL.8 compiler:

Execution cycles

```
%6:
      LCS   r0,$MEMORY+*s(r3)     Register scheduling      1
      INC   r3,r3,1               .                        1
      INC   r2,r2,1               .                        1
      CIS   cr,r0,0               Register usage           2+1
      STC   r0,$MEMORY+*t-1(r3)                            2
      JNB   cr,b26/eq,%6          Loop-mode jump           1

                                  Total cycles             9
```

instruction of the loop body. Thus, the store takes zero cycles. This code fragment also shows an example of reduction in strength: Rather than multiply the array index **i** by 4 (or even shift it left 2), an auxiliary variable is used as a pointer into the array and is bumped by 4 with a one-cycle ADD instruction each time through the loop.
2. Loops within the pre-fetch buffer are recognized by ROMP, and subsequent iterations of the loop are not re-fetched from memory. The branch which closes such a loop is thus reduced to one cycle and the entire memory bandwidth becomes available for data traffic. Real application programs have been observed in which the compiler

has generated these "tight" inner loops, and such programs approach the theoretical maximum rate of one instruction per cycle (10 MIPS at a 100-ns cycle time). System subroutines such as character string move are hand-coded to take advantage of high-speed looping within the pre-fetch buffer.

Although most ROMP instructions execute in only one cycle, additional cycles are taken when it is necessary to wait for data to be returned from memory for loads and branches. As a result, ROMP takes about 2.3 cycles on the average for each instruction. At the cycle time of 100 nanoseconds used in the RT PC, ROMP runs at about 4.3 MIPS.

Figure 2   Closing a loop with branch and execute

```
Closing a loop with branch with execute:

    int   x[50];

    for (i=0; i<50; i++) {   /* compute array elements */
        (body of loop)
        ...
        x[i] = y;
    }

ROMP object code, from the PL.8 compiler:

    %6:
        (body of loop)
        ...
        LS    r0,y(r1)         Load value of y
        A     r2,r2,r13        Increment x array pointer
        INC   r12,r12,1        Increment loop counter
        CI    cr,r12,50        Test loop termination
        BTX   cr,b25/lt,%6     Branch (with execute) if not done
        STS   r0,x(r2)         Store x[i]
```

The ROMP programming model

Here we describe the major features of the registers, instruction set, and addressing model of ROMP. More detail can be found in the references[7,8] and in the reference manuals for the RT PC.[9,10]

General-Purpose Registers. ROMP has sixteen 32-bit General-Purpose Registers (GPRs), as shown in Figure 3. The registers can be used for computation or as base registers, as with System/370. Register 0 has special meaning when used as a base register: The value 0 is used as the base rather than the contents of register 0. Thus, absolute addressing is provided by a convention on the base register name rather than by a separate addressing mode.

Some shift instructions consider the registers to be "paired" (e.g., 0 and 1, 14 and 15), with input from one register and output to the other register of the pair (an implicit operand). This deviation from true RISC style was made in order to be able to specify nondestructive shift instructions in the short (16-bit) format.

Other registers. The other registers which can be seen by the programmer are the System Control Registers (SCRs) shown in Figure 4. Most of these deal with hardware control of timers and interrupts or record exception conditions (page faults, program checks). Two are directly usable in application programs.

- The *Condition Status* (CS, Control Register 15) is the equivalent of the System/370 Condition Code. Results of comparisons and arithmetic operations are recorded here; the conditional branch instructions specify a bit in the Condition Status which determines whether the branch is taken. One bit is permanently zero, providing for unconditional branches (and no-ops). Another, the "test bit," can be loaded with any selected bit in any general register and then used as a branch condition.
- The *Multiplier/Quotient* (MQ, Control Register 10) register holds half of the 64-bit product or dividend for the Multiply Step and Divide Step instructions. It is an implicit operand of those instructions, and is the result of a trade-off between architectural elegance and hardware efficiency: As an implicit

Figure 4 ROMP System Control Registers

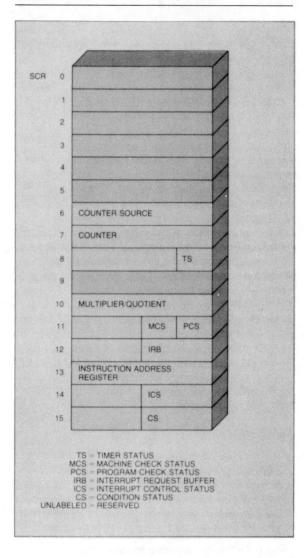

Figure 3 ROMP General-Purpose Registers

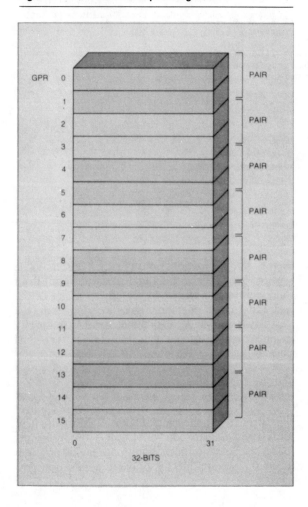

operand, the MQ need not be named in the instruction (thus the Multiply Step and Divide Step instructions can be 16 bits long) and it is implemented as a high-speed register separate from the general register file.

The Instruction Address Register (IAR) is contained in Control Register 13, but it is not needed directly by the programmer. Most branch instructions are implicitly relative to the contents of the IAR, and the value in the IAR can be loaded into a general register by the Branch and Link instruction when necessary.

SIMPSON AND HESTER

Instruction set. The ROMP provides a total of 118 instructions in the following ten classes:

Instruction Class	Number of Instructions
1. Memory Access	17
2. Address Computation	8
3. Branch and Jump	16
4. Trap	3
5. Move and Insert	13
6. Arithmetic	21
7. Logical	16
8. Shift	15
9. System Control	7
10. Input and Output	2
Total	118

The *Memory Access* instructions permit loading and storing data between the 16 GPRs and main memory. These instructions support four types of data:

- 8-bit (character) quantities
- 16-bit (halfword) quantities
- 16-bit algebraic (sign-extended halfword) quantities
- 32-bit (fullword) quantities.

Load Multiple and Store Multiple instructions are also included in this class. They permit loading or storing from one to 16 of the GPRs. A test and set instruction is provided for multiprocessor synchronization.

All Memory Access instructions compute the effective memory address as the sum of a GPR contents plus an immediate field specified in the instruction (base + displacement addressing). Two-byte memory access instructions provide a 4-bit immediate field, with 4-byte instructions providing a 16-bit immediate field.

The Memory Access instructions operate on data between memory and one or more GPRs. No memory-to-memory operations are provided. The architecture allows instruction execution to continue beyond a load instruction before the load is complete, if subsequent instructions do not use the loaded data. This increases system performance by overlapping memory access with subsequent instruction execution.

The *Address Computation* instructions compute memory addresses without changing the status of the condition codes. These instructions include a three-address add instruction (Compute Address Short),

increment, decrement, and 2- and 4-byte instructions which permit loading a GPR with a 4-bit or 16-bit immediate value, respectively. Separate Compute Address Lower and Compute Address Upper instructions are provided to load a 16-bit immediate value into either the lower half or upper half of a GPR. Two Address Computation instructions are provided specifically to aid in the emulation of 16-bit architectures. They allow the computation of a 16-bit quantity to replace the low-order 16 bits of a GPR without altering the upper 16 bits.

The *Branch* and *Jump* instructions are provided for decision making. Jumps are 2 bytes long, and provide a relative range of plus or minus 254 bytes. Branches are 4 bytes long and provide a range of up to plus or minus 1 megabyte. A group of Branch and Link (BAL) instructions are also provided for subroutine linkage.

Many branch and branch-and-link instructions have a delayed branch form (called "Branch with Execute") which allows overlap of the branch target fetch with execution of one instruction following the branch (called the subject instruction). Execution of the subject occurs in parallel with fetching of the target instruction, thereby eliminating dead cycles that would normally occur during fetching of the target instruction.

Three *Trap* instructions are provided for run-time address checking. These instructions compare a register quantity against a limit, and cause a program check interrupt if the limit is exceeded.

The *Move* and *Insert* instructions support testing the value of any bit in a GPR, and the movement of any of the four 1-byte fields in a GPR. A Move instruction is provided that allows moving any one of the 32 bits in a GPR to a test bit in the condition status register, with a corresponding instruction that moves the test bit value to any of the 32 bits in a GPR. A series of Move Character instructions are included that move any of the four 1-byte fields in a GPR to another 1-byte field in a GPR.

The *Arithmetic* class supports standard Add and Subtract operations in both single- and extended-precision modes. Other instructions in this class include absolute value, ones- and twos-complement, compare, and sign-extend. Also, Multiply Step and Divide Step instructions are provided. The Multiply Step instruction produces a 2-bit result per step, and can be used to construct variable-length multiply operations. The Divide Step instruction produces a single-bit result per step, and can be used to construct variable-length divide operations.

The *Logical* class provides AND, OR, XOR, and negation operations using two register quantities or one register and an immediate value. Also included in this class is a group of set and clear bit instructions that allow any bit in any GPR to be set to one or to zero.

The *Shift* class provides algebraic shift right, shift right, shift left, and left and right paired shifts. Shift amounts from 0 to 31 bits can be specified either as an immediate quantity in the instruction or as an indirect amount using the value in a GPR. The paired shifts provide nondestructive shifts that shift a specified GPR a given amount, and place the result in a different register (the other register of a register pair) without altering the source register.

Instructions in the *System Control* class are generally privileged instructions that are valid only in supervisor state. Included in this class are instructions that move GPRs to and from SCRs, set and clear SCR bits, Load Program Status, and Wait for interrupt. Also included is a nonprivileged Supervisor Call instruction.

Two instructions that load and store GPRs to I/O devices are included in the *Input and Output* class. These instructions are normally used to access control registers in the MMU or other system elements.

Memory addressing model

The basic concepts of memory addressing in ROMP are shown in Figure 5 and are similar to those of System/370. The smallest addressable storage unit is the 8-bit byte. Two bytes make a halfword, four bytes make a word (or fullword). Halfword and fullword quantities must be properly aligned on 2-byte and 4-byte boundaries in storage in order to be loaded and stored by the ROMP storage access instructions (in this area ROMP's memory model is that of System/360 rather than System/370). Strings of bytes (character strings) can begin on any byte address, but they are manipulated by subroutines rather than low-level ROMP instructions.

Memory addresses begin at 0 and increase "to the right," as in System/370. All quantities in storage are addressed by their leftmost (high-order) byte, without exception. This is true of the operands of load and store instructions and branch targets. The

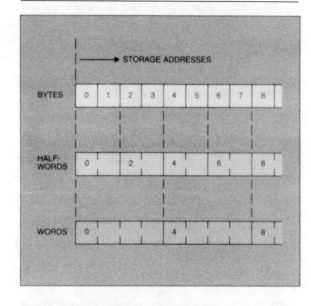

Figure 5 ROMP memory addressing with integral boundaries

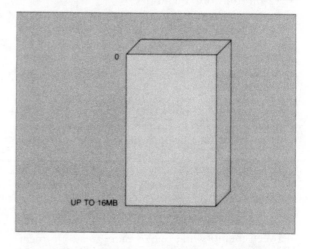

Figure 6 RT System real memory

bytes of arithmetic quantities are never reversed as they are moved between memory and registers.

When the virtual addressing mode of the ROMP MMU is enabled, there are three conceptual levels of addressing to be considered.

Real addressing. This is the lowest level, as depicted in Figure 6, the level that the programmer sees when running with virtual addressing turned off. Memory is a linear array of bytes starting at 0. Except for the recording of reference and change information, there

Figure 7 Mapping of 40-bit virtual addresses to real addresses

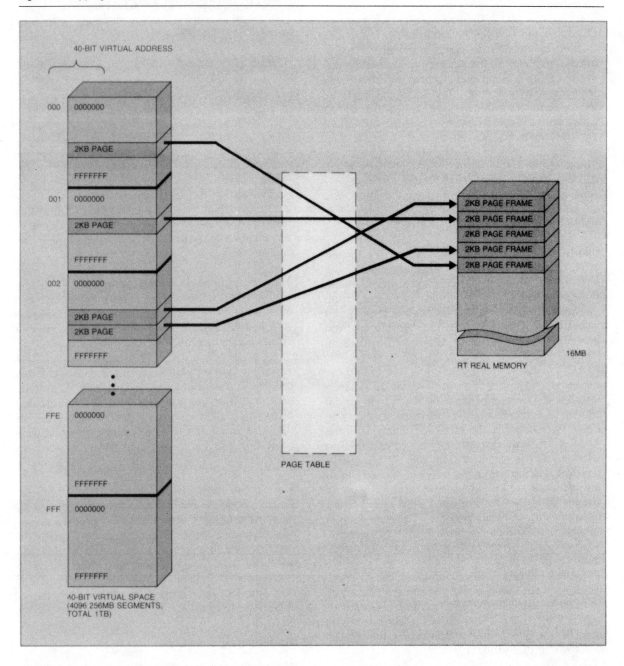

is no concept of "pages" at this level. Architecturally, real addresses are 32-bit quantities, but in the RT PC the maximum amount of memory that can be installed is 16 megabytes.

Long-form virtual addressing. This intermediate level, illustrated in Figure 7, becomes active when

the MMU is enabled for virtual address translation. Virtual memory can be viewed as a collection of *segments* of 256 megabytes each. There are 4096 possible segments, each named by a 12-bit *segment id*. Each segment is made up of 2K-byte pages. Virtual addresses in this level are 40 bits: 12 bits for the segment id, 17 bits for the page number within the segment, and 11 bits for the byte offset within the page. The total virtual space is thus 2^{40} bytes, or 1 terabyte.

Of course, this is virtual space. In reality only a tiny fraction of the 2^{40}-byte space is actually in use at once—only a few of the 4096 segments, and a maximum of only a few megabytes within each of those segments. The mapping of 40-bit virtual addresses to real addresses is done by the MMU, which signals a page fault to ROMP when an access to an unmapped page is attempted.

The programmer does not deal directly with 40-bit addresses. As is seen below, the ROMP hardware generates 32-bit virtual addresses, and the MMU constructs the 40-bit virtual address internally before translating it to real.

Short-form virtual addressing. This is the highest level, the level at which the programmer deals with virtual addressing. ROMP's address generation process is the same whether or not virtual address translation is enabled: Address computations result in 32-bit values, and 32-bit addresses are transmitted from ROMP to the MMU for loads, stores, and instruction fetches.

Inside the MMU, the first step of virtual address translation is the expansion of the 32-bit virtual address to a long-form (40-bit) address, as shown in Figure 8. To do this, the high-order four bits of the 32-bit short-form address are removed and used to select a 12-bit segment id from one of 16 *segment registers*. The segment registers are contained within the MMU and are loaded under control of the operating system; they are protected from modification by application programs. The 12-bit segment id is concatenated with the remaining 28 bits of the short-form virtual address to make a 40-bit virtual address.

The effect of this is that a program has a 32-bit window on the 40-bit world, in the form of a set of 16 of the possible 4096 256-megabyte segments. The segment to be used is selected by the top four bits of the 32-bit address, while the remaining bits are an offset within that segment.

For most purposes, the program is not aware of the presence of one or more segments in its 32-bit virtual space. With the AIX operating system, addresses of items on the stack lie in the range 30000000 through 3FFFFFFF (hex), while addresses of programs are in the range 20000000 through 2FFFFFFF. However,

Table 1   Page protection keys

Page Key	Type of Page	Access Key	Load	Store
00	System read/write	0	Yes	Yes
	User no access	1	No	No
01	System read/write	0	Yes	Yes
	User read-only	1	Yes	No
10	Public read/write	0	Yes	Yes
		1	Yes	Yes
11	Public read-only	0	Yes	No
		1	Yes	No

it is possible to make direct use of the segments by requesting that the operating system "map" a file to a segment, share one or more segments with other tasks, or use one of the segments to access the RT PC's memory-mapped I/O. A discussion of these uses is given below.

Memory protection. In real addressing mode, no memory protection is given. This mode is intended for use by low-level system programs such as interrupt handlers. Almost all application code runs in virtual addressing mode.

When virtual translation is enabled, one of two protection modes is selected. The most commonly used mode (for "normal" segments) is similar to that of System/370, in which a one-bit access key in the segment register is tested against a two-bit page protection key for the selected page, as shown in Table 1.

For "special" segments, a finer granularity of protection is provided. This mode is intended for use by database programs and others who need to distinguish between read/write and read-only access on items smaller than a page. Each page is divided into 16 "lines" of 128 bytes each, with read and write access granted on the individual line level. Details of this "line locking" function are discussed in References 7, 8, and 11.

Programming the ROMP

Almost all programming on the RT is done in high-level languages which hide low-level details such as the instruction set and the number of registers. These details are still important, for they affect the efficiency of the code that the compilers generate and thus the performance of RT programs. Some architectural features are pervasive, and show through the

SIMPSON AND HESTER

Figure 8   Conversion of 32-bit virtual addresses to 40-bit virtual addresses

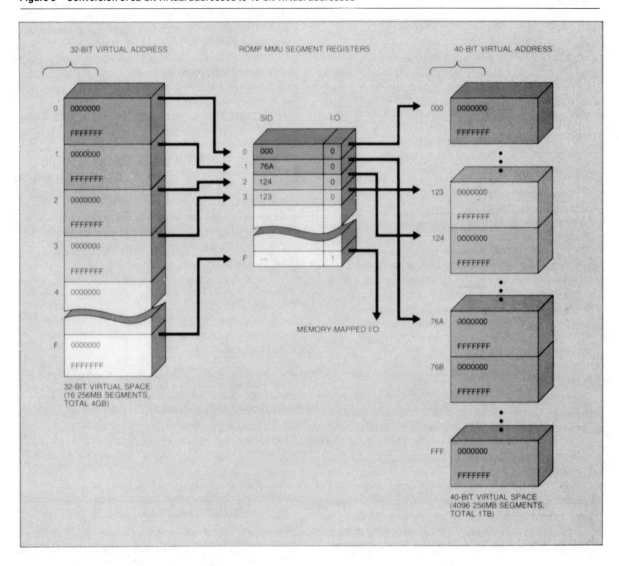

languages. They affect the methodology used by the programmer in designing and coding an application.

32 bits. On the RT, the natural unit of data is the 32-bit word. The general registers are 32 bits wide; hence, arithmetic on 32-bit quantities and 32-bit addresses is very efficient. The default integer size and pointer size for the various high-level languages on the RT is 32 bits.

Large linear memory space. There are no 64-kilobyte boundaries in the RT's addressing space. The smallest boundary is 256 megabytes, the size of a virtual storage segment. Almost all programs can be written with the presumption that any data item can be addressed with a standard 32-bit pointer; there are no distinctions between "near" and "far" pointers. There are no array size limitations such as 64K total entries or 64 kilobytes total space. Programs and data can easily be several megabytes in size.

Segments. A *segment* in the RT is much larger than the segments on most other machines, and it is used for different purposes. Each segment can be up to 256 megabytes and begins on a 256-megabyte boundary in the 32-bit virtual space; segments do not overlap. Up to 16 segments can be mapped at once, and the program can change the mapping through calls to the operating system.

RT segments are used to provide

- Data isolation, through multiple address spaces. The address space of a task is the collection of segments to which it has access. In the AIX operating system, for example, one segment will contain the private code for the process, another its private data, and another its stack. These segments are not mapped into the address spaces of other processes, and thus are completely isolated from the other processes.

- Data sharing, by mapping the same segment into several different processes. Private data remain isolated as described above.
- Different levels of protection, by assigning different hardware protection keys to different segments. Thus, a segment containing code (even private code) is normally read-only, while a data segment is read-write.
- Access to input/output, by assigning a segment to memory-mapped I/O.
- Mapped files, by mapping the image of a file on disk into a virtual storage segment.

The other traditional use for segments, which is to extend addressability beyond the natural address

---

Figure 9 Writing data to bit-mapped display using RT System's memory-mapped I/O

```
int            bus;              /* file descriptor for I/O bus              */
struct hwdbase busbase;          /* returned values of bus addresses        */
short          *regen_buf;       /* memory-mapped addr of display buffer     */
short          *p;               /* ptr to a location in display buffer      */

bus = open("/dev/bus",O_RDWR);   /* get read/write access to I/O space       */
ioctl(bus,HWDBASE,&busbase);     /* get starting addr of memory-mapped I/O   */
display_buf =                    /* compute starting addr of display buffer  */
    (short *) (busbase.hwdmem + 0xD80000);

p = display_buf +                /* point to proper location in display buf  */
    <offset of desired location>;
*p = <value>;                    /* store data into display buffer           */
```

Figure 10 **Random access to a mapped file on the RT System**

```
struct book                         /* structure mapping records in file  */
    char    isbn[16];
    char    author[50];
    char    title[100];
    char    publisher[50];
    int     year;
    ;
struct book *ptr;                   /* ptr to base address of mapped file */
int     bookfile;                   /* file descriptor                     */

bookfile =                          /* open the file for reading           */
    open(<filename>,O_RDONLY);
ptr =                               /* map file into virtual memory        */
    (struct book *)                 /* set "ptr" to its starting address   */
    shmat(bookfile,0,SHM_MAP|SHM_RDONLY);

/* print out the "author" field of the Nth record in the file              */

printf("author = %s\n",ptr[N].author);
```

width of the machine, is also possible in the RT but is not used nearly as often as on machines with smaller address widths. A 32-bit address spans 4 gigabytes, which is enough for most purposes. On the RT, this can be extended to 1 terabyte by manipulating the contents of the segment registers.

Memory-mapped I/O. On the RT, a single segment register is normally assigned to map the I/O address space rather than virtual memory. Access to this segment is controlled by protection hardware in the RT PC's I/O channel controller in a manner similar to the method used by the MMU to control access to pages of virtual storage. Thus, an application which

has not been explicitly granted access to the I/O memory map cannot accidentally trigger an I/O operation.

For applications which need to deal directly with I/O, it is simple to do this in high-level languages by assigning the appropriate values to pointers and then using assignment statements to read from and write to the I/O space. As an example, it is easy to code a C program which writes a screen full of graphics data to a bit-mapped display, as illustrated in Figure 9.

Mapped files. RT segments can be used to "map" files into virtual storage, as depicted in Figure 10.

After a file is opened, an operating system call converts the file identifier into an address in virtual storage (a pointer) at which the first byte of the file appears. From then on, the file can be treated as a large array or structure in virtual storage, and is read and written using assignment statements (i.e., load and store instructions). Actual I/O to the file is implicit and is done as needed by the paging supervisor. When the file is closed, modified pages are flushed out to their proper places in the file system.

This treatment of files can greatly simplify an application, especially those that must read and write files at random. Assuming that the file will fit into a 256-megabyte segment, it is simpler and more efficient to access elements by moving a pointer or adjusting an array index than it is to do explicit reads and writes through an I/O buffer.

Conclusions

The IBM RT PC's ROMP processor represents an effective adaptation of the RISC approach begun in the 801 to the real world of a small but powerful computer system product. Many cost-driven trade-offs had to be made, but even so the ROMP executes at a sustained rate of 4.3 MIPS, just under half that of an 801 with the same cycle time. This is done without the benefit of the 801's two caches.

ROMP is a good architectural base for future growth. All the size limits in the current implementation (12-bit segment ids, 16-megabyte real memory) can be increased without major architectural modifications. It is possible to add selected functions which are not normally considered part of the RISC domain as long as they are carefully chosen and known from measurements of actual code to pay back more in performance than they cost. Examples that come to mind are floating-point and character string operations.

The RT PC is truly a high-level language machine in that almost everything written for it has been in C, FORTRAN, or some other high-level language. The programming interface has been moved above the assembly language level. Because of this, it is even possible to change the ROMP's instruction set and still maintain the parts of the programming model that show through in high-level languages. Only the lowest-level routines in the operating system (interrupt handlers, for example) would need to be changed; applications would need only to be recompiled. This raising of the level of the programming interface may prove to be one of the major benefits of the RT PC in the long run.

RT and RT PC are trademarks of International Business Machines Corporation.

Cited references

1. M. E. Hopkins, "A perspective on the 801/Reduced Instruction Set Computer," *IBM Systems Journal* **26,** No. 1, 107–121 (1987).
2. G. Radin, "The 801 minicomputer," *SIGARCH Computer Architecture News* **10,** No. 2, 39–47 (March 1982). Revised version published in *IBM Journal of Research and Development* **27,** No. 3, 237–246 (May 1983).
3. M. Auslander and M. E. Hopkins, "An overview of the PL.8 compiler," *ACM SIGPLAN Notices* **17,** No. 26, 22–31 (June 1982); *Proceedings of the SIGPLAN '82 Symposium on Compiler Writing*, Boston, MA, June 23–25, 1982; published by the Association for Computing Machinery, 11 West 42nd Street, New York, NY 10036.
4. G. J. Chaitin, "Register allocation and spilling via graph coloring," *ACM SIGPLAN Notices* **17,** No. 26, 98–105 (June 1982); *Proceedings of the SIGPLAN '82 Symposium on Compiler Writing*, Boston, MA, June 23–25, 1982; published by the Association for Computing Machinery, 11 West 42nd Street, New York, NY 10036.
5. M. E. Hopkins, "Compiling for the RT PC ROMP," *RT Personal Computer Technology* (pp. 76–82), SA23-1057 (1986); available through IBM branch offices.
6. V. Markstein, J. Cocke, and P. Markstein, "Optimization of range checking," *ACM SIGPLAN Notices* **17,** No. 26, 114–119 (June 1982); *Proceedings of the SIGPLAN '82 Symposium on Compiler Writing*, Boston, MA, June 23–25, 1982; published by the Association for Computing Machinery, 11 West 42nd Street, New York, NY 10036. See also "The IBM RT PC Subroutine Linkage Conventions," *RT Personal Computer Technology* (pp. 131–133), SA23-1057 (1986); available through IBM branch offices.
7. P. D. Hester, R. O. Simpson, and A. Chang, "The IBM RT PC ROMP and Memory Management Unit Architecture," *RT Personal Computer Technology* (pp. 48–56), SA23-1057 (1986); available through IBM branch offices.
8. R. O. Simpson, "The IBM RT Personal Computer," *BYTE* **11,** No. 11, 43–78 (November 1986).
9. IBM Corporation, *IBM RT PC Advanced Interactive Executive Operating System Assembler Language Reference*, 59X7994 (1986); available through IBM branch offices.
10. IBM Corporation, *IBM RT PC Hardware Technical Reference*, Volume I, 75X0232 (1986); available through IBM branch offices.
11. A. Chang and M. F. Mergen, "801 Storage architecture and programming," *Proceedings of the 11th ACM Symposium on Operating Systems Principles*, 1987, to appear.

Richard O. Simpson *IBM Advanced Engineering Systems, Austin, Texas 78758.* Mr. Simpson has been involved with the architecture of the ROMP processor and memory management unit since 1981. Previously, he was part of the development groups for the IBM 5520 Administrative System, the Network Job Entry Facility for JES2, and a Federal Systems Division project to automate the U.S. Army's Pentagon Telecommunication Center.

Mr. Simpson joined IBM in 1969. He holds B.A. and M.E.E. degrees from Rice University, and is a Ph.D. candidate in computer science at the University of Texas at Austin.

Phillip D. Hester *IBM Advanced Engineering Systems, Austin, Texas 78758.* Mr. Hester is Engineering Center Manager for Advanced Engineering Systems in Austin, Texas. Previously, he was responsible for architecture and performance of the RT PC. He was also involved in the architecture, design, and implementation of the RT PC/RISC microprocessor and memory management unit. He has numerous patents and technical publications on RISC processors. Mr. Hester joined IBM Austin in 1976 after receiving a B.S. degree in electrical engineering from the University of Texas at Austin. While in IBM, he received an M.S. degree in engineering from the University of Texas in 1981. He is a member of Eta Kappa Nu and Tau Beta Pi.

Reprint Order No. G321-5301.

Gerry Kane, MIPS R2000 RISC ARCHITECTURE, © 1987, pages
2–1—2–15. Reprinted by permission of Prentice Hall, Inc., Englewood
Cliffs, N.J.

R2000 Processor Overview

The MIPS R2000 Processor consists of two tightly–coupled processors implemented on a single chip. The first processor is a full 32–bit RISC CPU. The second processor is a system control coprocessor (CP0), containing a TLB (Translation Lookaside Buffer) and control registers to support a virtual memory subsystem and separate caches for instructions and data. Figure 2.1 shows the functions incorporated within the R2000.

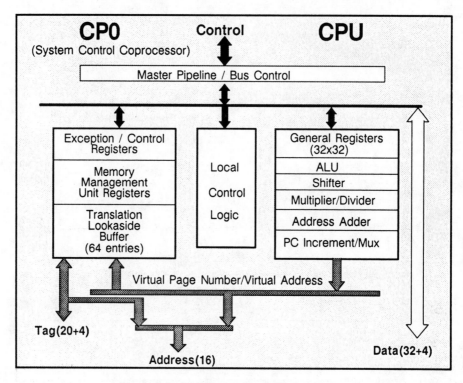

Figure 2.1 R2000 Functional Block Diagram

R2000 Processor Features

- **Full 32–bit Operation.** The R2000 contains thirty–two 32–bit registers, and all instructions and addresses are 32 bits.

- **Efficient Pipelining.** The CPU's 5–stage pipeline design assists in obtaining an execution rate approaching one instruction per cycle. Pipeline stalls and exceptional events are handled precisely and efficiently.

- **On–chip Cache Control.** The R2000 provides a high–bandwidth memory interface that handles separate external Instruction and Data caches ranging in size from 4 to 64 Kbytes each. Both caches are accessed during a single CPU cycle. All cache control logic is on chip.

- **On–chip Memory Management Unit.** a fully–associative, 64–entry Translation Lookaside Buffer (TLB) provides fast address translation for virtual–to–physical memory mapping of the 4–Gbyte virtual address space.

- **Coprocessor Interface**. the R2000 generates all addresses and handles memory interface control for up to three additional tightly-coupled external coprocessors.

R2000 CPU Registers

The R2000 CPU provides 32 general purpose 32-bit registers, a 32-bit Program Counter, and two 32-bit registers that hold the results of integer multiply and divide operations. The CPU registers are shown in Figure 2.2 and are described in detail later in this chapter. Note that there is no Program Status Word (PSW) register shown in this figure: the functions traditionally provided by a PSW register are instead provided in the *Status* and *Cause* registers incorporated within the System Control Coprocessor (CP0).

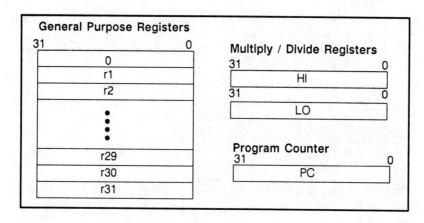

Figure 2.2   R2000 CPU Registers

Instruction Set Overview

All R2000 instructions are 32 bits long and there are only three instruction formats as shown in Figure 2.3. This approach simplifies instruction decoding. More complicated (and less frequently used) operations and addressing modes can be synthesized by the compiler using sequences of simple instructions.

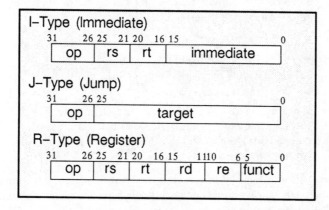

Figure 2.3   R2000 Instruction Formats

The R2000 instruction set can be divided into the following groups:

- **Load/Store** instructions move data between memory and general registers. They are all I–type instructions, since the only addressing mode supported is base register plus 16–bit, signed immediate offset.

- **Computational** instructions perform arithmetic, logical and shift operations on values in registers. They occur in both R–type (both operands and the result are registers) and I–type (one operand is a 16–bit immediate) formats.

- **Jump and Branch** instructions change the control flow of a program. Jumps are always to a paged absolute address formed by combining a 26–bit target with four bits of the Program Counter (J–type format, for subroutine calls) or 32–bit register addresses (R–type, for returns and dispatches). Branches have 16–bit offsets relative to the program counter (I–type). Jump and Link instructions save a return address in Register 31.

- **Coprocessor** instructions perform operations in the coprocessors. Coprocessor Loads and Stores are I–type. Coprocessor computational instructions have coprocessor–dependent formats (see the R2010 FPA instructions in **Chapter 7**).

- **Coprocessor 0** instructions perform operations on the System Control Coprocessor (CP0) registers to manipulate the memory management and exception handling facilities of the processor.

- **Special** instructions perform a variety of tasks, including movement of data between special and general registers, system calls, and breakpoint. They are always R–type.

Table 2.1 lists the instruction set of the R2000 Processor. A more detailed summary is provided in **Chapter 3** and a complete description of each instruction is contained in **Appendix A**.

R2000 Processor Programming Model

This section describes organization of data in registers and in memory and the set of general registers available. It also gives a summary description of all the R2000 CPU registers.

Data Formats and Addressing

The R2000 defines a 32–bit word, a 16–bit half word and an 8–bit byte. The byte ordering is configurable (configuration occurs during hardware reset) into either *big–endian* or *little–endian* byte ordering:

- When configured as a **big–endian** system, byte 0 is always the most significant (leftmost) byte, thereby providing compatibility with MC 68000® and IBM 370® conventions.

- When configured as a **little–endian** system, byte 0 is always the least significant (rightmost) byte, which is compatible with iAPX® x86, NS 32000®, and DEC VAX® conventions.

For purposes of exposition, bit 0 is always the least significant (rightmost) bit; thus bit designations are always little–endian (although no instructions explicitly designate bit positions within words).

Figures 2.4 and 2.5 show the ordering of bytes within words and the ordering of words within multiple–word structures for the big–endian and little–endian conventions.

OP	Description	OP	Description
	Load/Store Instructions		**Multiply/Divide Instructions**
LB	Load Byte	MULT	Multiply
LBU	Load Byte Unsigned	MULTU	Multiply Unsigned
LH	Load Halfword	DIV	Divide
LHU	Load Halfword Unsigned	DIVU	Divide Unsigned
LW	Load Word		
LWL	Load Word Left	MFHI	Move From HI
LWR	Load Word Right	MTHI	Move To HI
		MFLO	Move From LO
SB	Store Byte	MTLO	Move To LO
SH	Store Halfword		**Jump and Branch Instructions**
SW	Store Word		
SWL	Store Word Left	J	Jump
SWR	Store Word Right	JAL	Jump And Link
	Arithmetic Instructions	JR	Jump to Register
	(ALU Immediate)	JALR	Jump And Link Register
ADDI	Add Immediate	BEQ	Branch on Equal
ADDIU	Add Immediate Unsigned	BNE	Branch on Not Equal
SLTI	Set on Less Than Immediate	BLEZ	Branch on Less than or Equal to Zero
SLTIU	Set on Less Than Immediate Unsigned	BGTZ	Branch on Greater Than Zero
		BLTZ	Branch on Less Than Zero
ANDI	AND Immediate	BGEZ	Branch on Greater than or Equal to Zero
ORI	OR Immediate		
XORI	Exclusive OR Immediate	BLTZAL	Branch on Less Than Zero And Link
LUI	Load Upper Immediate	BGEZAL	Branch on Greater than or Equal to Zero And Link
	Arithmetic Instructions		**Coprocessor Instructions**
	(3-operand, register-type)		
ADD	Add	LWCz	Load Word from Coprocessor
ADDU	Add Unsigned	SWCz	Store Word to Coprocessor
SUB	Subtract	MTCz	Move To Coprocessor
SUBU	Subtract Unsigned	MFCz	Move From Coprocessor
SLT	Set on Less Than	CTCz	Move Control to Coprocessor
SLTU	Set on Less Than Unsigned	CFCz	Move Control From Coprocessor
AND	AND	COPz	Coprocessor Operation
OR	OR	BCzT	Branch on Coprocessor z True
XOR	Exclusive OR	BCzF	Branch on Coprocessor z False
NOR	NOR		**System Control Coprocessor**
	Shift Instructions		**(CP0) Instructions**
SLL	Shift Left Logical		
SRL	Shift Right Logical	MTC0	Move To CP0
SRA	Shift Right Arithmetic	MFC0	Move From CP0
SLLV	Shift Left Logical Variable		
SRLV	Shift Right Logical Variable	TLBR	Read indexed TLB entry
SRAV	Shift Right Arithmetic Variable	TLBWI	Write Indexed TLB entry
	Special Instructions	TLBWR	Write Random TLB entry
SYSCALL	System Call	TLBP	Probe TLB for matching entry
BREAK	Break	RFE	Restore From Exception

Table 2.1 R2000 Instruction Summary

Figure 2.4 Addresses of Bytes within Words: Big Endian

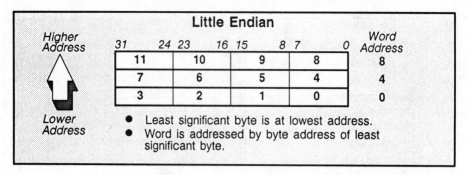

Figure 2.5 Addresses of Bytes within Words: Little Endian

The R2000 uses byte addressing, with alignment constraints, for half word and word accesses; half word accesses must be aligned on an even byte boundary and word accesses must be aligned on a byte boundary divisible by four.

As shown in Figures 2.4 and 2.5, the address of a multiple-byte data item is the address of the most-significant byte on a big-endian configuration, and is the address of the least-significant byte on a little-endian configuration.

Special instructions are provided for addressing words that are not aligned on 4-byte (word) boundaries (Load/Store-Word-Left/Right; LWL, LWR, SWL, SWR). These instructions are used in pairs to provide addressing of misaligned words with one additional instruction cycle over that required for aligned words. Figure 2.6 shows the bytes accessed when addressing a misaligned word with a byte address of 3 for each of the two conventions.

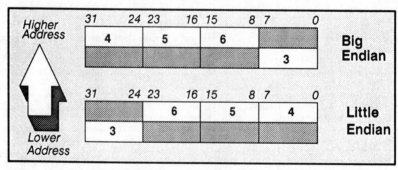

Figure 2.6 Misaligned Word: Byte Addresses

R2000 CPU General Registers

Figure 2.7 shows the R2000 CPU registers. There are 32 general registers, each consisting of a single word (32 bits). The 32 general registers are treated symmetrically, with two exceptions: *r0* is hardwired to a zero value, and *r31* is the link register for Jump And Link instructions.

Register *r0* may be specified as a target register for any instruction when the result of the operation is discarded. The register maintains a value of zero under all conditions when used as a source register.

The two Multiply/Divide registers (HI, LO) store the double-word, 64-bit result of multiply operations and the quotient and remainder of divide operations.

NOTE: In addition to the CPU's general registers, the system control coprocessor (CP0) has a number of special purpose registers that are used in conjunction with the memory management system and during exception processing. Refer to **Chapter 4** for a description of the memory management registers and to **Chapter 5** for a discussion of the exception handling registers.

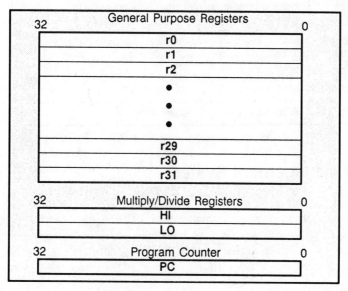

Figure 2.7 R2000 CPU Registers

R2000 System Control Coprocessor (CP0)

The R2000 can operate with up to four tightly-coupled coprocessors (designated CP0 through CP3). The System Control Coprocessor (or CP0), is incorporated on the R2000 chip and supports the virtual memory system and exception handling functions of the R2000. The virtual memory system is implemented using a Translation Lookaside Buffer and a group of programmable registers as shown in Figure 2.8.

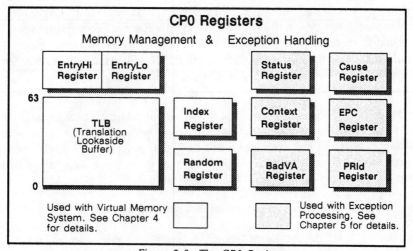

Figure 2.8 The CP0 Registers

System Control Coprocessor (CP0) Registers

The CP0 registers shown in Figure 2.8 are used to manipulate the memory management and exception handling capabilities of the R2000. Table 2.2 provides a brief description of each register. Refer to **Chapter 4** for a detailed description of the registers associated with the virtual memory system and refer to **Chapter 5** for descriptions of the exception processing registers.

Register	Description
EntryHi	High half of a TLB entry
EntryLo	Low half of a TLB entry
Index	Programmable pointer into TLB array
Random	Pseudo-random pointer into TLB array
Status	Mode, interrupt enables, and diagnostic status info
Cause	Indicates nature of last exception
EPC	Exception Program Counter
Context	Pointer into kernel's virtual Page Table Entry array
BadVA	Most recent bad virtual address
PRId	Processor revision identification

Table 2.2   System Control Coprocessor (CP0) Registers

Memory Management System

The R2000 has an addressing range of 4 Gbytes. However, since most R2000 systems implement a physical memory smaller than 4 Gbytes, the R2000 provides for the logical expansion of memory space by translating addresses composed in a large virtual address space into available physical memory addresses. The 4 GByte address space is divided into 2 Gbytes for users and 2 GBytes for the kernel.

The TLB (Translation Lookaside Buffer)

Virtual memory mapping is assisted by the Translation Lookaside Buffer (TLB). The on-chip TLB provides very fast virtual memory access and is well-matched to the requirements of multi-tasking operating systems. The fully-associative TLB contains 64 entries, each of which maps a 4-Kbyte page, with controls for read/write access, cacheability, and process identification. The TLB allows each user to access up to 2 Gbytes of virtual address space.

R2000 Operating Modes

The R2000 has two operating modes: *User* mode and *Kernel* mode. The R2000 normally operates in the User mode until an exception is detected forcing it into the Kernel mode. It remains in the Kernel mode until a Restore From Exception *(RFE)* instruction is executed. The manner in which memory addresses are translated or *mapped* depends on the operating mode of the R2000. Figure 2.9 shows the virtual address space for the two operating modes.

User Mode. In this mode, a single, uniform virtual address space (kuseg) of 2 Gbyte is available. Each virtual address is extended with a 6-bit process identifier field to form unique virtual addresses for up to 64 user processes. All references to this segment are mapped through the TLB. Use of the cache is determined by bit settings for each page within the TLB entries.

Kernel Mode. Four separate segments are defined in this mode:

- *kuseg.* When in the Kernel mode, references to this segment are treated just like User mode references, thus streamlining kernel access to user data.

- *kseg0.* References to this 512-Mbyte segment use cache memory but are not mapped through the TLB. Instead, they always map to the first 0.5 GBytes of physical memory.

- *kseg1.* References to this 512-Mbyte segment are not mapped through the TLB and do not use the cache. Instead, they are hard-mapped into the same 0.5-GByte segment of physical memory space as *kseg0*.

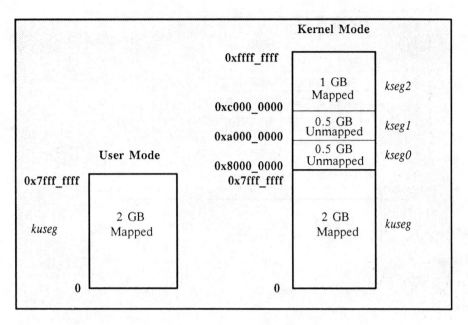

Figure 2.9 R2000 Virtual Addressing

- *kseg2.* References to this 1–Gbyte segment are always mapped through the TLB, and use of the cache is determined by bit settings within the TLB entries.

R2000 Pipeline Architecture

The execution of a single R2000 instruction consists of five primary steps:

1) **IF**—Fetch the instruction (I–Cache).
2) **RD**—Read any required operands from CPU registers while decoding the instruction.
3) **ALU**—Perform the required operation on instruction operands.
4) **MEM**—Access memory (D–Cache).
5) **WB**—Write back results to register file.

Each of these steps requires approximately one CPU cycle as shown in Figure 2.9 (parts of some operations lap over into another cycle while other operations require only 1/2 cycle).

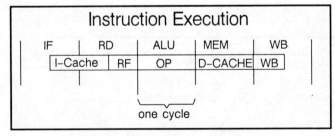

Figure 2.9 Instruction Execution Sequence

The R2000 uses a 5–stage pipeline to achieve an instruction execution rate approaching one instruction per CPU cycle. Thus, execution of five instructions at a time are overlapped as shown in Figure 2.10.

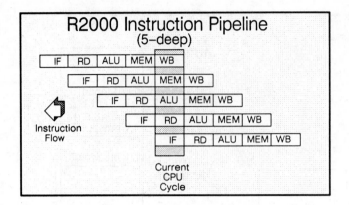

Figure 2.10   R2000 Instruction Pipeline

This pipeline operates efficiently because different CPU resources (address and data bus accesses, ALU operations, register accesses, and so on) are utilized on a non–interfering basis. Refer to **Chapter 3** for a detailed discussion of the instruction pipeline.

Memory System Hierarchy

The high performance capabilities of the R2000 Processor demand system configurations incorporating techniques frequently employed in large, mainframe computers but seldom encountered in systems based on more traditional microprocessors.

A primary goal of RISC machines is to achieve an instruction execution rate of one instruction per CPU cycle. The MIPS R2000 approaches this goal by means of a compact and uniform instruction set, a deep instruction pipeline (as described above), and careful adaptation to optimizing compilers. Many of the advantages obtained from these techniques can, however, be negated by an inefficient memory system.

Figure 2.11 illustrates memory in a simple microprocessor system. In this system, the CPU outputs addresses to memory and reads instructions and data from memory or writes data to memory. The memory space is completely undifferentiated: instructions, data, and I/O devices are all treated the same. In such a system, a primary limiting performance factor is memory bandwidth.

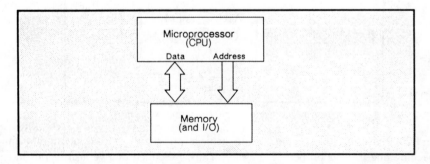

Figure 2.11   A Simple Microprocessor Memory System

Figure 2.12 illustrates a memory system that supports the significantly greater memory bandwidth required to take full advantage of the R2000's performance capabilities. The key features of this system are:

- **External Cache Memory**. Local, high–speed memory (called *cache* memory) is used to hold instructions and data that is repetitively accessed by the CPU (for example, within a program loop) and thus reduces the number of references that must be made to the slower speed main memory. Some microprocessors provide a limited amount of cache memory on the CPU chip itself. The external caches supported by the R2000 can be much larger; while a small cache can improve performance of some programs, significant improvements for a wide range of programs require large caches.

- **Separate Caches for Data and Instructions**. Even with high–speed caches, memory speed can still be a limiting factor because of the fast cycle time of a high–performance microprocessor. The R2000 supports separate caches for instructions and data and alternates accesses of the two caches during each CPU cycle. Thus, the processor can obtain data and instructions at the cycle rate of the CPU using caches constructed with commercially available static RAM devices.

- **Write Buffer**. In order to ensure data consistency, all data that is written to the data cache must also be written out to main memory. To relieve the CPU of this responsibility (and the inherent performance burden) the R2000 supports an interface to a write buffer. The R2020 Write Buffer captures data and addresses output by the CPU and ensures that the data is passed on to main memory.

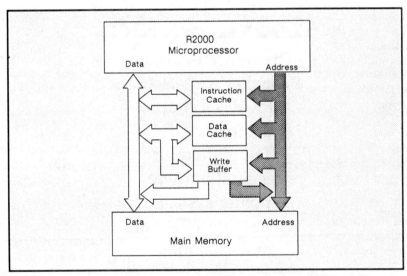

Figure 2.12 An R2000 System with a High–Performance Memory System

215

Reprinted from *Computer*, January 1989, pages 78–91. Copyright 1989 by
The Institute of Electrical and Electronics Engineers, Inc.

Precision Architecture

Ruby B. Lee

Hewlett-Packard Company

The Hewlett-Packard Precision Architecture provides a simple, comprehensive foundation for general-purpose computer systems. It is scalable, efficient, and extendible.

Hewlett-Packard designed Precision Architecture to serve as a common foundation for its computer systems, to enhance software portability, to provide price-performance advantages, and to streamline the company's hardware and software development, manufacturing, and support activities. Prior to this, each of HP's three major computer product lines, the HP3000, HP9000, and HP1000 systems, had different processor architectures, operating systems, and input-output systems.

This article describes the processor component of the Hewlett-Packard Precision Architecture system, henceforth referred to simply as "Precision." It describes the architecture's goals, how the architecture addresses the spectrum of general-purpose user information processing needs, and some architectural design trade-offs.

Goals. When HP charged the original architects with designing the new architecture, it presented us with some high-level, strategic goals. The architecture should be general purpose for use in commercial and technical applications. It should be scalable across technologies, cost ranges, and performance ranges and provide price-performance advantages. It should allow the leveraging of common hardware and software components. It should be designed with architectural longevity in mind, including features that enhance the possibility of a long, useful life for the 1990s and beyond. It should allow growth and extendibility. It should support multiple operating environments, for example, single-user and multiuser, centralized and distributed computing, and conventional and object-oriented environments. It should support the implementation of highly reliable, secure systems and real-time environments.

A version of this article appeared in *Proc. 22nd Hawaii Int'l Conf. on Systems Sciences*, Jan. 3-6, 1989, Kailua-Kona, Hawaii.

For the processor architecture, the technical mapping of these strategic goals resulted in a simple RISC-like execution model[1-3] with features for code compaction and dynamic path-length reduction, coupled with a more sophisticated set of extendibility and longevity features.

Precision execution model

For the execution model of the architecture, we mapped the scalability and price-performance goals into the following design guidelines:

• Precision instructions should be executable in a single cycle with simple (pipelined) processor hardware.

• Code compaction and dynamic execution time reduction should be considered for frequently executed operation sequences.

These guidelines resulted in an architecture where sometimes more than one operation was performed in one instruction cycle, and other times only a part of a more complex operation was performed by one instruction. We based these design decisions on extensive measurements and studies of the frequency of operations and operation sequences.[4-6] We made the basic assumption that high-level languages would be used for programming and that software and hardware would interact for

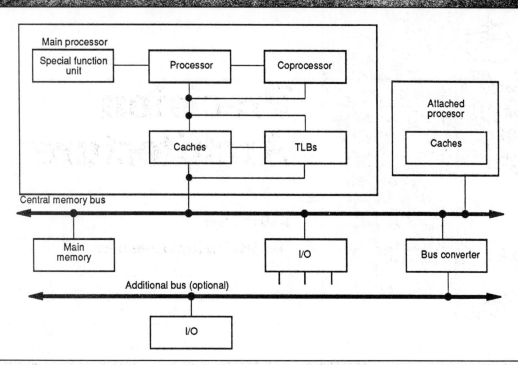

Figure 1. Typical system organization.

the most efficient execution.[1,4,5] For example, we assumed the use of high-level language optimizing compilers for optimizing code generated from user programs.

Figure 1 shows the modules in a typical system organization. Figure 2 shows the simple hardware needed for the execution unit. Figure 3 shows the registers, including the 32 general-purpose registers (GRs); the control registers (CRs), of which 25 are defined; the eight space registers (SRs); and the processor status word (PSW). I will describe the functions of these registers in the course of the article.

Table 1 summarizes the instruction set in terms of the generic operations implemented per instruction. The 53 generic instruction types can be expanded to 140 total instructions when we count all alternatives and options. The data types supported by the basic processor are signed and unsigned word, halfword, byte, packed and unpacked decimal numbers, 8-bit ASCII, and 16-bit international characters.

Simple hardware. The architecture has a general-register-based, load-store execution model with a simple execution engine

comprising an arithmetic logic unit (ALU) and a shift-merge unit (SMU).

There are 32 general-purpose registers,

where GR0 is a constant zero source as well as a bit-bucket destination. While using more than 32 simultaneously addressable

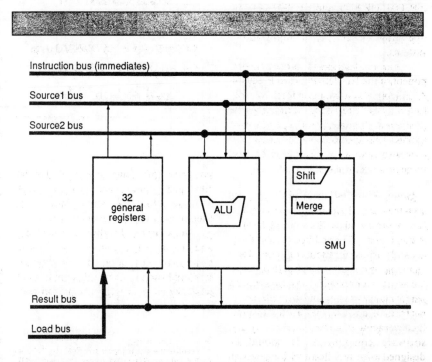

Figure 2. Execution data path.

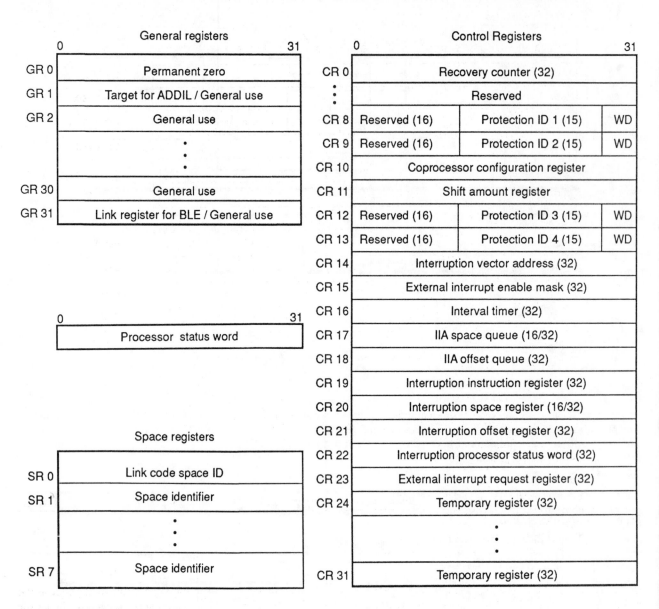

General registers

	0	31
GR 0	Permanent zero	
GR 1	Target for ADDIL / General use	
GR 2	General use	
	• • •	
GR 30	General use	
GR 31	Link register for BLE / General use	

0	31
Processor status word	

Space registers

SR 0	Link code space ID
SR 1	Space identifier
	• • •
SR 7	Space identifier

Control Registers

	0	31
CR 0	Recovery counter (32)	
⋮	Reserved	
CR 8	Reserved (16)	Protection ID 1 (15)	WD
CR 9	Reserved (16)	Protection ID 2 (15)	WD
CR 10	Coprocessor configuration register	
CR 11	Shift amount register	
CR 12	Reserved (16)	Protection ID 3 (15)	WD
CR 13	Reserved (16)	Protection ID 4 (15)	WD
CR 14	Interruption vector address (32)	
CR 15	External interrupt enable mask (32)	
CR 16	Interval timer (32)	
CR 17	IIA space queue (16/32)	
CR 18	IIA offset queue (32)	
CR 19	Interruption instruction register (32)	
CR 20	Interruption space register (16/32)	
CR 21	Interruption offset register (32)	
CR 22	Interruption processor status word (32)	
CR 23	External interrupt request register (32)	
CR 24	Temporary register (32)	
	• • •	
CR 31	Temporary register (32)	

Note: Space registers are either 16-bit or 32-bit in length.

Figure 3. Registers.

general registers sometimes decreases the number of memory accesses, the trade-off yields an increase in the process swap time, in the number of bits needed to specify register addresses in an instruction, and in the area and access time needed for a larger bank of registers. Specialized register structures to improve procedure calling[2,7] often have many hidden registers, incur-

ring complexity without the advantage of making an increased number of simultaneously accessible registers available to a good register allocator.[8]

Minimal decode instructions. To simplify instruction fetching and decoding, all Precision instructions are fixed-length 32-bit words. This eliminates, for example, the complexity of handling page faults

ple, the complexity of handling page faults during the fetching of a single instruction, which can happen for variable-length instructions.

Fixed-length instructions also enhance the use of fixed bit positions for time-critical operations, without waiting for decoding of the instruction. For example, since general register operands are always

```
                    1                   2                   3
 0 1 2 3 4 5 6 7 8 9 0 1 2 3 4 5 6 7 8 9 0 1 2 3 4 5 6 7 8 9 0 1
```

Format	Fields
opcode | r | r | s | i	LD/ST L
opcode | r | r/i | s | a | x | cc | e | m | r/i	LD/ST S/X
opcode | r | r/i | s | a | x | cc | e | cop | m | copr	COP LD/ST
opcode | r | i	Long IMM
opcode | r | r/i | c/s/e | i/0 | n | i	BR
opcode | r | r | c | f | e | r	ALU 3R
opcode | r | r | c | f | e | i	ALU RI
opcode | r | r/i | c | e | iptr/0 | r/ilen	ALU F
opcode | r/cr/0 | r/i/0 | s/0 | e | m | r/0	SYS
opcode | u	DIAG
opcode | r/u | r/u | u | e | sfu | n | u	SFU
opcode | u | cop | n | u	COPR

Abbreviations for field names

r	: general register specifier		f	: falsify condition c
s	: space register specifier		iptr	: immediate pointer
i	: immediate (or displacement or offset)		ilen	: immediate length
a	: premodify versus postmodify, or index shifted by data size		cr	: control register
x	: indexed (x=0) versus short displacement (x=1)		0	: not used (set to zeros)
cc	: cache hints		u	: undefined (can be defined as instruction extension)
e	: subop (opcode extension)		sfu	: special function unit identifier
m	: modification specifier		cop	: coprocessor unit identifier
n	: nullification specifier		copr	: coprocessor register
c	: condition specifier			

Figure 4. Instruction formats.

specified by the two leftmost register fields in any register format (see Figure 4), the reading of general registers can occur in parallel with instruction decoding. The target register, however, can be in any one of the three register fields in different instruction formats. This is an acceptable trade-off since the processor has ample time to decode the target register specification.

Combined operations. Many Precision instructions combine two operations into a single 32-bit instruction word. For example, in functional instructions (see Table 1) each instruction implicitly specifies an optional "conditional nullify" or "skip" feature in addition to the main arithmetic, logical, unit, or bit operation. In a single

cycle, as the data transformation operation is performed, the condition specified in the instruction is also evaluated. If the condition evaluates to true, then the following instruction is nullified. A nullified instruction has the effect of a NOP (no operation), with no changes to any architecturally visible state, including memory, and no side-effects like causing traps or nullification.

Conditional branch instructions also combine two operations into a single 32-bit instruction by allowing simultaneously a functional operation to be performed on two registers, a condition to be evaluated, and a PC-relative branch target to be calculated, with the branch taken only if the condition evaluates to true. This again achieves code compaction, eliminates the

need for storing condition codes in the processor, and enhances possibilities for reordering code in optimizing compilers.

Combined operations reduce both static code size and dynamic execution time, since only one instruction is needed rather than two or more.

Zero-cycle addressing and loading. The architecture makes extensive use of immediate data embedded within the instruction itself as one of the sources of operands. An immediate operand saves a memory load operation, provides effectively zero-cycle addressing, and does not require the use of a general register. Precision immediates are unusual in that they are "maximal length," that is, they fill up all unused bits in the fixed-length instruc-

Table 1. Instruction set.*

Memory Reference Instructions	Functional Instructions

Memory Reference Instructions

Load	{Word/Halfword/Byte} {Long/Indexed/Short} [Modified]
Store	{Word/Halfword/Byte} {Long/Short} [Modified]
Load	Word Absolute {Indexed/Short}
Store	Word Absolute Short
Load	Offset
Load	And Clear Word {Indexed/Short}
Store	Bytes Short

Branch Instructions

(a) Unconditional

Branch And Link {Displacement/Reg}
Branch Vectored
Branch External [and Link]
Gateway

(b) Conditional

Add {Reg/Immed} And Branch if {True/False}
Compare {Reg/Immed} And Branch if {True/False}
Move {Reg/Immed} And Branch if {True/False}
Branch On Bit {Variable/Constant}

System Instructions

(a) System Control

System Mask {Set/Reset/Move to}
Move {to/from} Control Register
Move {to/from} Space Register
Load Space ID
Break
Return From Interrupt
Diagnose

(b) Memory Management

Insert TLB {Instruction/Data} {Address/Protection}
Purge TLB {Instruction/Data} [Entry]
Probe Access {Read/Write} {Reg/Immed}
Load Physical Address
Load Hash Address

(c) Cache Management

Flush {Instruction/Data} Cache [Entry]
Purge Data Cache
Sync

Functional Instructions

(a) Arithmetic

Add {Reg/Immed} [with carry] [and Trap on {overflow/cond/overflow or cond}]
Sub {Reg/Immed} [with borrow] [and Trap on {borrow/cond/borrow or cond}]
Shift {One/Two/Three} And Add [and Trap on Overflow]
Divide Step

(b) Logical

Or	{Inclusive/Exclusive}
And	{True/Complement}
Compare {Reg/Immed} And Clear	
Add	Logical
Shift	{One/Two/Three} And Add Logical

(c) Unit and Decimal

Unit Xor
Unit Add Complement [and Trap on Condition]
Decimal Correct
Intermediate Decimal Correct

(d) Bit Manipulation

Extract {Variable Pos/Constant Pos} {Signed/Unsigned}
Deposit {Variable Pos/Constant Pos} {Reg/Immed}
Zero and Deposit {Variable Pos/Constant Pos} {Reg/Immed}
Shift Double {Variable Pos/Constant Pos}

(e) Long Immediate

Add Immediate Left
Load Immediate Left

Assist Instructions

(a) Special Function Unit Interface

Spop {Zero/One/Two/Three}

(b) Coprocessor Interface

Copr Load {Word/Doubleword} {Indexed/Short}
Copr Store {Word/Doubleword} {Indexed/Short}
Copr Operation

> **Key**
> Reg = register
> Immed = immediate
> Pos = position
> cond = condition

*Curly brackets indicate that one alternative within the curly brackets is selected for a given instruction, while square brackets indicate an optional feature that can be specified in the instruction.

tion and hence maximize the probability that a constant can be represented as immediate data within the instruction. Usually, this would imply that the sign position, in its traditional encoding as the leftmost bit of an integer value, would occur in variable positions. Precision solved this problem by encoding the sign position of these variable-length immedi-ates as the rightmost bit, simplifying decoding and sign extension.

Full-word immediates. Sometimes, even maximal-length immediates in an instruc-tion are not long enough, since a 32-bit immediate or displacement is needed. Pre-cision introduces 32-bit immediates in the instruction stream by using two fixed-length 32-bit instructions. For example, Load Immediate Left loads into a general register, GRi, a 21-bit immediate padded on the right with 11 zeros. A Load instruc-tion executed later, with this GRi as the base register, supplies the low-order bits of the 32-bit displacement value.

This method has the advantage that each instruction can still be a fixed-length

COMPUTER

32-bit word, simplifying instruction fetching and decoding. The alternative—variable-length instructions—requires either instruction alignment provisions with attendant memory wastage, or handling the complexity of a page-fault potentially occurring during an instruction fetch.

A trade-off in the use of immediates arises in encoding space versus operation orthogonality, that is, the size of the value that can be represented by the immediate versus the other options that can be specified in the fixed-length instruction. For instructions with a long immediate field, we chose to include only those instruction variants most frequently used rather than achieve full operation orthogonality with instructions where both operands come from registers.

Memory reference instructions. Effective address calculation for Precision load and store instructions uses the same execution unit (Figure 2) as add instructions and is based on the same guideline of single-cycle execution.

Static and dynamic displacements. All address calculations for load and store instructions are based on the base plus displacement, or base plus (shifted) index addressing modes, the most frequently used addressing modes.[9,10] Static displacements of 14 bits can be accomplished in one instruction, and 32-bit static displacements can be done with two instructions using a long immediate instruction, as described earlier. Using an index register, 32-bit dynamic displacements are possible.

Byte addressing. One reason Precision implements byte addressing rather than just word addressing is to allow the efficient movement of unaligned strings of bytes or characters, common in commercial computations.

A unique Store_bytes instruction simplifies such moves by allowing storage of any sequence of one to four bytes starting at any byte location within a 32-bit word. This includes *tribytes*, defined as three consecutive bytes in a word. Storing of tribytes comes free with byte addressing. In other architectures, unaligned byte moves would have required loading and masking of the destination word.

Address stride mechanisms. For indexed load instructions, the value in the index register can also be shifted by the data size to index bytes, halfwords, or

words. Moreover, the instruction can specify address modification of the base register, with support of both pre-modification and postmodification. A load or store operation combined with address modification is another example of combining two operations in a single instruction word.

A hardware-software trade-off resulted in the absence of indexed store instructions in the basic architecture. We chose to do this because achieving single-cycle execution would require a register file with three read ports rather than two. Coprocessor indexed store instructions exist, however, since the data register being stored comes from the coprocessor rather than the basic processor.

Another interesting encoding trade-off is that, in long-displacement load and store instructions, the timing of address modification (pre or post) is encoded by the same bit that encodes the sign of the displacement (increment or decrement). This prevented cutting in half the range of the 14-bit displacement while still allowing efficient accessing of stacks with the predecrement and postincrement options.

Delayed load effect. Optimizing compilers for Precision processors try to insert one or more instructions after a load instruction to prevent interlocked pipeline cycles. However, Precision processors will interlock if an instruction following a load instruction uses a register with a pending load. This hardware-software trade-off incurs insignificant additional hardware complexity while preserving code compaction by not requiring the insertion of NOPs after load instructions, as in some other architectures without such interlocks.[3,11] More significantly, the provision of hardware interlocks gives implementors the freedom to design different pipelines while guaranteeing object code compatibility.

Branch instructions. Precision implements delayed branching with some extra optimization features. In some architectures,[2,3,7,11] if a common instruction cannot be found, NOPs have to be inserted in the delay slot of a conditional branch, which can be executed for both paths of the branch. Precision achieves delayed branching with both static and dynamic code size reductions by enhancing the usage of the delay slot instruction following a conditional branch instruction. Conditional nullification is performed for backward branches only if the condition is false and for forward branches only if

the condition is true. For example, by closing loops with backward branches, compilers can always move the first instruction of the loop to the delay slot of the loop-closing backward branch, decreasing the loop size by one. By using forward conditional branches to rarely used code, software can again optimize the use of the delay slot instruction for the more frequently used fall-through path. If code is arranged so that backward branches are more likely to be taken than forward branches, then hardware can use the sign of the branch displacement as a static branch prediction bit.

Simple Branch And Link instructions are used as procedure call primitives, with the return address saved in a general register. A base-relative branch using this general register is used for subroutine return.

Functional instructions. Functional instructions execute a data transformation operation in a single pass through the ALU or SMU (see Figure 2).

Arithmetic instructions. The Add and Subtract arithmetic instructions come with the widest range of options (see Table 1). The Add And Trap on condition option allows range checking, often required by high-level languages, to be accomplished with minimal instructions.

Multiply and divide primitives. The Shift And Add instructions implement a simple integer multiply and accumulate function, using the standard ALU hardware (Figure 2) with a wider multiplexer on one port. Multiplication by small constants can be accomplished in a few cycles, and multiplication by a variable can be done typically by breaking the multiplier into 4-bit pieces.[5] The Divide Step instruction implements a single-bit non-restoring division operation and can be used in a sequence to perform integer division.

To implement full fixed-point integer multiply and divide in a single cycle would have required special hardware. We did not consider this cost-effective for a basic, general-purpose Precision processor because our studies of large collections of programs show that integer multiply and divide operations are rarely used, and multiplication usually occurs with a constant known at compile time.[5,6] Hence, we included only simple multiply and divide primitives in the basic instruction set, with floating-point instructions and integer

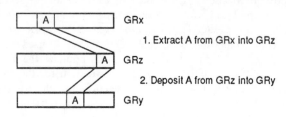

Figure 5. Arbitrary bit field movement.

multiply and divide instructions added as instruction-set extensions supported by optional hardware assists (described in the section on the Precision assists architecture).

Logical operations. The logical instructions allow efficient implementation of arbitrary Boolean conditions. For example, the Compare And Clear instruction first assumes a Boolean value of false by storing zero in the target register. The negation of the desired Boolean condition is used to conditionally nullify the following instruction. This instruction, if not nullified by the Compare And Clear instruction, will set the target register to true. Other architectures usually require a branch instruction to implement the equivalent Boolean function.

Unit and decimal primitives. Since a strategic goal for Precision Architecture is to support commercial applications, it must handle decimal operations in Cobol-like languages as well as alphanumeric code manipulation. The instruction set includes five instructions for parallel processing of small units (digits, bytes, and halfwords) within a word.[4,5] They are used for word-parallel string search and decimal arithmetic. The halfword units support the processing of 16-bit international character sets.

Unlike floating-point arithmetic, these instructions do not require significant additional hardware. Hardware support consists only of condition logic on the carry bits of each 4-bit group of the ALU. Cobol applications—important on HP3000 machines—have been found to run many times faster on Precision machines than on the previous non-Precision-based HP3000 machines.

Bit field manipulation. Although the main unit of transfer and operation is the 32-bit word, often it is desirable to be able to manipulate arbitrary bit fields within a word or across a word boundary. Examples include the efficient emulation of other instruction sets, bit-block transfers, unaligned byte moves, and field extraction from records.

The shift-merge unit implements efficient bit-field manipulation instructions (see Table 1). For example, Extract takes an arbitrary-length field from any portion of a word and creates a result with this field right justified, with optional sign extension. Deposit does the reverse operation, inserting a right-justified field into any portion of a target word, optionally clearing the rest of the target. Hence, in two instruction cycles Precision can perform an arbitrary bit field movement (see Figure 5). Other architectures usually simulate these instructions by a sequence of shifting and masking.

Extendibility and longevity features

Beyond the simple execution model described above, Precision also includes features designed to give the architecture a potentially longer useful life by allowing growth and extendibility of the architecture. Below, I will describe some of these aspects: the virtual memory model, access protection, the assists architecture, the interrupt system, and the input-output system and multiple processor support.

Virtual memory model. The Precision architects felt that the longevity of an architecture lies in the range of its addressing capabilities rather than in the size of its words or the specific operations implemented. While processing 64-bit integers rather than 32-bit integers might increase accuracy, we did not consider the trade-off in the hardware required for 64-bit datapaths throughout the processor to be cost effective for general-purpose computers.

However, computer usage has clearly tended towards the processing of larger programs and more data. Hence, the key to next-generation architectures is not as much the increase in data size from 32 to 64 bits as the increase in addressing range. Precision provides a 64-bit virtual address range, which is four billion times more virtual storage than in current architectures with 32-bit virtual addresses.[7,9,11]

The large virtual address space allows virtual addresses to be defined globally across processes. This contrasts with architectures where the same address can be used for different objects by different processes. An advantage is that address translation information does not have to change on a process switch. Global virtual addressing allows interacting processes to accumulate a stable working set of address translations despite frequent process switching.

Virtual address manipulation in the processor. Manipulating 64-bit virtual addresses efficiently with a 32-bit data path requires some ingenuity. Using the standard 32-bit ALU, effective address calculation in memory reference instructions is performed for 32-bit quantities to determine the byte offset within a virtual space. The virtual space, selected from one of the eight space registers or the implicit program space register, is then concatenated with the byte offset to give the full virtual address (see Figure 6a). Software conventions are commonly observed for the use of space registers.[4]

Different levels of the architecture are defined with respect to the size of the virtual space implemented: level-0 architecture with no space registers, level-1 architecture with 16-bit space registers, and level-2 architecture with the full 32-bit space registers. This allows the virtual memory to be scaled down for a lower cost Precision processor by reducing the width of each entry in its translation look-aside buffer and attendant data paths.

The architecture also incorporates a concept called "short pointers" to allow handling of 48-bit or 64-bit virtual

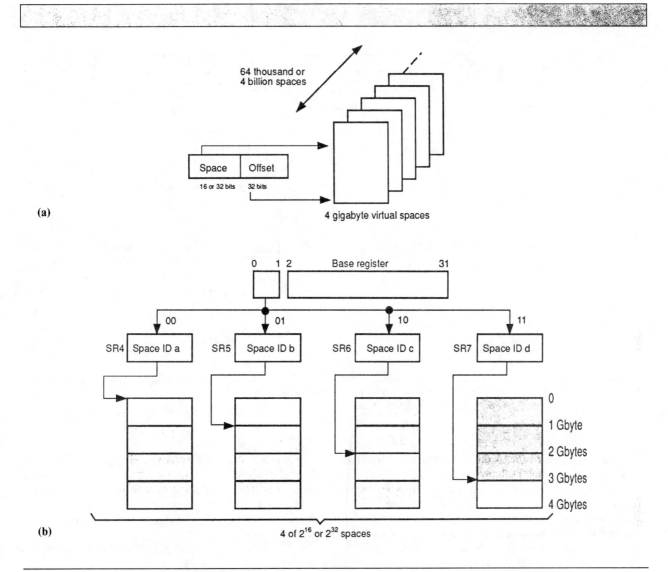

(a)

64 thousand or
4 billion spaces

| Space | Offset |

16 or 32 bits   32 bits

4 gigabyte virtual spaces

0 1 2   Base register   31

00   01   10   11

SR4 | Space ID a   SR5 | Space ID b   SR6 | Space ID c   SR7 | Space ID d

0

1 Gbyte

2 Gbytes

3 Gbytes

4 Gbytes

(b)   4 of 2^{16} or 2^{32} spaces

Figure 6. (a) Virtual memory organization and (b) short-pointer addressing.

addresses with short 32-bit pointers (see Figure 6b). It allows, at a given time, data access to four distinct virtual spaces, each space being one gigabyte in size. Long-pointer addressing provides access to four billion virtual spaces, each space being four billion bytes in size (Figure 6a). Short-pointer addressing allows pointers to be the same size—32 bits—as the standard integer data type, a situation often assumed by existing high-level languages like C. It also allows efficient passing of pointers via the 32-bit general registers.

Virtual space management in the memory-disk system. The virtual address is further partitioned into the space identifier, the virtual page number (VPN),

and the page offset. Each page has a fixed size of 2 kilobytes. The space identifier and the VPN are translated into a 21-bit physical page number (PPN), which is then used to access physical memory. If the physical page is not in memory, a page-fault occurs, and the missing page is brought in from the disk.

Two software tables are used: a hash table to index into a page directory (Pdir) table, which contains one entry for each physical page in the main memory. Each entry in the Pdir is either empty or contains the VPN of the virtual page mapped to that physical page slot. This has the advantage of reducing the size of the page tables to correspond to the size of the physical memory, rather than to the size of the

much larger virtual memory. Both the hash table and the page directory table permanently reside in physical memory for performance reasons.

To speed up the virtual to physical address translation process, a translation look-aside buffer (TLB) is defined as the processor's interface to the virtual memory system. This TLB acts as a cache for virtual to physical address translations. If an address translation is not in the TLB, a TLB miss occurs, handled either by a software interrupt routine or by a hard-wired sequence of operations. The architecture defines memory management instructions for inserting, changing, querying, and deleting entries in the TLB (see Table 1).

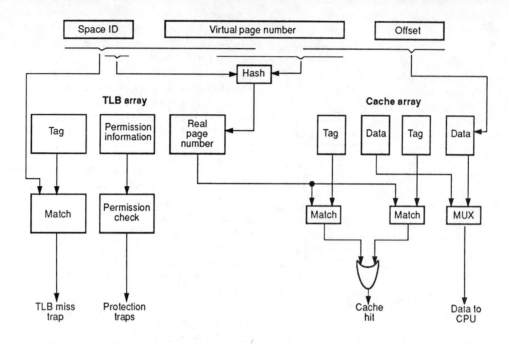

Figure 7. Virtual address translation, protection checking, and cache accessing.

Minimizing paging traffic. A dirty bit defined for every Pdir and TLB entry indicates if the page now differs from its disk image. This dirty bit is cleared to zero when the page is first brought in and when the page is written to disk, and remains clear as long as no writes to the page occur. The first time a program tries to write to that page, a dirty bit update trap occurs, which changes the dirty bit in both the Pdir and the TLB entry from zero to one. This allows the operating system to avoid writing out unmodified pages to the disk. The increase in system performance is well worth the slight overhead in TLB and Pdir management.

Address aliasing. A hardware-software optimization allows virtual cache indexing, which facilitates single-cycle loads from virtual memory. It does this by not allowing software to do address aliasing or mapping of different virtual pages to the same physical page. While address aliasing is of some use to software, it imposes significant performance degradations on hardware because it precludes the use of the virtual page as part of the index into cache memory.

For example, a virtual access could put data into the cache based on its index, and a later virtual access, using a different (aliased) address, would not find the data in the cache because the index was different in the virtual page portion. The second access would then go to memory, where it might get an inconsistent or stale copy of the data.

By effectively disallowing address aliasing, caches can use the virtual page number as part of the index without causing the stale data problem. This allows the cache to be accessed in parallel with the virtual address translation being done by the TLB (see Figure 7), without restrictions on the size of the cache. If address aliasing were allowed, either virtual address translation and cache accessing would have to be serialized, or the cache size would have to be restricted to that of the page size multiplied by the cache set-associativity.

Access protection. The architecture provides hardware support for access protection to be built into the storage unit and performed in the same cycle as virtual address translation and cache access (see Figure 7).

Precision protection checking is defined at the page level, to control access to the page in three dimensions: the type of access allowed (read, write, or execute),

the privilege level at which access is allowed, and the group of processes allowed access to the page. One reason for the choice of a 2-kilobyte page size rather than a larger one is so that access control can be defined at a finer granularity (useful in object-oriented environments, for example).

Privilege levels. For access rights checking, the architecture defines four hierarchical protection rings. The current privilege level of a process is checked against the privilege level for the read, write, or execute access being made to that page by this process.

Generalized supervisor/user transfers. This privilege-level mechanism allows a process to have different access rights over time without the overhead of changing TLB entries when access rights change or at process switch. Thus user programs (privilege level 3) can invoke the services of an operating system supervisor (privilege level 1) or kernel (privilege level 0) using an efficient procedure call rather than an interrupt or process switch. This can be done by a procedure call to a Gateway instruction, which branches to the body of the more privileged routine. The

COMPUTER

Gateway instruction can promote the privilege level while saving the caller's privilege level in the return address register so that it cannot be "forged" by the caller. On returning to the caller, a privilege-demoting branch instruction is used.

Access identifiers. The currently executing process can claim membership in up to four groups of pages simultaneously, each group having its own access identifier and write-disable bit, saved in four control registers. The access identifier allows each process sharing memory to access different domains in memory without the overhead of changing the TLB on process switch. Four access identifiers are provided to facilitate the controlled transfer of information between logical environments. These four access identifiers are checked against the protection identifier attached to the virtual page being accessed. A protection identifier of all zeros attached to a page allows public access to that page.

When set, the write-disable bit disallows writing for all privilege levels to the pages protected by the associated access identifier. This allows, for example, a single writer and multiple readers for a group of processes accessing a common protected domain of pages.

These protection features built into the architecture allow implementation of very secure, flexible environments. They might not be necessary for single-user or dedicated-controller environments, but they are necessary for efficient implementation of secure multiuser systems.

Assists architecture. One of the goals of Precision Architecture is to define a general-purpose, basic instruction set and allow future instruction set extensions. These future "assist" instructions could then be executed on optional hardware assists to speed up the processing of specialized computations, such as floating-point or graphics. An assist instruction defines the architectural interface between the processor, memory, and any future assist in terms of data movement operations, but we left specific functions performed by an assist for future definition.

Software compatibility. While other architectures define backward software compatibility with a previous instruction set,[10] the Precision assists architecture defines forward software compatibility with future assist instruction sets. In addition, software portability among Precision processors with different configurations of hardware assists is also achieved. These compatibility and portability goals are achieved by means of a transparent assist emulation trapping mechanism that automatically causes an interruption on detecting an assist instruction not supported by a hardware assist. This allows a software trap handler to perform the function required by the assist instruction, using the basic Precision instructions. Critical information needed for emulation is present in the interruption parameter registers, considerably speeding up the emulation routines.

SFUs and coprocessors. The architecture recognizes two classes of assists: special function units (SFUs) and coprocessors. SFUs are viewed as very tightly coupled to the main processor buses, serving as alternate functional units to the ALU or SMU in the execution unit of a basic Precision processor. As such, an SFU receives its operands from the general registers and places its result into a general register, like a basic ALU instruction. A 3-bit SFU identifier is attached to each SFU instruction, allowing up to eight SFUs simultaneously in a system.

We view a coprocessor as a hardware assist coupled to the processor at the level of the data cache or memory. As such, it has its own set of coprocessor registers, loaded from or stored to memory using the same virtual address translation and protection mechanism as the basic processor.

Coprocessor load/store instructions are like processor load/store instructions, except that the target/source registers are coprocessor registers rather than the processor's general registers. Coprocessor registers can be of a different size than processor registers; for example, the floating-point coprocessor registers are 64 bits wide.

Other than the coprocessor load/store instructions, there is only one other coprocessor instruction, where the operations to be performed by the coprocessor can be defined as an instruction extension. As for SFUs, a 3-bit coprocessor identifier is attached to each coprocessor instruction, allowing up to eight coprocessors or 16 logically different assists in a Precision configuration.

While an SFU provides execution-unit extendibility, a coprocessor also provides register-set extendibility.

An example of an assist is the floating-point coprocessor (see Figure 8). The Precision floating-point architecture allows highly pipelined implementations. It complies with the ANSI/IEEE 754-1985 floating-point standard, although not all operations and exceptions need to be supported by hardware, since an assists exception trap can be used for software support of unimplemented features.

For complex operations not frequent enough to justify the addition of assists hardware, a software call to a streamlined subroutine—called *millicode*—is used.

Interrupt system. In Precision Architecture, the term "interruptions" includes all abnormal events like memory faults, protection violations, computation exceptions, hardware malfunction, power failure, timer interrupts, and external interrupts. Synchronous interruptions (those caused by instruction execution) are precise interruptions across all Precision processors, allowing predictability and the leverage of software interruption handlers. Asynchronous interruptions (external to the instruction stream, like machine checks, power failure, and external interrupts) provide a standardized way of reporting malfunctions, saving state, and giving rapid real-time response to external conditions and requests.

Interruption registers. The interesting aspects of the Precision interrupt system are probably the ways in which the interruption registers are used for fast context switching, expediting interruption processing, and implementing precise interruptions even with delayed branching. There are six control registers (Figure 3) used to save state, such as the processor status word (PSW) of the interrupted program, the instruction causing an interruption, the virtual space and offset for data memory reference instructions, and the virtual spaces and offsets of the first two instructions processed upon returning from interruption servicing.

Fast context switch. Interruption servicing is implemented as a fast single-cycle context switch rather than a complete process swap. The information in the interruption registers is usually continuously updated by a Precision processor during normal instruction processing so that, on detecting an interruption, the processor only has to save the current PSW in the interruption PSW register, clear the current PSW, and pass the control flow to a vectored location in a dynamically relocat-

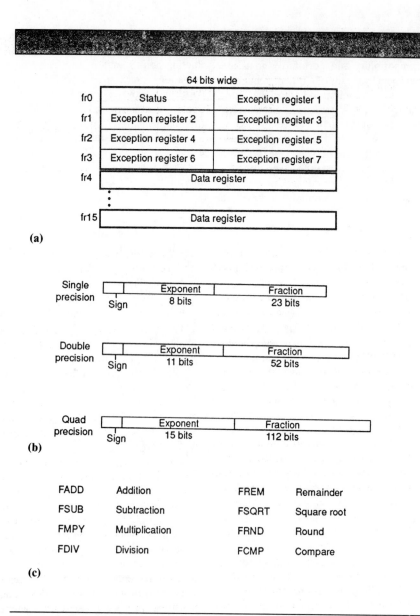

(a)

64 bits wide

fr0	Status	Exception register 1
fr1	Exception register 2	Exception register 3
fr2	Exception register 4	Exception register 5
fr3	Exception register 6	Exception register 7
fr4	Data register	
fr15	Data register	

(b)

Single precision — Sign, Exponent 8 bits, Fraction 23 bits

Double precision — Sign, Exponent 11 bits, Fraction 52 bits

Quad precision — Sign, Exponent 15 bits, Fraction 112 bits

(c)

FADD	Addition	FREM	Remainder
FSUB	Subtraction	FSQRT	Square root
FMPY	Multiplication	FRND	Round
FDIV	Division	FCMP	Compare

Figure 8. Floating-point coprocessor, including (a) floating-point registers, (b) floating-point data types, and (c) floating-point coprocessor instructions.

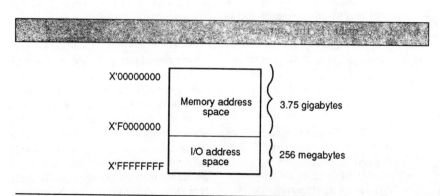

Figure 9. Physical address partitioning.

able interruption vector table. Clearing the PSW has the effect of disabling other interruptions, freezing the interruption registers, and enabling real mode addressing.

Eight control registers can be used as scratchpad registers for quick general-register saves under privileged software control. Upon completion of interruption processing, a Return From Interrupt instruction is executed, which restores the saved processor state and restarts execution at the interrupted instruction.

Precise interruptions with delayed branching. Delayed branching has been known to cause difficulties in interruption processing. Precision has easily solved this with the interruption instruction address (IIA) queue. The IIA queue consists of two instruction-return addresses, which are the first two instructions processed upon returning from the interruption. Interruptions caused by branch instructions are always taken after the branch instruction completes.

The hardware automatically collects in the IIA queue the addresses of the delay slot instruction, followed by the target instruction of the branch (generally non-contiguous addresses). Since the IIA queue saves the return addresses of the time-sequential instructions following an interruption, there is no restriction on a branch instruction occurring in the delay slot of another branch instruction.

Flexible external interrupts. There are 32 external interrupt classes, each of which can be individually masked by privileged software. When an external interrupt occurs, its corresponding interrupt pending bit is set in the external interrupt request register. If the corresponding mask bit in the external interrupt mask register is also set, an external interrupt is taken.

Debugging and diagnostic hooks. The architecture provides debugging support traps to aid in software development. A Break instruction can be used to insert software checkpoints anywhere in the code, causing a break trap when executed. This instruction allows software encoding of bits within the instruction, which will be ignored by the hardware but interpreted by the software in the Break trap handler.

Pages can also be tagged by two trap-enable bits that cause a trap whenever any reference is made to that page, or only whenever a store is made to that page. Traps can also be enabled whenever a

COMPUTER

branch is taken, or whenever the privilege level of the running process is promoted or demoted.

A recovery counter is defined to facilitate the implementation of fault recovery in software rollback schemes and for single-step debugging. It can be enabled to cause an interrupt after the execution of a predetermined number of instructions.

Precision Architecture also includes a Diagnostic instruction, whose only defined field is the 6-bit major opcode field. The rest of the instruction can be defined for implementation-specific operations, like accessing pipeline registers or implementation-specific mode bits, not otherwise directly accessible by software. This instruction has proven very useful in boot-up, self-test, and diagnostic routines.

I/O system and multiple processor support. The architecture defines a memory-mapped input-output system, with I/O devices mapped to the top sixteenth of the four-gigabyte physical address space (see Figure 9). A Precision I/O module can be interrogated and controlled by software via load and store instructions. I/O addresses are not cached, and software maintains cache coherency for direct memory access by means of explicit cache control instructions.

A simple semaphore operation, Load And Clear Word, resembles the test-and-set indivisible operation in earlier architectures.[10] Instructions for purging and flushing the translation look-aside buffers and caches allow software to maintain TLB and cache coherency when necessary.

Bus standards have also been defined for hardware-managed TLB and cache coherency, in which case software sees only a single cache and a single TLB. The architecture does not constrain the type of asymmetric multiple processor support implemented by the total hardware-software system.

Precision processor implementations

While describing the range of Precision products is beyond the scope of this article, I will give some processor references and describe a typical pipeline.

First-generation Precision processors have been implemented in a variety of technologies, including transistor-transistor logic,[12] n-type metal-oxide semiconductor,[13] complementary metal-

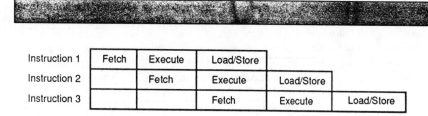

Figure 10. Typical pipeline.

Instruction 1	Fetch	Execute	Load/Store		
Instruction 2		Fetch	Execute	Load/Store	
Instruction 3			Fetch	Execute	Load/Store

oxide semiconductor,[14] and emitter-coupled logic (in a prototype), with a variety of clock speeds, cache support, and TLB support, over a range of performance and cost. These processors are used in both the HP3000 series 900 business computer line and the HP9000 series 800 technical computer line.

Figure 10 shows a typical pipeline for a Precision processor.[12] In the Fetch stage, the fetched instruction is decoded at the same time as the reading of the general registers. During the Execute stage, the operands are routed through the ALU or SMU, where a functional operation or address calculation occurs, and the condition is also evaluated if necessary. At the end of the Execute stage, the result is stored in the general registers and also bypassed to the next Execute stage if necessary.

There are no pipeline penalties for delayed branching, since the target address is calculated during the Execute stage at the same time the condition is evaluated for a conditional branch. This is done in time to fetch either the target instruction or the sequential instruction in the next cycle. Similarly, there are no pipeline penalties for load or store instructions, except when the register being loaded is used in the immediately following instruction. This situation is minimized by Precision optimizing compilers using code reordering.

Attainment of the SPECTRUM goals

In the spirit of architectural acronyms,[2,3,7,9,11] I will take the liberty of defining a SPECTRUM architecture as one with the following goals:

- Scalable implementations
- Price-performance advantages
- Extendible architecture

- Commercial applications
- Technical applications
- Reusable components
- Unconstrained lifetime
- Multiple environments

This makes Precision a SPECTRUM architecture, since the above goals include most of the major ones enunciated for its design. These goals are more similar to those addressed in the design of architectures like the IBM 360/370 architecture[10] and the DEC VAX architecture[9] rather than to those of RISC microprocessor architectures.[2,3,7,11]

However, the Precision execution model shares many features common to these RISC architectures.[2,3,7,8,11] These include features like register-based execution, simple load-store interface to memory, delayed branching, simple addressing modes, fixed-length instructions, and three-register nondestructive functional instructions. Such architectural features can usually be implemented with simple, pipelined processor hardware, where single-cycle execution is achievable for most instructions. Since the hardware requirements are simple, these architectures are scalable in the sense that they can be implemented by low-cost hardware or by higher cost, higher performance processors, which have very fast processor clock frequencies. A variety of process technologies with different densities, speeds, and costs can be used.

Since Precision instructions are executable in a single cycle by simple hardware, we can say that the architecture has price-performance advantages—more instructions can generally be executed in a given amount of time by less costly processors than in architectures with large, complex instruction sets.[9,10] However, simply executing more instructions in a given amount of time does not necessarily imply that more useful work is accomplished, especially if very little is accomplished in an average instruction.[2,3,7,11] For this reason, Precision instructions try to combine frequent instruction pairs, like Compare and Branch, into one instruction. This saves both static code space and dynamic execution time, since one instruction replaces two and only one execution cycle is needed for both operations.

In fact, all Precision functional instructions have a built-in skip operation; memory reference instructions can have base register address modification operations; and conditional branch instructions combine both the condition generating operation and the branch operation in one instruction. In addition, the conditional branch nullification scheme and the conditional trapping scheme allow both static and dynamic code optimizations for looping, jumps to error routines, and range checking. The use of maximal-length immediates also helps to reduce the number of load instructions and the execution time involved.

Note that, in computer systems with disks, tapes, graphics accelerators, and other I/O devices, the cost of the processor subsystem is important, although not necessarily the dominating factor in system cost. Similarly, the performance of the processor subsystem is important, but not necessarily the dominating factor in system performance.

The Precision assists architecture allows flexible instruction-set extendibility without sacrificing software compatibility. In fact, the built-in assists emulation trap allows software to be compatible among Precision systems with different configurations of hardware assists and even with future, as yet undefined, assists. The Diagnose instruction also allows implementation-specific instruction-set extensions. This is useful for implementing reliable and serviceable systems.

The fact that Precision processors have been used in both the commercial HP3000 and the technical HP9000 product lines attests to the general-purpose nature of the architecture. Decimal operations are supported for Cobol applications, while efficient coprocessor integration contributes to high performance for floating-point applications. The most frequently used Precision instructions are quite different for Cobol, Fortran, or C applications.

The Precision machine models have leveraged or reused key components like hardware VLSI processors, floating-point processors, cache and TLB controllers, and standard bus controllers. Both the HPUX (Unix) and MPE-XL operating systems can run, unmodified, on all Precision processor systems. By defining not only user-visible architecture, but also system-visible architecture, Precision Architecture has defined not just an applications binary interface,[7] but also a systems binary interface. Naturally, when object code is compatible at the most privileged systems level, it is also compatible at the least privileged user-applications level. Precision Architecture, together with Precision bus standards, has provided the potential for streamlining software, hardware, and input-output developments.

The longevity of Precision Architecture is certainly unconstrained by its large 64-bit virtual address space, since this is four billion times larger than current 32-bit virtual address architectures.

The virtual memory structure and the built-in access protection features allow the implemention of multiple operating environments, since a large amount of addressability is provided, with provisions for various kinds of access control and protection for different domains of pages. The flexible bit-manipulation features enhance the emulation of older instruction sets, contributing to easy migration from older HP machines. The external interrupt system allows environments requiring fast, real-time response to asynchronous events. The access protection features, machine checks, power-fail interrupt, and diagnostic features provide hooks for implementing secure, highly reliable, and serviceable systems.

P recision Architecture has a simple execution model, where each instruction can be executed in a single cycle by a simple, scalable processor. This is enhanced by code compaction and execution time reduction features for the efficient processing of frequent operation sequences. The architecture provides a 64-bit virtual address space to support growing user needs and flexible protection mechanisms to implement secure multi-user systems. Moreover, the assists architecture provides forward compatibility with new instructions and register sets that can be added, with these instructions executed transparently by either hardware assists or software emulation.

Precision Architecture provides a systems binary interface for software compatibility at both applications and systems levels. It forms the basis for the consolidation of hardware and software production. The architecture has been refined through extensive performance measurements and analysis and tested against various hardware implementations and software environments. It combines successful architectural ideas evolved from the past with several innovative features to support both current computing needs and future cooperative computing environments. □

Acknowledgments

The Precision program, initially called "Spectrum," was started by Joel Birnbaum at Hewlett-Packard Laboratories, Palo Alto. The original architecture design team consisted of Allen Baum, Hans Jeans, Russell Kao, Michael Mahon, Terence Miller, Steve Muchnick, William Worley, and myself. This team surveyed the ground, set all the major architectural directions, and produced the first version of the HP Precision Architecture in 1982. Subsequently, many individuals contributed to the refinement of the architecture, including Steve Boettner, Bill Bryg, Mike Fremont, Dave Fotland, Carol Thompson, Craig Hansen, Jerry Huck, Dave James, Dan Magenheimer, and too many others to list here completely. The architecture would not have existed in its present form without their efforts.

The program flourished with the continuing support of John Young and Dean Morton. I would also like to acknowledge the dedicated Hewlett-Packard implementation team members who worked on the Precision processors, coprocessors, operating systems, compilers, I/O systems, bus standards, performance measurement and analysis, debuggers, databases, networks, graphics enhancements, VLSI technology, CAD tools, manufacturing, marketing, sales, support, and management. It is through their efforts that the Precision Architecture has been instantiated in a spectrum of real-world machines, environments, and applications.

References

1. J.S. Birnbaum and W.S. Worley, Jr., "Beyond RISC: High-Precision Architecture," *Hewlett-Packard J.*, Vol. 36, No. 8, Aug. 1985.

2. D. Patterson, "Reduced Instruction Set Computers," *Comm. ACM*, Vol. 28, No. 1, Jan. 1985, pp. 8-21.

3. J. Hennessy et al., "MIPS: A Microprocessor Architecture," *Proc. Micro-15*, IEEE, Oct. 1982.

4. M.J. Mahon et al., "Hewlett-Packard Precision Architecture: The Processor," *Hewlett-Packard J.*, Vol. 37, No. 8, Aug. 1986, pp. 4-21.

5. K.W. Pettis and W.B. Buzbee, "Hewlett-Packard Precision Architecture Compiler Performance," *Hewlett-Packard J.*, Vol. 38, No. 3, March 1987, pp. 29-35.

6. J.A. Lukes, "HP Precision Architecture Performance Analysis," *Hewlett-Packard J.*, Vol. 37, No. 8, Aug. 1986, pp. 30-39.

7. R.B. Garner et al., "The Scalable Processor Architecture (Sparc)," *Proc. 26th Compcon*, 1988, pp. 278-283.

8. G. Radin, "The 801 Minicomputer," *Proc. SIGArch/SIGPlan Symp. Architectural Support for Programming Languages and Operating Systems*, ACM, Palo Alto, Calif., March 1982, pp. 39-47.

9. W.D. Strecker, "VAX-11/780: A Virtual Address Extension to the DEC PDP-11 Family," *Proc. NCCC*, June 1978, pp. 967-980.

10. *IBM System/370 Principles of Operation*, Form No. GA22-7000, IBM, Poughkeepsie, N.Y., 1970.

11. J. Moussouris et al., "A CMOS RISC Processor with Integrated System Functions," *Proc. 31st Compcon*, March 1986, pp. 126-131.

12. D. Fotland et al., "Hardware Design of the First HP Precision Architecture Computers," *Hewlett-Packard J.*, Vol. 38, No. 3, March 1987, pp. 4-17.

13. S. Mangelsdorf et al., "A VLSI Processor for HP Precision Architecture," *Hewlett-Packard J.*, Vol. 38, No. 9, Sept. 1987, pp. 4-11.

14. A. Marston et al., "A 32b CMOS Single-Chip RISC Type _____ *Int'l Solid-State C_____* pp. 28-29.

Ruby B. Lee is a manager of a VLSI processor design team at Hewlett-Packard. She is a founding member of the Precision Architecture program and a principal designer of the processor architecture, the assists architecture, and a VLSI _____ plementing Precision Architecture. _____ imary inventor of four patents on _____ rchitecture, with more patent applications in _____ rogress.

_____ BA from Cornell University, an MS _____ science from Stanford University, _____ electrical engineering from Stanford _____ s written several papers on parallel _____ or organizations, performance _____ mputer architecture and design, _____ architectures, testing, and testa-

_____ an contact the author at Hewlett-_____ ompany, Bldg. 42U7, 19447 _____ Ave., Cupertino, CA 95014.

TWO DAY HOLD SLIP

HOLD UNTIL 7/6

LAST NAME:

GUJARATHI

"Architectural Tradeoffs in the Design of MIPS-X" by P. Chow and M.
Horowitz, *The Proceedings of the 14th International Symposium on Computer Architecture*, 1987, pages 300–308.

Architectural Tradeoffs in the Design of MIPS-X

Paul Chow and Mark Horowitz

Computer Systems Laboratory
Stanford University
Stanford, CA 94305

Abstract

The design of a RISC processor requires a careful analysis
of the tradeoffs that can be made between hardware
complexity and software. As new generations of processors
are built to take advantage of more advanced technologies,
new and different tradeoffs must be considered. We examine
the design of a second generation VLSI RISC processor,
MIPS-X.

MIPS-X is the successor to the MIPS project at Stanford
University and like MIPS, it is a single-chip 32-bit VLSI
processor that uses a simplified instruction set, pipelining and
a software code reorganizer. However, in the quest for higher
performance, MIPS-X uses a deeper pipeline, a much simpler
instruction set and achieves the goal of single cycle execution
using a 2-phase, 20 MHz clock. This has necessitated the
inclusion of an on-chip instruction cache and careful
consideration of the control of the machine. Many tradeoffs
were made during the design of MIPS-X and this paper
examines several key areas. They are: the organization of the
on-chip instruction cache, the coprocessor interface, branches
and the resulting branch delay, and exception handling. For
each issue we present the most promising alternatives
considered for MIPS-X and the approach finally selected.
Working parts have been received and this gives us a firm
basis upon which to evaluate the success of our design.

Introduction

The first generation reduced instruction set processors
(IBM 801[1], RISC[2,3] and MIPS[4,5]) have shown the
importance of making the correct tradeoffs across the
boundary that separates hardware complexity and software
functionality. Hardware should only be used to support
features that clearly improve performance. As
implementation technology improves, new features can be
considered and new tradeoffs must be made.

The goal of the MIPS-X project was to combine a new
technology, a 2µm, 2-level metal CMOS process, with the
knowledge and experience gained from the first generation
RISC machines, to build a single processor with a peak rate of

20 MIPS and then to use 6-10 of these processors as the nodes
in a shared memory multiprocessor. The resulting machine
would be about two orders of magnitude more powerful than
a VAX 11/780 minicomputer.

We describe here the design of the single processor, MIPS-
X. The overriding principle was to keep the design as simple
as possible. The original MIPS team was heavily involved in
the initial architectural discussions, and they helped steer
MIPS-X away from the kinds of trouble that they faced with
MIPS. The major areas of concern were control related, of
which the most important were considered to be instruction
decode and exception handling. Both were not considered
early enough in the MIPS design and created difficult
implementation problems in the final chip.

The design of the instruction format was straightforward
since we religiously adhered to a maxim given in the first
working document on MIPS-X. It stated, "The goal of any
instruction format should be:
1. Simple decode,
2. simple decode, and
3. simple decode.
Any attempts at improved code density at the expense of CPU
performance should be ridiculed at every opportunity."
Needless to say, all instruction sets considered for MIPS-X
were fixed format 32-bit words and the amount of decoding
was minimal. The effects of having this simple instruction
format is discussed in the conclusions.

Not all areas were as stable as the instruction decode.
Before presenting the major tradeoffs we made in the MIPS-X
design, the next section describes the basic architecture of the
processor and the following section gives an overview of the
hardware and organization of the machine. This is followed
by several sections, each discussing a major design issue in
MIPS-X, the solution used and the rational for that decision.

MIPS-X Architecture

The goal of the MIPS-X project was to design a
microprocessor with an order of magnitude more performance
than the original MIPS processor. MIPS-X borrows heavily
from the original MIPS design; it is again a heavily pipelined
machine, and the resulting pipeline interlocks are handled by
the supporting software system. MIPS-X differs from MIPS
in that it aims for single-cycle execution using a much faster
clock (20 MHz), a deeper pipeline and better implementation
technology.

The high instruction rate means that memory bandwidth is
an important consideration. At the projected clock frequency

230

of 20 MHz it is very difficult to satisfy instruction and data fetch requirements across the available package pins. To alleviate this problem, MIPS-X has a 2K-byte, on-chip instruction cache (Icache). Only instructions that miss in the Icache pass through the package pins. The Icache is placed above the datapath, in the area of the chip that is normally used for microcode storage and processor control. Data references and instruction references that miss in the Icache are handled by a large 64K word external cache (Ecache). The Ecache uses a shared bus to communicate with main memory. An added benefit of this two-level cache is that it provides a second port to memory; the processor can fetch an instruction from the Icache at the same time it is accessing off-chip data.

A deep pipeline is used to allow the machine to start a new instruction every cycle. Each instruction is divided into five pipeline stages. They are described in Figure 1. All control is hardwired.

IF	Instruction fetch.
RF	Instruction decode and register fetch.
ALU	ALU or shift operation
MEM	Wait for data from memory on a load and output data for a store.
WB	Write the result into the destination register.

Figure 1: MIPS-X Pipestages

The machine uses a load-store architecture; the only memory operations are explicit loads and stores. The use of the ALU cycle depends on the instruction being executed. For compute instructions, this cycle performs the desired computation, for memory instructions it is used to compute the address of the desired memory location and for branch instructions, it is used to compute the condition. All memory operations use the same addressing mode; the contents of a register are added to a 17-bit signed offset to produce a 32-bit address. There are 32 general purpose registers in the datapath with a 32-bit ALU and a funnel shifter for compute operations.

Although a compute instruction finishes its computation during the third pipeline cycle (ALU), the result is not written back into the register file until the last pipeline cycle. This delayed writeback is done to make instructions only change machine state during their last pipeline cycle, making exception handling much easier. Bypassing is used to reduce the number of pipeline interlocks.

All instructions are restartable so MIPS-X will support a dynamic, paged virtual memory system. To help implement such a system, MIPS-X supports both maskable and nonmaskable interrupts. For systems requiring more complex interrupt handling, an external interrupt coprocessor can be added. MIPS-X also provides two operating modes, system and user, that execute in separate address spaces to provide the protection needed to implement an operating system. The current mode is stored in the PSW and it can only be changed while executing in system mode.

A Hardware Overview

The major components of MIPS-X are the instruction cache data array, the instruction register and the datapath. The datapath is composed of the register file, the execution unit, PC unit and the tag store for the instruction cache. The organization of these parts is shown in Figure 2.

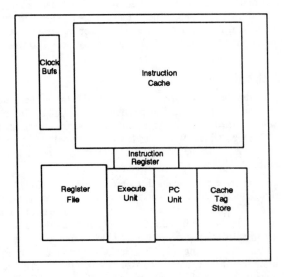

Figure 2: MIPS-X Floorplan

The instruction cache is organized as an 8-way set-associative cache, with 4 sets (rows) and 16 words in each block (line). A sub-block replacement scheme is used so there are 512 valid bits, one per word, as well as the 32 tags. These are located in the datapath to decrease the time needed to detect an instruction cache miss.

The instruction register latches the output from the instruction cache and predecodes some fields of each instruction. It also controls the flow of data during cache misses so that instructions can be written into the cache. During a cache miss, the instruction is latched in the instruction register from the data bus while it is going to the cache memory array. This latch provides a very useful testing feature by allowing the processor to run with the cache disabled.

The register file contains 31 general purpose registers and a hardwired constant zero register. It is useful to have a read-only register as a place to write unwanted data. The constant zero was chosen because it is used as a source value for many instructions such as loading immediate values by doing an add immediate to Register 0. Registers to handle two levels of bypassing and the memory data registers are also in this section.

Shifting and ALU operations are done in the execute unit. It contains a 64-bit to 32-bit funnel shifter and a 32-bit ALU. There is also a special register, called the MD register, that is used during multiplication and division instructions.

The program counter, or PC unit, contains a displacement adder for branches, an incrementer and a chain of shift registers to save the PC values of the instructions currently in execution. Having both the displacement adder and the incrementer means that as soon as the branch condition is determined the PC bus can be driven with the correct value. The PC values in the shift chain are needed to restart the machine after an exception.

In a small area above each section of the datapath is local instruction decoding and control for that section. The overall control of the machine is handled by two finite state machines located in the PC unit. One of them is used to handle Icache misses and the other one does instruction *squashing* during exceptions and branches. Squashing an instruction converts it into a *no-op* instruction.

Critical Paths

To run the processor at or above 20 MHz meant that much attention had to be paid to possible critical paths. In each cycle, we tried to minimize the number of series operations as much as possible. Whenever feasible, a signal was given a full phase to be decoded and driven from one section to another.

There were a few paths that we felt were most likely to be critical paths and we spent a lot of time concentrating on them. The most important of these involved external data fetches. In the specification for the pipeline, addresses would be computed during $\phi1$ of the ALU cycle and driven to the address pads during $\phi2$. The Ecache would be accessed during the MEM cycle. Even assuming that the address could be driven off the chip by the end of ALU, completing a fetch in 50 ns would be tight because of the address buffer delay, memory access time and setup time for the fetched data. Getting the result of the tag compare back in a cycle seemed impossible since this would also involve delay through some comparators. To ease the constraint on getting the tag compare back, we decided to use a *late-miss* signal. This meant that the cache would inform the processor at the beginning of the WB cycle whether the cache access during MEM was successful. If there was a miss, then the processor would effectively go back and re-execute $\phi2$ of MEM to try the access again. This loop would continue until the cache got the data and signaled a hit. Throughout the design we had to be careful not to unnecessarily add delay to the memory-fetch path.

Other paths that we tried to optimize included the path from branch condition generation to driving the PC Bus, instruction cache hit detection, squeezing the ALU time into 1 phase to get the address out by the end of the cycle and doing register reads and writes in one cycle. The latter two were strictly circuit design issues and are not discussed any further here.

The Instruction Cache

Advances in processor architecture and VLSI technology have increased faster than the improvements in packaging technology. This has meant that high-performance VLSI processors have become memory bandwidth limited. For example, if we assume that one instruction is fetched every cycle while, on average, data is only fetched every third cycle,

then MIPS-X will have an average bandwidth of 26 MWords/s and a peak bandwidth of 40 MWords/s. Clearly, on-chip memory would help to alleviate this bottleneck. For MIPS-X, we built an on-chip 512-word instruction cache and the tradeoffs made in its design are described in detail elsewhere[6]. We will only discuss the salient features here.

The instruction cache was the first part of the chip to be designed. We first fixed a die size that we felt had enough area to implement the functionality we desired yet small enough that we could expect a reasonable yield of working parts. The datapath and control would take about half of the area inside the padframe so the cache was allocated the remaining area fixing its area and aspect ratio. The other main constraint on the cache was that the cycle time had to be less than the 50ns clock cycle. Given these constraints we investigated many different floorplans and organizations, trying to minimize the average cost of an instruction fetch. This cost is a function of the cache hit rate, the miss penalty, and the cache access time.

We found that the performance of the cache was more sensitive to the the miss service time than the miss ratio. This meant that the implementation details of the cache were more important than the cache organization because the implementation affected how quickly we could determine whether an address hit in the cache. With our pipelining, this meant the difference between stalling the machine for 2 or 3 cycles on a cache miss. By placing the tag and valid-bit stores in the datapath close to the PC unit a 2-cycle miss could be realized. This lengthened the datapath by the number of cache tags and meant that we could not have smaller block sizes because more tags would make the datapath too long. However, the benefits of having fewer cache miss cycles far outweighed the slightly lower miss rates achievable by having smaller blocks.

Initial simulations of this organization yielded disappointing results. Using a set of medium size programs we achieved miss rates that averaged over 20%. We felt that real programs would have worse miss rates, pushing the cost of an instruction fetch close to 1.5 cycles. We found a way to reduce the number of cache miss cycles to 1 by writing the missed instruction into the Icache as soon as it got back onto the chip, but since accessing external data was already one of the critical paths we did not want to risk extending the cycle time to complete the write. Instead we realized that the 2 cache miss cycles could be used to fetch back 2 instructions, the one that missed and the next one to be executed. Doing this double fetch did not affect the critical path and, in fact, was easier to do than fetching back only one instruction because it minimized the disruption of the pipeline. Fetching back 2 words almost halves the miss ratio, driving down the cost of an instruction fetch to that of a single-cycle miss. The key realization here was that there was extra cache bandwidth available and that we could use it to fetch back the next instruction, significantly improving the cache miss ratio without impacting the cycle time of the machine. Fetching back more words would not be advantageous because the bandwidth of the cache is fully used.

Trace driven simulations show that with our set of large Pascal and Lisp benchmarks, the cache has an average miss rate of 12% resulting in an average instruction executing in 1.24 cycles.

The Coprocessor Interface

The coprocessor interface was considered from the very beginning of the design. It also led to some of the most interesting discussions within the MIPS-X design team. We spent considerable time trying to find an efficient interface that would give reasonable performance and still fit within the constraints of VLSI packaging and design. This problem was exacerbated by the presence of the on-chip instruction cache, since now all instructions would not be visible to the outside world.

The proposal for the first instruction set had a single bit in every instruction to specify whether the instruction was for the CPU or a coprocessor. For instructions with the coprocessor bit set, MIPS-X would perform all the addressing calculations, but would not affect any of its stored data. That is, all coprocessor memory instructions still used the processor to generate the addresses and the required control signals, while the coprocessor either acted as a source or sink of the data. To make the coprocessor instructions visible outside of the processor, a dedicated bus was required to transfer the instruction off the processor chip. This scheme had 2 disadvantages: all interprocessor communication had to go through memory, and a coprocessor bus was required. A minor concern was that half the opcode space was devoted to the coprocessor; there had to be a more efficient encoding.

The next instruction format divided the opcode space into three instruction types: memory operations, branches and compute operations. The memory and compute instructions had a 3-bit field to specify the coprocessor number, branches were only done on the main processor. If Coprocessor 0 was specified then the instruction was for the main processor, otherwise the instruction was for one of the 7 available coprocessors. To branch on a coprocessor condition, the coprocessor would first be told to assert a single input to the main processor and a *branch on coprocessor true* or *branch on coprocessor false* would be executed to test the status of that input. Several coprocessors could be connected by wire-oring their outputs. This scheme still had the problem that data transfers between processors must be done through memory.

It was then proposed that all coprocessor instructions must be non-cached, removing the need for a coprocessor bus. The issue of pins and pin bandwidth was heavily debated within the MIPS-X design team. Pins on the processor were in short supply and devoting approximately 20 of them to the coprocessor interface seemed excessive. The question was not just whether there were enough pins available. Without the coprocessor bus, MIPS-X would need only about 90 signal pins, a relatively small number by today's standards. Rather the argument focused on what would be the best use of these pins if we had them. It was not at all clear that using them for the coprocessor interface was the most effective use of the pins. To prevent coprocessor instructions from being cached, a bit in the instruction cache would be set when an instruction being loaded was detected to be a coprocessor instruction. If the bit was set during an instruction fetch that missed, the coprocessor would get the instruction off the memory bus as the main processor read the instruction from memory during the cache miss cycle.

The obvious disadvantage of this approach was that all coprocessor operations incurred an overhead from the internal cache miss. Our initial benchmarks indicated that this would not cause a significant performance loss, but when we generated traces from some floating point intensive code we realized a significant percentage of the instructions were floating point instructions. This caused a re-examination of the decision to not cache coprocessor instructions, and led to the coprocessor scheme that was finally chosen.

The opcode encoding of the machine was changed again, this time making coprocessor operations a form of memory operation or more accurately, memory instructions became a type of coprocessor instruction. Coprocessor instructions work in this scheme by using the address lines to transmit the coprocessor instruction. A memory instruction takes a 17-bit offset constant and adds it to the contents of a register to compute the memory address. If the memory system ignores the cycle, it is possible to pass the 17-bit offset constant to a coprocessor as an instruction. The instruction would include a 3-bit field to specify the coprocessor being addressed, although the processor does not need to know the format of these instructions. This scheme has several advantages over our earlier ideas. A coprocessor instruction bus is not required, since the instructions are sent out over the address pins. Only one extra pin is required to tell the memory system to ignore the cycle. Additional pins can now be used for alleviating the pin bandwidth problem in other parts of the system. Using coprocessor load and store instructions, data can be directly transferred between processors by making the coprocessor supply or read data on the data bus instead of the memory. Also, the coprocessor instructions can be cached just like all the other instructions. The disadvantages of this scheme are that there are fewer bits to specify the coprocessor instructions, and all data to and from the coprocessor's registers must be transferred through the main processor registers first before it can be sent to memory.

Having to transfer all data through the main processor registers was still thought to be inefficient for heavy floating point computation. This lead to a further modification of the instruction set to add *load floating* and *store floating* instructions. These instructions provide one special coprocessor with its own load and store instructions, which we assume will be a floating point unit (FPU). The interface now allows one special coprocessor to load and store its registers directly to memory, without passing through the main processor, in a single instruction. All other coprocessors require one extra cycle for memory loads/stores.

One final tweaking of the interface was to remove the coprocessor branch instructions. The main reason for their removal was the problem of saving state in the coprocessors across exceptions. The solution was to just read a coprocessor status register into a main processor register and then branch according to the value of that register. This change eliminated the last set of problems we had discovered with the coprocessor instructions.

By using the address lines, the resulting coprocessor interface has instructions that can be cached, does not require a large coprocessor bus, allows efficient communication between the processor registers and the coprocessor registers, and lets a single coprocessor have direct access to memory.

Branches

Having set out the initial architecture of the machine, we quickly ran into the problem of branches, and branch delays. Branches have a considerable effect on the performance of a computer especially one that is pipelined as deeply as MIPS-X. The effects of branches in a pipelined machine are particularly noticeable because branches interrupt the flow of the pipeline. Decisions about the design of the pipeline and the type of branch scheme used are not independent. Control complexity is a serious issue.

We very quickly decided to eliminate the use of condition codes in MIPS-X if possible. This decision was motivated by two facts. First, instruction trace statistics indicated that a prior compute operation infrequently generated the condition code needed for a branch. In roughly 80% of the branches an explicit compare operation must be performed to set the condition codes. A previous analysis[7] of empirical data showed that the number of instructions saved by condition codes was very small and essentially useless. Second, condition codes generate state that needs to be saved and restored during exceptions. Handling condition codes in a pipelined machine is difficult because when an exception occurs, great care must be taken to ensure that the correct condition codes are saved. It seemed to us that condition codes provide little benefit and have potential complexity problems. In particular, generating code to use condition codes efficiently is not as straightforward as one might expect. All the branch schemes considered for MIPS-X contained an explicit compare in the branch. This actually reduces the amount of control logic required because there is no need to worry about how to save this state.

Two arithmetic operations are required to execute a branch instruction. One is to compute the branch condition and the other is to compute the branch destination. A machine that uses condition codes computes the branch condition before the actual branch instruction and saves the condition in a condition code register. The first idea conceived for implementing branches in MIPS-X computed the condition in the branch instruction, but did not compute the branch destination. Instead the branch destination was made explicitly visible in the architecture. The user would have to load a register called *PC+1* with the branch destination. The branch instruction computes a condition and then selects *PC+1* or the next sequential instruction depending on the computed condition. An observation was made that many inner loops contain several forward branches due to constructs like if-then-else statements so it would be good to have several *PC+1* registers. Four was felt to be sufficient. This would allow the compiler to hoist the destination address calculations out of the loop. Without this feature, the contents of *PC+1* would have to be loaded from a register for each branch within the loop for each iteration of the loop.

This scheme still had the problem that there was some state that must be saved (the *PC+1* registers) when an exception occurred. Also, deciding how to use the *PC+1* registers could be cumbersome for the compiler system. Finally, with four special registers, it was no longer clear that this solution was easier to implement than simply including a separate adder to compute the destination while the ALU performed the comparison. At this point in the design, adding a little hardware to the datapath to make the control simpler was the wisest choice so we added the separate adder to compute the destination.

During this period we also became concerned about the effect of the branch delay slots on the machine's performance. Often in a pipelined machine one or more instructions following a branch are fetched before the result of the condition evaluation is known. If these instructions are executed, then the machine is said to have a *delayed branch* meaning the effect of the branch occurs after the actual branch instruction. The number of cycles or *delay slots* that execute after the branch instruction and before the actual branch occurs is called the *branch delay*. Filling these delay slots is not a simple task[8, 9, 10] and affects the overall performance.

In the MIPS-X pipeline, it is most straightforward to implement a branch with a delay of two. The ALU is used to compute the branch condition during the third (ALU) pipestage. Filling two delay slots did not seem very promising. Using data from MIPS instruction traces, we expected over 50% of the slots to remain empty[8]. This performance problem lead to discussions about how to reduce the branch delay to 1 cycle, and whether we could use branch prediction to help reduce the wasted cycles[11, 12].

A *quick compare*[3] was proposed as a method to reduce the branch delay. In this scheme, simple comparisons between the two source registers are done before the ALU cycle. This comparison would be performed at the end of the RF cycle by placing a comparator on the output of the register file. Only equality and sign comparisons can be obtained using this method since there is not enough time for an arithmetic operation. Other conditions such as *greater than* would require two steps. The ALU operation is done first and the result is stored in a register. This result is then used in a quick sign compare instruction.

The main question that needed to be resolved initially was what percentage of branches could be handled by a quick compare. Statistics from Katevenis's thesis indicate that by changing the compiler slightly, about 80% of all branches can be converted into quick compares[3], but this means that 20% of all branches take two cycles. Our initial statistics indicated that the number of branches that could be handled using a quick compare was between 70% and 80%.

The quick compare was eventually dropped because it could potentially lengthen the processor cycle time. The comparator circuit must operate on the source buses leading to the ALU and since the values on the buses could come from a bypass source it was possible that the buses would not be stable until late into that cycle, particularly for a previous memory fetch because the data would only be back at the very end of the cycle. For the quick compare to operate, we would need to perform a compare on these values and then use this result to select the correct address of the next instruction. The potential increase in cycle time discounted its slight advantage in the average number of cycles it takes to complete a branch. In retrospect, our decision was correct. In the final machine, the delay from the generation of the branch signal to driving the correct value on the PC Bus is long (measured to be about 20 ns). Even providing a full phase to drive this path leaves it on a critical path.

Left with a branch delay of 2, we investigated branch prediction as a way to reduce the effective branch delay. There were two prediction algorithms tried: branch cache, and static prediction. The branch cache was quickly discarded when we discovered that it had to be fairly large (much greater than 16 entries) to get a high hit rate. It would also affect the size of our instruction cache. Besides, it never did much better than static prediction and was much more complex. Static prediction would use information at compile time (possibly with profiling) to predict which way a branch would go.

To make use of the prediction information we considered implementing *squashing*, the ability to convert an instruction into a *no-op* if the branch did not go in the predicted direction. In MIPS, the instructions in the branch delay slots are always executed. The strategy for choosing instructions is to first try to move an instruction from before the branch into the slot. If no instructions can be moved past the branch the next choice is to find instructions from the destination or the sequential path that have no effect if the branch goes the wrong way. Thus if you predict correctly, the slot performs a useful instruction and if the branch goes the other way, the slot instruction is simply wasted. The last alternative is to place a *no-op* instruction in the slot. Squashing relaxes the restriction on the second choice for instructions. It allows any instruction from the branch destination to be placed in the slot, even when there is an adverse effect if the branch goes the wrong way. The machine squashes the instruction (turns it into a *no-op*) if the branch goes the wrong way.

With squashing there are three options for dealing with the instructions in the delay slots giving three possible branch types: *no squash* where the slot instructions are always executed, *squash if don't go* where the slot instructions are executed if the branch takes and *squash if go* where the slot instructions are executed if the branch does not take. Since we decided to use static prediction, and in the static case most branches go, MIPS-X only has the first two types of branches. This requires only one bit in the instruction to specify how to deal with the instructions in the slots.

Various combinations of one and two-slot schemes with and without squashing were evaluated. The results are shown in Table 1. The *no squash* scheme is the same as used in MIPS where the instructions in the slots are always executed. The *always squash* scheme only uses the *squash if go* and *squash if don't go* actions for the instructions in the branch slots. The *squash optional* scheme includes the use of branches with *no squash* instructions in the slots as well as having branches with squashing. It can be seen that by allowing squashing the efficiency of branches is much better.

Branch Scheme	Cycles/Branch[2]
2-slot no squash	2.0
2-slot always squash	1.5
2-slot squash optional	1.3
1-slot no squash	1.4
1-slot always squash	1.3
1-slot squash optional	1.1

Table 1: Average Cycles per Branch Instruction for Various Branch Schemes

[2]If all of the branch delay slots could be filled with useful instructions, then we would achieve the ideal of a 1 cycle branch. Any no-op instructions in the branch delay slots are attributed to the cost of the branch so a branch with 2 no-ops in its two delay slots is deemed to have a cost of 3.

The scheme we finally chose uses the full compare and *squash optional* with two slots. Our initial estimates about the cost of the double slots turned out to be slightly optimistic. Where we predicted the average branch would take 1.3 cycles, results using the actual reorganizer showed that the average branch took about 1.5 cycles for small benchmarks using traditional optimization. However, we have since developed better optimization techniques and our most recent results show that even with large Pascal and Lisp benchmarks the average branch takes 1.27 cycles.

Implementing squashing was a gamble because we were not completely sure how it would affect exception handling at the time we made the commitment to use it. It turned out that they mesh together very well as described in the next section.

Exception Handling

As the design of the machine progressed, our concentration shifted from the functions the machine was going to perform to how these functions were going to be controlled. MIPS-X benefited greatly from the experience gained during the MIPS design. Handling exceptions in MIPS caused the most complexity in the machine because of the large number of possible states in the processor during an exception. These states were the result of the processor trying to complete the instructions that occurred conceptually before the fault but still in the pipeline, and reloading the partially full pipeline on a return from an exception. The goal for MIPS-X was to require as few states as possible to handle an exception so the state machine design would not be difficult. The underlining rule was to *keep it simple, stupid*[13].

In some ways exception handling in MIPS-X followed the MIPS model. Exceptions are not vectored so the exception handler must first determine the cause of the exception. On MIPS there was an on-chip *surprise register* where this information was stored. MIPS-X relies instead on a separate off-chip interrupt control unit that contains this information. The PSW does contain bits that determine whether the exception was caused by an interrupt, arithmetic overflow or a non-maskable interrupt.

MIPS-X differed from MIPS in how exceptions affected the pipeline. The MIPS exception sequence started with the pipeline being flushed of as many instructions as possible that were already executing. Then the program counter (PC) was zeroed and the return PCs saved from the PC chain. The flushing of the pipeline caused a great many extra states and added a lot of complexity.

In MIPS-X the pipeline is halted when an exception occurs. No instructions are completed. The PC is immediately set to zero and the shift chain of old PC values is frozen, saving the addresses of the instructions that are still in the pipeline. The current PSW is placed in PSWold, interrupts are turned off and the machine is placed into system mode. The exception routine, located at address zero in system space, begins execution by first saving the three PCs from the PC chain and PSWold onto the system stack. Once the state of the interrupted process is saved, then PC shifting can be enabled and interrupts unmasked if desired. The restart sequence involves reloading the PC chain with the three saved PCs and then doing three special jumps using the contents of the PC chain; the PC chain is used to store the return addresses during the return sequence. Interrupts must be disabled both during machine state saving and restoring.

During the discussions about how branches were to be implemented, there was some concern about the effects the branch implementation would have on exception handling. The original feeling was that having more branch slots would require more state in the machine and implementing squashing branches would make the state machine even more complicated. The squash proponents argued that the hardware needed to freeze the pipeline during an exception could be used to implement squashing branches. They not only convinced the design team, they also turned out to be correct. Squashing two branch slots only requires a single extra input to the squashing finite state machine that is used to handle exceptions. Branch squashing and squashing for exceptions are very similar.

The general scheme used to no-op an instruction is quite simple. All that needs to be done is to set a bit in the destination specifier for that instruction. This bit is used by the register file to determine whether to perform a write or not. There are 2 lines in the machine that can set this bit, Exception and Squash. Exception no-ops the instructions in the ALU and MEM stages of the pipeline, while Squash no-ops the instructions currently in the IF and RF stages of the pipeline. The only added complexity occurs with the Mult/Div register and the PSW which contains the only visible state outside of the register file. Writes to these locations are also prevented by Exception and Squash.

There is only one exception generated on chip and it is a trap on overflow in the ALU or the multiplication/division hardware. At the start of the design it was felt that detecting overflows and generating a trap was too complex to do. The original solution was the concept of a *sticky overflow* bit. If an overflow occurred then the sticky overflow bit would be set in the PSW. This bit could then be checked at a later time to determine whether an overflow had occurred. This meant that it would not be possible to precisely detect the occurrence of the overflow but at least it was possible to indicate the presence of an incorrect result. We began looking for other overflow mechanisms when we discovered that the sticky overflow bit interacted badly with bypassing. Instead of making the hardware simple, it seemed to make the PSW harder to design.

Several other simple schemes were then proposed. One was a *SetOnAddOverflow* instruction that just routed the overflow bit from the ALU into the most significant bit of the ALU result. This instruction could then be used to determine whether the addition causes an overflow by simply testing for the sign of the result. Another suggestion was a *Branch on Overflow* instruction that caused a branch if the result of the branch comparison overflowed. These were minimal hardware solutions that would provide some small support for overflow detection.

At this point the exception hardware had been designed and we observed that generating a true *trap on overflow* was not difficult; in fact it was simpler than the original sticky overflow bit. We decided to abandon the sticky overflow bit for a maskable trap on overflow.

Control

Our overriding goal for the control section was to keep it as simple as possible. In part we accomplished our goal by eliminating hardware features that would complicate the machine without providing significant performance advantages. We also tried to keep a uniform view of the hardware, trying to reuse the same control mechanism for many features. Merging exceptions and squashing, and merging memory instructions and coprocessor operations were examples of this strategy. Finally, we eliminated the global controller for the machine and replaced it with a set of smaller controllers, one for each section of the datapath. We further partitioned the design so that a single designer was responsible for both the datapath and control in his section, giving each designer the incentive to make his control section simpler. Most of the machine control is simple decoders, many generated automatically using PLA generators.

One technique that MIPS-X used to great advantage was a qualified clock, called $\psi1$, to latch the control state of the machine. This clock is the $\phi1$ clock qualified with *not external cache miss* and *not internal cache miss*. When either cache misses, the $\psi1$ clock does not rise, and the control state does not shift down the pipeline control latches. The lack of a $\psi1$ clock causes the machine to execute the *previous* $\phi2$ phase before retrying the $\phi1$ phase. This simple technique made temporary stalling of the entire pipeline very easy, and allowed us to implement the late miss described earlier without greatly increasing the machine complexity. Since the $\psi1$ clock is only allowed to clock control state latches, its pulse width can be quite narrow (about 10 ns). As long as the miss signal is monotonic, it is possible to detect a cache hit after the data has been latched in the machine without stalling the machine.

Together these control techniques were quite successful. The control was nicely divided among the 4 main datapath sections, with the only two finite state machines (FSMs) residing in the PC unit. These FSMs handle instruction cache misses and instruction squashing during exceptions and squashed branches. The state diagrams for the two machines are shown in Figures 3 and 4. These FSMs are implemented as simple shift registers with a very small amount of random logic and occupy less than 0.2% of the total area of the chip.

Status and Conclusions

The MIPS-X project began in earnest during the summer of 1984. By January 1985, we had settled on an initial version of the instruction set, and had written an instruction level simulator for the machine. We were able to use much of the software system that was created for MIPS for MIPS-X as well. This greatly reduced the software development effort. The compiler/simulator system generated instruction traces that we used to gather cache statistics and fine tune the architecture. By April 1985, the architecture had stabilized and work on the detailed design accelerated. We ran our first instruction through a detailed functional simulator of the entire processor during the summer. The final design was taped out at the end of April 1986 and we received first silicon back in October.

The processor was designed to run at a clock rate of 20

MHz, executing an instruction every cycle, yielding a peak performance of 20 MIPs. Timing analysis showed that the version that was shipped in April would run at about 16 MHz. Initial timing tests have shown that the part is fully functional and it runs at the projected 16 MHz clock rate. We are now fixing the critical paths so that we can achieve our goal of 20 MHz. The die is 8.5 mm by 8 mm and has a total of 108 pins of which 84 are for signals and 24 are for power and ground. There are about 150K transistors, two thirds of which are in the instruction cache. The power dissipation is less than 1 W.

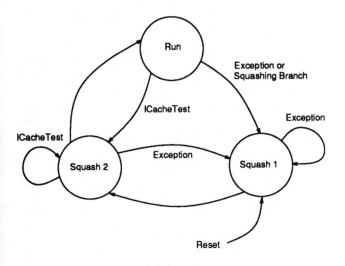

Figure 3: Squash Finite State Machine

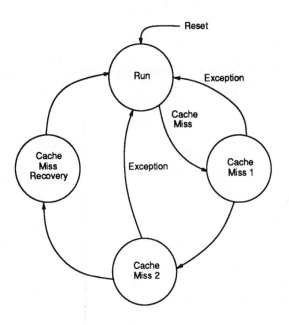

Figure 4: Cache Miss Finite State Machine

Simulations of our large Pascal benchmarks show that 15.6% of all instructions are no-ops due to unused branch delays or other pipeline interlocks that cannot be optimized away. For Lisp, this number increases slightly to 18.3% due to a larger number of jumps and many load-load interlocks caused by chasing car and cdr chains[14]. When the memory system overhead is included (delays from Icache and Ecache misses), the average instruction requires about 1.7 cycles meaning MIPS-X should have a sustained throughput above 11 MIPs. Our benchmark programs have static code sizes in the range of 50 KBytes to 270 KBytes so we cannot get exact numbers for the effects of the external cache because most of the benchmarks fit entirely. Smith's numbers[15] are not large enough so we used much larger traces[16] to derive the Ecache effects.

The performance of a machine is based on three factors: the number of instructions executed (path length), the number of cycles per instruction and the cycle time. Ideally, all three factors should be minimized but we have shown that by having simple instruction decode we can significantly decrease the latter two factors without adversely affecting the path length. Comparison of Pascal programs with a VAX 11/780 shows that MIPS-X executes about 25% more instructions but executes the programs about 14 times faster for unoptimized code. The static code size for MIPS-X is also about 25% greater than VAX code. The Stanford compiler system was used and the only difference was in the back end code generators. However, when MIPS-X code is compared to the Berkeley Pascal compiler, the path length is 80% longer and the speedup is only 10 times faster than the VAX. Much of this difference may be due to poorer code from our VAX code generator. We feel that when we get the results for optimized code, the numbers will be somewhere inbetween.

The goal of the MIPS-X project from the beginning was to learn from MIPS and design a simpler yet faster processor. The emphasis in all design decisions throughout the project was simplicity: minimize state and keep the control simple. The implementation of MIPS-X has shown that it is possible to implement a high performance microprocessor that supports coprocessors, without requiring complex control or hundreds of pins.

Acknowledgements

The MIPS-X research project has been supported by the Defense Advanced Research Projects Agency under contract #MDA903-83-C-0335. Paul Chow was partially supported by a postdoctoral fellowship from the Natural Sciences and Engineering Research Council of Canada.

Many people have contributed to the MIPS-X research effort. Malcolm Wing, Arturo Salz, Karen Huyser, Anant Agarwal, Scott McFarling, C.Y. Chu, Steve Richardson, Steve Tjiang, John Acken, Richard Simoni, Glenn Gulak, Kathy Cuderman, Takeshi Tokuda, Eugen Reithmann, Steven Przybylski, Chris Rowen, Norm Jouppi, Thomas Gross, John Gill and John Hennessy deserve special thanks for their contributions to the project.

References

1. G. Radin, "The 801 Minicomputer", *Proc. SIGARCH/SIGPLAN Symposium on Architectural Support for Programming Languages and Operating Systems, ACM, Palo Alto*, March 1982, pp. 39-47.

2. D. Patterson and C. Sequin, "A VLSI RISC", *Computer*, September, 1982, pp. 8-21.

3. M. Katevenis, "Reduced Instruction Set Computer Architectures for VLSI", Computer Science Division (EECS) UCB/CSD 83/141, Univ. of CA at Berkeley, October 1983.

4. J. Hennessy, et al., "The MIPS Machine", *COMPCON*, IEEE, Spring 1982, pp. 2-7.

5. S. Przybylski, T. Gross, J. Hennessy, N. Jouppi, C. Rowen, "Organization and VLSI Implementation of MIPS", *Journal of VLSI and Computer Systems*, Vol. 1, No. 2, December, 1984, pp. 170-208.

6. Anant Agarwal, Paul Chow, Mark Horowitz, John Acken Arturo Salz and John Hennessy, "On-chip Instruction Caches for High Performance Processors", *Proceedings, Stanford Conference on Advanced Research in VLSI*, March 1987, pp. 1-24.

7. J.L. Hennessy, N. Jouppi, F. Baskett, T.R. Gross and J. Gill, "Hardware/Software Tradeoffs for Increased Performance", *Proc. SIGARCH/SIGPLAN Symposium on Architectural Support for Programming Languages and Operating Systems, ACM, Palo Alto*, March 1982, pp. 2-11.

8. Thomas Gross, *Code Optimization of Pipeline Constraints*, PhD dissertation, Stanford University, December 1983, Available as Stanford University CSL Technical Report 83-255.

9. John Hennessy and Thomas Gross, "Postpass Code Optimization of Pipeline Constraints", *ACM Transactions on Programming Languages and Systems*, Vol. 5, No. 3, July, 1983, pp. 422-448.

10. Scott McFarling and John Hennessy, "Reducing the Cost of Branches", *Proceedings, 13th Symposium on Computer Architecture*, June 1986, pp. 396-403.

11. J.E. Smith, "A Study of Branch Predition Strategies", *Proceedings, Eighth Symposium on Computer Architecture*, May 1981, pp. 135-148.

12. Johnny K. F. Lee, Alan Jay Smith, "Branch Prediction Strategies and Branch Target Buffer Design", *Computer*, January, 1984, pp. 6-22.

13. Butler W. Lampson, "Hints for Computer System Design", *IEEE Software*, Vol. 1, No. 1, January, 1984, pp. 11-30.

14. Peter Steenkiste, *LISP on a Reduced-Instruction-Set Processor: Characterization and Optimization*, PhD dissertation, Stanford University, 1987, To appear in 1987.

15. Alan Jay Smith, "Cache Memories", *Computing Surveys*, Vol. 14, No. 3, September, 1982, pp. 473-530.

16. Anant Agarwal, Richard L. Sites and Mark Horowitz, "ATUM: A New Technique for Capturing Address Traces Using Microcode", *13th Annual International Symposium on Computer Architecture*, IEEE, June 1986, pp. 119-127.

"The CLIPPER Processor: Instruction Set Architecture and Implementation"
by W. Hollingsworth, H. Sachs, and A.J. Smith, *Communications of the ACM*, February 1989, Volume 32, Number 2, pages 200–219.

THE CLIPPER® PROCESSOR: INSTRUCTION SET ARCHITECTURE AND IMPLEMENTATION

Intergraph's CLIPPER microprocessor is a high performance, three chip module that implements a new instruction set architecture designed for convenient programmability, broad functionality, and easy future expansion.

WALTER HOLLINGSWORTH, HOWARD SACHS, and ALAN JAY SMITH

The Intergraph CLIPPER[1] employs a new high performance computer architecture currently implemented as a three chip module, consisting of a processor chip and two cache and memory management unit (CAMMU) chips (see Figure 1); the processor is also available separately. It uses a new "simplified" instruction set and satisfies the key aspects of RISC designs [41] (limited and simple instruction set; maximum use of registers and minimal references to memory; and emphasis on optimizing the instruction execution pipeline). The machine has a 32-bit architecture, with a 32-bit bus data path, 32-bit registers, 32-bit data paths on chip, and a separate 32-bit virtual address space for the system and each user address space. There are nine addressing modes, permitting memory addresses to be computed from most of the useful combinations of the program counter, register contents and/or a displacement of 12, 16, or 32 bits. Instructions are 2, 4, 6, or 8 bytes long, with their length, address mode, and opcode specified in the first two bytes for efficient decoding. Data types include bytes, halfwords, words (32 bits), longwords (8 bytes), and single (4 bytes) and double (8 bytes) precision floating point. Three user visible register sets are available: 16 user and 16 supervisor general purpose 32-bit registers, and 8 floating point registers of 64 bits each. There are also the usual control registers (program counter, program status word, system status word)

and some internal registers used by the processor. Eighteen traps are implemented and 128 system calls are provided. Floating point operations conform to the IEEE 754 standard [6].

The CLIPPER microprocessor uses caching and virtual memory as the standard mode of operation. The associated CAMMU chips each contain a 4 Kbyte cache, a translation lookaside buffer (TLB), and a translator. One CAMMU is used for instruction references and the other for data; the CAMMUs not only provide caching, but also implement protection, detect page faults, and watch the system bus to ensure multiple cache consistency. A full 32-bit address space is provided for the operating system and for each user process; the address space is *not* partitioned via high order address bits.

The floating point unit is on the CLIPPER processor chip. Instruction execution is pipelined with up to five instructions in the pipeline. Interlocks and dependency checks are provided in the pipeline hardware, so that no compiler inserted no-ops are needed for correct operation. Some complicated operations and diagnostics are implemented as instruction sequences in a small, on-chip ROM, called the Macro Instruction ROM (MIROM); all other instructions are hardwired. No microcode is used. The machine has 168 instructions, of which 101 are directly hardwired.

Two versions of the CLIPPER processor have been introduced. The C100, first available in 1986 from Fairchild Semiconductor, was implemented in 2 micron CMOS, was 167 K square mils, and used 132,000 transistors. The C300, available in 1988 from Intergraph Corporation, is implemented in 1.5 micron CMOS, is 285K square mils, and uses 174,000 transistors. Per-

---

[1] The trademark *CLIPPER* was chosen to reflect the principal architect and general manager's preference for spending his weekends sailing [34].

CLIPPER is a trademark of Intergraph Corporation.

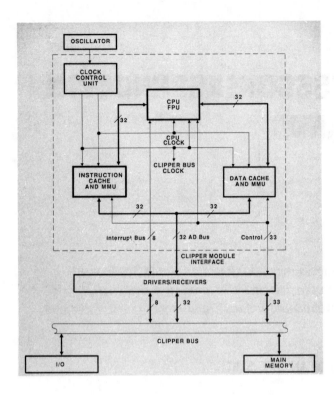

FIGURE 1. Schematic Diagram of CLIPPER

thus made to design a new instruction set architecture, using the previous experience of the designers and the latest thinking in the computer architecture research community.

Fashions in computer architecture have varied widely over the last few years, changing from the "baroque" or "rococo" of the 1970s to the "minimalist" 1980s. It was widely believed in the 1970s that hardware would be very cheap, and software difficult and expensive; therefore as much functionality as possible should be moved to the hardware, resulting in complex architectures such as the DEC Vax [10, 24]. The problems with such a complex architecture are that it is very difficult to obtain good performance as a function of the amount of logic needed, it is difficult to get compilers to actually generate instructions that use the machine features, and the machine is hard (time consuming, expensive) to design, build, and debug [18, 19].

The popular thinking in computer architecture shifted in the 1980s toward very simple architectures, as originally implemented in the Cray machines (CDC 6400, 6600, 7600), studied and implemented in the IBM 801 [36], and further studied and popularized by the RISC project at Berkeley [32, 33] and the MIPS project at Stanford [19]. The essence of such machines is a simplified instruction set, which permits a hardwired implementation, a very simple instruction encoding which permits rapid decoding and effective pipelining, a load/store architecture, which greatly simplifies the control logic, and effective use of registers to cut memory traffic. Some such machines, such as RISC [32, 33] and MIPS [19] have carried these concepts to their limits by requiring fixed length instructions, almost all of which execute in one cycle. The fixed length instructions result in a significant increase in code size [14], increasing memory traffic and cache miss ratios. The single cycle execution requirement increases the machine cycle time; CLIPPER has more compact code and a shorter cycle time than such very simple machines. Some discussion of the RISC/CISC issues appear in [7] and [14].

The choice was thus made to design a new instruction set architecture (ISA). The instructions, the module design, and the functional partitioning were chosen to permit mainframe level performance, and to permit future compatible mainframe implementations. The continuing and increasing adoption of the easily ported UNIX* [37] as the standard operating system for academic, software development, and workstation environments made a new ISA commercially feasible.

Outline and Context
It is possible to describe a "computer" at many levels. The *instruction set architecture* (*ISA*) refers to the computer instruction set as expressed in binary or in assembly language and its functions; the ISA is usually described in the "principles of operation" manual. We

formance measurements show that the C100 implementation is 3 to 15 times as fast as a Vax 11/780 (averaging more than five times faster) and is somewhat faster than a Vax 8600. The C300 is about twice as fast as the C100. The peak execution rate in CLIPPER instructions for the C100 is 33 MIPS and 50 MIPS for the C300. Additional information on CLIPPER is available in [3] and [13].

Motivation and Design Philosophy
CLIPPER was designed and built to fulfill the need for a very high performance, microcomputer chip-based computer. The immediate applications for such a processor are in high performance workstations and "super-minicomputer" shared machines. To introduce some historical perspective, the highest performance commercial mainframe in 1976 was the IBM 370/168, which for the kind of workloads expected on CLIPPER (C, Fortran, Pascal), had performance comparable to that of the C100 CLIPPER.

When the CLIPPER project began 1982–83, no existing commercial computer architecture permitted a high performance implementation on a microprocessor chip with the necessary instruction set and architectural features. At the time, architectures available on microprocessors failed to permit high performance implementations, and most other architectures failed to be easily implementable on a chip or to provide a reasonable range of features. There were also commercial barriers to using existing architecture. The decision was

---

* UNIX is a trademark of AT&T Bell Laboratories.

use the term *design architecture* to refer to the highest level description of an implementation, i.e., the block diagram and parameter level. Below that are gate and circuit level descriptions.

This article focuses primarily on CLIPPER's instruction set architecture, and examines the design architecture and related issues such as performance, design tradeoffs, design implications, and areas for possible future expansion.

MEMORY ARCHITECTURE AND DATA TYPES
Memory Architecture
First, we'll provide a *brief* overview of the memory architecture of the CLIPPER microprocessor. A much more detailed description, including a discussion of the CAMMU, is provided in [3].

Address Space
In normal operation, CLIPPER uses virtual memory, although unmapped (real memory) mode is also possible. The supervisor and each user process has its own 32-bit virtual address space, defined by the PDO (page directory origin) register in the CAMMU, which contains the physical memory address of the base of the first level of the page map for the process. The page map is implemented in two levels: the first level is the page directory, and the second level contains the page tables. The page size is 4 Kbytes, which is large enough for efficient I/O [38], keeps the TLB miss ratio down, and provides enough unmapped bits that set selection in the 4 Kbyte caches can be effectively overlapped with translation [39]. The page size is also small enough to avoid unreasonable levels of internal fragmentation. No address bits are used to partition the address space, as in the Vax and MIPS machines [9], so such a partitioning isn't an obstacle to increased address space size as technology evolves.

Caching
Two cache and memory management chips (see Figure 1) provide most of the support for the memory architecture; one is used for data and the other for instructions; each is connected to the processor by its own 32-bit address/data bus. Each CAMMU has a TLB and a translator. The TLB is set associative with 128 entries organized as 64 sets of 2 elements each. Protection is provided on a page basis, with each page table entry specifying permission for the process to read, write, and/or execute from the page in supervisor and/or user state; protection bits are cached in the TLB. Page faults, protection faults, and memory errors are detected by the CAMMU and a trap code is returned to the processor for supervisor action.

Each CAMMU also contains a 4 Kbyte cache memory, organized as 128 sets of two 16-byte lines. The caching policy (copy back, write through, uncacheable) is defined on a per page basis and can vary from page to

page; caching policy bits are attached to each page table and TLB entry. The CAMMU is capable of "watching" the system bus and acting to maintain cache consistency when there are multiple CAMMUs on the bus and/or when I/O operations reference data resident in the local cache. Specifically, shared data is marked "shared" and is cached write-through. Bus operations labeled as "I/O" or "shared write-through" are recognized by the CAMMU. I/O reads to lines that are dirty in the cache are preempted and the cache supplies the data. Single word I/O writes and shared write-throughs on the bus update the local copy, if any, and quad-word writes invalidate the local copy.

The low order eight pages of the supervisor address are permanently mapped by the CAMMU to provide access to Boot ROM (residing on the system bus), I/O, which is addressed via reads and writes to memory addresses, and low main memory. Trap and interrupt vectors reside in low memory. The CAMMUs are controlled by reads and writes to the I/O region of memory.

Bit Ordering
The C100 model of the CLIPPER was designed to use a consistent, *"little endian"* [23], numbering system for bits, bytes, and words, in which the most significant bit is in the highest numbered bit of the highest numbered byte, and internally, CLIPPER remains little endian. Figure 2 shows the instruction formats, in which the bit, byte, and word numbering may be observed. The "first parcel" is the first two bytes of the instruction stream; the remaining bytes of the instruction or the bytes of the following instruction(s) will appear in the second, third, and fourth parcels. This numbering system is also used in the Dec VAX, Intel 80386, and National 32000 [21]. This contrasts with the System/370 [22] in which the most significant bit is the lowest numbered bit of the lowest numbered byte; bits, bytes and words are numbered in increasing order from left to right, with the MSB at the left. The Motorola 68000 also uses a "big endian" scheme, but numbers bits in the opposite order from bytes and words [28].

In the C300 version, CLIPPER can function in either a little-endian or big-endian mode, although internally the little-endian–ness is retained. The appropriate byte order is selected at power-up time by tying a pin to either +5v or ground. When operating in big-endian mode, CLIPPER internally reverses the order of half words in the instruction buffer, reverses the order in which double word operands are loaded/stored, and changes the byte and half-word addressing to reference the correct byte or half word within a word. As a result, data can be exchanged with a big-endian machine without reversing the bytes or changing the byte numbering. It also facilitates upgrading low performance (big-endian) machines with higher performance, CLIPPER-based products. (In contrast, when data is exchanged between a Vax and an IBM 370, bytes must be explicitly swapped.)

INSTRUCTION FORMATS - NO ADDRESS

REGISTER

15		8	7		4	3		0
OPCODE			R1			R2		

CONTROL

15		8	7			0
OPCODE			BYTE			

QUICK

15		8	7		4	3		0
OPCODE			QUICK			R2		

MACRO

15		9	8	7	6		0
OPCODE		P	0	0 0		CODE	
0 0 0 0 0 0 0 0			R1			R2	

31   24 23   20 19   16

16-BIT IMMEDIATE

15		8	7		4	3		0
OPCODE			1 0 1 1			R2		
S	IMMEDIATE							

31 30   16

32-BIT IMMEDIATE

15		8	7		4	3		0
OPCODE			0 0 1 1			R2		
IMMEDIATE LOW								
S	IMMEDIATE HIGH							

47 46   32

INSTRUCTION FORMAT - WITH ADDRESS

RELATIVE

15		8	7		4	3		0
OPCODE		0	R1			R2		

PC-RELATIVE PLUS 16-BIT DISPLACEMENT

15		8	7		4	3		0
OPCODE		1	1 0 0 1			R2		
S	DISPLACEMENT							

31 32   16

RELATIVE PLUS 12-BIT DISPLACEMENT

15		8	7		4	3		0
OPCODE		1	1 0 1 0			R1		
S	DISPLACEMENT					R2		

31 30   20 19   16

PC-RELATIVE PLUS 32-BIT DISPLACEMENT

15		8	7		4	3		0
OPCODE		1	0 0 0 1			R2		
DISPLACEMENT LOW								
S	DISPLACEMENT HIGH							

47 46   32

RELATIVE PLUS 32-BIT DISPLACEMENT

15		8	7		4	3		0
OPCODE		0	1 1 0			R1		
0 0 0 0 0 0 0 0 0 0 0 0						R2		
DISPLACEMENT LOW								
S	DISPLACEMENT HIGH							

63 62   48

RELATIVE INDEXED

15		8	7		4	3		0
OPCODE		1	1 1 1 0			R1		
0 0 0 0 0 0 0 0			RX			R2		

31   24 23   20 19   16

16-BIT ABSOLUTE

15		8	7		4	3		0
OPCODE		1	1 0 1 1			R2		
S	ADDRESS							

31 30   16

PC INDEXED

15		8	7		4	3		0
OPCODE		1	1 1 0 1		0 0 0 0		
0 0 0 0 0 0 0 0			RX			R2		

31   24 23   20 19   16

32-BIT ABSOLUTE

15		8	7		4	3		0
OPCODE		1	0 0 1 1			R2		
ADDRESS LOW								
S	ADDRESS HIGH							

47 46   32

FIGURE 2. CLIPPER's Instruction Formats

Data Types

The selection of data types represents a compromise between apparent functionality, which is enhanced by a large number of data types, and implementability, which is easiest when the number of types is small. The data types supported by the CLIPPER architecture include signed and unsigned bytes, half words (2 bytes), words (4 bytes) and long words (8 bytes). There are also single and double precision (4 and 8 bytes, respectively) floating point numbers. This set of data types is sufficient to implement programming languages such as C, Fortran, and Pascal with direct hardware support provided for most language operations. (Initially, as suggested in [18], little support for bytes or half words was intended, but further examination of programming needs showed that more direct hardware support was required.)

At this time CLIPPER does not provide decimal numbers, strings, or precision beyond that of long words or double precision floating point as hardware specified data types. Strings can be easily implemented via software; CLIPPER also provides three string manipulation instructions (move, compare, fill) as Macro ROM sequences. Extended precision can be obtained via software when needed.

CLIPPER also imposes *alignment restrictions* on data items, as do other RISC and RISC-like processors. All data items must be stored on a boundary which is a multiple of its size [29]. This restriction generally causes little difficulty, and simplifies the processor implementation considerably. For CLIPPER, there is no implementation problem with *line crossers* (fetch or store requests spanning a pair of cache lines) or *page crossers* (fetch or store requests spanning a page boundary), since line and page crossers are impossible for data loads and stores. Instructions can span page boundaries, but no problem occurs since the instruction stream is fetched sequentially, four (aligned) bytes at a time.

REGISTERS AND MODES OF OPERATION
User and Supervisor General Purpose Registers

There are two sets of 16 general purpose registers (GPRs), one referenced by user mode programs and one by supervisor mode programs. The mode of the program is determined by a bit in the system status word (SSW). Two privileged instructions allow data transfers between user and supervisor registers.

Using separate user and supervisor register sets speeds up interrupt and trap handling, and makes CLIPPER especially suitable for real time applications, since registers don't need to be stored or restored when interrupts occur. The selection of 16 registers was determined by several factors, including the number of bits conveniently available for register addressing and the fact that 16 registers represent a good tradeoff; 16 registers are enough for local working storage without inducing unreasonable overhead for saving and restoring them at procedure call time. The C compiler provided by Intergraph [29] saves and restores only those

registers that have been modified, and passes the first two arguments in registers. For comparison, we note that both the Vax and the IBM 370 have 16 GPRs. Lunde's results [25] suggest that 8 to 10 registers are almost always sufficient. Analyses in [14] show that with intra-procedure register allocation, no improvement in load/store traffic is obtained with more than 16 registers; even with interprocedural register allocation, minimal improvement is obtained with more than 16 registers. Eight registers, however, are too few.

The idea of register windows was first proposed by Baskett and was implemented in the Berkeley RISC project [32]; the motivation was that loads and stores due to procedure calls and returns could be avoided by simply moving to a new set of registers, using shared registers to pass parameters and results. Analyses in [14] show that with fewer than 100 registers, interprocedural register allocation results in less memory traffic than register windows; even with a total of 256 registers, register windows only outperform interprocedural register allocation by a small amount. Large register sets, such as those used in register windows, however, have a number of disadvantages [18, 33]: they require substantial chip area, only a small fraction of the registers are in use at any one time, process switching time is much larger since all registers need to be stored and restored, and larger register files are slower due to distance and circuit drive requirements. Register windows also require a mechanism to address across windows, so that nonlocal variables can be referenced [41]. For some projects (RISC II, SOAR), register access time has been a primary determinant of cycle time [14]. The decision, therefore, to use 16 user and 16 supervisor GPRs seems to be fully justified.

Floating Point Registers

CLIPPER provides a set of eight double precision floating point (FP) registers accessible in both user and supervisor states; floating point instructions refer to these. This is similar to the IBM 370 design, in which there are four FP registers. Eight registers provide sufficient storage for temporary operands, whereas four are insufficient in the absence of memory to register operations other than load and store. Four registers are clearly insufficient to permit interprocedural register allocation. (For non-numerically intensive programs, Lunde found that three floating point registers were usually sufficient. We expect a workload that is more numerically intensive than that analyzed by Lunde.)

Processor Status Registers

Three additional program addressable registers are provided, the *program counter* (*PC*), the *program status word* (*PSW*), and the *system status word* (*SSW*). The **program counter** contains the address of the instruction about to be *issued*, i.e., the instruction in the pipeline that will be released and allowed to modify the processor state (write into a register or store a result). The internal registers containing addresses of instructions following the currently issued instruction in the pipe are not user addressable.

The **program status word (PSW)** is primarily used to hold status information (condition codes, trap codes) and to set those aspects of the processor state that the user process is permitted to modify, such as floating point trap enables. Four bits of *condition code* are provided (negative, zero, overflow, carry), and five bits of floating point exception status, as required by IEEE 754 standard, are also available. Six bits are used to enable/disable floating point traps, and two more to specify the floating point rounding mode. A trace trap bit is available. Four bits are used to record program traps (e.g., trace trap, illegal operation), and four more to record system trap types (memory error, page fault, etc.). The PSW may be read or written by the user process.

The last status register is the **system status word (SSW)**. The SSW is used, among other things, to record the interrupt number and level, to enable interrupts, to set the mode (user/supervisor) and to set the protection key. The SSW may only be written in supervisor state. Its use is further described in [3].

INSTRUCTION FORMATS AND ADDRESSING MODES
Addressing Modes

The CLIPPER microprocessor has a *load/store architecture*; i.e., most of the references to memory are via load and store instructions in contrast to both the IBM 370 and DEC Vax which make extensive use of their register/memory operations (370 RX type instructions) and memory-to-memory (370 SS type) instructions. Eliminating most RX and SS instructions substantially simplifies the processor implementation by eliminating

control logic and especially by simplifying recovery from traps and interrupts such as page faults and memory errors. As noted in [41], all modern, simplified architectures are load/store. The lack of RX and most SS-type instructions increases CLIPPER code size above that for such densely encoded CISC (complex instruction set computer) processors such as the Vax, the National 32000 and the Intel 80386, but provides considerably denser code than RISC processors such as the SUN Sparc and the IBM ROMP. (CLIPPER does have some SS operations implemented in the MIROM.) For RISC-I [32], a $2/3$ increase in number of instructions over the Vax was observed, using a very primitive compiler for RISC. Table I shows static code sizes (the size of the text segment of the object file) for a number of standard benchmarks compiled on a number of machines; data in [14] shows that static and dynamic code sizes are very closely correlated. There are two advantages to small code sizes: there is less memory traffic, which is a limiting factor in most multiprocessor designs, and cache miss ratios are lower, since working sets are smaller; see [14] for analyses and comparative miss ratios.

For *load* and *store* instructions, CLIPPER provide nine addressing modes, which appear in Figure 2. These nine address modes represent those judged to be important for convenient programming plus those that "come for *free*;" i.e., those that can be trivially generated with the logic and data paths already available. For a 32-bit architecture, a register + 32-bit displacement mode (relative with 32-bit displacement) is very useful. The long 32-bit displacement eliminates the aggravating addressability problem posed by the 12-bit displacement of the IBM 370. The register + 12-bit displacement mode saves 4 bytes, if only a short displacement is

TABLE I. Code Size of Several Standard Benchmarks (in bytes)[a]

Machine	Code Sizes							
	doduc.f	livermore loops.f	linpack.f	whet.c	smith.f	dhry.c	NAS Kernels.f	Average Ratio
Vax (Unix 4.3 BSD)	86832	24908	9016	1900	6448	1276	21404	
	(1.0)	(1.0)	(1.0)	(1.0)	(1.0)	(1.0)	(1.0)	1.0
IBM PC/RT (ACIS 1.0)	*	41696	16792	*	10872	1632	*	
	—	(1.67)	(1.86)	—	(1.69)	(1.28)	—	1.63
Sun 3/280 (Sun Unix 4.2/3.4)	134372	29572	9388	2600	7064	1616	23372	
	(1.55)	(1.19)	(1.04)	(1.37)	(1.10)	(1.27)	(1.09)	1.23
Sun 4 (Sun Unix 4-3.2)	141280	29944	13104	3152	12248	1792	30976	
	(1.63)	(1.20)	(1.45)	(1.66)	(1.90)	(1.40)	(1.45)	1.53
Sequent (32032)	95396	*	6960	2024	5876	1368	16516	
	(1.10)	—	(0.77)	(1.07)	(0.91)	(1.07)	(0.77)	0.81
Sequent (80386)	100112	*	7264	2224	8556	1384	16776	
	(1.15)	—	(0.81)	(1.17)	(1.33)	(1.08)	(0.78)	1.05
CLIPPER	114680	24584	8976	1904	7816	1376	24456	
	(1.32)	(0.99)	(1.00)	(1.00)	(1.21)	(1.08)	(1.14)	1.11

[a] Code size in bytes is shown for the text part of the object file for the compiled version of each of several standard benchmarks: Doduc, Livermore Loops [27], Linpack [11], Whetstone [8], NAS Kernels [1], and a synthetic benchmark used by one author (Smith). In parentheses below the size is the ratio of that size to the size of the code for the VAX, using the compiler distributed with 4.3BSD UNIX. The average ratio (arithmetic average of the ratios) is shown at the right. In each case, the smallest code size obtained is shown; code sizes vary with the level of optimization. An asterisk means that the program would not compile.

needed, and the relative (register with no displacement) mode requires two bytes less. Register + displacement addressing is often used for array and stack references, and local variables.

Absolute addressing is provided with 16-bit or 32-bit address constants. Absolute addressing is typically used for references (e.g., calls) to independently compiled code segments, and in the 16-bit form, for references to low memory and within small programs.

A PC-relative address mode would have been very useful in the IBM 370 [35], and such modes are provided by CLIPPER. The PC can be used with 16- or 32-bit displacement or with a register (GPR) displacement. Most of the time, the short displacement should be sufficient; in [35] 99 percent of the branches were expressible in 16 bits or less as an offset from the PC. PC relative addressing is used primarily for branches and the PC + GPR mode for computed gotos and case statements.

Finally, a two register address mode (relative indexed) is provided, which facilitates addressing when both the base and index addresses are in registers, as well as when an array is passed as a parameter.

Four important aspects of the way the address mode is specified are evident in Figure 2. First, the address mode and opcode are *always* defined in the first instruction parcel (first two bytes), so there is no (slow) sequential decoding of the instruction; subsequent bytes can be immediately routed (as to the adder) without further examination. This encoding provides many of the supposed advantages of fixed length instructions that are used in RISC and MIPS. Second, 4 bits are used to specify the addressing mode, and only 8 of the 16 possible combinations are currently assigned, leaving the remainder available for future extensions. Third, there is no indirect addressing mode, a mode which is very difficult to implement efficiently. Finally, some of the address modes result in unused bits in some fields, which could be used in the future to generate more than 32 bits of virtual address.

To estimate the frequency of use of the various addressing modes, we examined data from the literature. In [35], addressing calculations for System/370 RX type instructions used no register 1.1 percent of the time, one register 85.6 percent of the time, and two registers 13.3 percent of the time; the RX type instruction forms an effective address as the sum of a 12-bit displacement and the contents of up to two registers. Data in [12] indicates that for the Vax, 61 percent of the operand addresses were displacement + register, and 23 percent were just register. Displacements from a register were most often one byte long. For the PDP-11 [31], most of the operand addresses were specified in a register (with or without increment or decrement), and most of the remainder were displacement + register. Based on the data cited and further data in [16] and [44], we would expect the *relative* {(R)}, *relative with 12-bit displacement* {(R) + disp}, and *PC Relative with 16-bit Displacement* {(PC) + disp} to account for the bulk of the address

mode use. In fact, as shown in Table VII for one (unrepresentative) benchmark, those address modes are common, as are also the *PC Relative with 32-bit Displacement* {(PC) + disp)} *and Relative Indexed* {(RX) + (R)}. The former is appropriate to large programs, such as Spice, and the latter for numerical programs making many array references. We again note that many of the address modes provided "*come for free*"; e.g., the relative address mode is a displacement mode with no displacement. If each address mode had required significant additional logic, fewer modes would have been justified or included.

Instruction Formats
Figure 2 shows the available instruction formats. Those instructions using addresses have already been discussed; next we'll comment on instructions which do not contain memory addresses.

Register-to-register instructions are specified in two bytes. Register-immediate operations can be specified in 2, 4, or 6 bytes, depending on the size of the immediate constant. Immediate constants are often small; 69 percent of the immediate operands can be encoded in 4 or fewer bits and 96 percent in 8 or fewer bits [18]; the corresponding figures from [16] are 60 percent and 70 percent. The availability of the *quick* format (which provides a 4-bit unsigned constant) and the 16-bit immediate format aid code density.

The *control* opcode is used when the operation requires a small (8-bit) constant only, as for the *calls* (system call) instruction. The *macro* opcodes are used to invoke operations implemented via instruction sequences in the on-chip ROM, such as the string move (*movc*) instruction.

INSTRUCTION SET
The CLIPPER instruction set is fairly conventional and reflects the experience of its designers with respect to two factors: what is needed for convenient and efficient programmability, and what can be easily implemented in hardware. Table II shows the set of opcodes. Most of the entries are self-explanatory, and we will discuss only those that are interesting or worth explaining.

Floating Point
The CLIPPER microprocessor is unusual in that its floating point unit is on the processor chip; the floating point execution unit is also used to compute the integer multiplication, division and mod operations. Floating point arithmetic operations are performed as specified in the IEEE 754 standard. As noted earlier, there is a separate set of eight floating point registers, and all floating point operations are register to register. The floating registers may loaded or stored from/to main memory, or from/to the general purpose registers.

Branches and Condition Codes
The approach chosen for CLIPPER for controlling program execution is that of condition codes, which are set

TABLE II. Operations and Opcodes

Instruction Type	Variants and Op Codes
Load	address (loada), byte (loadb), byte unsigned (loadbu), double floating (loadd), floating status (loadfs), halfword (loadh), halfword unsigned (loadhu), immediate (loadi), quick (loadq), single floating (loads), word (loadw)
Store	byte (storb), double floating (stord), halfword (storh), single floating (stors), word (storw)
Move	double floating (movd), double floating to longword (movdl), longword to double floating (movld), word (movw), processor register to word (movpw), single floating (movs), supervisor to user (movsu), user to supervisor (movus), single floating to word (movsw), word to processor register (movwp), word to single floating (movws)
Add	double floating (addd), immediate (addi), quick (addq), single floating (adds), word (addw), word with carry (addwc)
Subtract	double floating (subd), immediate (subi), quick (subq), single floating (subs), word (subw), word with carry (subwc)
Multiply	double floating (muld), single floating (muls), word (mulw), word unsigned (mulwu), word unsigned extended (mulwux), word extended (mulwx)
Divide	double floating (divd), single floating (divs), word (divw), word unsigned (divwu)
Negate	double floating (negd), single floating (negs), word (negw)
Modulus	word (modw), word unsigned (modwu)
Scale-by	double floating (scalbd), single floating (scalbs)
Convert	double floating to single (cnvds), double floating to word (cnvdw), rounding double to word (cnvrdw), rounding single to word (cnvrsw), single floating to double (cnvsd), single floating to word (cnvsw), truncating double to word (cnvtdw), truncating single to word (cnvtsw), word to double floating (cnvwd), word to single floating (cnvws)
And	immediate (andi), word (andw)
Or	immediate (ori), word (orw)
Exclusive-or	immediate (xori), word (xorw)
Not	word (notw), quick (notq)
Shift arithmetic	immediate (shai), longword (shal), word (shaw), longword immediate (shali)
Shift logical	immediate (shli), longword (shll), word (shlw), longword immediate (shlli)
Rotate logical	immediate (roti), longword (rotl), word (rotw), longword immediate (rotli)
Compare	double floating (cmpd), immediate (cmpi), quick (compq), single floating (cmps), word (cmpw)
Test and set	(tsts)
Compare characters	(cmpc)
Initialize characters	(initc)
Move characters	(movc)
Pop word	(popw)
Push word	(pushw)
Save registers rn . . . r14	(savew$n$)
Save floating registers fn . . . f7	(saved$n$)
Save user registers	(saveur)
Restore registers rn . . . r14	(restw$n$)
Restore floating registers fn . . . f7	(restd$n$)
Restore user registers	(restur)
Branch conditional	(b*): less than (bclt), less than or equal (bcle), equal (bceq), greater than (bcgt), greater or equal (bcge), not equal (bcne), less than unsigned (bcltu), less or equal unsigned (bcgtu), greater or equal unsigned (bcgeu), not carry (bnc), carry (bc), overflow (bv), not overflow (bnv), negative (bn), not negative (bnn), floating unordered (bfn)
Branch floating exception	(bf*): floating any exception (bfany), floating bad result (bfbad)
Call	(call)
Call supervisor	(calls)
Return from subroutine	(ret)
Return from interrupt	(reti)
Trap on floating unordered	(trapfn)
Wait for interrupt	(wait)
No operation	(noop)

by one instruction and read and used by a subsequent instruction; this is similar to what is done on the IBM 370. Using condition codes for branching yields better performance and less complexity than an instruction that both tests and branches.

Four standard condition codes—N (negative), Z (zero), V (overflow) and C (carry)—are set in the PSW after certain operations. There are five floating point exception signalling codes: FX (floating inexact), FU (floating underflow), FD (floating divide by zero), FV (floating overflow), and FI (floating invalid op). Compare instructions normally set the N and Z flags; since the compare is executed by performing a subtraction, V and C may also be set.

There are two standard branch instructions. *Branch on condition* tests the NZVC PSW bits; the list of possibilities is shown in Table II. The *branch on floating exception* tests either for any exception or for a bad result (floating invalid, divide by zero, overflow). Branch instructions use the standard addressing modes, as defined in Figure 2, where the R2 field holds the condition code field that specifies the type of branch.

Implemented directly in the hardwired instruction set are the *call* and *return* (*ret*) instructions. The call instruction decrements the stack pointer (defined by the register in the R2 field), pushes the address of the next instruction onto the stack, and then loads the PC with the target address. *Return* reverses the process.

Macro Instructions

The CLIPPER processor chip includes a small ROM (known as the *Macro Instruction ROM*), which holds various useful code sequences. The MIROM contents are regular instructions, *not microcode*. Microcode requires a two-level decode [19] (instructions need to be decoded into microinstructions, and then decoded and executed), and microcoded machines tend to be slower than hardwired ones. Approximately half of the MIROM is devoted to diagnostic code to be used for chip testing and sorting during manufacturing. The remainder implements complex operations that are often found as single (usually microcoded) instructions on CISC machines. Implementing these functions as MIROM sequences increases code density and readability, instruction fetch penalties (misses, sequential fetch delays) and memory traffic decrease, and less instruction cache space is used. The MIROM concept has other advantages: (1) new instructions can be easily added; and (2) custom versions of the processor can be easily designed and implemented.

A Macro instruction actually represents a branch into the ROM; the instruction fetch unit starts fetching instructions from the ROM at the address specified by the macro opcode. Next, we'll briefly discuss the instructions implemented in the MIROM; the operation of the MIROM is described in more detail later.

Instructions to save and restore general registers (save registers (*save*wn), restore registers (*restw*n), save floating registers (*saved*n), and *save user registers* (*saveur*)) are implemented in the MIROM as a sequence of consecutive store (or load) operations, starting from a given register number and continuing through register 14. The floating point register saves and restores are implemented similarly.

Three string (storage to storage) instructions are currently implemented in the MIROM: *movc* (copy a string of characters from/to nonoverlapping fields), *initc* (initialize a string with the contents of a register; primarily used for clearing buffers), and *cmpc* (compare two character strings). These instructions may be interrupted and restarted.

All of the conversion operations, and negate floating, scale by, and load floating status (see Table II) are implemented in the ROM.

The *return from interrupt* (*reti*) instruction restores the processor state after trap or interrupt processing. The *wait for interrupt* (*wait*) instruction causes the processor to halt pending the arrival of an enabled interrupt. The interrupt routine then determines whether to continue execution.

Test and Set

The cost and performance advantages of multiple microprocessor computer systems sharing a common memory are currently quite compelling [40]. The *Test and Set* (*tsts*) instruction is the instruction chosen for CLIPPER to implement the locks used in multiprocessor and multiprocess synchronization. As a single, indivisible operation, it loads the contents of a main memory location into a specified GPR, and sets bit 31 of the given main memory word to 1. Indivisibility is achieved by making the lock word noncacheable, and holding the main memory bus for the entire operation (which is a read/modify/write). A processor may either loop, continually testing the lock until it is released, use the *wait* instruction to sleep, or task switch. Test and set is also used by the IBM 370 and the M68000; the Vax provides seven instructions for locking and synchronization, some of which are equivalent to test and set. Test and set locks may be either cacheable or noncacheable. If they are cacheable, the local copy is updated and any remote copies are invalidated; in any case, the *tsts* operation always references main memory.

Opcode Assignment

As shown earlier in Figure 2, the high order byte of the first parcel of each instruction *always* contains the instruction opcode. As noted earlier, this greatly facilitates rapid execution, by always permitting immediate instruction decode. The assignment of bits to opcodes is shown in Figure 3. Of the possible 256 operation codes available from 8 bits, 85 instructions (including sets of instructions) are defined, and 104 of the bit combinations are used. (Some opcodes used to implement instructions that may be executed only from the MIROM are not shown in Figure 3.) That leaves over 140 possible opcodes for future expansion. In general, we have

Instruction Opcode/Mnemonic Summary

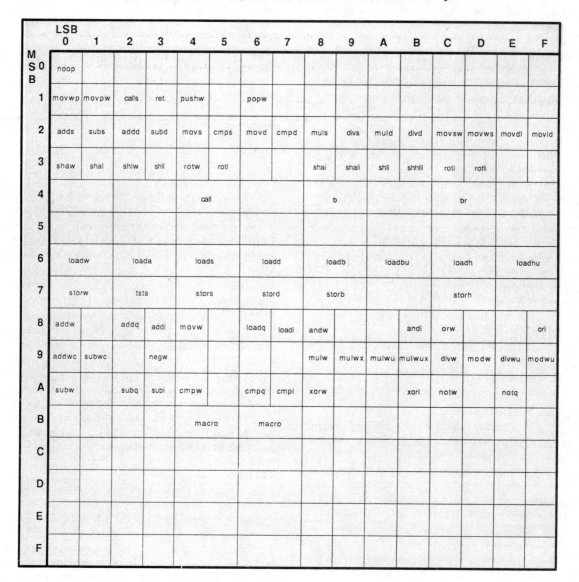

MSB \ LSB	0	1	2	3	4	5	6	7	8	9	A	B	C	D	E	F
0	noop															
1	movwp	movpw	calls	ret	pushw		popw									
2	adds	subs	addd	subd	movs	cmps	movd	cmpd	muls	divs	muld	divd	movsw	movws	movdl	movld
3	shaw	shal	shlw	shll	rotw	rotl			shai	shali	shli	shhlli	roti	rotli		
4					call					b			br			
5																
6	loadw		loada		loads		loadd		loadb		loadbu		loadh		loadhu	
7	storw		tsts		stors		stord		storb				storh			
8	addw		addq	addi	movw		loadq	loadi	andw			andi	orw			ori
9	addwc	subwc		negw					mulw	mulwx	mulwu	mulwux	divw	modw	divwu	modwu
A	subw		subq	subi	cmpw		cmpq	cmpi	xorw			xori	notw		notq	
B					macro		macro									
C																
D																
E																
F																

Macro Instruction Code Field (Opcode B4)

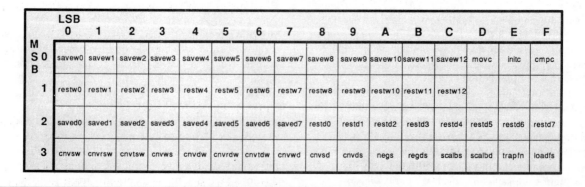

MSB \ LSB	0	1	2	3	4	5	6	7	8	9	A	B	C	D	E	F
0	savew0	savew1	savew2	savew3	savew4	savew5	savew6	savew7	savew8	savew9	savew10	savew11	savew12	movc	initc	cmpc
1	restw0	restw1	restw2	restw3	restw4	restw5	restw6	restw7	restw8	restw9	restw10	restw11	restw12			
2	saved0	saved1	saved2	saved3	saved4	saved5	saved6	saved7	restd0	restd1	restd2	restd3	restd4	restd5	restd6	restd7
3	cnvsw	cnvrsw	cnvtsw	cnvws	cnvdw	cnvrdw	cnvtdw	cnvwd	cnvsd	cnvds	negs	regds	scalbs	scalbd	trapfn	loadfs

FIGURE 3. Assignment of Bits to Opcodes

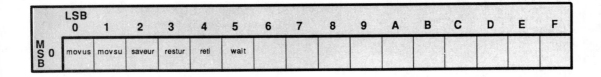

Privileged Macro Instruction Code Field (Opcode B6)

	LSB 0	1	2	3	4	5	6	7	8	9	A	B	C	D	E	F
MSB 0	movus	movsu	saveur	restur	reti	wait										

FIGURE 3. (*Continued*)

made a conscious effort to allow the CLIPPER architecture to evolve with user needs and technology trends; reserving a significant number of opcodes is one part of that effort.

INTERRUPTS, TRAPS AND SUPERVISOR CALLS

The CLIPPER microprocessor provides for 402 exception conditions: 18 hardware traps, 128 programmable supervisor calls and 256 vectored interrupts. The number of hardware traps can be expanded to 128.

A *trap* is an exception that relates to a condition of a single instruction, e.g., page fault, memory error, overflow, etc. *Interrupts* are events signalled by devices external to the CLIPPER module.

Intrap and Return Sequences

The recognition by the hardware of a trap or interrupt causes entry to a macro instruction sequence, *INTRAP*, which in noninterruptible mode performs a context switch to supervisor mode, stores the PC, PSW, and SSW on the supervisor stack, and transfers control to the trap or interrupt handler through the *vector table*. The vector table is a table in low memory containing two-word entries; each entry contains the address of the trap or interrupt handler and the new SSW. The *reti* (return from interrupt) sequence is a noninterruptible sequence which restores the system to the correct user or supervisor environment. Interrupts and traps are prioritized, with logic within the processor giving service to the highest priority event. Traps are permitted during interrupt and trap handling but result in an unrecoverable fault; page fault traps must be avoided during fault handling.

Traps

When a trap occurs, all instructions prior to the trapping instruction are completed (including those in the floating point unit), and all instructions that follow the trapping instruction are flushed from the pipeline.

Traps can be classified into several groups: data memory, floating point arithmetic, integer arithmetic, instruction memory, illegal operation, diagnostics, and supervisor calls.

Data memory and *instruction memory traps* include *correctable and uncorrectable memory errors*, *page faults*, and *protection faults*. In each case, the CAMMU recognizes the exception and maintains copies of the protection bits taken from the page table entries in the TLB.

The five *floating point arithmetic traps* are *invalid operation*, *inexact result*, *overflow*, *underflow*, and *divide by zero*. There are trap enable flags for each of these in the PSW, as well as exception flags in the PSW which are set when the corresponding events occur. An overall floating point trap enable flag (also in the PSW) can be used to disable all floating point traps.

The *trace trap* causes a trap at the end of the current instruction. A MIROM sequence is considered to be a single instruction for tracing purposes. Tracing is disabled on entry to the INTRAP sequence and trace trap handler.

Supervisor calls are implemented as traps triggered by the *calls* instruction. There are potentially 128 supervisor call codes; the CLIX® system (the Intergraph port of Unix) [30] uses approximately 60 of them.

Interrupts

Interrupts are signalled externally to the processor and appear as signals on the interrupt pins of the system bus. An interrupt is taken only when no traps are pending except the trace trap, interrupts are enabled, all instructions currently in the pipeline have completed, and string instructions have either completed or have saved sufficient state to be able to restart. (Long string instructions periodically test for pending interrupts, and if there are any, save their state and permit the interrupt to be processed.) With the exception of the string instructions, interrupts are not accepted during MIROM sequences.

There are 16 prioritized interrupt levels, with 16 interrupts of equal priority within each level. Interrupt processing can be interrupted by an event of higher priority.

DESIGN ARCHITECTURE

As explained earlier, the term *design architecture* refers to the architectural implementation at a fairly high level. Figure 4 shows the major components of the CLIPPER processor and the major interconnections in a simplified fashion. Somewhat more detail is shown in

---

® CLIX is a trademark of Intergraph Corporation.

Figure 5. As can be seen from those figures, the processor is divided into six major sections: the *instruction bus interface* (including an instruction prefetch buffer), the *macro instruction unit*, the *instruction control unit*, the *floating point unit*, the *integer execution unit*, and the *data bus interface*. Table III shows the fraction of the chip area occupied by various processor sections; the remainder of the area is occupied by other minor components or empty space.

Instruction Bus Interface

The instruction bus (described in more detail in [3]) is a bi-directional 45-line bus connecting the CPU chip to the Instruction CAMMU. The interface contains receivers (RCV) and drivers (DRV), and a 64-bit (8-byte) instruction buffer on the processor chip. Instructions are prefetched into this buffer, and are then fed into the instruction control unit as needed. A branch never hits in this buffer because there is no mechanism to detect that a branch target address is within the buffer; on a successful branch, the instruction buffer is cleared. The Instruction CAMMU contains its own instruction counter, and will feed the next 4 bytes of the instruction stream into the instruction buffer every time the next

instruction line of the instruction bus is clocked. While within a cache line, the ICAMMU can deliver 4 bytes every 2 CPU cycles (60 ns), and the CPU can at its maximum rate execute 2 bytes (one parcel, or one 2-byte instruction) every CPU cycle (30 ns).

A multiplexor (MUX) that can accept instructions from either the instruction buffer or the Macro Instruction ROM and feed them to the instruction control unit is also associated with the instruction bus interface.

Macro Instruction Unit

The Macro Instruction ROM (MIROM) is an on-chip ROM (1 K entries × 47 bits) that implements complicated instructions as sequences of simpler *hardwired* instructions; the opcode for the MIROM implemented instruction is effectively a branch target address into the ROM; the MIROM does *not* contain microcode. Each entry in the MIROM contains two instruction parcels plus the next instruction address and a stop bit.

The set of legal opcodes for ROM instructions is a superset of the standard instruction set, including, for example, the conditional branch within the MIROM itself; those ROM-only instructions are not shown in Table II or Figure 3.

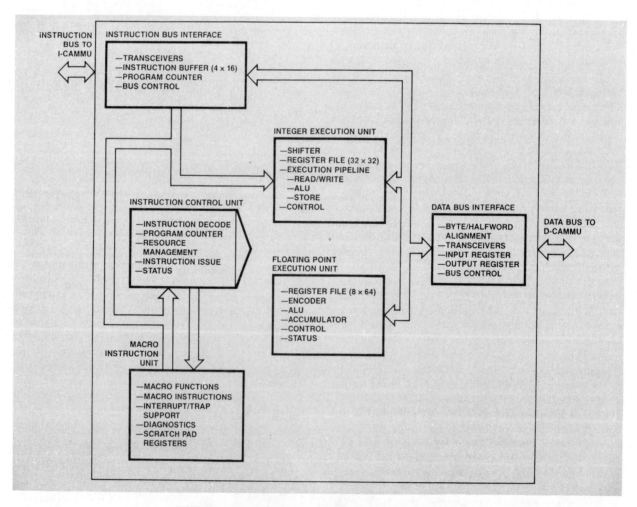

FIGURE 4. Simplified Diagram of CLIPPER's Major Components

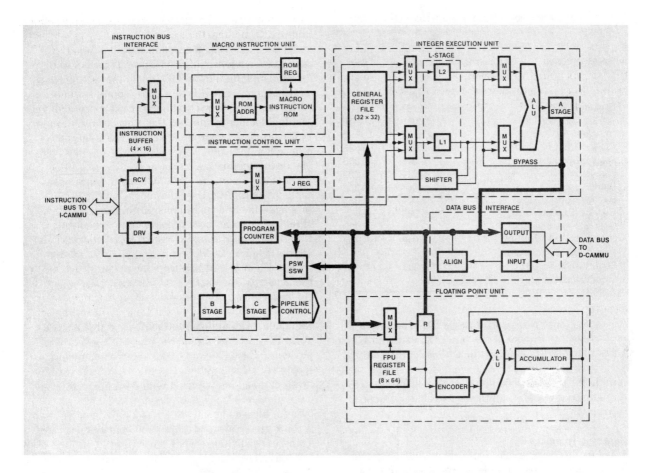

FIGURE 5. Detailed Diagram of CLIPPER's Major Components

In addition to the regular registers, there are 16 scratch registers (12 regular and 4 floating point) accessible only from instructions in the MIROM. The instructions in the MIROM also have a mechanism to reference the registers specified by the R1 and R2 fields of the Macro instruction (see Figure 2).

Integer Execution Unit
The integer execution unit contains the general register file (16 user GPRs, 16 supervisor GPRs, and 12 scratch registers), the shifter, and the ALU. The register file has three ports, permitting two reads and one write during the same machine cycle.

The shifter implements the shift and rotate instructions and is designed as a serial double bit shifter. Single and double bit shifts occur in one cycle; larger shifts require multiple cycles. Data in [20] shows that for a particular System/370 workload, only 1.9 percent of all shifts were for more than 3 bits.

The ALU (arithmetic/logic unit) implements integer addition and subtraction, bitwise logical operations, and register-to-register transfers. The address mode additions are also performed by the ALU; each requires only one pass through the ALU, since no address computation requires more than one add.

Floating Point Unit
CLIPPER is unusual among current microprocessors in having its floating point unit (FPU) on chip. Multiplication uses a Booth algorithm [2] which produces products iteratively, two bits per clock cycle for single precision (2 bits/3 cycles for double precision) in the C100 and 8 bits per cycle in the C300. Typically, one clock time is needed for round and one (3 in the C300) for normalize. Division uses a nonrestoring shift and subtract algorithm, producing 1 bit per three clocks in the C100 and 8 bits per seven clocks in the C300. Associated with the FPU is the floating point register file, which contains eight regular and four scratch-pad 64-bit floating point registers; the latter are accessible only from code running in the Macro Instruction ROM. The floating point unit is also used to perform integer multiply and divide.

The floating point unit operates in parallel with respect to the rest of CLIPPER. Although only one floating point operation can be executed at a time, operations that neither use the FPU nor rely on its output can be issued steadily while the FPU completes the current operation. As a result, much of the execution time for floating point operations will overlap that of other instructions.

TABLE III. Area Allocations for Functions on CLIPPER Chip

Processor Section	Fraction of Area	
	C100	C300
Floating Point Unit	0.25	0.507
(Floating Point Control)	(0.067)	(0.082)
Execution Unit	0.187	0.096
(Register File)	(0.05)	(0.019)
(ALU)	(0.053)	(0.016)
ROM	0.056	0.025
Program Counter	0.013	0.006
Instruction Buffer	0.014	0.023
Branch Logic	0.041	0.032
B-stage Control Logic	0.074	0.037
C-stage (Execution) Logic	0.083	0.062
Data Memory Interface	0.026	0.022
Status Logic (PSW, SSW, Trap and Cond Codes)	0.048	0.032
Other (interconnect, misc and unused)	0.208	0.158

Floating point exceptions may be out of sequence with respect to the rest of the instruction stream. When a floating point trap occurs, the address of the floating point instruction may be recovered from a special register; the PC value pushed on the system stack can potentially be quite far from the address of the trapping instruction.

Data Bus Interface
The data bus interface consists principally of receiver and driver circuits for the data bus, and a shifter for aligning byte and half word operands. It is connected to all of the major functional units of the CPU via the S-bus so it can receive and deliver operands in the most expeditious manner.

Instruction Control Unit and CPU Pipeline
The heart of the CLIPPER processor is the instruction control unit (ICU), which is responsible for decoding instructions and controlling instruction execution. The ICU is shown in Figure 5, and the instruction execution pipeline is shown in Figure 6.

The ICU has several components. The program counter contains the address of the instruction about to be issued; to *issue* an instruction means to allow it to run to completion (i.e., modify registers or memory), provided no traps occur. Figure 6 shows two boxes, called the "B stage" and "C stage." Each consists of a set of decoding logic and registers for holding partially decoded instructions and the corresponding instruction address. The B stage is responsible for instruction decoding and resource management; resource management keeps track of which functional units are busy and allows instructions to advance to the issue stage only if the necessary units are available. The C stage holds the fully decoded instruction, and controls the operation of the integer execution unit and the floating point unit. The J register (Figure 5) is used to hold immediate values (including address offsets and address

constants). The PSW and SSW registers are also located in the ICU.

There can be one instruction in each of the B and C stages. Shown preceding the B stage (Figure 6) is the instruction buffer (IB), which holds 4 parcels (8 bytes) of instructions, or up to four instructions.

The last stage of the pipeline consists of parallel integer and floating point execution units. These two execution units can operate in parallel, with one active instruction in the FPU and one instruction in each of the three stages of the integer execution unit (IEU). Those three stages are operand fetch (L stage), arithmetic (A stage: ALU or shifter) and operand write (O stage—to either registers or elsewhere). It takes three cycles for an instruction to pass through the IEU—one to read from the registers into the ALU, one to pass through the ALU or shifter, and one to write the results. There is a bypass from the output of the ALU to the input, so that results can be immediately reused in the next instruction.

LAYOUT, AREA, AND PHYSICAL PARAMETERS
Table III shows the fraction of the chip used for various purposes. The C100 (and C300) are implemented respectively using 2-micron (1.5-micron) CMOS, with two levels of metal interconnect with a 6.5 micron (5.2 micron) pitch, one polysilicon level with 2.0 micron (1.5 micron) gates and a 4.0 micron (3.2 micron) pitch, a 250 Å thick gate oxide, and 2.0 micron contacts and vias. Transistor switching speeds range from 0.5 ns (0.35 ns) to 3.0 ns, depending on gate size and load. The chip dissipates 0.5 (1.5) watts. The processor cycle time is 30 ns (20 ns), which is also the minimum time to execute an instruction. The power supply is required to provide 0 and +5 volts. The processor chip has 132 (144) pins. The chip size is 10.55 × 10.24 (13.45 × 14.12) millimeters; the package is 0.9 in.^{2} (1.025) and is surface mounted.

PERFORMANCE
CLIPPER was conceived of and designed as a high performance processor, and design decisions and tradeoffs have been made whenever possible to achieve higher performance. That high performance has indeed been achieved is evident from the instruction execution times shown in Table IV. The minimum instruction execution time is one CPU cycle time, or 30 ns in the C100 and 20 ns in the C300. The peak program execution rate is thus 50 MIPS on the C300.

Benchmark results have been obtained both from real machines running current software and from an instruction set timing simulator. The simulator shows an average of 5 to 6 clock cycles per instruction including memory delays for typical integer programs on the C100. That works out to about 5 to 7 MIPS on the C100 and 1.8 to 2.0 times that for the C300.

Table V shows the results of the Dhrystone [43], Whetstone [8], Linpack [11], Livermore Loops [27], Stanford, Smith and Doduc benchmarks on the C100 (33 MHz) and C300 (50 MHz) CLIPPER, the Vax 8600,

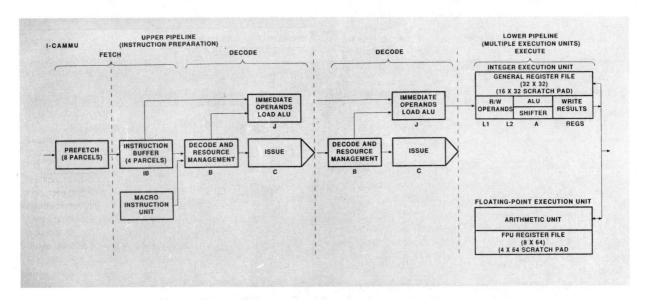

FIGURE 6. CLIPPER's Instruction Execution Pipeline

8800, and 11/785, and the SUN 3/50 (with 68881), 3/280 (with 68881), 386i/250 (with 80387) and 4/280. Whetstone and Dhrystone are in C; the others are in Fortran. All runs were with *unoptimized code*; published data usually shows optimized results. All runs were made by one of the authors personally, using the same source code in all cases, and should be comparable. Results have been normalized to the Vax 8600, since we no longer have access to a Vax 11/780. The Vax 11/780 is typically considered to be a 1 MIPS (millions of instructions per second) machine, and the Vax 8600 is approximately four times as fast, or 4 MIPS. (Actually, the Vax has a CISC instruction set, and thus generally runs at about 0.5 MIPS [12]. The Vax 11/780 runs about as fast as an IBM System/370 machine running at 1 MIPS on a scientific workload.)

While there is considerable variation among the various benchmarks, the C100 CLIPPER is approximately 1.3 times as fast as a Vax 8600, or a little over 5 MIPS. The C300 CLIPPER is about 2.5 times as fast as a Vax 8600, or about 10 MIPS. Performance ratings of all machines shown would be higher with fully optimized code.

Hardware Monitor Measurements

A limited number of programs have been run on a C100 CLIPPER and measured with a hardware monitor, and also traced. Here we summarize the measurements taken from an execution of the SPICE circuit simulator on an MOS memory cell circuit. SPICE is a large double precision numerical program, and the results are not representative for other workloads.

The execution time was 8.64 seconds at 33MHz; 1.37 seconds of system time and 7.27 seconds of user time. The instruction cache miss ratio in user state was 14 percent and the data cache miss ratio 10 percent; for system state, the miss ratios were 2.3 percent and

3.9 percent. User state data references were 69 percent read and 31 percent write; in supervisor state, the figures were 54 percent and 46 percent. Instructions were 85 percent fixed point, 12 percent point, 10 percent branch and call, and 3 percent other. The percentages of the most common instructions in user state are shown in Table VI. 33 percent of the branches were unconditional, and 67 percent were conditional. The frequencies of the various address modes are shown in Table VII. Data types for compares were 47 percent quick, 32 percent double, 13 percent word, and 9 percent immediate. Floating point instructions were 28 percent add double, 31 percent subtract double, 30 percent multiply double and 9 percent divide double. 11.7 percent of the instructions were "quick" types.

Performance versus Cycle Time and Cycles/Instruction

For a given instruction set architecture, CPU performance is inversely proportional to the product of cycle_time and cycles/instruction. CLIPPER achieves its high level of performance via a careful tradeoff of these two factors, rather than forcing all instructions to execute in one cycle, as is suggested by many RISC proponents [18, 33, 36].

The disadvantage to the single cycle per instruction approach is that not all instructions are equally complex, and the cycle time must accommodate the longest single cycle instruction; conversely, partitioning an instruction into a larger number of sequential phases provides more possibilities for overlap. For these reasons, the CLIPPER designers chose to implement the instruction set in the manner of a traditional mainframe, whereby the longer and more complex instructions are permitted more cycles to complete. The CPU cycle time in the C100 (30 ns) was chosen as a design goal, on the basis that the technology available at the time of chip

TABLE IV. Execution Times for Common Instructions

Instruction	C100		C300	
	Time (Clocks)	Time (ns)	Time (Clocks)	Time (ns)
Add Word	1	30	1	20
Logical	1	30	1	20
Move Word	1	30	1	20
Load Word/Pop	4–6	120–180	3–5	60–100
Store Word/Push	8	180	5	100
Branch (not taken)	4	120	4	80
Branch (taken)	7–9	210	7–9	140–180
Multiply word	26	720	14	280
Floating Add Single	25	750	12	240
Floating Add Double	27	810	13	260
Floating Multiply Single	24	720	13	260
Floating Multiply Double	69	2070	17	340
Floating Divide Single	110	3300	50	1000
Floating Divide Double	183	5490	71	1420

Note: Floating point times vary; figures given are averages.

TABLE V. Benchmark Results

Unoptimized code in all cases. (Quality of optimizers varies; published results are usually from optimized code.) Each set of data (with one exception) consists of two rows. The first row of each pair contains the raw performance numbers. The second row of the pair shows the data normalized to the Vax 8600 (first column). In the second row, in all cases, bigger is better. The row "average ratio" represents the (arithmetic) average speed ratio of the machines to the Vax 8600.

Benchmark	Machine								
	VAX 8600	VAX 11/785	CLIPPER C100	SUN 3/50	SUN 3/280	VAX 8800	SUN 4/280	CLIPPER C300	SUN 386i
Dhrystone 1.1	5893	1889	8670	1732	3942	7936	10489	17005	7246
(dhrystones)	1.0	.32	1.47	.30	.67	1.35	1.78	2.89	1.23
Whetstone (double)	1648	600	2048	617	909	2352	2765	5259	1202
(kilowhetstones)	1.0	.36	1.24	.38	.55	1.43	1.68	3.19	.73
Whetstone (single)	1935	692	3429	696	972	2667	4000	7026	1587
(kilowhetstones)	1.0	.36	1.77	.36	.50	1.38	2.07	3.63	.82
Linpack	.536	.218	.792	.077	.105	.777	.585	1.40	.195
(mfLops)	1.0	.41	1.48	.14	.20	1.45	1.09	2.61	.36
Livermore Loops	.521	.198	.529	.070	.095	.617	.484	.990	.185
(mfLops)	1.0	.38	1.02	.13	.18	1.18	.93	1.90	.36
Stanford (ms)	863	2356	561	2435	1143	582	698	347	694
Composite—non-FP	1.0	.37	1.50	.35	.76	1.48	1.24	2.49	1.24
Stanford (ms)	1538	4274	1132	4630	2481	1119	1163	675	1685
Composite—FP	1.0	.36	1.34	.33	.62	1.37	1.32	2.28	.91
Smith (sec)	236	589	176	708	412	156	208	102	287
	1.0	.40	1.34	.33	.57	1.51	1.13	2.31	.82
Smith (ave)	1.0	.308	1.23	.470	.385	1.51	1.23	2.35	.698
Doduc (sec)	140	355	203	639	449	95	110	83.9	359
	1.0	.39	.84	.22	.31	1.47	1.27	1.67	.39
Average Ratio	1.0	.37	1.32	.30	.48	1.41	1.37	2.53	.76

Figures for Dhrystones [43], Whetstones [8], Linpack [11] and Livermore Loops [27] are given in number of units per second. "mfLops" is "millions of floating point operations per second." Figures for Stanford, Smith and Doduc are given in units of time. Linpack matrices with leading dimension of 201. Livermore loops mflops are harmonic mean, vector length 468. The "Smith (ave)" line gives a weighted average of subcomponents of the Smith benchmark, normalized to the same weighted average for the Vax 8600 (paper in preparation).

TABLE VI. Instruction Frequencies, Spice Program

Instruction	Percentage	Cumulative
load double floating	11.58	11.58
load address	9.87	21.45
load word	9.71	31.16
add word (fixed)	7.65	38.81
branch conditional	6.57	45.38
store double floating	5.42	50.80
subtract quick	5.26	56.06
shift arithmetic immediate	4.19	60.25
move word	3.84	64.09
multiply double	2.63	66.72
compare quick	2.53	69.25
subtract double	2.52	71.77
load immediate	2.43	74.20
add quick	2.41	76.61
move double	2.28	78.89
add double	2.26	81.15
store word	1.69	82.84
load quick	1.48	84.32
move longword to double	1.29	85.61
branch	1.28	86.89
compare double	1.26	88.15
return	0.95	89.10
call	0.95	90.05
compare immediate	0.91	90.96
push word	0.74	91.70
divide double	0.72	92.42
compare word	0.66	93.08
and immediate	0.51	93.59

fabrication would permit the basic instructions (e.g., add, logical operations) to complete in one cycle. Longer instructions were allowed to take as many cycles as necessary, and the appropriate hardware support was placed on-chip to ensure that the instructions executed correctly in the presence of traps, interrupts, and data and register dependencies.

As a result, in 1986 it was possible to build a 33 Mhz part and in 1988, a 50 MHz part. This compares with speeds of about 16 MHz for the initial Sparc implementation (1987), and 8 MHz for the initial MIPS Corp. implementation (1986). The minimum instruction time for those machines is one cycle, so the peak instruction rate of CLIPPER is substantially higher.

Performance Improvement
There are two approaches to improving the performance of an implementation of a given instruction set architecture. The first is technology scaling, by which faster technology and denser packaging (or a smaller chip) permit the machine to run faster without any changes in the design architecture or even in the circuit diagram.

For the most part, performance improvements in scaling from one technology (e.g., 2-micron CMOS) to another (e.g., 1.5-micron CMOS) are independent of the actual absolute value of the cycle time. The cycle time in a machine is limited by the longest signal path (including gate delays) within a cycle; halving the longest

path almost halves the cycle time. CLIPPER has already improved in performance significantly through the scaling and semiconductor process improvements that occurred in going to the C300, which also has a much improved floating point unit relative to the C100, as well as other minor functional changes.

In considering the performance of CLIPPER, the factor most strictly limiting performance on a high performance microprocessor is the memory interface [26]. As is discussed in more detail in [3], CLIPPER is most strictly limited by memory delays, despite the two buses (one each for instructions and data), and the fact that those busses are short and that each is dedicated to communication between a pair of chips. In scaling any processor, the limiting factor will continue to be the memory interface, which does not scale as well as other aspects of the machine.

The other approach to improved performance is a redesign which decreases the number of cycles per instruction. In general, this can be accomplished by the use of more logic. This type of redesign has already occurred in going from the C100 to the C300, as is shown in Table IV. There we see that by redesigning the floating point unit, floating instruction times have decreased significantly. Similar improvements are possible in other multicycle instructions. In comparison, the Amdahl 470V/6 required 5 to 6 cycles per instruction, and that was roughly halved for the 580. The DEC Vax 11/780 needed about 10 cycles per instruction [12], which was reduced to about 6 cycles for the 8600 [15]; the cycle time was only reduced from 200 ns to 80 ns, but the total performance was improved by a factor of almost five. The next versions of CLIPPER will be complete reimplementations with the mean number of cycles per instruction reduced substantially.

CONCLUSIONS
The Intergraph CLIPPER microprocessor was designed from scratch to provide high performance, cost effectiveness, convenient programmability, and an architecture that can be expanded as technology improves and the art of computer architecture design advances.

Among the important characteristics of CLIPPER are a load/store, fully hardwired architecture, full feature

TABLE VII. Frequencies of Address Modes for Spice Benchmark

Address Mode	Frequency (all instructions)	Frequency (all address modes)
12(r1)	15.66	31.48
32(pc)	10.77	21.65
(r1)	8.04	16.16
16(pc)	7.85	15.78
[rx](r1)	4.82	9.69
32(r1)	1.62	3.26
abs32	0.75	1.51
[rx](pc)	0.23	0.46
Total	49.74	

instruction set with complex instructions implemented in an on-chip ROM, an instruction set encoding that permits very fast decode, compact code, very fast cycle time, a sophisticated pipeline, on-chip floating point, and high performance. To minimize the costs of using CLIPPER in a product, CLIPPER is available as a small module containing the processor, two cache and mem-

ory management units, and the clock; thus the user doesn't have to build his own cache or memory management system. Opcodes and address modes have been left available, so that the instruction set and address space may be easily expanded.

We believe that CLIPPER represents a good set of design choices.

TRADEOFFS AND EXTENSIONS

Instruction Set Choice

Why Not "Pure RISC"? The current research trend in computer architecture is to design machines with extremely simple instruction sets. The term *RISC*, named after the Berkeley RISC project [32], is sometimes taken to mean a machine with a simple, load/store architecture; it can also be used to refer to a machine with a specific set of "features," including fixed length 32-bit instructions, single cycle execution, and register windows. This specific set of features is only one means to high performance; as is noted in [32]: "we somewhat artificially placed the following design constraints on the hardware."

We decided not to use register windows for several reasons. Flynn [14] shows that register windows do not improve memory traffic in comparison to good register allocation mechanisms, and the large number of registers can increase the cycle time [19, 33]. Fixed length instructions increase code size, memory traffic and cache miss ratios; data in Table I demonstrate that CLIPPER code is reasonably compact. The benefits of fixed length instructions are obtained in CLIPPER by placing the opcode and address mode in the first parcel (two bytes) of the instruction, so that efficient decoding is possible. Single cycle execution means that the cycle must be long enough to accommodate the longest single cycle instruction; CLIPPER allows instructions to take as many cycles as necessary. As with all RISC designs, CLIPPER is a load/store architecture, which only increases the code size slightly (see Table I), while greatly simplifying the pipeline control and interrupt and trap handling. Finally, the benefits of the more useful complex instructions (such as copy string and fill buffer) are obtained through the use of the MIROM; no complexity has been added to the implementation or the actual hardwired instruction set.

Why Not "More CISC", and What We Chose Not To Include.

There is a certain intellectual appeal to taking commonly needed software functions and implementing them in single instructions. Extreme examples are instructions to manipulate queues and compute polynomials, but we can include such reasonable operations as the three memory address instruction in this class. There are several problems with this approach. First, the number of gates available on a chip in current technology is not sufficient to implement these instructions entirely in hardware; microcode would have been required. Existing microcoded machines tend to be slow. (see [19, 33, 41] for extensive and detailed discussions of this issue.)

A natural form of computation is memory-to-register, register-to-memory, or memory-to-memory, but such instructions are not provided for three reasons:

1. It is very simple to generate the corresponding code sequences. Very few extra instruction bytes are needed,

since the total number of operand specifiers is almost the same.

2. There is usually little savings in execution time, since the same sequence of operations must occur.

3. There is *considerable* additional complexity, because of the difficulty of handling memory traps and interrupts, especially page faults. In particular, if there are multiple memory references per instruction, then there can be multiple page faults; an extreme case occurs with the M68000 which permits an indirect indexed address mode.

Some complicated instructions seen in the IBM/370 and DEC Vax (e.g., translate, translate and test, edit, queue, polynomial, etc.) were omitted because of their substantial complexity, and the fact that the same functionality can be reasonably implemented in software. In practice, a compiler is seldom able to generate these instructions even when they are needed. All existing studies show that a small number of opcodes account for the large majority of all instructions executed; (see e.g., [5, 35]). For many of the same reasons, we omitted complicated branch instructions (such as decrement, test, and branch if less than zero).

Protection domains were limited to those possible from the protection bits assigned to page frames (see [3] for further discussion), since very few operating systems are prepared to take advantage of ring-structured protection domains or similarly complex designs. Likewise, a segmented address space was avoided, due to the inflexibility it imposes on the use of memory, including the impediments it provides to increases in the address space size, and the fact that the same functionality is obtained by protection bits on pages. General purpose registers were selected over dedicated registers (e.g., index, data, and address registers) for programming flexibility and generality.

A compatibility mode is not necessary in CLIPPER since it is not an upward compatible extension of an existing architecture. Not having to provide this feature greatly simplified the design, avoided undesirable architectural compromises, and permitted increased performance.

Extended precision arithmetic was not considered to be sufficiently useful at the time CLIPPER was designed to justify the area required to implement it in hardware. Extended precision is currently implemented with instruction sequences, and opcodes are available to implement extended precision in the hardwired instruction set in the future.

Possible Additions

One of the limiting factors in the design of a microprocessor is the silicon area available and the area required for each gate. For that reason, some features originally considered were deferred until future CLIPPER versions. For example, a delayed branch can reduce the pipeline penalty due to successful branches. The problem with a delayed branch is that of saving the state when a trap (e.g., a page fault) or interrupt occurs between the time the branch decision is made (the delayed branch instruction) and the time that it takes effect (one or two instructions later). Because of its sophisticated pipeline, the existing CLIPPER chips simply don't have the space to implement this feature. (This is in contrast to various RISC chips which can easily include a delayed branch because each instruction executes in one cycle, thus only a very small amount of state has to be saved when a page fault occurs.) In addition to the delayed branch, a delayed load and vector instructions are also possible future enhancements.

Pipeline Control
CLIPPER is pipelined, and the pipeline is fully hardware controlled, with all interlocks (including checks for register dependencies) enforced with hardwired logic. This is in contrast to designs such as MIPS [4], where the compiler must reorganize code and insert no-ops as necessary. Some claim [19] that hardware pipeline control increases the cycle time, but this is disputed by others [33]. We chose to use hardware control deliberately because (1) it is a burden to require that the compiler understand the pipeline and inserts no-ops as necessary; (2) it is an unreasonable burden on the assembly language programmer and/or code generator to overcome the lack of hardware; (3) the implications of (1) and (2) are that without interlocks, code will tend to be "buggy"; (4) compilers and programs become implementation dependent; instead of just depending on the instruction set architecture, they depend on the precise features of the pipeline for correctness. Object code is thus not portable between different implementations of the same instruction set architecture. We regard (4) to be the most serious of these problems.

On-Chip Cache or Larger Instruction Buffer
Considerable study was devoted to the question of whether CLIPPER should have an on-chip cache or a significantly larger instruction buffer than the current 8 bytes. We do not have space here to discuss the reasons for the existing choice in detail (see [3]), but the basic problem is that given the limited chip area, we were unable to put enough cache or

buffer on the chip to yield a useful performance improvement. For example, the 68030 (which was available in 1987) has only 256 bytes of instruction cache and 256 bytes of data cache; such small caches are of little use, and much of the potential utility of the small instruction cache is obtained from the 8-byte instruction buffer used in CLIPPER. In addition, there are problems of virtual versus real addressing, synonyms, cache flushing, and cache consistency [39]. A 2- or 3-level cache (on chip, CAMMU chip, cache board) is a future possibility.

Address Space Size
Almost any shortcoming in a computer architecture can be overcome except too small an address space; this is the reason that DEC was finally forced to design the Vax ("virtual address extension") as a replacement for the PDP-11. CLIPPER provides a flat, uniform (not partitioned) 32-bit address space. Because of the availability of additional address modes, it will be possible to define modes which produce more than 32 bits of virtual address. More than 32 bits of physical addressing can be obtained by changing the format of the page tables. These changes are straightforward and require few user programs to undergo conversion. We expect that within 10 or 15 years, both physical and virtual addresses will need more than 32 bits.

Better Multiprocessor Cache Consistency
As explained in [3], the CLIPPER CAMMU implements a bus watch cache consistency protocol; it watches memory transactions on the bus, and maintains cache consistency in a system with multiple CPUs and shared writeable areas of memory. The algorithm implemented requires that shared writeable data be marked, and thus the CAMMU need only take action when the reference is marked shared. Because the present CAMMU can do only one thing at a time, consistency operations interfere with normal CPU access, and thus the use of this mode should be minimized. With improved technology, we expect that it will be possible to implement a much more sophisticated bus interface, with a dual-ported cache directory and an optimized consistency algorithm such as is described in [42].

Acknowledgments. The Advanced Professor Division of Intergraph Corporation (formerly part of Fairchild Semiconductor) consists of over one hundred people, including those doing architecture, software, circuits, CAD, marketing, and manufacturing, all of whom contributed to this project. We want to especially note and thank Vern Brethour, James Cho, Rich Dickson, Duncan Gurley, John Kellum, Kevin Kissell, David Neff, and Ray Ryan, all of whom had major design and implementation roles throughout most of the project.

Alan Jay Smith's research in computer architecture and computer system performance is supported in part by the National Science Foundation under grants CCR-8202591 and MIP-8713274. Some research results obtained under this funding are presented in this article.

REFERENCES
1. Bailey, D.H., and Barton, J.T. The NAS Kernel Benchmark Program, NASA Tech. Memo. 86711, August 1985.
2. Cavanagh, J. *Digital Computer Arithmetic—Design and Implementation.* McGraw-Hill, New York, 1984.
3. Cho, J., Smith, A.J., and Sachs, H. The Memory Architecture and the Cache and Memory Management Unit for the Fairchild CLIPPER, UC Berkeley CS Division Tech. Rep. UCB/CSD 86/289, March, 1986.
4. Chow, F., Himmelstein, M., Killian, E., and Weber, L. Engineering a RISC compiler system. In *Proceedings of the IEEE Compcon*, San Francisco, Calif., March, 1986, pp. 132–137.
5. Clark, D., and Levy, H. Measurement and analysis of instruction use in the VAX-11/780. In *Proceedings of the 9th Annual Symposium on Computer Architecture* (Austin, Texas, Apr. 1982), pp. 9–17. (Also *Computer Architecture News 10*, 3.)
6. Cody, W.J., Coonen, J.T., Gay, D.M., Hanson, K., Hough, D., Kahan, W., Karpinski, R., Palmer, J., Ris, F.N., and Stevenson, D. A Proposed radix- and word-length-independent standard for floating point arithmetic. *IEEE Micro 4*, 4 (Aug. 1984), 86–100.
7. Colwell, R.P., Hitchcock C.Y., III, Jensen, E.D., Brinkley Sprung, H.M., and Kollar, C.P. Computers, complexity and controversy. *IEEE Comp. 18*, 9 (Sept. 1985), 8–19.
8. Curnow, H.J., and Wichman, B.A. A synthetic benchmark. *Comput. J. 19*, 1 (Feb. 1976), 43–49.
9. DeMoney, M., Moore, J., and Mashey, J. Operating system support on a RISC. In *Proceedings of the IEEE Compcon* (San Francisco, Calif., March, 1986), pp. 138–143.
10. Digital Equipment Corp., *VAX Architecture Handbook*, 1981.
11. Dongarra, J.J. Performance of various computers using standard linear equations software in a Fortran environment. *Comp. Arch. News 13*, 1 (Mar. 1985), 3–11.

12. Emer, J.S., and Clark, D.W. A characterization of processor performance in the VAX-11/780. In *Proceedings of the 11th Annual Symposium on Computer Architecture* (Ann Arbor, Mich., June 1984), pp. 301–309.

13. Fairchild. *CLIPPER 32-bit Microprocessor User's Manual*. Prentice Hall, Englewood Cliffs, N.J., 1987.

14. Flynn, M., Mitchell, C., and Mulder, J. And now a case for more complex instruction sets. *IEEE Comp.* (Sept. 1987), 71–83.

15. Fossum, T., McElroy, J., and English, W. An Overview of the VAX 8600 System, *Digital Tech. J. 1* (Aug. 1985), 8–23.

16. Grochowski, E.T. An Instructor Tracer for the Motorola 68010, MS Project Report, Computer Science Division, EECS Dept., University of California, Berkeley, Calif., May, 1986.

17. Hansen, P.M., et al. A performance evaluation of the Intel iAPX 432, *Comp. Arch. News 10*, 4 (June 1982), 17–26.

18. Hennessy, J., Jouppi, N., Baskett, F., Gross, T., and Gill, J. Hardware/software tradeoffs for increased performance. In *Proceedings of the Symposium on Architectural Support for Programming Languages and Operating Systems* (Sigarch Computer Architecture News, 10, 2, March, 1982), pp. 2–11.

19. Hennessy, J. VLSI processor architecture, *IEEETC C-23*, 12 (Dec. 1984), 1221–1246.

20. Huck, J. Comparative analysis of computer architectures, Computer Systems Laboratory Tech. Rep. 83-243, May, 1983, Stanford University, Stanford, Calif.

21. Hunter, C., and Farquhar, E. Introduction to the NS16000 architecture. *IEEE MICRO 4*, 2 (Apr. 1984), 26–47.

22. IBM Corporation. IBM Systems/370 Principles of Operation, Form Number GA22-7000-5, IBM, Poughkeepsie, New York, 1976.

23. Kirrmann, H. Data format and bus compatibility in microprocessors. *IEEE MICRO 3*, 4 (Aug. 1983), 32–47.

24. Levy, H., and Eckhouse, R. *Computer Programming and Architecture: The VAX-11*, Digital Press, Bedford, Mass., 1980.

25. Lunde, A. Evaluation of Instruction Set Processor Architecture by Program Tracing. Tech. Rep., Dept. of Computer Science, Carnegie-Mellon University, July, 1974.

26. Mateosian, R. System considerations in the NS32032 design. In *Proceedings of the NCC*, 1984, pp. 77–81.

27. McMahon, F. The Livermore Fortran Kernels: A Computer Test of the Numerical Performance Range, Tech. Rep. UCRL-53745, Lawrence Livermore National Laboratory, December, 1986.

28. Motorola Corporation *16-Bit Microprocessor User's Manual*. 3rd Edition, 1982.

29. Neff, D. C compiler implementation issues on the CLIPPER microprocessor. In *Proceedings of Compcon* (San Francisco, Calif., Mar. 1986), pp. 196–201.

30. Neff, L. CLIPPER microprocessor architecture overview. In *Proceedings of Compcon*. (San Francisco, Calif., Mar. 1986), pp. 191–195.

31. Neuhauser, C.J. Analysis of the PDP-11 Instruction Stream. Tech. Rep. 183, Computer Systems Laboratory, Stanford Electronics Laboratories, Stanford University, Stanford, Calif. 94305, February, 1980.

32. Patterson, D.A., and Sequin, C.H. A VLSI RISC, *IEEE Comp. 16*, 9 (Sept. 1982), 8–20.

33. Patterson, D. Reduced instruction set computers. *Commun. ACM 28*, 1 (Jan. 1985), 8–21.

34. Perry, T. At work or play, he's the captain. *IEEE Spect. 24*, 6 (June 1987), 56–59.

35. Peuto, B., and Shustek, L. An instruction timing model of CPU performance. In *Proceedings of the 4th Annual Symposium on Computer Architecture* (College Park, Md., Mar., 1977), pp. 165–178.

36. Radin, G. The 801 Minicomputer. *IBM J. Res. Devel. 27*, 3 (May, 1983), 237–246.

37. Ritchie, D.M., and Thompson, K. The UNIX timesharing system. *Commun. ACM 17*, 7 (July, 1974), 365–375.

38. Smith, A.J. Input/output optimization and disk architecture: A survey. *Perform. Eval. 1*, 2 (1981), 104–117.

39. Smith, A.J. Cache memories. *Comp. Surv. 14*, 3 (Sept. 1982), 473–530.

40. Smith, A.J. Problems, directions and issues in memory hierarchies. In *Proceedings of the 18th Annual Hawaii International Conference on System Sciences* (Honolulu, Jan. 2–4, 1985), pp. 468–476. Also available as UC Berkeley CS Report UCB/CSD84/220.

41. Stallings, W. Reduced instruction set computer architecture. In *Proceedings of the IEEE 76*, 1 (Jan. 1988), pp. 38–55.

42. Sweazey, P., and Smith, A.J. A class of compatible cache consistency protocols and their support by the IEEE futurebus. In *Proceedings of the 13th Annual International Symposium on Computer Architecture* (Tokyo, June, 1986), pp. 414–423.

43. Weicker, R.P. Dhrystone: A synthetic systems programming benchmark. *Commun. ACM 27*, 10 (Oct. 1984), 1013–1030.

44. Wiecek, C.A. A case study of VAX-11 instruction set usage for compiler construction. In *Proceedings of the Symposium on Architecture Support for Programming Languages and Operating Systems*. Palo Alto, Calif., March, 1982.

CR Categories and Subject Descriptors: C.1.1 [**Processor Architectures**]: Single Data Stream Architectures—*Pipeline Processors, SISD Architectures, Von Neumann Architectures*; C.4 [**Performance of Systems**]; C.5 [**Computer System Implementation**]: Microprocessors
General Terms: Design, Measurement, Performance
Additional Key Words and Phrases: CLIPPER, Instruction Set

ABOUT THE AUTHORS:

WALT HOLLINGSWORTH works for Intergraph in Palo Alto, California, and is one of the CLIPPER architects. He has over 29 years of computer design experience beginning with navigation computers at Honeywell, the Sigma mainframes of SDS/Xerox, and has also worked at Telefile and Cray Research. He received a BSEE from Lamar Tech in 1960. Author's Present Address: Intergraph Corporation, Advanced Processor Division, 2400 Geng Road, Palo Alto, CA 94301.

HOWARD SACHS is Vice President and General Manager of Intergraph Corporation's Advanced Processor Division. He has extensive experience in computer design, and is the chief architect of Intergraph's CLIPPER microprocessor. Author's Present Address: Intergraph Corporation, Advanced Processor Division, 2400 Geng Road, Palo Alto, CA 94301.

ALAN JAY SMITH received a B.S. degree in electrical engineering from the MIT, and M.S. and Ph.D. degrees in computer science from Stanford University. He is currently a Professor in the Computer Science Division of the Department of Electrical Engineering and Computer Sciences, University of California, Berkeley, California, where he has been on the faculty since 1974, and was vice chairman of the EECS department from July, 1982–June, 1984. His research interests include the analysis and modeling of computer systems and devices, computer architecture, and operating systems. Author's present address: Alan Jay Smith, Department of Electrical Engineering and Computer Science, University of California at Berkeley, Berkeley, CA 94720.

Reprinted from *Computer*, September 1987, pages 59–69. Copyright © 1987 by The Institute of Electrical and Electronics Engineers, Inc.

A Survey of RISC Processors and Computers of the Mid-1980s

Charles E. Gimarc and Veljko M. Milutinović

Purdue University

Several years have elapsed since the early reduced computer architecture research was conducted at IBM, Stanford, and Berkeley. In this article, we briefly survey modern reduced instruction set computer architectures. A survey of this type helps illustrate the application areas into which RISC philosophy has moved, the wide range of technologies being used for processor implementation, features that seem to be common with all designs, and unique features introduced to solve specific problems. Finally, although this survey does not provide much depth on each architecture, we will provide interested readers with a more extensive list of references.

Definition of RISC

It seems to be difficult to provide a precise definition of a RISC architecture. The original reduced instruction set computer research, in which an attempt was made to reduce the semantic gap, produced a design philosophy that can be stated as follows[1,2]:

(1) Analyze target applications to determine which operations are used most frequently.

> We briefly survey modern RISC architectures, illustrating common features, range of applications, implementation technologies, and some unique characteristics of today's RISC machines.

(2) Optimize the datapath design to execute these instructions as quickly as possible.

(3) Include other instructions only if they fit into the previously developed datapath, are relatively frequent, and their inclusion will not slow the execution of the more frequent instructions.

(4) Apply a similar strategy to the design of other processor resources. Include a resource only if it is justified by its frequency of use, and its inclusion will not slow other, more frequently used, resources.

(5) Push as much complexity as reasonable from runtime hardware into the compile-time software.

Within RISC design philosophy, one must be free to make tradeoffs across boundaries of architecture/implementation, hardware/software, and compile-time/runtime.

When a processor design is based upon RISC philosophy, the resulting architecture typically has features in common with other RISC designs. Inclusion or exclusion of particular features should not be used as a measure of a RISC design, however. As you will see in this survey, several computers that are definitely RISC designs have features generally not considered part of a RISC design. Some features commonly seen in reduced instruction set computers are[3,4,5]

- single cycle execution of most instructions,
- load/store instruction set,

- hardwired instruction decoding,
- relatively few instructions and address modes,
- fixed instruction format for simple decoding,
- complexity pushed into optimizing compiler,
- highly pipelined datapath for much concurrency,
- large register set (windowed or not windowed),
- many levels of memory hierarchy, and
- instruction set designed for a specific application class.

A brief study of rating RISC designs based upon a similar set of characteristics was done by Tabak[6] in 1986. This type of rating is useful, but must be carefully applied and interpreted. The danger in using a list such as this is that computers with features contrary to those listed may not be interpreted as RISC designs. For example, some of the surveyed computers have microcoded instruction decoders, large instruction sets, and small register sets, but are still definitely RISC designs. The important issue is that RISC philosophy is followed in the design of a processor for a specific application.

Controversy

Currently there is much controversy over several issues relating to comparison between reduced instruction set computers and complex instruction set computers. The controversy can be divided into two broad categories. First, what differentiates a RISC from a CISC? And second, how does one make reasonable and useful performance measurements for comparisons?

Many of the features now seen in reduced instruction set computers have been extensively used in complex instruction set computers. Some of the features, such as pipelined datapath, caching, and register windowing, are often viewed as attributes of a RISC design.[7] One advantage that RISC designs have is the existence of a coherent philosophy statement. Originally, RISC designs were targeted for a specific application and therefore optimized for execution of a well defined class of programs. Characteristically, CISCs are designed for a broad range of applications and consequently include support for many different programming environments. It is evident that there is now a trend away from the narrow RISC

application and to a more general purpose design, again confusing the difference between RISC and CISC. RISC proponents often see instruction set size and complexity as a major feature of "RISCy" designs.

Many of the popular performance measurement techniques are of questionable value when comparing RISC performance with CISC performance. Typically, the effects of operating system overhead, compiler optimization, and multiple register sets are not properly considered. Benchmarks related to number of application transactions per second are more meaningful than simply measuring instructions executed per second.

What processors are out there?

Twenty-one processors are included in this survey. Table 1 presents a list of the surveyed processors with a brief description of each. It is apparent that RISC design has moved out of the university and into the marketplace. Fifteen processors are either currently available for purchase, or will be available this year. Three computers are part of continuing research at Stanford University and the University of California, Berkeley. Three computers are in the design stage and will become embedded signal processors for defense computers.

RISC designs are available as single-chip microprocessors, very large scale integration chip sets with more powerful functions, single-board computers, and superminicomputers. The ARM processor is marketed as VLSI Technology's VL86C010 microprocessor, indicating that some of these processors can appear under different names. A wide range of circuit technologies are used in their implementation. The Whetstone and AMD 29300 processors are bipolar VLSI devices with emitter coupled logic (ECL) internal cells and transistor-transistor logic (TTL) interfaces. Most designs are N-type metal oxide semiconductor (NMOS) or complementary metal oxide semiconductor (CMOS) implementations with geometries of one to three microns. The highest performance processors are being designed for gallium arsenide (GaAs) implementa-

tion. These processors have the longest time to their introduction as a product.

One of the typical characteristics of a RISC design is a certain narrowness of target application. Table 1 indicates a wide range of individual applications, plus some designs with a very broad application space. Many designs target scientific, engineering, computer-aided engineering (CAE), and computer-aided design (CAD) applications. Almost universally, these use some variant of a Unix operating system. Five of the designs—ARM, Dragon, FAIM-1, SOAR, and SPUR—target symbolic processing and artificial intelligence applications. Most of these are used in multiprocessor configurations. All three GaAs designs and the CAP target signal, data, and image processing applications. The GaAs processors have the advantage of raw speed. The CAP processor has the potential of massive parallelism. The Transputer and MIPS-X processors were designed with general purpose multiprocessing in mind. Four designs—AMD 29300, Spectrum, Ridge 32, and Whetstone—have a broad application target.

Characteristics of GaAs material require changes in architecture when compared to designs in silicon. Of these characteristics, the major design implications are higher off-chip/on-chip delay ratio and lower transistor count per chip. Each of the three GaAs processors address these issues in similar ways, with deep pipelines, processing functions spread over several chips, small instruction sets, and complex memory hierarchies.

This survey is not exhaustive for several reasons. Relatively low cost, high performance computers are an extremely competitive business arena, and many manufacturers will not release details of their current or future products. Several new products are scheduled for introduction in 1987 and will appear between the time of writing this article and its publication. Several manufacturers market products as RISC or RISC-like that we feel do not follow the RISC design philosophy closely enough for inclusion. Other processors are too early in their design phase and will have to be discussed another time, after their designs have stabilized. We included some designs that may not be RISC processors because they exhibit some important RISC features. The Defense Advanced Research Project Agency (DARPA) is funding research for the development of GaAs and CMOS RISC processors. These CMOS processors

COMPUTER

Table 1. Description of RISC processors.

Processor	Manufacturer	Configuration	Technology	Application
Accel	Celerity Computing	Single-board CPU and workstation	Uses NCR 32000 MOS chip set	Multiuser scientific and general purpose with Unix support
ARM	Acorn Computers	Microprocessor and single-board computer	2 to 3 μ MOS, 25K transistors	Workstation for HLL programming and real time AI
AMD29300	Advanced Micro Devices	Chip set to construct custom computer	Bipolar LSI with ECL internal and TTL interface	Construct target architecture without custom VLSI
CAP	IT&T Advanced Technology Center	Slave multiprocessor array	1.2 to 3 μ CMOS, 120K to 600K transistors	Signal processing, image processing, and scientific calculations
Clipper	Fairchild	Single-board computer	3 chips of 2 μ CMOS, total of 836K transistors	Scientific programming in a Unix environment
CRISP	AT&T	Microprocessor	1.75 μ CMOS, 172K transistors	General purpose
Dragon	Xerox PARC	Multiprocessor workstation	2 μ CMOS	Symbolic processing, AI
FAIM-1	Schlumberger, Palo Alto	Multiprocessor workstation	Custom VLSI CMOS	Symbolic processing, AI
MIPS	MIPS Computer Systems	Microprocessor, chip set, and minicomputer	2 μ CMOS, 100K transistors	General purpose programming with Unix support
Pyramid 90X	Pyramid Technology	Superminicomputer	Schottky TTL	Scientific programming and graphics with Unix support
Ridge 32	Ridge Computers	Workstation and superminicomputer	STTL and MOS VLSI in multiple chips	Scientific programming and graphics with Unix support
ROMP	IBM	Microprocessor chip set	2 chips of 1.8 μ NMOS with a total of 111K transistors	Scientific and graphics workstation with Unix support
Spectrum (HP Precision Architecture)	Hewlett-Packard	CPU family	1.5 μ NMOS, 115K transistors	Scientific, business, and instrumentation computing with Unix support
Transputer	INMOS	Microprocessor family	2 μ NMOS, 250K transistors	Multiprocessor
Whetstone I, Whetstone II	Integrated Digital Products	Single-board computer, one-chip CPU	Bipolar VLSI with ECL internal and TTL interface	Plug-in replacement general purpose computer
MIPS-X	Stanford University	Microprocessor chip set	2 μ CMOS	Updated MIPS, multiprocessing
SOAR	University of California, Berkeley	Microprocessor and processor board	NMOS, 35K transistors	Smalltalk-80 programming system workstation
SPUR	University of California, Berkeley	Multiprocessor workstation	3 chips in 2 μ CMOS	Parallel processing research in Lisp environment
CDC GaAs	Control Data	Microprocessor chip set	3 chips of 10K gates each in HIIL GaAs	Embedded computers for signal processing
McD GaAs	McDonnell Douglas	Microprocessor chip set	E-JFET GaAs, 41K transistors in 2 chips	Embedded computers for signal processing
RCA GaAs	RCA and Purdue University	Microprocessor chip set	ED-MESFET GaAs	Embedded computers for signal processing

Table 2. RISC processors instruction set features.

Processor	Number of Instructions	Decoder	Instruction Length
Accel	142 integer, 126 floating point	Microcoded	90% are 16 bits, 10% are 32 or 80 bits
ARM	?	Programmable logic array	All 32 bits
AMD29300	Variable	Hardwired or microcoded	32 bits
CAP	33 general, 7 scientific, 9 SIMD support	Hardwired; vector units are either 16 or 32 bits	16 or 32 bits
Clipper	101 general, 61 macroinstructions	Hardwired with 2048-word macroinstruction ROM	Multiples of 16 bits
CRISP	33	Decoder unit	16, 64, and 96 bits
Dragon	approx. 150	Programmable logic array	8, 16, 24, or 40 bits
FAIM-1	64	Finite state machine	?
MIPS	?	Hardwired	All 32 bits
Pyramid	90	Microcoded	32, 64, or 96 bits
Ridge 32	170	Microcoded	16, 32, and 48 bits
ROMP	112	Hardwired with 256 words of microcode	16 or 32 packed to 32 bits
Spectrum	140	PLA with millicode	All 32 bits
Transputer	16	Programmable logic array	All 8 bits
Whetstone	18 basic, 181 total	Basic instructions have hardware decode	16 bits
MIPS-X	< 32	Hardwired, distributed	All 32 bits
SOAR	20	Hardwired	All 32 bits
SPUR	28 general, 10 Lisp support, 25 floating point	Hardwired CPU and FPU	All 32 bits
CDC GaAs	29 CPU, 31 FCOP, 6 MMU	Hardwired	Multiple; depends on execution unit
McD GaAs	< 64	Hardwired	All 32 bits
RCA GaAs	< 64	Hardwired	32 and 64 bits

are not treated in this survey because they are still early in their development cycle.

Organization of this survey

Since this is a survey of modern RISC designs, we will not discuss the IBM 801, RISC I, RISC II, and SU-MIPS. Also, we included the early commercial products from Pyramid and Ridge only in the tables as a reference. All of these computers have been extensively treated in the literature. We will refer to the early research RISCs when such reference illustrates a common trait, change in design philosophy, or enhancement of a familiar design feature.

This article is organized into sections comparing groups of common features. We investigate the CPU design first, emphasizing instruction set, datapath, and memory system design. Next we investigate the RISC as a system, emphasizing multiple execution units, coprocessor support, multiprocessing, operating system support, language support, and family requirements. Finally, we briefly compare performance.

CPU issues

Instruction set. A tabulation of features related to the instruction set appears in Table 2. The size of instruction sets in this

survey ranges from a minimum of 16 instructions for the Transputer to approximately 268 for the Accel with floating-point support. Even though the instruction set size and instruction length differ for all the surveyed RISC machines, they all use instruction formats that allow rapid decode through use of a consistent opcode field.

Accel designers chose not to limit the processor to too few commands. The instruction set includes 142 integer processor unit instructions and 126 floating-point unit instructions. Ninety percent of the instructions are 16 bits long, the rest are 32 or 80 bits long. This large instruction set is reduced in terms of format and register orientation.

The AMD 29332 ALU has a symmetrical and regular instruction set of byte-aligned and variable-length data manipulation instructions. A complete central processing unit instruction set is constructed out of the arithmetic logic unit instructions, with fields to manipulate registers, coprocessors, and other parts of the CPU. Instructions are limited to 32 bits since all datapaths support a 32-bit word.

The CAP instruction set can be divided into three subsets. Thirty-three instructions execute primarily in the scalar processor. Seven floating-point or scientific instructions are present, and nine instructions are devoted to control of the single instruction, multiple data (SIMD) processor array. Two formats are used, with the 32-bit format split between two vector processors. Vector processors are 16-bit machines.

Fairchild chose to split the Clipper instruction set into two parts, with 101 "simple" instructions forming the basic instruction set. These are all multiples of 16 bits in length. Complex or application-specific instructions may be added to this set through coding into the macroinstruction unit.

The CRISP 33-member instruction set contains instructions of 16, 64, and 96 bits in length. The first bit of each instruction determines length. A major departure from other RISC processors, this design uses memory-to-memory instructions that can execute in one cycle. Also, this instruction set provides direct support of multiplication and division.

Dragon allows variable-length byte-encoded instructions. Consequently, the decode logic is quite complex.

Most of the 64 instructions of the FAIM-1 processor can execute in a single cycle.

Like the earlier RISC designs, and in contrast to most modern RISC designs, MIPS has fixed-length instructions, a single address mode, and all instructions 32 bits long. It uses three instruction formats. Like the MIPS processor, Stanford's MIPS-X implements its full instruction set in only 32-bit words. A five-bit opcode field allows only 32 instructions. Multiplies and divides are performed iteratively. It uses only one address mode and four instruction formats.

Most ROMP instructions (79) are 16 bits wide, and the remaining 39 fit into a 32-bit word. Some instructions have both two-byte and four-byte versions depending upon address modes. All instructions are packed into 32 bits upon fetch by the

ROMP CPU.

In the Transputer, single-byte instructions decouple instruction format from the word length of the machine. There are several 16- and 32-bit Transputer models. All instructions are byte aligned with a four-bit opcode field.

To allow compatibility with an existing user base, the Whetstone simulates the Data General Nova instruction set. The manufacturer asserts that the processor uses 18 basic instructions, a subset of the Nova instruction set. All 181 Nova instructions are then mapped into this set of 18, presumably by the compiler. Instructions and data are in 16-bit words.

Each SOAR instruction contains a bit that enables or disables tag checking, allowing conventional programming languages to compile to SOAR instructions. Three instruction lengths (one, two, and three bytes) are used in the instruction set.

All SPUR instructions fit into a 32-bit word, with opcode and register fields aligned. The 55 instructions can be divided into general operations, Lisp support, and floating-point support groups.

The CDC processor instruction set may be divided into three subsets, one for the central processing unit, one for the floating-point coprocessor, and one for the memory management unit. Length of an instruction depends upon where it is executed.

A six-bit opcode field is used for both the McD and RCA processors' instructions. All instructions in the McD processor are 32 bits long, while the RCA processor allows some 64-bit instructions.

In this survey are two basic instruction decoder designs and several interesting combinations. Recall that the original RISC examples all used hardwired logic decoders for the simplest and fastest possible instruction decode. Most of the example processors (12) employ some form of strictly hardware instruction decode. A hardwired decoder, as in CAP, MIPS, MIPS-X, SOAR, SPUR, CDC, and RCA, implies that an area of the CPU chip is designed with minimized logic to decode the instruction set. The MIPS-X processor uses a distributed design with partial decode at the register in which the fetched instruction is placed, and the remainder of the decode at the functional elements in the datapath. The McDonnell Douglas references did not specify instruc-

tion decoder design, but in view of the time required to decode, a hardwired decoder seems the appropriate choice. The FAIM-1 employs a finite state machine controlled by instruction opcodes as the method of decode. Three examples (ARM, Dragon, and Transputer) employ programmable logic arrays in the decode path. Use of a PLA is effectively the same as hardwired decode, but does not use minimized logic design. Also, it is much simpler to reprogram a PLA for instruction set modifications than to redesign a hardwired decoder.

Two processors, Accel and Ridge 32, use microcoded instruction decoders and also have the largest instruction sets. The Accel design is built around an NCR32000 CPU and support devices. The CPU is microcodable, allowing specification of a rich instruction set with RISC attributes. The Ridge processors are microcoded, with most instructions executed by a one-instruction microsequence.

The AMD 29300 may be used to implement a RISC CPU with either hardwired or microcoded instruction decode. It requires only the proper control signals for the ALU, registers, coprocessor, and other units in the proper time sequence.

Four processors—Clipper, ROMP, Spectrum, and Whetstone—use a combination of hardwired and microcoded instruction decode techniques. The Clipper has hardwired decode of 101 instructions. A 2048-word macroinstruction ROM is provided, currently with 61 instructions, to allow support of specific programming environments. More macroinstructions may be added by the user. ROMP uses hardwired decode for instruction prefetch and memory data requests. A 256-word microprogram store is used for execution control. Hewlett-Packard's Spectrum processors use hardwired decode for most instructions and a millicode store in virtual memory for implementation of complex instructions. The Whetstone processors use hardwired decode for the basic 18 instructions, with microcode interpretation of the 181-instruction Nova 1200 instruction set.

The CRISP processor employs a separate Prefetch and Decode Unit to break each instruction into fully decoded 192-bit words. These decoded instructions are then loaded into a Decoded Instruction Cache for access by the Execution Unit. The FAIM-1 processor employs a separate Instruction Stream Memory to select, format, and deliver decoded instructions to the Evaluation Processor Unit.

Table 3. RISC processors datapath features.

Processor	Pipeline Stages	Register Set	Delayed Branch	Execution Units
Accel	3	48 32-bit register windows with overlap of 16, 512 windows	Yes, with delay of 2	Separate integer and floating point units
ARM	3	32 32-bit, 25 for user	No, compiler rescheduling	1 plus fetch incrementer
AMD29300	2	Variable	Yes, plus reorganizer	2: execute and fetch/decode
CAP	?	16 per processor	Send both options, do according to data mask	Scalar unit plus vector data and address units
Clipper	3	16 user, 16 special, 16 supervisor, all 32-bit	?	2: integer and floating point, all on chip
CRISP	3	32 32-bit, as a stack cache	Branch folding	2: prefetch and decode, and execution units
Dragon	?	?	Static branch prediction	2: instruction fetch, execute
FAIM-1	2	Stack	Yes	2: evaluation and switching processors
MIPS	5 (see Figure 1)	32 general purpose, 1 PC, 2 arithmetic, no windows	Yes, with reordering	2: CPU and system coprocessor. Separate data and address units
Pyramid	3	528 32-bit in 16 windows of 64	Yes	Separate instruction fetch and execution units
Ridge 32	4	16 32-bit with overlap windows	Branch prediction	2: instruction fetch, execute
ROMP	3	16 32-bit, 10 system, 4-port register file	Yes, branch with execute instruction	1
Spectrum	5	32 32-bit general purpose	Yes, with reorganization	1 CPU plus coprocessors
Transputer	?	6 32-bit	?	2: execute, I/O
Whetstone	3	4	?	3: arithmetic, address, I/O
MIPS-X	5	32 32-bit general purpose	Yes, with squash instruction, delay of 2	Separate execution and PC
SOAR	3	80 32-bit dual port with 8 register windows, using overlap of 8, and 8 global	Yes, with delay of 1 cycle. Must do type checking.	1
SPUR	4	32 32-bit registers in each window, using overlap of 6 and 10 global	Yes, with cancel compare instruction	1, but instruction and data fetches concurrently
CDC GaAs	6	16 32-bit general purpose	Yes, with reorganization and delay of 2	1
McD GaAs	4	16 32-bit general purpose, 16 32-bit special	Yes, with reorganization and delay of 1	1
RCA GaAs	5 + 2 waits	16 with variable size windows or background loading	Yes, with ignore instruction and delay of 2	Separate execution and PC units

Datapath. Datapath design is quite complex in all the surveyed processors. All 21 examples have pipelines of depth ranging from two stages in the AMD 29300 to seven stages (five plus two wait stages) in the proposed RCA GaAs processor. Generally, the shorter the cycle time, the deeper the pipeline. This phenomenon is primarily due to two factors. First, all example processors are designed to attempt to begin a new instruction each clock cycle. The MIPS processor can begin any instruction each clock cycle. Most other processors have some subset of instructions that require use of the pipeline for more than one cycle. Second, the processors have memory access and wiring delays that make up a large fraction of the clock cycle period. Thus, more cycles must be allocated for memory access instructions. Table 3 presents some important datapath features for the surveyed processors.

The Pipeline Stages column of Table 3 gives the number of CPU pipeline stages, but not details about how they overlap on successive instructions, nor the function of each stage. (Those details are available in the references.) The MIPS processor pipeline deserves special attention because of its complexity. Figure 1 illustrates the pipe for four instructions. It is difficult to give a number-of-stages figure for this design because there are half- and full-cycle stages, and concurrent activities within each instruction execution. The clock cycle is 60 nanoseconds divided into two 30-nanosecond phases. Complexity is partially due to the requirement to execute all instructions in one cycle.

Several register set designs were used, with most processors using an organization with 16 to 32 32-bit registers. All the surveyed RISC designs attempt to gain performance advantages through (1) the speed of an on-chip variable store and (2) the compiler's ability to effectively use locality of program variables. Both windowed and unwindowed register files occur. Thirteen processors have register files with no windowing. Several nonwindowed designs, and even windowed designs such as SOAR, use *load multiple* or *store multiple* instructions to speed context switches. Table 3 gives window size details of the five windowed examples.

The ARM processor resembles the Pyramid design in the sense that it employs an extremely large number of registers. A few processors, such as the ROMP and AMD 29300, have four-port register files, allowing multiple reads and writes in a single clock cycle. The AMD allows expansion of the register file in length and width by adding more register chips. The Transputer has an extremely small register file. Even though only three registers are available for ALU operations, the Transputer maintains a workspace pointer in the register stack pointing to the first variable in memory. A delay of one cycle is thus incurred at each variable access. MIPS-X maintains 33 bits on each variable in the register file. The 33rd bit allows a read and write to be performed in a single cycle. The CRISP and FAIM-1 processors use a stack-based register file organization. In CRISP, a separate stack cache appears to the compiler as memory, is arranged as a circular buffer, and allows two reads and one write per cycle. Processors using stacks do not have the register allocation

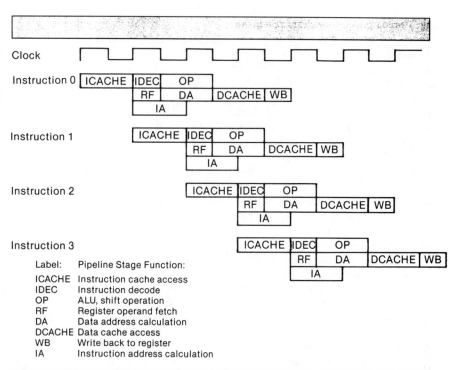

Figure 1. MIPS computer systems pipeline.

problems that other RISC processors' compilers have.

Most of the example processors divide CPU tasks into subtasks for separate execution units. A greater degree of concurrency is allowed at the expense of increased chip resource requirements and more complex control. Twelve processors (ARM, AMD, CAP, CRISP, Dragon, MIPS, Pyramid, Ridge, Transputer, Whetstone, MIPS-X, and RCA) have separate units for concurrent ALU execution and I/O operations. In most processors the I/O unit includes a separate ALU for address computation. The CAP divides execution into a scalar unit and separate vector data and vector address units. The Transputer I/O units are unique in providing four bidirectional links to other Transputers. The I/O unit coordinates the queueing of transmitted and received messages. The Whetstone divides tasks even further with separate address and I/O units. The SPUR processor is unique in performing independent and concurrent data and instruction fetches. Two logically separate units (prefetch and decode, and execution) in the CRISP are connected by a decoded instruction cache. This organization allows each unit to operate autonomously, with no central controller. Many processors use coprocessors to perform complex operations such as caching, memory man-

agement, and floating-point computations.

Several different shifter designs are included in the datapath of RISC processors. SPUR uses a simple unit that allows one-bit right or one-, two-, and three-bit left shifts. Due to timing constraints, RCA requires two instructions to perform a shift. The first instruction loads data into the shifter. A second instruction executes the shift and writes back results. Other processors use barrel or funnel shifters.

As in the original Stanford MIPS, some of the surveyed processors do not have hardware to manage pipeline interlocks. The processors with stated software interlocks are MIPS-X, MIPS, McD, RCA, and Spectrum. Of these, all but Spectrum appeared to be influenced by the SU-MIPS design.

Three processors (ARM, Clipper, and CDC) followed the Berkeley lead by providing hardware interlocks. Most processors provide register bypass paths to allow availability of a result of a computation for the next instruction.

Most processors use delayed branching to accommodate the condition when a branch is not taken. The ARM processor does not allow delayed branching. Three processors (CRISP, Ridge, and Dragon) use branch prediction in the compiler to increase the efficiency of delayed branching. The compiler sets or clears a bit in the branch instruction depending upon the likelihood of a branch taken. In CRISP, the technique of "branch folding" allows most branches to execute in zero time. This technique makes use of a dynamically generated "next address" field in each decoded instruction. In most processors, the compiler or reorganizer moves code to fill one or two slots following a branch with something more useful than *nop* instructions. The deeper the pipeline, the more difficult it is to fill the slots. For example, the deep pipelines of CDC and RCA processors have two delay slots to fill with code reorganization.

An interesting feature added to the MIPS-X processor consists of two versions of branch instructions. For a nonsquashed branch, instructions in the delay slots always execute. A squashed branch is used when both delay slots are not filled. Branch destination instructions are put into the slots and changed to *nop* instructions if the branch is not taken. SPUR performs a similar operation with its cancel compare instructions. To keep the processor array synchronized in CAP, instructions for *branch-taken* and *branch-not-taken* are transmitted by the scalar processor to the array processors. Computation then continues first with the taken instructions, then with the not-taken instructions, according to a branch condition mask.

Memory system. Because of the need to keep instructions and data supplied to the processors, RISC memory systems are necessarily quite complex. Several levels of memory hierarchy are used, often with data and instructions separated. Virtual memory is universally supported in the surveyed processors.

A hierarchical memory is one in which parts of the total storage space exist at different physical distances from the CPU, and at different operational speeds. It is currently not possible to build all the desired memory at a speed in which it can be accessed by the pipeline without delay. Several memory structures are possible, but the most common includes an on-chip instruction buffer of sufficient size to hold the next few instructions. This buffer is kept full by prefetch logic. Next is an on-chip or off-chip instruction and/or data cache. Some processors cache both data and instructions, others have just one or no cache. Finally, main memory exists off-chip and often off the processor board. Of course, access time increases as distance

from the CPU or size of the memory system increases.

Six processors use on-chip instruction prefetch buffers in addition to instruction or data caches. CAP uses RAM in the vector processors as local instruction storage. Clipper, Transputer, and Dragon use a four-word instruction buffer. SPUR has a 512-byte prefetch buffer (used as cache) with a reported 70 percent hit ratio. On-chip instruction or data caches are implemented in five of the surveyed processors. ARM has a shared instruction and data cache. Future plans include splitting the on-chip cache for greater flexibility. CAP also has 256 kilobits of local RAM used to cache instructions and data in each vector processor. Each Dragon processor has an on-chip fully associative cache. The Transputer has one kiloword of on-chip memory to store instructions and data. MIPS-X processor has a 512-word on-chip instruction cache.

All the processors without on-chip cache use some form of off-chip cache for data or instructions. The Accel processor board uses three distinct on-board cache systems. A 64-kilobyte cache holds instructions. To support virtual addressing, a 32-kilobyte four-way set associative address translation cache is used. And a 64-kilobyte stack register cache is used for expansion of the CPU registers.

Separate MMU chips in the Clipper implement separate external data and instruction caches. Each cache contains four kilobytes of two-way set associative memory. The instruction cache is reported to have a 96 percent hit ratio. A program counter inside the instruction cache MMU reduces CPU-to-MMU bus bandwidth requirements. The data cache supports copy back, write through, and noncacheable control schemes. With two MMU chips, instruction and data access can occur concurrently.

The MIPS processor uses separate instruction and data caches of up to 16 kilowords each. Cache control for both, and memory management, are on the CPU chip, while memory resides off-chip. A write buffer chip in MIPS allows up to four writes to be queued, freeing the CPU.

Ridge processors use a 256-byte instruction cache and no data cache. Spectrum uses separate instruction and memory caches, both located on the CPU board. A

three-level cache scheme is implemented in the Whetstone processor. The CPU directly accesses 128 kilobytes of very fast main memory. Separate on-board and off-board cache memories allow physical memory expansion up to 32 megabytes. Cache memory is updated through a separate DMA interface with the system disk.

In addition to an instruction buffer, MIPS-X uses an expandable 16- to 64-kiloword external direct mapped instruction cache. This cache is designed to minimize memory bus traffic.

Separate 128-kilobyte instruction and data caches are located on the SPUR processor board. The Berkeley Ownership algorithm insures cache consistency in a multiprocessor environment. All three GaAs processors use separate instruction and data caches. Due to chip resource constraints, the caches must be located off-chip. The CDC processor, like Clipper, uses two MMU chips to separate instruction and data cache control. Each CDC cache is one kiloword, direct mapped.

System issues

Division of functions. All the surveyed processors reflect different approaches to the design of reduced instruction set computer systems. Many of the processors divide system functions across chip boundaries, allowing integration of a large amount of functionality. Almost all these processors provide floating-point support utilizing the IEEE 754 standard. Floating-point support usually is provided by a separate coprocessor chip.

The Accel processor is available through Celerity computers with one or two floating-point units. The floating-point unit is physically separate from the CPU and loads data and instructions through the CPU registers.

As a user configurable system, the AMD processor allows connection of separate ALU, multiplier, and floating-point units, encouraging inclusion of only necessary functions. Each unit is a separate VLSI chip.

CAP is unique in that it implements an array of 20 identical RISC processors with memory on a single integrated circuit. This array chip employs software-based fault tolerance, necessary with such an extremely large device, by disabling faulted processors or memories. A multiprocessor array can be constructed from one or more CAP chips, depending upon the application. A scalar execution unit

COMPUTER

fetches instructions and provides control for an array of CAP chips that comprise the parallel execution unit. Each processor on the array chip has a microinstruction set similar to other bit slice processors, containing *and*, *add*, *or*, and *sub* type instructions. CAP may be treated as a collection of SIMD processors, each operating in synchrony on its own data.

The Clipper processor board uses three chips of two different functions. The CPU/FPU chip contains execution circuitry. Floating-point support is included on the same chip as the integer execution unit to avoid delays associated with moving floating-point operands between chips. Two combined cache and memory management unit chips are used on the Clipper board. One CAMMU chip manages instruction cache and memory access, and the other one manages operand cache and memory. This arrangement allows overlapped instruction and data access. Floating-point operations are performed on-chip for greater performance. This eliminates moving instructions and data to a coprocessor.

The Dragon processor is used in a workstation of one to ten identical processors with a shared memory. Cache in each processor mediates between processor and memory, reducing bus traffic—typically the bottleneck in shared memory systems.

FAIM-1 is a fully distributed multiprocessor system with no shared memory. Each processing element, called a Hectagon, contains an Evaluation Processor, Switching Processor, Post Office (topology dependent hardware), Instruction Stream Memory, Scratch Memory, and Associative Memory. Hectagons are connected together into hexagonally arranged Surfaces. Surfaces can also be connected into larger structures. The memory system is a highly parallel associative store. FAIM-1 is used as a hardware accelerator unit attached to a host Lisp processor. The prototype FAIM-1 will have 19 processors, but the system can be scaled to an arbitrarily large number of processors.

The MIPS system is implemented as a three-chip set. A CPU chip contains all integer execution, memory management, and cache control. A tightly coupled floating-point processor supports IEEE single- and double-precision operations. A write buffer chip provides queueing of memory access. This allows the CPU to continue its task without waiting for a write to complete.

The IBM ROMP processor is implemented in two devices, a CPU chip and a separate memory management unit. CPU and MMU communicate over a 32-bit parallel packet switched channel. A floating-point accelerator board is available for inclusion in the IBM RT PC system.

The Spectrum processor is designed to support a wide range of applications. Three kinds of assist processors are available. Coprocessors may be added for graphics or floating-point support. Special function units can be added to perform fixed-point arithmetic, encryption, emulation, and other functions. Finally, multiprocessing units can be added to the system.

Transputer is a RISC processor for parallel processing. Each processor has four dedicated 10 megabit-per-second interfaces to other Transputers or peripherals. Other processing units, such as communications link adapter, graphic, or floating-point, can be added to the system. Multiprocessor performance can scale linearly with the number of processors.

Whetstone uses three independent processors to perform arithmetic/logic, memory/address, and DMA-I/O operations. An optional floating-point unit is also available.

MIPS-X differs from the original SU-MIPS in the inclusion of coprocessor support. MIPS-X is designed as a processor in a shared memory multiprocessor system. To that end, memory bus traffic is minimized by keeping the cache miss ratio very small through use of a large (16- to 64-kiloword) external cache. Simulations indicate that six to eight processors may share the same memory without noticeable performance degradation due to bus contention.

The SOAR processor is implemented as a board for use with a Sun workstation. The SPUR processor follows development of RISC I, RISC II, and SOAR at Berkeley. It provides support for Common Lisp and IEEE 754 floating-point standards in a parallel processing environment. SPUR is a general purpose processor with some Lisp support. Three types of chips comprise the majority of the SPUR processor. A CPU performs integer execution and instruction fetch. A cache controller chip manages the memory and the instruction cache. A separate FPU implements the IEEE standard. The FPU tracks CPU instructions and fetches required instructions from the instruction cache.

The CDC system uses four major integrated circuits. A CPU executes most instructions with a RISC processor. Up to four different coprocessors can be used to augment the instruction set, with execution capabilities for specific applications. A floating-point coprocessor (FCOP) is being developed. The operand and instruction caches are each controlled by their own memory management unit. System devices interconnect through 32-bit parallel operand and instruction data buses, a 24-bit parallel instruction address bus, and a 26-bit parallel operand bus. Each of the system chips is pipelined.

The McD GaAs processor design was derived from the SU-MIPS microprocessor. Modifications include reduction in transistor count and complexity, and the addition of two coprocessor interfaces for floating-point operations. The CPU performs all fetch operations. The FPU loads all instructions in parallel with the CPU, executing only the ones that apply to floating-point operations. A system controller chip contains interrupt management, clock generation, and low-speed I/O operations.

Operating system/language support. The dominant operating system supported on new RISC processors is Unix or one of its variants. The ARM, Clipper, MIPS, Pyramid, Ridge, and Spectrum processors all have applications that run under a resident Unix-type operating system. The Unix processors all support some subset of the C, Pascal, Fortran, Ada, and Cobol programming languages. Optimizing compilers exist for all these languages.

The ROMP processor was designed to support IBM's PL.8 compiler. The two Berkeley processors, SOAR and SPUR, support Smalltalk and Lisp. SPUR was designed to also allow execution of untagged languages. Dragon was designed primarily to execute Lisp, but also provides support for Cedar and Smalltalk. The FAIM-1 processor was designed around the OIL intermediate language, a high-level symbolic processing language. CRISP is based upon the Bell Labs C Machine, and was optimized for execution of programs written in the C language.

All three GaAs processors were designed for high level language execution. The CDC specifically supports, through the development of optimizing compilers, the Pascal and Ada languages. Whetstone represents a departure from the norm of

Table 4. RISC processors performance.

Processor	Cycle Time/Clock Rate	Instruction Rate (MIPS)
Accel	100 ns	3.2 MIPS
ARM	8 MHz	3-4 MIPS
AMD29300	125 ns	4-5 MIPS
CAP	I: 10 MHz, II: 25 MHz	12.5 MIPS peak, scalar unit
Clipper	33 MHz	5 MIPS
CRISP	16 MHz	> 10 MIPS
Dragon	10 MHz	5 MIPS per CPU
FAIM-1	?	?
MIPS	16.6 MHz	8 MIPS
Pyramid	125 ns	2-4 MIPS
Ridge 32	125 ns	1-4 MIPS
ROMP	170 ns	2 MIPS
Spectrum	30 MHz	10.8 MIPS
Transputer	50 ns	10 MIPS
Whetstone	50 ns	5-13.3 MIPS
MIPS-X	20 MHz	> 10 MIPS
SOAR	400 ns	See text
SPUR	150 ns	?
CDC GaAs	5 ns	91 MIPS
McD GaAs	10 ns	100 MIPS
RCA GaAs	200 MHz	200 MIPS peak

this survey by supporting an existing user base in the RDOS, SLICE, and IRIS systems.

Family requirements. A few processors were designed under the constraint of compatibility with an existing family of processors. The HP Spectrum gained some complexity by the requirement of object code compatibility with existing Hewlett-Packard computers. This level of compatibility carries with it a great marketing advantage, since users can experience at least a two times performance increase with existing applications by changing hardware.

The Whetstone design was completely constrained by the requirement of assembly code compatibility with Data General Nova 1200 computers. This provides a reduced architecture product that is software compatible with an existing user base. Both Ridge Computers and Pyramid Technology are working on new additions to their existing RISC-based computer products.

Advanced Micro Devices has announced a new AMD 29000 RISC processor. This 25-megahertz device, with 192 registers configured as a stack cache, a four-stage pipeline, provisions for macroinstructions (similar to the Clipper), and

single-cycle instruction execution, will be the next step beyond their current AMD 29300 series devices.

Performance notes

The processors in this survey can be divided into two performance groups. The largest group contains those processors with silicon implementations. From Table 4 we can see that most processors have cycle times in the range of 30 nanoseconds to 400 nanoseconds. The data in the Instruction Rate column are, where possible, average processing rates from measured or simulated benchmarks, and not peak processing rates. Transputer's 10 MIPS rate may be misleading, since it relies on the assumption that all instructions and operands reside in the on-chip RAM, with no external memory delays. Overall processing rates of multiprocessors such as SPUR, Transputer, and Dragon are scalable on the number of active processors.

A second performance group contains the gallium arsenide processors. These three processors are designed for a 200-megahertz clock. The clock rates and instruction rates are an order of magnitude

greater than those possible from silicon processors. The difference in instruction rate figures for the CDC and McD processors is most likely due to the measurement method.

SOAR's performance is compared to other Smalltalk systems, the Xerox Dorado, and the VAX 11/780. Benchmarks show SOAR operating at 50 percent of the Dorado rate and about six times faster than the VAX. Choice of benchmark has a tremendous effect on performance measurement, since SOAR is a language specific processor.

Reduced instruction set computers have quickly moved into many different application areas, indicating that the RISC philosophy can be applied to special purpose processors as well as to large general purpose computers. Most of these computers were designed for engineering and scientific computing. Few of the surveyed processors possess every characteristic commonly attributed to RISC designs. Most share some CISC characteristics, providing additional processing capacity for a given application. In fact, it is interesting to note that every processor surveyed contained architectural features typically attributed to CISCs, and every CISC feature was represented in at least one RISC design, indicating that in future designs good and useful architectural concepts will survive.

It should be obvious that an optimizing compiler is an integral part of any RISC design. Most RISCs use some form of delayed branching and also require code reorganization for optimum performance. The development of optimizing compilers and reorganizers often lags behind development of new computing hardware. One must be certain these tools exist for the language in which their applications programs are to be implemented.

We can expect to see more introductions of RISC machines in 1987 and beyond. Several of the recently introduced processors have begun to find their way into commercially available systems (such as Clipper in Opus Systems personal mainframe computers, Integraph workstations, and an IBM PC accelerator card). We can expect this trend to continue as software support of these processors matures. □

Acknowledgment

This research has been partially supported by NCR.

References

General References

1. D.A. Patterson and J. Hennessy, "Response to 'Computers, Complexity, and Controversy'," *IEEE Computer*, November 1985, pp. 142-143.

2. M.G.H. Katevenis, *Reduced Instruction Set Computer Architecture for VLSI*, Ph.D. Thesis, University of California, Berkeley, Calif., October 1983.

3. R.P. Colwell, C.Y. Hitchcock III, E.D. Jensen, H.M.B. Sprunt, and C. P. Kollar, "Computers, Complexity, and Controversy," *IEEE Computer*, September 1985, pp. 8-19.

4. J.R. Mashey, "RISC, MIPS, and the Motion of Complexity," *Proc. UNIFORUM*, February 1986.

5. M.E. Hopkins, "A Definition of RISC," *Proc. International Workship on High-Level Computer Architecture*, Univ. of Maryland, College Park, Md., 1984, pp. 3.8-3.11.

6. D. Tabak, "Which System is RISC," *IEEE Computer*, Vol. 19, No. 10, October 1986, pp. 85-86.

7. N. Mokhoff, "New RISC Machines Appear as Hybrids with Both RISC and CISC Features," *Computer Design*, April 1, 1986, pp. 22-25.

8. R. Weiss, "RISC Processors: The New Wave in Computer Systems," *Computer Design*, Vol. 26, No. 10, May 15, 1987, pp. 53-73.

Accel Processor

9. *C1260/C1230 ACCEL Architecture Overview*, Celerity Computing, pn. 650 902, December 1985.

10. N. Mokhoff, "Unix-Based CAE RISC Architectures and Software Products Link to PCs and Supercomputers," *Computer Design*, February 15, 1986, p. 96.

ARM Processor

11. "At 3 MIPS, RISC Processor is among Fastest Chips Around," *Electronics*, August 26, 1985, pp. 48-49.

AMD 29300 Processor

12. B. Case, "Building Blocks Yield Fast 32-Bit RISC Machines," *Computer Design*, July 1, 1985, pp. 111-117.

CAP Processor

13. S.G. Morton and F. Tse, "ITT CAP—A Parallel RISC Architecture for Personal Supercomputing," ITT-Advanced Technology Center, Shelton, Conn., March 1986.

CLIPPER Processor

14. H. Sachs, "The Fairchild CLIPPER Microprocessor Family—A High Performance 32-Bit Processor," *Proc. WESCON '85*, IEEE, N.Y., November 1985.

15. H. Sachs and W. Hollingsworth, "A High Performance 846,000 Transistor UNIX Engine—The Fairchild CLIPPER," *Proc. WESCON '85*, IEEE, N.Y., November 1985.

16. H. Sachs, "Improved Cache Scheme Boosts System Performance," *Computer Design*, November 1, 1985.

CRISP Processor

17. D.R. Ditzel, H.R. McLellan, and A.D. Berenbaum, "The Hardware Architecture of the CRISP Microprocessor," *Proceedings, 14th Annual International Symposium on Computer Architecture*, IEEE Computer Society Press, Los Alamitos, Calif., June 1987, pp. 309-319.

Dragon Processor

18. H.J. Hindin, "High-End Workstations Incorporate New Technologies," *Computer Design*, October 15, 1985, pp. 30-38.

19. L. Monier and P. Sidhu, "The Architecture of the Dragon," *Proc. COMPCON*, IEEE Computer Society Press, Los Alamitos, Calif., 1985, pp. 118-121.

FAIM-1 Processor

20. J.M. Anderson, W.S. Coates, A.L. Davis, R.W. Hon, I.N. Robinson, S. V. Robison, and K.S. Stevens, "The Architecture of FAIM-1," *IEEE Computer*, Vol. 20, No. 1, January 1987, pp. 55-65.

MIPS Processor

21. M. DeMoney, J. Moore, and J. Mashey, "Operating System Support on a RISC," *Proc. COMPCON S'86*, IEEE Computer Society Press, Los Alamitos, Calif., March 1986.

22. J. Moussouris, L. Crudele, D. Freitas, C. Hasen, E. Hudson, R. March, S. Przybylski, T. Riordan, C. Rowen, and D. Van't Hof, "A CMOS RISC Processor with Integrated System Functions," *Proc. COMPCON S'86*, IEEE Computer Society Press, Los Alamitos, Calif., March 1986,

Ridge Computers

23. *Ridge Processor Reference Manual*, Ridge Computers, No. 9008-C, September 1985.

24. E. Basart, "The Ridge Operating System: High Performance through Message-Passing and Virtual Memory," *Proc. 1st International Conference on Computer Workstations*, IEEE Computer Society Press, Los Alamitos, Calif., November 1985, pp. 134-143.

25. E. Basart, "RISC Design Streamlines High-Power CPUs," *Computer Design*, July 1985.

ROMP Processor

26. D.E. Waldecker and P.Y. Woon, "ROMP/MMU Technology Introduction," *IBM RT Personal Computer Technology*, Form No. SA23-1057, 1986, pp. 44-47.

27. P.D. Hester, R.O. Simpson, and A. Chang, "The IBM RT PC ROMP and Memory Management Unit Architecture," *IBM RT Personal Computer Technology*, Form No. SA23-1057, 1986, pp. 48-56.

28. D.E. Waldecker, C.G. Wright, M.S. Schmookler, T.G. Whiteside, R.D. Groves, C.P. Freeman, and A. Torres, "ROMP/MMU Implementation," *IBM RT Personal Computer Technology*, Form No. SA23-1057, 1986, pp. 57-65.

Spectrum Precision Architecture

29. J.S. Birnbaum and W.S. Worley,Jr., "Beyond RISC: High-Precision Architecture," *Proc. COMPCON S'86*, IEEE Computer Society Press, Los Alamitos, Calif., March 1986, pp. 40-47.

30. D.S. Coutant, C.L. Hammond, and J.W. Kelly, "Compilers for the New Generation of Hewlett-Packard Computers," *Proc. COMPCON S'86*, IEEE Computer Society Press, Los Alamitos, Calif., March 1986, pp. 48-61.

Transputer Processor

31. C. Whitby-Strevens, "The Transputer," *Proc. 12th Annual International Symposium on Computer Architecture*, IEEE Computer Society Press, Los Alamitos, Calif., June 1985.

32. K. Smith, "Inmos Finally Unveils the 32-Bit Transputer," *Electronics*, October 7, 1985, pp. 20-21.

33. "The Transputer Spawns a Radically New Computer," *Electronics*, October 7, 1985, pp. 43-45.

Whetstone Processor

34. Whetstone I and Whetstone II Product Technical Briefs, Integrated Digital Products Corp., Anaheim, California, 1986.

35. P. Goodrich, "Simple System Approach Increases Throughput," *Mini-Micro Systems*, May 1985.

36. P. Goodrich, "What Is It? Making Sense out of the RISC Confusion," *Data Base Monthly*, June 1986, pp. 30-33.

MIPS-X Processor

37. M. Horowitz and P. Chow, "The MIPS-X Microprocessor," *Proc. WESCON 85*, IEEE, N.Y., November 1985, pp. 6/1.1-6/1.6.

SOAR Processor

38. D. Ungar, R. Blau, P. Foley, D. Samples, and D. Patterson, "Architecture of SOAR: Smalltalk on a RISC," *Proc. 11th Annual International Symposium on Computer Architecture*, IEEE Computer Society Press, Los Alamitos, Calif., June 1984, pp 188-197.

Published in *IEEE Computer*, September 1987, by Charles Gimarc and Veljko Milutinovic.

SPUR

39. M.D. Hill, S.J. Eggers, J.R. Larus, G.S. Taylor, G. Adams, B.K. Bose, G.A. Gibson, P.M. Hansen, J. Keller, S.I. Kong, C.G. Lee, D. Lee, J.M. Pendleton, S.A. Ritchie, D.A. Wood, B.G. Zorn, P.N Hilfinger, D. A. Hodges, R.H. Katz, J. Ousterhout, and D.A. Patterson, "SPUR: A VLSI Multiprocessor Workstation," *Report No. UCB/CSD 86/273*, University of California, Berkeley, Calif., December 1985.

CDC GaAs Processor

40. E.R. Fox, K.J. Kiefer, R.F. Vangen, and S.P. Whalen, "Reduced Instruction Set Architecture for a GaAs Microprocessor System," *IEEE Computer*, October 1986.

McDonnel Douglas Processor

41. T.L. Rasset, R.R. Niederland, J.H. Lane, and W.A. Geideman, "A 32-Bit RISC Implemented in Enhancement Mode JFET GaAs," *IEEE Computer*, Vol. 19, No. 10, October 1986, pp. 60-68.

RCA GaAs Processor

42. V. Milutinovic, D. Fura, and W. Helbıg, "An Introduction to GaAs Microprocessor Architecture for VLSI," *IEEE Computer*, March 1986, pp. 30-42.

43. W. Helbig and V. Milutinovic, "Architecture and Design of a 32-Bit GaAs Microprocessor," *High-Level Language Computer Architectures*, (V. Milutinovic, ed.). Computer Science Press, Rockville, Md., 1986.

Charles E. Gimarc is currently a doctoral student in electrical engineering at Purdue University. He has held design engineering positions at Texas Instruments and Ampex Corp. He has also been a computer systems engineer in the Digital Signal Processing Laboratory at the Georgia Institute of Technology. His research interests include computer architectures for digital signal processing.

Gimarc received a BSEE degree from Texas A&M University and an MSEE from the Georgia Institute of Technology. He is a student member of the IEEE and the Audio Engineering Society.

Veljko M. Milutinović is on the faculty of the School of Electrical Engineering at Purdue University. He has published over 60 technical papers, two books, and four edited books. His current interests include VLSI computer architecture for GaAs, high-level language computer architecture, and artificial intelligence computer architecture. He has consulted for a number of high-tech companies and is currently involved in the industrial implementation of a 32-bit VLSI microprocessor for GaAs technology, with responsibilities in the microarchitecture domain.

Milutinović received his PhD from the University of Belgrade in 1982. He is a senior member of the IEEE and is on the Euromicro board of directors.

Readers may write to Milutinović at the School of Electrical Engineering, Purdue University, West Lafayette, IN 47907.

WHERE THERE'S RISC, THERE'S OPPORTUNITY

As more vendors field pure RISCs and streamline CISCs,
VARs, OEMs and system integrators
could realize price/performance breakthroughs

Andrew Allison, Contributing Editor

In late 1987, AT&T Co. and Sun Microsystems Inc. announced plans to outfit Sun's SPARC reduced instruction set computer (RISC) microprocessor with a new UNIX operating environment. In a related announcement, Areté Systems Corp., a manufacturer of multiprocessor systems that support 16 to 256 users, revealed that it would build high-performance computers based on Sun silicon—the scalable processor architecture chip—by the latter part of 1988. (Areté promises superminicomputer performance at supermicrocomputer prices.)

These developments, along with Xerox Corp.'s endorsement of the SPARC chip, should send a strong signal to value-added resellers and system integrators competing in

the microcomputer, workstation and super-microcomputer arenas. RISC architecture, along with streamlined complex instruction set computer (CISC) processors and the UNIX operating system, will dramatically change price/performance of products from add-in processors to systems, from microcomputers to minicomputers.

And price/performance is the name of the game, especially in the hotly contested workstation market. Manufacturers of the workhorses in this class—currently dominated by Motorola Inc.'s MC68020 microprocessor—are beginning to embrace RISC concepts and to recognize the performance leaps they offer. "Competitive high-performance workstations require the use of RISCs," says Forest Baskett, vice president of R&D at workstation vendor

MINI-MICRO SYSTEMS/January 1988

"Where There's Risk, There's Opportunity" by A. Allison, *Mini-Micro Systems*, January 1988, pages 49–62.

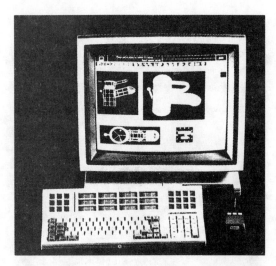

The Intergraph InterPro 200 *workstation series uses the Clipper RISC chip to pack added functionality into the same package used for the original InterPro 32C, the first merchant-market RISC workstation.*

Silicon Graphics Inc. He adds, "Sun's SPARC microprocessor offers 2-to-3 times, and MIPS Computer Systems Inc.'s R2000 about 4 times, the performance of the MicroVAX 3000 in workstation implementations."

These developments also climax 14 months of RISC ventures since *Mini-Micro Systems* last investigated RISC technology and products ("RISCs challenge mini, micro suppliers," MMS November 1986, Page 127). Since then, the benefits of streamlined architecture have become clear. With several "pure RISC" system implementations and well-established CISC architectures being streamlined by the incorporation of RISC features, the methodology has entered the mainstream of computer systems design.

Microcomputers take RISC plunge

Like the microprocessors on which they are based, RISC microcomputers fall into two categories: powerful, typically application-specific,

---

RISCs are register-rich with time to share

RISC (more accurately, streamlined) architectures make use of several "reduced instruction set computer" techniques to minimize the total number of clock cycles required to execute programs. Instruction-set simplification, which typically eliminates microcoding, greatly reduces the amount of control logic and hence makes possible powerful single-chip implementations. Also, load-and-store architectures reduce the delays associated with data access. Up to 50 percent of the instructions executed in a typical CISC (complex instruction set computer) access data memory, and less than 20 percent are register-to-register operations. In a load-and-store architecture executing the same functions, these percentages may well be reversed.

Because streamlined processors use registers more extensively, they typically have a minimum of two sets of 16 working registers. Some offer as many as 16 banks of 32, often overlapped to facilitate parameter passing. The use of register-rich architectures originated with the University of California at Berkeley researchers and contrasts with the Stanford University-IBM Corp. approach, which stresses compiler technology.

At current levels of compiler optimization, reduced instruction sets typically require 15 percent to 20 percent more, albeit faster, instructions to execute the same functions as complex ones. While this puts

Separating the instruction *and data paths, a common feature of current RISC implementations, helps lower the clock cycles per instruction.*

a premium on instruction-memory bandwidth, the data-memory bandwidth requirements of register-oriented architectures are much lower than for memory-oriented architectures. As a result, streamlined architectures frequently use separate instruction and data paths (i.e., Harvard architecture, see Diagram). Dual caches, sometimes with their own

add-in processors for standard buses; and general-purpose systems.

Add-in processors based on the Novix Inc. family of microRISCs, for example, are being used in image-processing applications such as graphics, image enhancement, OCR (optical character recognition) and machine vision. The FORTH programming language, directly executed by Novix's NC series, is also well-suited to motion-control and disk (especially optical-disk) controllers. Robotics applications are also proving popular.

Calay Systems Inc., a leading supplier of design-automation systems for printed-circuit board (PCB) layout, introduced an NC4000-based product in September 1986. The RPR-7 Autorouting Accelerator, a $19,000 Q-bus-compatible PCB autorouting processor with up to 2M bytes of local grid storage (externally expandable to 16M bytes) and 1M byte of program memory, runs Calay's routing software 15 times faster than a Digital Equipment

Corp. VAX-11/780—equivalent to 15 MIPS. Another example of an add-in product is the Fast9 PC/AT coprocessor from Quintek Ltd., which incorporates nine T414 or T800 transputers, each with 1M byte of RAM. This

---

Price/performance is the name of the game in the hotly contested workstation market.

$25,950 add-in processor is said to deliver 13.5 MFLOPS (million floating point operations per second).

For general-purpose systems, MIPS Computer has been the leading board-level RISC supplier, but it is de-emphasizing this area in order to concentrate on various systems. However, the board-level products, typically VMEbus-compatible, provide a relatively painless way

---

MMUs (memory-management units) are also common, and single-cycle cache access is a significant advantage.

An instruction cache can be viewed as a dynamically alterable, writeable control store. This capability facilitates optimization for execution of high-level languages or specific applications. It may include allocation of the internal resources, e.g., of registers between general-purpose and cache utilization.

Get over pipeline stalls

Most modern processors employ pipelining. If the execution of one instruction depends upon the results of a preceding one, the pipeline must be halted until the results are available, and it often must be flushed and refilled. The most common cause of a pipeline "bubble" is a branch instruction and, instead of simply clearing the pipeline, many streamlined processors continue to execute instructions until the branch destination becomes available. This uses machine cycles that otherwise would be wasted (delayed branching). Some RISC architectures attempt to predict the branch destination instead.

Streamlining is also influencing traditional microprocessor design. Tom Johnson, manager of technical communications for Motorola Inc.'s Microprocessor Group, points out that, "New technology tends to merge with old to obtain the best of both worlds." He adds, "Streamlining is an implementation methodology that can equally well be

applied to existing architectures." For example, the average cycles per instruction has declined for successive implementations of the MC68000 architecture—from 12 for the 8-MHz 68010 to 5.5 for the 20-MHz 68030.

Johnson says, "The applicable streamlining techniques, especially those that reduce memory-bandwidth requirements, have been incorporated into the 68030." Specifically, execution-unit control points and several instructions have been hardwired, and the instruction and data paths have been separated (each with its own 256-byte on-chip cache). A three-stage pipeline was determined to be the best trade-off between architecture and performance, but the MMU has been brought onboard, and a highly autonomous bus controller prioritizes bus accesses. The multiple internal operations occurring in parallel reduce the effective cycle time of the two-cycle execution unit towards the RISC goal of an instruction per cycle, and Motorola is claiming for the 68030 double the performance of the 68020. Motorola has also been working on a "pure- RISC" design, the M78000. Intel Corp. has acknowledged that it too is developing a RISC chip.

Johnson also draws attention to a frequently overlooked aspect of RISC technology development in pointing out that, "The development of RISCs is resulting in very rapid advances in compiler technology, the benefits of which accrue to all computer architectures, RISC, CISC or hybrid."

for OEMs to gain access to RISC technology. Because any developer of RISC machines would find it difficult to market the product without one, such subsystems will proliferate.

An evolving relationship between MIPS Computer and Prime Computer Inc. illustrates the flexibility provided by the board-level approach. When Prime, an early OEM of the MIPS Computer boards, concluded it was not cost-effective to develop the graphics capability needed for high-end workstations, the two companies went to Silicon Graphics. Now, MIPS Computer supplies board-level products to Silicon Graphics, which integrates its geometry engine and then supplies Prime which, in turn, adds its own software and support value.

Advances on the systems front

The first "microRISC" system to market, IBM Corp.'s RT PC, was introduced on Jan. 21, 1986. With a base price of $11,700, roughly

MIPS Computer's R2000 *chip incorporates a 10-MIPs CPU, a memory-management unit and cache control in a custom 100,000 transistor package.*

Sparking an interest in microRISC

The SPARC, scalable processor architecture, from Sun Microsystems Inc. (manufactured by Fujitsu Microelectronics Inc.) is a University of California at Berkeley-style RISC (reduced instruction set computer). It has load-and-store architecture, delayed branches and up to 32 banks of 24 overlapped (by eight) registers and eight global registers in the IU (integer unit). The initial implementation of the IU, in a single Fujitsu 20,000 gate array, has six register banks. Floating-Point operations are carried out in a companion FPU (floating point unit) with 32 working registers. These initially were implemented as a controller interfacing the Weitek Corp. 1164/65 chip-set. Provision has also been made for a second, implementation-definable, coprocessor.

In addition to Fujitsu, the SPARC architecture has been licensed to Cypress Semiconductor Corp. and Bipolar Integrated Technology Inc. for marketing as a merchant-market microprocessor and to AT&T Co. for use in workstation products. This broad-based licensing makes it very likely that SPARC will become widely used.

Also, "microRISCs," like the SPARC are catching the eye of many OEMs, because they are so compact that they can be accommodated in moderately sized gate arrays and standard cells. That compactness and the availability of powerful ASIC (application-specific integrated circuit) design tools will encourage the development of application-specific processors (ASPs). Likely targets include

floating-point, vector and digital signal processors. In fact, several ASP graphics processors have already reached the market. RISC-based compute, file and terminal-network servers, back-end (database management), front-end (communications and network control), and other I/O processors have also begun to appear—as have artificial-intelligence-specific microprocessors. Because of the impact of transferring data across chip boundaries and between levels of the memory hierarchy, ASPs will be integrated into extraordinarily powerful single-chip implementations as circuit density continues its relentless advance.

At the end of last November, MIPS Computer responded to Sun's aggressive entry into the microRISC market with the announcement of three semiconductor manufacturing licencees of its own: Integrated Device Technology Inc., LSI Logic Corp. and Performance Semiconductor Corp. This multiple licensing of microRISC architectures seems certain to spread, limiting their proliferation and rapidly driving down the price of high-performance 32-bit microprocessors.

Although all of the currently available RISC microprocessors are implemented in CMOS, their low transistor count makes them suitable for a broad range of semiconductor technologies. SPARC, for example, is being implemented in ECL (emitter-coupled logic) and in GaAs (gallium arsenide) semiconductors.

Sun Microsystems' Sun-4/200 *workstation, based on Sun's SPARC microprocessor, delivers performance comparable to DEC's VAX 8700.*

The 4M-byte maximum memory, 200K-byte Whetstones floating-point performance, inadequate graphics and I/O performance, and a lack of connectivity (especially local area network support) inhibited the acceptance of the RT. Just over a year after the RT's introduction, IBM announced enhancements:

• 1-micron/100-nsec CMOS versions of the initial 1.8-micron/170-nsec NMOS CPU and MMU (memory-management unit) in a single-board implementation;

• 1M-byte dynamic memory chips quadrupled the memory board capacity to 4M or 8M bytes and the system maximum to 16M bytes;

• Quadrupled disk transfer speed (to 1.08M bytes per second), and high-resolution color and monochrome support.

double that of the PC/AT at the time. IBM claimed the RT PC offered about 3 times the AT's performance. The ROMP (Research/Office Products Division Microprocessor) used in the RT PC is a full 32-bit, three-stage pipelined derivative of an IBM RISC minicomputer, the 801, that was never introduced. Its AIX (Advanced Interactive Executive) operating system, developed under contract by Interactive Systems Corp., is an "enhanced" (read proprietary) version of UNIX System V Release 1, with selected Release 2 and Berkeley 4.2 BSD improvements.

'Competitive high-performance workstations require the use of RISCs.'

At the same time. IBM replaced the original National Semiconductor Corp. NS32081 floating-point unit with a standard Motorola MC68881 unit (on the motherboard) and added an optional floating point accelerator. More than 80 percent of the new system's cost was said to be based on IBM products and technology.

WHERE THE CHIPS FALL	NC4000	T800	R2000	5100	SPARC	AM29000
First delivered	1985	1985	1986	1987	1987	1987
Developer	Novix	Inmos	MIPS	Ridge	Sun	AMD
Instructions[1]	48/48	22/9	79/75	70/60	89/43	115/N/A
Technology	CMOS	CMOS	CMOS	CMOS	CMOS	CMOS
Registers[2]	ext.	4	32	16	120	192[4]
Pipeline stages	none	none	5	3	4	4
Harvard architecture	Y	N	N	Y	N	Y
Cycle time (nsec)[3]	167	50/150	60	62.5/125	60	40
Transistors	16K	238K	100K	50K	50K	N/A
On-chip subsystems (cache (K bytes)/MMU/FPU)	–/N/N	4/N/Y	–/Y/N	–/Y/N	–/N/N	–/Y/N

Notes: [1]Instructions/single-cycle instructions
[2]Excluding integral FPU registers
[3]Processor/main memory buses (if different)
[4]Dynamically assignable (stack-cache/registers)

Source: compiled from industry sources

With the introduction of IBM's PS/2 Model 80 and OS/2, it seems likely that the RT PC will become the company's vehicle for penetrating the UNIX market. However, when compared with the other microRISC workstations introduced last year, the RT PC's performance remains unexciting (see Table). Another upgrade, incorporating the PS/2 Micro Channel Architecture and other enhancements, is expected soon. Like the other established minicomputer and superminicomputer suppliers, IBM faces nettlesome problems in trying to market competitive workstation products, without cannibalizing its established product lines.

RISCy maneuvers among minicomputer makers

The handful of RISC (reduced instruction set computer) minicomputer suppliers—among them Ridge Computers Inc., Pyramid Technology Corp., Computer Consoles Inc. and Harris Corp.—will feel the market heat generated by "microRISCs." Only Ridge, which delivered the first RISC minicomputers as workstations, in September 1983, seems to have anticipated the threat. During 1986, the company repositioned itself as a general-purpose UNIX system supplier with the introduction of the Ridge 3200, which offers about the same performance as Sun Microsystems Inc.'s Sun-4 and a System V-based implementation of UNIX (RX/V) incorporating the TEN/PLUS user interface developed by Interactive System Corp.

Last September, Ridge introduced a high-performance microRISC system, the 5100. This single-board implementation of Ridge's architecture puts the CPU on the same Fujitsu Microelectronics Inc. 1.5-micron CMOS 20,000 gate-array as Sun's IU (integer unit). The implementation uses branch-prediction, instead of the more common delayed-branches technique, and an MMU (memory-management unit) that accesses separate, 32K-byte-to-128K-byte instruction and data caches in a single cycle. A companion FPU (floating point unit) is implemented in another Fujitsu gate array.

Running at 16 MHz to maintain compatibility with Ridge's 125-nsec (8-MHz) backplane timing, the 5100, according to Ridge, delivers about twice the performance of the Sun-4 and 10 percent to 20 percent more performance than the MIPS Computer Systems Inc. M/1000.

Despite the RISC plunge by this handful of vendors, only one major traditional minicomputer manufacturer has fully embraced RISC technology. Hewlett-Packard Co. continues to shift its product line to implementations of its Performance Architecture. Originally announced in February 1986, the Spectrum products suffered delays caused by difficulty in attaining backward compatibility, primarily with the I/O portion of HP's MPE XL operating system. Delivery began in November 1986 of the first of the new products, the 3000 Series 930, based on a 125-nsec TTL (transistor-to-transistor logic) implementation of the architecture.

This was followed last May by the UNIX-based 9000 Series 840S, and by the 825S in August. The Series 800 is an extension of the HP 1000 and HP 9000 technical computer product lines, with the 840S offering about 35 percent better performance than the 825S.

The first shipments of systems using a single-chip NMOS (N-channel metal-oxide semiconductor) implementation, the 3000/950 and 9000/850S, occurred last September and October, respectively. The 930 is roughly equivalent in performance to the (16-bit) 3000 Series 70, while the 950 is 2-to-2.5 times more powerful. The 850S offers about twice the performance of the 825S. A new low-end product, the 925 (positioned between models 52 and 58 and intended to compete with Digital Equipment Corp.'s MicroVAX 3000), is scheduled for introduction this Spring.

Meanwhile at DEC, RISC remains a research curio. "Digital is always investigating new technology, and, as has been publicized in the past, we have evaluated and implemented RISC machines in research," says Dom LaCava, manager of DEC's Low-End Systems Group. "The fundamental business assumption for offering a RISC machine is that it offers superior price/performance over current computer architectures. However, this price/performance is not without sacrifice—incompatibility with more than 10 years of software investment by applications developers and our customers."

DEC's position contrasts sharply with that of HP, which has (with some difficulty) switched to a source-compatible RISC architecture. LaCava does add, "If we discover through our customers that the benefits of RISCs outweigh the costs, Digital certainly has the capability to implement computers with this type of CPU." Actually, MicroVAX processor implementations have been selectively incorporating RISC methodology for several years, and it can only be a matter of time before DEC responds to the market.

RISC MICROCOMPUTER MOUNTS THE VAX ATTACK

Company	Product	Microprocessor	Dhrystones	DP Whetstones	DP LINPACK KFLOPS	Backplane	Base price*
digital	VAX-8700	N/A	10,416	2,670	970	VAXBI	$433K
IBM	RT PC	ROMP	6,500	1,400	300	AT	$20K
mips	M/1000	R2000	23,700	7,900	1,100	VME	$59.2K
RIDGE	5100	5100	23,020	7,000	1,960	proprietary	$109K
SUN	Sun-4/200	SPARC	19,000	N/A	1,100	VME	$85.5K

Source: compiled from industry sources

MIPS Computer was the next microRISC supplier to market, with the joint introduction of the R2000 processor (a 100,000-transister unit, with a 10-MIPs CPU and cache control) and the M/500 system in May 1986. In a comparison of RISC microcomputer performance, the M/500 outperforms the DEC VAX 8600 superminicomputer at about one-tenth the price—$38,000 versus $350,000. The company introduced faster processors, single-board computers and systems in March (M/800) and July (M/1000) of 1986. John Moussouris, vice president of engineering at MIPS, expects to achieve "a better than 50 percent speed improvement per year." Unlike most of the current crop of RISC microcomputers, the MIPS systems are marketed as network servers and general-purpose systems, rather than as workstations.

In June 1986, workstation supplier Intergraph Corp. announced its first RISC workstation, the InterPro 32C. This CAE system, based on the (then Fairchild Semiconductor Corp.'s) Clipper chip, offers 6M bytes of RAM, an 80M-byte fixed disk drive and a 1.2M-byte flexible disk drive, a 15-inch 1,184-by-884-pixel color monitor, an Ethernet controller, three RS232 ports, keyboard and mouse, plus UNIX System V, for $25,000. Stressing the performance gains associated with RISCs, John Hubbard, Intergraph's executive manager of workstation marketing, reports that, "The Clip-

per-based system has 6-to-10 times the performance of the NS32032-based product that it replaced."

Intergraph has made a major commitment to the Clipper chip. In June 1986, the company added 10 Clipper-based products to its Inter-Pro line: the InterAct series of dual-screen and the InterView series of large-scale digitizing

---

Well-established CISC architectures are being streamlined by the incorporation of RISC features.

---

workstations, along with two VMEbus-compatible plot, file and compute servers. In September 1987, Intergraph announced that it would purchase Fairchild's entire Clipper operation as part of the latter company's sale to National Semiconductor Corp., and that it would actively pursue design wins for the component as well as pursue hardware and software enhancements.

Also in June 1986, Texas Instruments Inc. introduced the Explorer II, an artifical-intelligence workstation based on the CLM (Compact LISP Machine) microprocessor originally developed by TI as a DARPA (Defense Advanced Research Projects Agency) project. The CLM is a 32-bit RISC-like processor microprogrammed to support Common LISP. The high performance of RISC architectures and the relative ease with which they can be optimized makes them attractive for AI applications. Other RISCs available from TI include a family of digital signal processors and the TMS34010, a 6-MIPS RISC-based graphics processor.

The following month, Sun announced a RISC-based workstation. Based on a CMOS gate-array implementation of a RISC architecture developed by Sun, the Sun-4 is said to offer 4-to-5 times the performance of the Sun-3, which uses the 16.67-MHz 68020-68881 combination and the same Weitek Corp. floating point accelerator. Sun expects to increase processor performance fivefold within two years. A diskless, entry-level Sun-4/260 system with 8M bytes of memory and a monochrome monitor is priced at $39,900 and, like the other micro-RISC suppliers, Sun is also offering server configurations. Sun-3 systems, with which the Sun-4 is source-code compatible, can be upgraded by swapping CPU boards.

Clearly, RISC design methodology is having a significant impact on microcomputer systems. In the workstation market, the pre-eminence of the 68020 chip is being challenged by microRISCs and Intel Corp. 80386-based products. Dave House, senior vice president and general manager of Intel's Microcomputer Component Group suggests, "It's just a matter of time before the engineering workstation market becomes a 386 market." However, despite the instant popularity of 80386-based MS-DOS emulation engines, this claim should be taken with a grain of salt.

Independent benchmark tests consistently show the 68020 outperforming the 80386 in the UNIX environment and Motorola claims twice the performance of the 68020 for the recently introduced 68030, first sampled last year. System suppliers and value-added resellers currently committed to the Motorola products will do well to think carefully before even considering a switch to Intel. The demand for MS-DOS compatibility can be met much less expensively with high-performance PC/AT clones, and it will be two or three years at best before OS/2 application software becomes a factor in the workstation market.

MicroRISCs, in contrast, do represent a viable challenge to 680X0-based products. They offer 2-to-3 times the performance of today's 68020-based workstations, and the gap seems more likely to widen. Furthermore, unlike the MS-DOS world, workstation applications are largely written in high-level languages and run under UNIX, making them relatively easy to port to new architectures. The de facto standardization of the VMEbus in this market further facilitates substitution. Two of the leading workstation suppliers, Sun and Apollo Computer Inc., have already made their decision, developing RISCs for high-performance applications.

But, most resellers won't have the wherewithal to devote the significant effort necessary to develop their own RISC, despite the fact it is perhaps an order of magnitude less than for a CISC. However, integrating a RISC microprocessor will be less difficult and less expensive for many of them. Intergraph's Hubbard, for example, points out that, "Although we had done some of the preliminary design work

---

Intergraph has said that it will pursue design wins for the Clipper chip and explore software and hardware enhancements.

---

ahead of time, it took only 90 days from receipt of our first Clipper silicon to demonstrating the InterPro 32C at a trade show." It is, of course necessary to have available UNIX support (OS, compilers and support software) to achieve this kind of turnaround. As another example, the design of Calay's RPR-7, which started as a long-shot alternative to a bit-slice implementation, took about six months.

As might be expected, the general-purpose, multiuser market has more stringent criteria. Rick Gimble, director of product marketing at Sequent Computer Systems Inc., says: "Sequent's architecture allows for incorporation of new microprocessors, and it may be that ultimately a RISC will be the best solution. However, that will not happen until a product establishes enough momentum to create massive software support [i.e. database], rather than the UNIX, C and FORTRAN typically offered." The cost of porting and validating the software required for general-purpose systems is prohibitive for most suppliers. Nevertheless, Intergraph, MIPS and Sun are all offering network servers, and RISCs are beginning to penetrate the general-purpose systems market. Departmental processors will be the next class of products to feel the price/performance pressure engendered by RISCs.

A reseller considering the use of microRISC components or systems should carefully bal-

---

Board-level products, typically VME-compatible, offer OEMs painless access to RISC technology.

---

ance the price/performance benefits against the costs. In addition to conversion cost, supplier viability and the level of support available must be considered—as must the actual performance increments likely to be achieved. One caution: real performance may bear little relationship to benchmark data provided by the supplier. Consequently, great care should be taken to match the benchmarks to the intended use.

Particular attention should be paid to arithmetic requirements (i.e., the mix of integer, single-precision and double-precision floating-

point) and to cache use (most published benchmarks are small programs that don't overflow cache). Another thing to keep in mind is the relative ease with which RISC-based systems can be optimized for specific applications. This is good-news/bad-news for resellers because it will inevitably increase vertical integration on the part of system suppliers.

The risks associated with committing to a new processor can be alleviated by careful attention to standards and transportability. Keep the benefits of these in mind when developing your own hardware and avoid CPU-dependent code like the plague. □

Andrew Allison is a management consultant specializing in minicomputer and microcomputer technology, products and markets. Before establishing his practice in 1977, he was with Digital Equipment Corp., Rolm Corp. and Advanced Micro Devices.

Section 6: An Assessment of RISC

6.1 Background

For many years the general trend in computer architecture has been toward increasing CPU complexity: more instructions, more addressing modes, more specialized registers, and so on. The RISC movement represents a fundamental break with the philosophy behind that trend. Naturally, the appearance of RISC systems, and the publication of papers by its proponents extolling RISC virtues, has led to a reaction from what might be called the mainstream of computer architecture.

The work that has been done on assessing the merits of the RISC approach can be grouped into two categories

- *Quantitative:* attempts to compare program size and execution speed of programs on RISC and CISC machines that use comparable technology.
- *Qualitative:* examination of issues such as high-level language support and optimum use of VLSI real estate.

The success of the RISC approach in the marketplace is far from assured. As research, development, and product introduction continues, the assessment goes on. The articles in this section should give the reader an appreciation of the current status of that assessment.

6.2 Article Summary

The first article, "MIPS, Dhrystones, and Other Tales," serves to introduce the topic of quantitative assessment. The author points out the pitfalls of quantitative comparison and discusses several alternative techniques. Results are presented that compare some RISC and CISC machines.

The next two articles compare the Berkeley RISC machines to other contemporary computers. The Berkeley RISC machines are the best-documented and most-studied RISC systems. "Re-Evaluation of the RISC I" attempts to decouple the effects of a large register file from a reduced instruction set and to analyze the program size and execution time effects of the latter. "RISC Watch" assesses the performance of the second Berkeley machine, the RISC II.

"The Effect of Instruction Set Complexity on Program Size and Memory Performance" attempts to determine the effect of instruction set complexity on cache memory performance and bus traffic. The authors used a set of benchmark programs and several compilers for machines of varying instrucion set complexity.

"Toward Simpler, Faster Computers" provides a qualitative comparison of RISCs and CISCs.

Although recent RISC and RISC-like processor offerings appear to offer substantial price/performance advantages over CISC, current and forthcoming CISC processors continue to dominate the market. "Applications Determine the Choice of RISC or CISC" examines the reasons for the continued success of pure CISC machines.

The next article, with two responses, reports on a large and ongoing effort at Carnegie Mellon University to provide a comparative assessment of RISCs and CISCs. This is a thorough and probing analysis of the issues involved. Finally, "And Now a Case for More Complex Instruction Sets" takes the CISC side of the controversy and presents arguments in favor of CISCs.

MIPS, DHRYSTONES AND OTHER TALES
Omri Serlin

Summary: Simple performance indices are desirable, but can never capture the complex factors involved. Lack of standards and independent certification further detract from the usefulness of such popular measures as MIPS, Dhrystones, Whetstones, and Linpack MFLOPS. End users should rely on applications-related workloads to compare competing systems.

(This is a revised version of an article from the April, 1986 issue of the *Supermicro* newsletter; a condensed version of this article also appeared in the June 1st, 1986 issue of *Datamation*.)

+++

The recent "RISC MIPS" vs. "real MIPS" debate has refocused the industry's attention on computer performance measurement. But the quest for simple measures of computer performance dates back to the very early days of the modern digital computer[1]. Over the years, many different performance indexes have been developed, including MIPS, Whetstones, Dhrystones, LINPACK MFLOPS, and transactions/second (tps), to name a few.

There are several reasons for the continuing, intense interest in this subject. End-users would like to have simple performance indicators so that they could make straight-forward comparisons of several competing alternatives. Another end-user concern is capacity planning: the ability to predict when a particular system would have to be augmented or replaced in order to service the expected future load.

Manufacturers are concerned with performance measurements that help designers optimize future hardware architectures, operating systems, and language compilers for their intended applications.

Journalists and Wall Street analysts love to construct neat comparison tables, replete with dollars-per-MIPS factors, which are always popular with readers in the industry and the investment community.

Technical economists use performance indices to chart the chronological progress of technology, such as the decline in the cost-per-computation over the years. Technology trend charts have also played an important role in, for example, the debate about Grosch's Law and the merits of distributed vs. centralized computing[2].

What's wrong with simple indicators?
There are two key problems with such indicators. First, there is a fundamental difficulty in reducing a set of complex considerations and conditions into one simple number. It is not reasonable to expect that a single number could meaningfully characterize a computer system, just as it is unlikely that a single number could capture the essence of the various factors that affect the "goodness" of an automobile, a much simpler system.

Moreover, different users may value each aspect of the system's performance quite differently. A user with a transaction processing application is interested in the efficiency of the I/O system, database software, and communication protocols. Such a user is likely to be concerned with the magnitude and the consistency of the system's response time, but may care little for the CPU's ability to process floating point operations, or the compilation speed of the various compilers. In a technical, scientific, real-time or university environment, the set of priorities may be quite different.

The second problem is that, contrary to common misconception, there are no accepted industry standards for computing the value of MIPS or tps. Thus there is no assurance whatever that MIPS ratings reported for various system from various manufacturers are comparable in any sense. The recent arrival of RISC machines on the scene aggravates the problem.

Problems with "Standard" Benchmarks

Even when a sort of a standard does exist (e.g., Whetstones, Dhrystones, and LINPACK MFLOPS), there is no independent authority to certify performance claims. For example, Jack Dongarra of the Argonne National Laboratory, who publishes the very-widely-used results of the LINPACK benchmark, gives no guarantees regarding the authenticity of the performance data, which is supplied by a variety of sources. (He did tell this author, though, that he has "a 90% confidence in the numbers... I know the performance of the machines, and it matches the numbers").

Another complicating factor with the "standard" benchmarks is that multiple versions exist, which are not always identical. For example, version 1.0 of the Dhrystone benchmark, distributed by AT&T's Rick Richardson, whose results are posted on USENET and are widely quoted, yields about 15% better results relative to the version distributed by Reinhold Weicker, the benchmark's author. Richardson's "Version 1.1" is, supposedly, much closer to Weicker's intent.

A third difficulty is that the standard benchmarks can be run under a variety of conditions. For example, the Dhrystone benchmark can be run with and without registers. The Whetstone benchmark exists in single and double precision versions. Linpack can be run with standard, rolled, or assembly-coded BLAS (a key subroutine); in long or short precision; with 100 or 1000 equations; and with or without compiler directives to help in multiprocessor situations. Reported results often neglect to state these important conditions.

Operational problems can also lead to complications. For example, in 1985, grossly understated results were published in the press for one of AT&T's new 3B machines under the AIM Unix benchmarks. The problem was that, in interpreting the benchmark results, the machine's clock period was assumed to be much longer than it actually was. Most standard benchmarks are self-timing and rely on the system's hardware clocking facilities; any errors in interpreting these facilities, or in adapting the benchmark to use the internal clock, could seriously affect the results. It is generally better to repeat the test in a loop enough times so it can be timed with a stop watch.

Finally, reported results often neglect to mention important environmental factors that could have a significant impact. Among these: the operating system version; the machine's memory speed, when several options are available; the compiler version, and level of optimization invoked; the disk transfer rate and capacity (in I/O benchmarks); whether or not a floating point accelerator or coprocessor was employed; and so on. No serious comparison should ever be attempted unless the environment for each run is completely specified, and its implications understood.

Major Vendors' Approach

Major computer manufacturers rarely publish MIPS ratings for their systems; although DEC did advertise 6 MIPS for its 8650 system, and HP publicly claims 4.5 MIPS for the Spectrum processor in the models 3000/930 and 9000/840. Vendors are worried, on the one hand, that they may penalize themselves unnecessarily by quoting a conservative figure; and on the other, that some user might consider their claims excessive enough to justify legal action. Similar considerations apply with other performance measures for which there is no standard derivation procedure.

Instead, IBM and other major manufacturers typically characterize their new machines in relation to previous models. Performance data for that determination is usually derived from running a "job mix" of several representative programs on the new and old machines. With a few exceptions, manufacturers are very reluctant to publicly describe the exact procedure and programs used in deriving their relative performance figures; possibly because they do not wish competitors or users to be able to reproduce these.

Large vendors often have no company-wide standards for establishing relative performance. In 1982, for example, one Hewlett Packard division was characterizing the engineering-oriented Series 9000 (based on a proprietary, 32-bit microprocessor) as a 1 MIPS machine. At the same time, another HP division was claiming 3 MIPS for a much-lower cost, 16-bit A900 measurement and control computer. The two divisions were (and still are) using entirely different procedures to derive their performance claims. HP did introduce performance measurement standards for Spectrum-based models, which are currently being offered by two independent divisions.

Among major vendors, IBM is probably the most meticulous in measuring relative performance. To compare the low-end of 4300 series (4331 and 4341 models), introduced in 1979, to the older, System/370 models, IBM used a new suite of benchmarks, called the "Standard

Intermediate Systems Workload". The programs, developed jointly by SPD and several of the marketing divisions, included 7 typical commercial batch jobs, used to determine internal (CPU) performance; a transaction-oriented, CICS-based benchmark; and an interactive benchmark consisting of a collection of scripts simulating users doing various types of work under the VM operating system.

Great care was taken to assure identical conditions (peripherals, operating system parameters, etc.); when this was impossible, the differences were clearly enumerated. (Such differences are often due to differing characteristics of successive generation of equipment. Sometimes, however, even major vendors may have difficulty assembling substantial, identical configurations of several machines for "non productive" benchmark work). All told, more than 100 runs were required to complete the load under a variety of specified operating systems and other conditions. The internal IBM report on the results included more than 60 pages of small print and dozens of tables and charts.

Yet because IBM is highly compartmentalized into multiple, autonomous divisions, even today there is no single work load that can be used to compare the complete line of compatible mainframes (4300, 308X, 309X), even when using the same operating system. Incompatible operating systems (DOS/VSE, MVS, VM) further complicate the problem. The non-compatibles systems (S/1, S/36, S/38) present an even tougher problem, since their operating systems, support software, and language compilers are so drastically different than those for the mainline offerings.

Still, some progress has been made. Three key IBM performance centers (at Poughkeepsie and Endicott, NY; and Washington, DC) are today using a common workload to measure performance under the MVS operating system. The workload appears to be an extension of the SPD SISW mentioned above; it includes commercial batch, engineering/scientific batch, TSO interactive, IMS on-line, and CICS on-line work. Most of the measurements under this workload were performed on 308X and 4381 models; some portions were also run on the 4361 Mod 5 (in Germany).

Two internal IBM documents describe the results in exhaustive detail, one for MVS/370 and one for MVS/XA (the latter is the MVS version for the newer systems with 31-bit addressing; the original 360/370 used 24 bit addressing). These documents, while not generally available, are distributed to IBM sales people and are often discussed with prospective buyers.

International Data Corp. (Framingham, MA) is one of several independent organizations that have over the years attempted to provide their own relative performance measures, not just for IBM, but also for other vendors' gear. However, IDC numbers were not based on actual testing. Instead, they were derived from a paper-and-pencil formula, which assigned a performance basis of 45 "cuples" to the IBM System/370 Model 158-3, and relied mostly on the published IBM relative performance claims thereafter.

IDC never described this formula publicly, nor did it ever reveal how it derived numbers for non-IBM machines. There is reason to believe that the process included a good deal of "guesstimating" and group consensus. IDC decided to stop publishing its relative performance numbers, apparently because it reached the conclusion that the process by which they were derived was no longer adequate.

IBM goes on the Offensive

IBM became so concerned about performance claims by competitors vis-a-vis the latest 4381 models that, in mid-March, 1986, it hosted a special consultants' seminar on the subject, and even gave a special briefing dealing with performance measurement to the *Wall Street Journal*. IBM was principally worried about performance claims that suggested that DEC's 8650 and 8800 and DG's MV/20000 were considerably better in absolute performance and in price/performance relative to the latest 4381 Models 11, 12, 13 uniprocessor, and the dyadic Model 14.

In the presentation (which used "Vendor A" and "Vendor B" as thin disguises for DEC and DG, respectively), IBM showed how under different benchmarks and conditions, different conclusions could be drawn regarding the 4381 in relation to the competing machines. The 4381 gave best account of itself in engineering & scientific tasks requiring long (64 bit) precision, which IBM claims is really needed by the majority of such applications.

Based on direct testing of the DEC 8600, plus published claims of DEC and of DG relative to DEC, and using such published results as LINPACK, IBM concluded that, in long precision Whetstones, the 4381-14 dyadic matches DG's MV/20000 and is about 86% as fast as the DEC 8800. However, in long-precision LINPACK, as well as in running NASTRAN in LP, the 4381-13 matches the MV/20000, and the 4381-14 beats the 8800 by a factor of more than 1.5. The obvious moral of the story: simple numbers can't tell all; a detailed look behind the scenes is required for full understanding.

The origin and meaning of MIPS

One of the earliest attempts to characterize computer performance, in more meaningful terms than just its Add and Multiply execution times, was done around 1960 by IBM staffer J.C. Gibson[3]. He performed several *dynamic instruction traces* on programs written for the IBM 650 and 704 machines, and came up with his Gibson Mix, which made it possible to compute the execution time of an "average" instruction. The inverse of this measure became known as KIPS (later, MIPS): the number of average instructions executed per second.

A dynamic instruction trace requires either software or hardware instrumentation to record the type of each instruction as it is being executed. By performing such traces on a large (and, presumably, representative) body of programs, it is possible to determine how often a particular type of instruction is likely to be used in typical programs. Given the frequency of, and execution time for each instruction class, it is then possible to develop the execution time for an average instruction. Figure 1 shows such a Gibson Mix computation for a fairly representative non-IBM computer system from the early 1970s.

Fig. 1
Deriving MIPS from a Gibson Mix
For a 1970-Vintage Supermini

Instruction Category	Gibson Mix %	cpi	Weighted cpi
Load/Store	31.2	1.9	0.593
Add/Subtract	6.1	1.8	0.110
Multiply	0.6	10	0.060
Divide	0.2	18	0.036
Floating Add/Subtract	6.9	4	0.276
Floating Multiply	3.8	10	0.380
Floating Divide	1.5	18	0.270
Search/Compare	3.8	2	0.076
Test/Branch	16.6	1	0.166
Shift	4.4	2.8	0.123
Logical	1.6	1.3	0.021
No Memory Reference	5.3	1	0.053
Indexing	18.0	0	0.000
Cycles per average instruction (cpai) =			2.164

$$\begin{aligned} \text{MIPS} &= 1 / (\text{cpai} \times \text{cycle time in us}) \\ &= 1 / (2.164 \times 0.6) \\ &= 0.77 \end{aligned}$$

Source: O. Serlin, except mix % data: J.C. Gibson (see note 3).

Representative of the many other notable attempts at deriving performance figures based on instruction tracing was the one done in 1963 by Kenneth E. Knight on the IBM 704 and 7090 "scientific" and 705 "commercial" computers (see *Datamation*, September 1966, pp. 40-54). Knight computed his measure for 225 systems introduced between 1944 and 1963; but he was principally interested in quantifying technological change, rather than in accurate characterization of the performance of individual machines relative to each other.

At least three important recent architectures have been characterized by instruction frequencies obtained by tracing. Figures 2, 3, and 4 give the results for the IBM System/370, DEC VAX 11/780, and the Motorola 68000 family.

Fig. 2

System/370 Ten Most Frequent Instructions

Instruction		% Executions
BC -	Branch on Condition	20.2
L -	Load	15.5
TM -	Test under Mask	6.1
ST -	Store	5.9
LR -	Load Register	4.7
LA -	Load Address	4.0
LTR-	Test Register	3.8
BCR-	Branch on Register	2.9
MVC-	Move Characters	2.1
LH -	Load Halfword	1.8

Source: *IBM RT PC Computer Technology*, IBM Form No. SA23-1057, 1986, p. 81.

The chief advantage of the mix-based MIPS calculation was its simplicity. MIPS could be readily calculated from published instruction execution times, if one assumed Gibson's frequency data was correct for the specific target machine. The key drawback of the method was that this was rarely a correct assumption.

MIPS figures are useful only for comparisons among members of the same architectural family; they cannot be relied upon to compare systems which are architecturally substantially different. The following examples illustrate this point.

Some of the subtleties and difficulties involved in mix-based MIPS calculation can be seen by examining Figs. 1-4. For example, Gibson had provided a significant category for *indexing instructions* (e.g., "add 1 to index register 3"), which were popular on some computers in the late 1950s. Such instructions are not needed by most modern architectures, which permit any register to be used in indexing operations. Note in Figure 1 that the indexing category is weighted at zero, because the particular supermini involved (an SEL 86) had no indexing instructions, and entailed no indexing time penalty.

Fig. 3
DEC VAX 11/780 Instruction Frequencies

Group Name	Types	Frequency %
SIMPLE		83.60
	Move instructions, simple arithmetic operations, boolean operations, simple & loop branches, subroutine call & return.	
FIELD		6.92
	Bit field operations	
FLOAT		3.62
	Floating point operations, integer multiply & divide	
CALL/RETURN		3.22
	Procedure call & return; multiple register push & pop	
SYSTEM		2.11
	Privileged operations, context switch, system services, request & return, queue manipulation, protection probe instructions	
CHARACTER		0.43
	Character & string instructions	
DECIMAL		0.03
	Decimal instructions	

Source: Emer, J.S. & Clark, D.W.: *A Characterization of Processor Performance in the VAX 11/780*, 11th Int'l Symposium on Computer Architecture, June 1984, p. 304.

Will the real MIPS please stand?

An excellent illustration of the value of this caveat is the great "RISC vs. CISC" debate. While there is no accepted definition of the term, the general aim of RISC architectures is to obtain enhanced performance by simplifying the underlying hardware, so that it handles only a small set of (hopefully) the most-frequently-used instructions. More complex (and hopefully rare) instructions are delegated to the software; for example, the in-line "millicode" in the HP Spectrum architecture.

Fig. 4: Performance of the Motorola 68000 family

	68000	68010	68020		
			0% hit	64% hit	100% hit
Cycles/Av. Instruction	12.567	12.107	7.682	7.159	6.373
MIPS @ 8 MHz	0.64	0.66	-	-	-
MIPS @ 10 MHz	0.80	0.83	-	-	-
MIPS @ 12.5 MHz	-	1.03	1.63	1.74	1.96
MIPS @ 16.6 MHz	-	-	2.17	2.33	2.62

Hit rate is for the on-chip instruction cache.

Cycles/average instruction derived from actual instruction tracing.

Source: MacGregor, D. & Rubinstein, J.: *A Performance Analysis of MC68020-based Systems*; IEEE Micro, December 1985, pp. 55, 56.

How well a RISC machine achieves this aim can be measured by the number of clock cycles per average instruction (cpai). The ultimate goal of a RISC machine is to come as close to 1 cpai as possible; i.e., the great majority of executed instructions should take 1 clock. HP claims its Spectrum is at the 1.6-1.7 cpai level. The IBM RT PC, according to IBM published literature, averages 3 cycles per instruction. Once the cpi figure is established, MIPS can be directly calculated as 1/(cpai x us) where us = microseconds/cycle.

When comparing such RISC MIPS to those from conventional architectures, the key question is whether a given function or task at the user level translates into the same number of instructions on the two systems. The formal measure of this property is the *dynamic path length*. The information released to date is somewhat sketchy; but it seems to indicate that at least some RISC machines tend to be substantially more verbose than conventional CISC implementations. For example, there is some evidence that C programs compiled on the IBM RT PC produce 20%-40% more code than the same programs using the same compiler on the DEC VAX 11/780.

In translating *object code* from current HP3000 programs to Spectrum, an expansion factor of about 6:1 has been observed; i.e., each HP3000 instruction translates on the average into *six* Spectrum instruction. However, recompilation with native Spectrum compilers reduces the expansion factor to about 20%.

(It is also possible to run unmodified HP3000 binary code on a *simulator* running on the Spectrum. The simulator executes about 16-20 instructions for each simulated instruction. However, the simulator is said to run very nearly at 1 cpai on the 8 MHz Spectrum, achieving nearly 8 MIPS).

In making its MIPS claims for the Spectrum, HP carefully eliminated some of the verbosity sources, in order to make such claims more comparable with previous HP models and competitors' systems. Actual instruction counts were obtained by a passive (non-obtrusive) analyzer co-processor. Then these counts were reduced by accounting for Nullifies and TLB misses.

Nullifies are instances when the compiler can't find a useful instruction to stuff in the slot following a delayed branch; in such cases, a No-Op must be executed. Approximately 3-4% of all instructions fall in this category. Spectrum TLB misses are handled by software; a count of actual TLB misses is taken, and the estimated number of instructions involved in handling the miss is subtracted. Clearly, it would not be meaningful to compare MIPS from code sequences containing a great deal of No-Ops and TLB handling to code that performs the same function, but is not burdened by such excess baggage.

A third example is the Inmos Transputer, used most notably in Floating Point Systems' T-Series hypercube. Inmos claims 10 MIPS for its fastest version, while FPS claims a more modest 7.5 MIPS for a the slower version it is using. Both claims are several times higher than such leading 32-bit microprocessors as the Motorola 68020 or Intel's 386.

However, the Transputer's architecture is extremely rudimentary: it has no addressable registers at all, just a 3-level stack; and its basic instruction set features only sixteen 8-bit instructions. More complex instructions must be constructed *at run-time* using the basic set. This suggests that the Transputer's dynamic path lengths should be much greater than conventional machines', although Inmos claims this is not the case.

Furthermore, the Transputer's performance claims are based on finding all instructions and data in the 2KB on-chip memory, which is too small for realistic programs. Since the Transputer is so far programmable only in Occam, a unique language, none of the benchmarks couched in C, Pascal, Fortran, or other current languages can be run on it; so its true performance relative to conventional processors remains untested.

Synthetic Benchmarks

Well before RISC or the Transputer became hot issues, it was realized that instruction-level performance figures, such as MIPS, would always be unreliable in comparing systems whose underlying architectures are dissimilar. Furthermore, as more end-user activity became directed to high-level languages, the ability of the compiler to produce good (optimized) code became an increasingly important performance measure.

Synthetic benchmarks were developed in response to one or both of these needs. The goal is to create a simple, relatively small program that approximates the way typical applications, coded in high-level languages, behave. In particular, the synthetic benchmark is supposed to mimic the relative frequencies of the various types of high-level language statements and constructs, and the types of data structures real programs deal with, but in the framework of a manageably-small program.

Collecting dynamic execution statistics for high-level language programs is much more difficult than obtaining instruction traces, because it is generally impossible to determine language constructs from the resulting machine-level instruction sequences generated by the compiler. Hence designers of synthetic benchmarks are forced to rely on a mixture of static and dynamic data from a wide variety of sources[4]. Such benchmarks are therefore not accurate in reflecting the nature of typical programs. However, since they are cast in terms of specific programs, which are usually self-timing, they are far less subject to interpretation or "personal creativity" than are MIPS ratings.

Two of the best-known synthetic benchmarks are the Whetstone and Dhrystone programs. The Whetstone benchmark was developed in the early 1970s by Curnow and Wichman[5] at the U.K.'s National Physical Laboratory. It is based on statistics originally collected by Wichman from 949 programs compiled with the interpretive "Whetstone" Algol-60 compiler. However, its most popular implementation today is in Fortran. The program is constructed so as to represent the execution of one million "Whetstone instructions". The inverse of the measured run-time (in seconds) yields millions of Whetstone instructions per second, or simply (mega) Whetstones. A double-precision version of this benchmark merely changes the definitions of the relevant variables from single- to double-precision. The Whetstone benchmark is heavily biased towards numerical computing and floating point operations; in a general sense, it is representative of scientific and engineering applications. Some representative Whetstone ratings are shown in Figure 5.

Fig.5
K Whetstone Results, Single Precision

HP3000/930	2841.
IBM 4381-11	~2000.
DEC 11/780	1152.
HP1000/A900	1042.
MicroVAX II	877.
Sun 3/50	860.
Counterpoint	833.
Apollo 3000	780.
IBM RT PC	200.

Source: DEC: *Digital Review*, Jan. 1986, p.77; all others: company claims.

Dhrystone is a more recent benchmark, developed by Reinhold P. Weicker of Siemens, and first reported in 1984[4] as an Ada program. Dhrystone's emphasis is on the type of data and operations encountered in system, rather than numerical, programming. It contains 100 statements, of which 53 are assignment type, 32 are control statements, and 15 are procedure and function calls. C and Pascal versions also exist. Results are stated as thousands or millions of Dhrystones per second, or simply Dhrystones. Figure 6 shows a few Dhrystone results from the version distributed by AT&T's Rick Richardson, and reported by him regularly on USENET.

Fig. 6
Some Dhrystone Benchmark Results
(Best values, with registers)

IBM 3090/200	31,250*
Amdahl 5860	28,846*
HP3000/930	10,000
Alliant FX/8	7,655
DEC VAX 8600	7,142
Intel 386/16MHz	6,133
Gould PN9080	4,922*
Intel 386/12½MHz	4,794
NCR Tower 32	4,545
Sun 3/180	3,846
Celerity C1200	3,468
Pyramid 90x	3,333
HP9000/500	1,724#
IBM RT PC	1,698
DEC 11/780	1,640*
DEC MicroVAX II	1,399*
IBM PC/AT	1,388

* Version 1.1; all others Version 1.0.
\# Without registers.

Source: Rick Richardson, report of March 31, 1986; except IBM RT PC: & HP 3000/930; company claim.

A number of synthetic Cobol benchmarks have been proposed over the years. Perhaps the best known is the so-called "U.S. Steel Benchmarks"[6,] which consist of eleven "tests". They have been run on numerous systems since 1965. Results are presented as a productivity index relative to the IBM 1460; namely, the time for running the tests on the 1460 divided by the time on the tested machine. Under these tests, the IBM 3081 Model K yielded an index of 5505, while a DEC VAX 11/780 did 500.

The LINPACK benchmark

For the past several years, Jack J. Dongarra of the Argonne National Laboratory has been publishing the results of the so-called "LINPACK benchmark". LINPACK is a collection of Fortran subroutines for solving systems of linear equations. The benchmark consists of solving, in double-precision, a set of 100 such equations. Another version, which solves a set of 1,000 equations, has been recently introduced. Often used to compare the performance of supercomputers and vector processors, the benchmark has now been run on engineering workstations and even some personal computers. Results are given in terms of both LINPACK MFLOPS (millions of floating-point operations per second), and in relative terms, with the performance of the Cray 1S set at 1.0, and with faster machines registering under 1.0. Some selected LINPACK results are shown in Figure 7.

Fig. 7
Some LINPACK Results
(Best values, long precision, Fortran)

Machine	Ratio	MFLOPS
Cray XMP2 (1 proc.)*	0.50	24.
IBM 3090/200 w/VF*	1.0	12.
Cray 1S*	1.0	12.
Flt.Pt.Systs. FPS264*	2.2	5.6
Amdahl 5860 w/HSFPF	3.1	3.9
Alliant FX/8, 8 CEs*	4.9	2.5
IBM 3081K	5.7	2.1
IBM 4381 Mod 13	10.	1.2
DEC VAX 8800	12.	0.99
DEC VAX 8650	17.	0.70
HP3000/930	21.	0.57
Sun 3/160M w/FPA	30.	0.40
Celerity C1200	58.	0.21
DEC VAX 8200	80.	0.15
DEC MicroVAX II	97.	0.13
DEC 11/780 w/FPA	101.	0.13
IBM PC/AT w/80287	1054.	0.012

* Rolled BLAS.

Source: Dongarra, J.J.: *Performance of Various Computers Using Standard Linear Equations Software in a Fortran Environment;* Argonne National Laboratory Technical Memorandum No. 23, April 16, 1986. *HP 3000/930: Company claim.*

Transaction Processing

On line transaction processing (OLTP) is increasingly important in commercial applications (see Datamation, August 1, 1985, pp. 60-68). A transaction processing system maintains a typically-large database, to which multiple users at local and remote terminals have access, for both inquiries and updates. The transaction processing programs are generally small and not very demanding in terms of CPU utilization. Rather, the performance of the system is chiefly affected by the efficiency of its system and database software, I/O facilities, and communications protocols.

Performance measurements of such systems are best characterized in terms of transactions/second (tps), or tps/processor when more than one processor is available. A synthetic benchmark has been proposed[7]. This benchmark, dubbed the DebitCredit or DtCt benchmark, stipulates equivalent of 10,000 bank tellers doing an account update transaction once every 100 seconds, thus presenting the system with a load of 100 transactions/sec. The benchmark further specifies that 95% of all transactions must have a 1 second or less response time. The vendor is free to configure the lowest-cost system that will do the job, but is expected to report a cost-per-tps according to a specified formula. For less-demanding applications, the benchmark can be scaled down by reducing the number of tellers and the size of the relevant files.

Although this benchmark is hardly typical, it is the only one applicable to OLTP that has been given wide publicity to date. Several manufacturers, including IBM, DEC, NCR, Tandem, Stratus, and several others have performed this benchmark, although not all have reported results.

Unfortunately, since the benchmark is couched in functional terms only, it is open to some interpretation; reporting of the results often does not include key parameters, such as scaling. A compact description of the benchmark, along with critical analysis of its weaknesses, and a proposed standard reporting checklist, is contained in reference 8[8].

In measuring the on-line transaction performance of its IMS system, IBM has been using a standard workload developed in the late 1970s, based on GUIDE and SHARE user group surveys of IMS customer workloads. It represents an order entry and inventory control application. A subset of this workload has also been used to measure the transaction throughput of the relational database system, DB2. Performance measurements for both IMS and DB2 take place at the Santa Teresa Lab in San Jose, CA. Some DB2 measurements have been reported in reference 9[9].

Caveat Emptor
Measuring computer power is objectively difficult, and, due to competitive market pressures, politically explosive. It is, perhaps, futile to expect vendors to reveal how they derive their performance claims. Users should, whenever possible, test performance under loads that represent their typical applications; and employ wall-clock (stop-watch),

rather than internal timing. Users should insist that any benchmark results supplied by vendors or third parties should include complete environmental specifications, and complete specifications of the benchmark's version (an actual listing of the program would not be amiss).

Computer suppliers, like car manufacturers, should qualify all performance claims with a caveat of some sort. IBM already leads the way; some of its performance publications now carry the disclaimer, "Performance data determined by IBM in a controlled environment. Results obtained in other environments may vary significantly".

Footnotes and References

1. John von Neumann and his collaborator Herman Goldstine wrote about instruction frequency counts in technical reports they published in 1947-1948.

2. Industry gadfly Dr. Herbert R.J. Grosch informally stated his "law" in the 1950s as "proof" that large-scale systems were more cost effective than smaller, distributed systems. The law stated that a computer's performance is proportional to the square of its price; i.e., for double the price, a user should be able to get a system with four times the power. The debate about Grosch's Law raged on in the 1960s, until advancing VLSI technology made distributed processing (and later, personal computing) widely accepted. Even now the debate refuses to die; see *Grosch's Law Revisited* by Philip Ein-Dor (CACM, February 1985, pp. 142-151).

3. While the Gibson Mix was never published in the trade or professional press, I remember from first-hand knowledge that Gibson Mix data was already industry lore around 1964. Years later, Gibson did publish a 4-page, internal IBM Technical Report (TR-00.2043, June 18, 1970), which documented the mix data and gave a very terse description of the traces done on the IBM 704 and 650 machines in 1959, from which the mix was derived.

4. Weicker, Reinhold P.: *Dhrystone: A Synthetic Systems Programming Benchmark*, CACM, October, 1984, pp. 1013-1090.

5. Curnow, H.J., & Wichman, B.A.: *A Synthetic Benchmark*, Computer Journal, February 1976, pp. 43-49. Whetstone (Leicester, U.K.) was the site of the English Electric Co.'s Atomic Power Division, where the interpretive Algol-60 compiler for the English Electric KDF9 computer was developed in the early 1960s. Interpreters for the Whetstone compiler were developed for three other British computers as well. Such interpreters made it possible for Wichman to collect run-time statistics on the frequencies of the various Algol constructs from 949 programs; that data was used as the model for the Whetstone benchmark.

6. Now called the Cobol Analysis System, and available through G.E. McKinzie, 1509 Muriel St., Pittsburgh, PA 15203.

7. See Anon et. al., *A Measure of Transaction Processing Power*, Datamation, April 1, 1985, pp. 112-118.

8. See *FT Systems* Newsletter, No. 47, July 1986, pp. 2-8. The publication is available from ITOM International Co., POB 1450, Los Altos, CA 94023.

9. See *InfoDB*, Summer, 1986 (Vol. 1, No. 2). The publication is available from Colin J. White Consulting, POB 20651, San Jose, CA 95160.

Contributions . . .

Re-evaluation of the RISC I

J. L. Heath,
North Dakota State University
Fargo, ND 58105

1. INTRODUCTION

Recently reported research <3> indicates that the RISC I, a reduced instruction set computer, is able to outperform conventional processors. The validity of these results has, however, been questioned <7> since factors not directly related to the size and speed of the instruction set may have been utilized to the RISC I's advantage. By removing these extraneous factors, and re-evaluating the RISC I, this paper hopes to more completely evaluate the reduced instruction set computer.

2. BACKGROUND

The Reduced Instruction Set Computer is a relatively new concept in computer architecture. The most publicized example of the reduced instruction set design philosophy is the RISC I, a 32 bit microprocessor which has been developed at the University of California, Berkeley. The results reported for the RISC I, when compared to conventional microprocessors, indicate that the RISC I offers improved performance when executing compiled C programs. The tests used in this evaluation compared the performance of the RISC I to the MC68000, the Z8000, and several other processors. The performance of these processors was measured via benchmark programs which were written in C and translated into machine language using a compiler.

There are, however, two factors other than the reduced instruction set which may have affected the performance of the RISC I. These are the register window (together with the large number of registers) and the type of compiler used for the C programs.

The register scheme, 138 registers allocated in overlapping groups of 32, provide a means of context switching which may have significantly increased the performance of the RISC I.

The programs written for the RISC I were compiled with the use of a peephole optimizer. The same programs when written for the conventional processors were compiled with a portable compiler. This discrepancy between the compilers used for the different machines being compared may have served to disproportionately benefit the RISC I.

Reprinted with permission from *Computer Architecture News*, March 1984,
pages 3–10. Copyright © 1984 by J.L. Heath.

297

3.   ALTERNATIVES

There are two alternative methods of comparing the processors in question (within the context of using benchmark programs to measure performance). The first method is to use an optimized compiler for the conventional machines. The second method involves eliminating the effects of the register window and the optimizing compiler from the results of the RISC I, and comparing these results to similar studies performed for the other machines.

Both methods are useful for comparing the performance of different types of machines. The first method allows the highest performance levels of each processor to be measured, with the optimal use of all machine resources. The second method serves to isolate the benefits incurred by the reduced instruction set.

4.   PREVIOUS STUDIES

The only major performance evaluation of the RISC I was done at Berkeley <3,4>. This evaluation involved writing a set of benchmark programs in C and compiling them for the RISC I and for several conventional processors. As stated earlier, the RISC I programs were compiled with a peephole optimizer whereas portable compilers were used on the other machines. The programs used in this evaluation included a subset of five programs from the Carnegie-Mellon test package. Processors used in this study were the RISC I, the Motorola MC68000, the Intel 8086, the DEC LSI-11/32, the Z8000, the VAX 11/780, the PDP 11/70, and the BBN C/70.

In 1981, Electronic Design News used a subset of seven programs from the Carnegie-Mellon test package to evaluate four processors <2>. Five of these programs were also used by Berkeley to evaluate the RISC I. The EDN study tested the Motorola MC68000, the Zilog Z8000, the DEC LSI-11/23, and the Intel 8086.

The programs used in each of these studies are indicated in Table 1.

By comparing the results of the EDN study to the Berkeley study for the MC68000 and the Z8000, it is apparent that the compiler used at Berkeley was relatively inefficient. One blatant example in support of this statement is the MC68000 programs which, when coded by hand, averaged over six times faster than the programs generated by the Berkeley C compiler (the hand coded programs were also smaller than the compiled C code).

The results of both the Berkeley and EDN studies are shown in Tables 2 and 3.

The results shown in Tables 2 and 3 indicate that the RISC I performance is comparable to that of the MC68000 and the Z8000. Although this would seem to justify the reduced instruction set computer philosophy, the results may be excessively biased in favor of the RISC I by the presence of, and use of, the large set of registers and the register window. This bias may be justified by the rationale that the implementation of both features was facilitated by the

```
+------------------------------------------------------------------+
!                            TABLE 1                               !
!                                                                  !
!                   Carnegie-Mellon Benchmarks                     !
!                                                                  !
!                                                                  !
!                                                                  !
!        EDN   UCB      benchmark          description             !
!                                                                  !
!         *               A          I/O interrupt kernel          !
!         *               B          I/O kernel with FIFO          !
!         *     *         E          Character-string search       !
!         *     *         F          Bit set, reset, test          !
!         *     *         H          Linked-list insertion         !
!         *     *         I          Quicksort                     !
!         *     *         K          Bit-matrix transposition      !
!                                                                  !
+------------------------------------------------------------------+
```

implementation of the small instruction set, i.e. the chip area necessary for the registers was available only because of the small amount of chip area used in the implementation of the instruction set.

5.   RE-EVALUATING THE RISC I

In order to eliminate the effects of the RISC I's register window, it was necessary to hand code each of the five Carnegie-Mellon benchmark algorithms directly in RISC I assembly code. Each program was run on a RISC I simulator to ensure correct program execution and to measure the execution times. These programs minimized the effects of the register window by only using 32 of the available registers. One residual benefit of the register windows does, however, remain; that is the contents of the registers used by the programs were not restored to the original register contents. Although this practice may violate some of the criteria set forth in the EDN study, the effects should be no more significant than those resulting from some of the 'questionable' practices used in the code written for the MC68000 and the Z8000 <4>.

The results of this study are also shown in Table 2 and 3.

6.   RISC I SIMULATOR

The simulator used for the RISC I programs was written in FORTRAN and run on an IBM computer system. The simulator implements each RISC I assembly language instruction as a FORTRAN subroutine. To run on the simulator, the RISC I program must therefore be transformed into a sequence of FORTRAN subroutine calls. This method of implementation, although somewhat slow, allows a large degree of flexibility, together with the ability to easily monitor the execution of the assembly language program.

One benefit of this type of simulator is that extensive and detailed knowledge of the hardware is not required. That is, since the instructions do not need to be represented as bit strings, the op codes for the particular instructions are not needed.

TABLE 2

Benchmark Results, Program Size

Assembled C Code

Benchmark	RISC I	processor MC68000	Z8000
E	144	115 (0.8)*	129 (0.9)*
F	120	144 (1.2)	180 (1.5)
H	176	123 (0.7)	140 (0.8)
I	992	694 (0.7)	1091 (1.1)
K	288	316 (1.1)	374 (1.3)

average   (0.9)   (1.12)

Machine Language Programs

Benchmark	RISC I	processor MC68000	Z8000
E	112	44 (0.39)*	66 (0.59)*
F	84	36 (0.43)	44 (0.52)
H	164	106 (0.65)	96 (0.59)
I	692	266 (0.38)	386 (0.56)
K	232	74 (0.32)	110 (0.47)

average   (0.43)   (0.55)

* numbers in parenthesis indicate the number of times
  larger than the RISC I program.

TABLE 3

Benchmark Results, Program Execution Time

Assembled C Code

Benchmark	RISC I	MC68000		Z8000	
E	460	1228	(2.8)*	421	(0.9)*
F	60	288	(4.8)	242	(4.0)
H	100	160	(1.6)	137	(1.4)
I	50400	206640	(4.1)	149760	(3.0)
K	430	1720	(4.0)	1278	(3.0)
average			(3.5)		(2.5)

Machine Language Programs

Benchmark	RISC I	MC68000		Z8000	
E	417	244	(0.59)*	134	(0.32)*
F	83	70	(0.84)	70	(0.85)
H	66	153	(2.32)	135	(2.05)
I	39449	33527	(0.85)	66000	(1.67)
K	772	368	(0.48)	369	(0.45)
average			(1.01)		(1.07)

* numbers in parenthesis indicate the number of times slower than the RISC I program.

TABLE 4

Dynamic Programming Statistics

instruction	average frequency of execution	
	machine language programs	assembled C programs
ADD	25 %	27 %
SUB	24	20
JMPR	25	15
other	26 *	38

* no single instruction in the 'other' category
accounted for more than 8 % of the total.

There are, however, some disadvantages to this type of simulator. Perhaps the major drawback is that the simulator does not represent a von Neumann machine, i.e. the instructions and data are not indistinguishable.

Before comparing the results, it should be noted that while the programs for the EDN study were coded by the processor manufacturers, Motorola and Zilog, the hand coded RISC I programs represent a first attempt at writing RISC I machine code. Therefore, the results may be slightly biased against the RISC I.

7. DYNAMIC PROGRAMMING STATISTICS

One additional feature of this simulator allows the dynamic programming statistics (i.e. the frequency of execution of individual instructions) to be gathered. The dynamic statistics for the five benchmark programs are given in Table 4.

8. CONCLUSIONS

Several general observations may be made from comparing the results of the various studies. These are:

A) The discrepancy (both in program size and speed of execution) between the compiled C code and the hand written code (for both the Z8000 and the

MC68000) indicate that the compiler used for these processors was not able to generate efficient code for those machines.

B) The hand coded RISC I programs were comparable, in terms of program size and speed of execution, to the results from the MC68000, the Z8000, and the compiled C code of the RISC I. Remember that the hand coded programs did not make use of the RISC I's register window or the large number of registers.

C) Comparing the results of individual programs indicates that for specific tasks the RISC I offers significantly better performance than either of the other processors. For instance, when executing benchmark H (Linked-list insertion), the RISC I performed much better than the other two processors.

D) The dynamic programming statistics reveal that the RISC I makes extensive use of a very small subset of its already small instruction set. This indicates that a disproportionate increase in processor performance may be obtained by increasing the speed at which this subset of instructions executes. This conclusion is not limited to reduced instruction set computers; it is, however, predicated on the assumption that the processor's software is written to effectively use these instructions.

1. Jan L. Heath, "A Study of Reduced Instruction Set Computers", M.S. Thesis, EEE Dept., North Dakota State University, 1983

2. R. Grappel, and J. Hemenway, "A tale of four uPs: Benchmarks quantify performance," Electronic Design News, Vol. 26, No. 7, April 1, 1981, pp. 179-265.

3. D. Patterson, and C. Sequin, "A VLSI RISC," IEEE Computer, Vol. 15, No. 9, September, 1982, pp. 8-18.

4. R. Piepho, "Comparative Evaluation of the RISC I Architecture Via the Computer Family Architecture Benchmarks," Research Project, University of California, Berkeley, August 17, 1981.

5. D. Patterson, and D. Ditzel, "The Case for the Reduced Instruction Set Computer," Computer Architecture News, Vol. 8, No. 6, October, 1980, pp. 25-33.

6. D. Fitzpatrick, D. Patterson, C. Sequin, et al., "A RISCy Approach to VLSI," Computer Architecture News, Vol. 10, No. 1, March 1982, pp. 28-32.

7. R. Colwell, C. Hitchcock III, E. Jensen, "Peering Through the RISC/CISC Fog: An Outline of Research," Computer Architecture News, Vol. 11, No. 1, March 1983, pp. 44-50.

RISC WATCH

David A. Patterson

Computer Science Division
Department of Electrical Engineering and Computer Sciences
University of California
Berkeley, California 94720

There have been several new computers and new studies relating to Reduced Instruction Set Computers (RISC) since our last article in *Computer Architecture News*. The first report is on RISC II, a much more aggressive implementation of the Berkeley RISC architecture. The studies of RISCs in new areas include floating point, big benchmarks, Lisp, and ECL. After reviewing the last stages of the Berkeley RISC project, I list the commercial RISCs, and conclude with a short description of our next project.

RISC II

We have just finished testing RISC II, a 32-bit NMOS microprocessor at Berkeley by Manolis Katevenis and Robert Sherburne. This 41,000 transistor chip is 25% smaller than RISC I even though it has 60 more 32-bit registers. Both designs were fabricated at λ of 2 microns (4 micron drawn gate length).

Like RISC I, RISC II worked on first silicon. This time, however, the performance was close to what we predicted—because of careful design and extensive Spice simulation of critical data-path delays and because of Crystal,[1] a MOS timing verifier developed by Prof. John Ousterhout. The predicted RISC II cycle time (i.e. execution of a register-to-register instruction) was 480 ns. In the lab, RISC II chips run at 500 ns per instruction (8MHz clock, VDD=5V, VBB=VSS=0V, room temperature, 1.25 Watts power dissipation).

Our architectural studies assumed 400 ns per instruction (10MHz clock) to predict performance of Berkeley RISCs. Benchmark simulations show that even at 500 ns, RISC II runs integer C programs faster than a 8-MHz iAPX-286, 10-MHz NS 16032, 12-MHz 68000, or 18-MHz HP 9000 CPU.

We resubmitted RISC II at smaller geometries ($\lambda = 1.5$). The resulting chip is, of course, about half the size—about 25% smaller than the 68000—yet runs at 330 ns per instruction (12MHz clock, VDD=5V, VBB=VSS=0V, room temperature, 1.8 Watts dissipation). Details on RISC II will be presented at the International Solid State Circuits Conference in San Francisco in February, 1984. [2]

FLOATING RISCS

Floating point arithmetic was ignored in our original studies because we rarely use floating point and because of the difficulty of implementation. Tim

Sippel studied floating point arithmetic and found that floating point routines written in C run only slightly faster on RISC than assembly language routines on the 68000, but neither is a match for a VAX. [3]

I have revised and summarized his study in the table below. The revisions include

- Using the measured cycle times of RISC II instead of the estimated time;

- Using the 10 MHz, 0 wait state 68010 in a SUN 2 workstation instead of the slower 8 MHz, 2 wait state 68000 of the Dual 8312 workstation;

- Using a faster floating point co-processor. Sippel originally estimated the performance of RISC with hardware support based on an 8-MHz 8087 co-processor. Here, I estimate the performance of based on the Weitek floating point chips.[4] This 2-chip set executes single precision floating add, subtract, and multiply in less than 1 microsecond. (Weitek also provide chips that are nearly twice as fast.) I have assumed that a double precision version of the Weitek chips would execute add, subtract, and multiply in 2 microseconds (not including the time to pass operands.) I also assume that divide takes 5 times as long as multiply.

The next question is selecting a floating point benchmark. The most widely quoted floating point benchmark is the Whetstone[5,6], usually written in Fortran. We have no Fortran compiler for RISC II, but as the original Whetstone was written in Algol-60, we translated it into C.

Let me describe the circumstances of this experiment, to avoid misunderstandings. The motivation is comparability: showing relative CPU performance for the same software, and not giving the best possible performance for each architecture. This table shows single user CPU time using the UNIX[†] C compiler and the transcendental function library routines written in C. You can get better numbers for RISC II and the VAX if you write the transcendental routines in assembly language, if you use a more highly optimizing C compiler, if you use the Fortran version of this program with the VMS compiler, or if you calculate only single precision numbers.[‡] The point, however, is to reduce the number of variables in this study so that we can can more accurately compare CPU time. It is increasingly important to use the UNIX C compiler to compare CPU performance as Digital Equipment Corporation is now selling Berkeley UNIX, and Datamation estimates that more than 20% of the minicomputers sold in 1984 will be running some version of UNIX.[7]

The two variables in this table are the machines and the type of floating point support. RISC II, with the hypothetical double precision Weitek chip, is about half the speed of a 780 with the optional floating point accelerator, and faster than the standard 780 with microcoded floating point. The RISC II speed

---

[†] UNIX is a Trademark of Bell Laboratories.

[‡] For example, RISC II can run the Whetstones in single precision (using floating point arithmetic written in C) five times faster than double precision, and using the VMS Fortran compiler and VMS assembly language transcendental routines improves double precision performance by a third on the VAX.

Whetstone Benchmark in C		
(Double Precision using UNIX C compiler)		
(Transcendentals written in C)		
(Measuring single-user CPU time)		
Machine	Floating Point implementation	Time (sec.)
VAX 11/780	hardware	2.2
VAX 11/750	hardware	3.4
RISC II (12MHz)	hardware	4.5
VAX 11/780	microcode	5.5
RISC II (8MHz)	hardware	6.4
VAX 11/750	microcode	8.4
68010 (10MHz)	assembly	41.5
RISC II (12MHz)	C	67.1
RISC II (8MHz)	C	101.7

will be difficult to improve, for most of the floating point time is spent sending the operands between RISC II and the coprocessor. The software floating point routines written in C for RISC II are more than an order of magnitude slower than the coprocessor version.

Our interpretation of these results is that RISCs alone are not an effective vehicle for floating point applications, and that the CPU-coprocessor interface is an area we want to improve in future RISCs.

BENCHMARKS: BIGGER AND BETTER

The performance predictions for RISCs were based on small programs. This small size was dictated by the reliability of the simulator and compiler, the available simulation time, and the inability of the first simulators to handle UNIX system calls. I am sure that RISC advocates would like to know whether the performance predicted by the small programs holds for the larger ones.

The first step was finding a large benchmark. The large program that had the widest interest was the compiler. The compiler is usually a popular program on most systems and, as a large program, it likely strains the system.

Jim Miros ran his RISC C compiler and the VAX C compiler on both RISC II (simulated) and the VAX-11/780 (actual), and found that RISC II can compile faster the VAX-11/780.[8] (Since the RISC simulator cannot handle system calls, Miros made a version of each compiler with stubs in place of the system calls to make the comparison fair.) A 10 MHz RISC varied from 60% to 80% faster, just as the small programs predicted. I have revised his numbers for the 8 and 12 MHz RISC II and included them in the table below.

UNIX C Compile Time Benchmarks										
(Measuring single-user CPU time)										
(VAX-11/780 vs. 8 & 12 MHz RISC II)										
Compiled Program		VAX C Compiler					RISC C Compiler				
name	size	on VAX	on RISC		$\frac{VAX}{RISC}$		on VAX	on RISC		$\frac{VAX}{RISC}$	
	(lines)	(secs)	8mhz	12mhz	8	12	(secs)	8mhz	12mhz	8	12
ld.c	1587	27.9	21.0	13.9	1.3	2.0	35.2	22.4	14.8	1.6	2.4
sort.c	873	17.4	13.2	8.7	1.3	2.0	20.0	13.2	8.7	1.5	2.3
puzzle.c	118	5.2	3.6	2.4	1.4	2.2	7.3	4.8	3.2	1.5	2.3
TOTAL	2578	50.5	37.8	25.0	1.3	2.0	62.5	40.4	26.7	1.5	2.3

The 12 MHz RISC II runs either compiler more than twice as fast as the VAX-11/780. It is interesting to note that the VAX compiler runs faster than the RISC compiler on the same computer (50.5 vs. 62.5 or 25.0 vs. 26.7) even though the code generator was simpler for RISC (simpler instructions mean fewer decisions). It turns out that the heart of the UNIX C compiler is a pattern matching routine that matches the partially compiled object code to templates, so more instructions per program means more calls to this routine, thus slower compilation. However, even if we compare the RISC C Compiler running on RISC II to the VAX C Compiler running on the VAX-11/780, the 12MHz RISC II can still compile twice as fast.

PAPER STUDIES: Lisp and ECL

Carl Ponder studied how well RISCs could run Lisp.[9] His report was not based on implementing a Lisp system on RISC II, but was estimated by translating the output of VAX Lisp compilers to RISC II machine code. The Franz Lisp and PSL compilers generated VAX assembly code, which Ponder translated to RISC II. The next question was again what to use to compare performance. The mixture of competing programming environment philosophies, competing language factions, and competing companies has made Lisp benchmarking difficult. Dick Gabriel of Stanford, for example, has been working on the problem for two years and has yet to publish his results. Disregarding the warnings of the dangers of Lisp benchmarking, the table below lists compiled programs only and summarizes the results of running one highly recursive Lisp program on several machines.

Given that special case optimizations can result in a difference in performance of a factor of 8 on the same machine running the same language, it is dangerous to draw strong conclusions from this table. Ponder concludes that we can, at worst, expect better performance from RISC II than the VAX 11/750 for comparable Lisp systems.

Compiled TAK Lisp benchmark in Franz Lisp			
Machine	Lisp Dialect	Time (secs)	*Optimizations*
68010 (10MHz)	Franz Lisp	13.7	*(none)*
VAX 11/780	Franz Lisp	8.3	*(none)*
RISC II (8MHz)	Franz (est)	4.4	*direct call; tail recursion*
VAX 11/750	Franz Lisp	3.6	*fixed arithmetic*
RISC II (12MHz)	Franz (est)	2.9	*direct call; tail recursion*
68010 (10MHz)	Franz Lisp	2.5	*direct call; fixed arithmetic*
VAX 11/780	Franz Lisp	1.1	*direct call; fixed arithmetic*

Compiled TAK Lisp benchmark in PSL			
Machine	Lisp Dialect	Time (secs)	*Optimizations*
VAX 11/750	PSL	7.1	*(none)*
RISC II (8MHz)	PSL (est)	2.6	*direct call; tail recursion*
RISC II (12MHz)	PSL (est)	1.7	*direct call; tail recursion*
VAX 11/750	PSL	1.4	*direct call; fixed arithmetic*

Richard Blomseth investigated whether the RISC philosophy applies to computers built with technologies other than custom MOS.[10] He used a SCALDstation to design "Big RISC," a RISC II CPU built from ECL 100K chips. The timing verifier supplied a time estimate of the logic delays on the worst case path. Depending on your belief about wire delays and cache hit ratios, "Big RISC" is 4 to 8 times faster than RISC II, and the CPU fits on one large board.

Our conclusion is that the RISC philosophy works well for ECL 100K machines.

DOCUMENTED RISCS

In addition to the work mentioned above, several reports were written on the Berkeley RISC experiments. Jim Peek, the lead designer on RISC I, finished a report on the VLSI circuitry of RISC I.[11] Manolis Katevenis, the student who was principally responsible for the micro-architecture of RISC I and RISC II, has finished a dissertation that describes the rationale for RISCs, explains the micro-architecture of RISC II, and suggests directions for the next generation of machines.[12] Robert Sherburne, the lead circuit designer of RISC II and the last remaining RISC student, is completing his dissertation; in it, he analyzes the trade-offs in the circuit design of microprocessors and describes the ideas behind the circuits of RISC II.[13]

WILL OTHERS TAKE RISCS?

We stopped working on the RISC project a while ago, and it was interesting to see if others would pick up the ideas, and if so, when.

John Hennessy of Stanford started the MIPS project[14] shortly after we started the RISC project. They have recently fabricated a chip that works at the speed that meets or exceeds the performance predicted in his papers. MIPS can run Pascal programs about as fast as the DEC 20/60, or more than five times faster than a 8 MHz 68000. Like the IBM 801 project, MIPS relies on highly optimizing compilers in addition to streamlined computers to get high performance at low cost.[15] Our studies report you can build a RISC faster than traditional computers even if both use the same simple compiler technology,[16] and Stanford has shown that the performance gap between RISCs and traditional machines is even greater when both use the same highly optimizing compiler technology.[17]

Three companies are selling RISC machines—at least according to their marketing departments. The Ridge Thirty-Two is a TTL minicomputer with a simple pipelined load/store architecture.[18] Pyramid has adopted the register window scheme of RISC I and also followed the load/store style of instruction set in building a TTL minicomputer.[19] INMOS has recently announced a single-chip VLSI computer with on-board memory and a simple instruction set.[20] All three companies claim performance exceeding the VAX-11/780, with INMOS claiming the largest advantage.

These three companies may not be the only ones to take risks, for according to one article[21] says

> "A number of computer and chip makers including IBM, TRW, Fairchild Semiconductor, Hewlett-Packard, and Digital Equipment are reportedly investigating RISC architectures."

Although I doubt DEC is calling them RISCs, I certainly found it interesting that DEC's single chip VAXs do not implement the whole VAX instruction set.[22] A MicroVAX traps when it tries to execute some infrequent but complicated operations, and invokes transparent software routines that simulate those complicated instructions.

APPLES AND ORANGES

Fair comparisons of RISC architectures to traditional designs are difficult, and it certainly would be wonderful if "both architectures were designed from scratch in the same technology."[23] If we look at the technology used to build the CPU, most would conclude that the Mead/Conway 3 or 4 micron NMOS puts RISCs at a disadvantage. A RISC built either from the NMOS technology used to build the 68010 or the TTL gate arrays of the VAX-11/750 would certainly be faster, and we could build a much faster RISC using either the 1500 TTL chips in the VAX-11/780 CPU or using the 2 micron double level metal NMOS technology to build the 140,000 transistor MicroVAX 32.[24]

SUN 2 provides an answer to questions concerning the memory systems for RISCs. This machine has a 10 MHz 68010 that runs with no wait states with up to 4 megabytes of memory (built from 64K chips). This speed includes translating addresses from virtual to physical memory. The complete 2-level virtual memory tables—not just a translation buffer—are included on the same multibus board with the CPU. The 8MHz RISC II could run without wait states using this same scheme and same memory system. The 12MHz RISC II would require a new board design, either using the faster 256K memory chips or by building a cache like those found on the VAX-11/750 and the VAX-11/780.

RISCING BERKELEY'S FUTURE?

After working with C and UNIX, we decided to pick an architectural project that had far different problems and challenges. Experimental programming environments and objected-oriented computers seemed interesting, but traditional architectural support has meant:

- complex instruction sets; and
- poor performance.

In January 1983 we started our third architecture/VLSI course sequence, and our goal is to reverse that trend.

Our test vehicle is Smalltalk-80[†], an object-oriented programming language and programming environment created by the Software Concepts Group of Xerox PARC. This group has spent the last decade developing systems that improve programmer productivity, in part by using more computing power.

The only machine that has demonstrated adequate Smalltalk-80 performance is the Dorado,[25] an ECL minicomputer that costs over $100,000. Traditional computers have not been a good match for Smalltalk-80. The DEC Smalltalk-80 implementation for the VAX-11/780,[26] for example, is 15 to 30 times slower than the Dorado.[27]

Our next machine is called Smalltalk On A RISC, or SOAR[‡]. We hope SOAR will show that a Reduced Instruction Set Computer can be a low cost, high performance Smalltalk machine.

ACKNOWLEDGEMENTS

I thank the Berkeley students who had the courage to take our course sequences and to build "real stuff." Thanks also to Ricki Blau, Susan Eggers, Richard Fateman, Manolis Katevenis, Randy Katz, John Ousterhout, Allene Parker, Yale Patt, Carlo Séquin, and Nick Tredennick who gave valuable suggestions that improved the quality of this paper.

This research was sponsored by Defense Advance Research Projects Agency (DoD) ARPA Order No. 3803 Monitored by Naval Electronic System Command under Contract No. N00034-K-0251.

[†] Smalltalk-80 is a Trademark of Xerox Corporation.
[‡] SOAR is not a Trademark of Bell Laboratories nor of Xerox Corporation.

References

1. J.K. Ousterhout, "Crystal: A Timing Analyzer for nMOS VLSI Circuits," *Proc. Third Caltech Conference on Very Large Scale Integration*, pp. 57-70, 1983.

2. R.W. Sherburne, M.G.H. Katevenis, D.A. Patterson, and C.H. Séquin, "A 32b NMOS Microprocessor with a Large Register File," *31st International Solid States Circuit Conference*, San Francisco, February 23-25, 1984.

3. T. Sippel, "Floating RISCs," M.S. Project Report, U.C. Berkeley, September 1982. (Unpublished)

4. F. Ware, "Pipelined IEEE Floating Point Processor," *Compcon*, February 28-March 3, 1984.

5. H.J. Curnow and B.A. Wichmann, "A Synthetic Benchmark," *Computer Journal*, vol. 19, no. 1, 1975.

6. B.A. Wichmann and H.J. Curnow, "The Design of Synthetic Programs," in *Benchmarking: Computer Evaluation and Measurement,*, pp. 89-114, John Wiley & Sons, London, 1975.

7. J.W. Verity, "Minis Lose out to PCs," *Datamation*, vol. 29, no. 11, pp. 44-52, November 1983.

8. J. Miros, "A C Compiler for RISC I," M.S. Project Report, U.C. Berkeley, September 1982. (Unpublished)

9. C. Ponder, "... but will RISC run LISP? (a feasibility study)," Computer Science Technical Report No. UCB/CSD 83/122, U.C. Berkeley, August 1983. M.S. Project Report.

10. R. Blomseth, "A Big RISC," Computer Science Technical Report No. UCB/CSD 83/143, U.C. Berkeley, November 1983. M.S. Project Report.

11. J.B. Peek, "The VLSI Circuitry of RISC I," Computer Science Technical Report No. UCB/CSD 83/135, U.C. Berkeley, June 1983. M.S. Project Report.

12. M.G.H. Katevenis, "Reduced Instruction Set Computer Architectures for VLSI," Computer Science Technical Report No. UCB/CSD 83/141, U.C. Berkeley, October, 1983. PhD Dissertation.

13. R.W. Sherburne, *Processor Design Tradeoffs in VLSI*, U.C. Berkeley, May, 1984. PhD Dissertation (in preparation).

14. J. Hennessy, N. Jouppi, F. Baskett, A. Strong, T. Gross, C. Rowen, and J. Gill, "The MIPS Machine," *Proc. Compcon*, pp. 1-7, San Francisco, California, February 1982.

15. G. Radin, "The 801 Minicomputer," *Proc. Symposium on Architectural Support for Programming Languages and Operating Systems*, pp. 39-47, Palo Alto, California, March 1-3, 1982.

16. D.A. Patterson and R.S. Piepho, "RISC Assessment: A High-Level Language Experiment," *Proc. Ninth International Symposium on Computer Architecture*, Austin, Texas, April 26-29, 1982.

17. F.C. Chow, "A Portable Machine-Independent Global Optimizer—Design and Measurements," Computer Systems Laboratory Technical Note No. 83-254, Stanford University, December, 1983. PhD Dissertation

18. D. Folger and E. Basart, "Computer Architectures – Designing for Speed," *Compcon*, pp. 25-31, February 28-March 3, 1983.

19. R. Ragan-Kelley, "Performance of the Pyramid Computer," *Compcon*, February 28-March 1, 1983.

20. I. Barron, P. Cavill, D. May, and P. Wilson, "Transputer does 5 or more MIPS even when not used in parallel," *Electronics*, pp. 109-115., November 17, 1983.

21. C. Barney, "Fewer Instructions Speed Up VLSI," *Electronics*, vol. 55, no. 23, pp. 101-102, November 17, 1983.

22. B. Supnik and I. Evans, "MicroVAX 32 -- A VAX-Compatible Microprocessor," *Compcon*, February 28-March 3, 1984.

23. S.J. Metz, "Letter to the Editor," *Computer Architecture News*, vol. 11, no. 5, December 1983.

24. J. Beck, D. Dobberpuhl, M.J. Doherty, E. Dorenkamp, R. Grondalski, D. Grondalski, K. Henry, M. Miller, R. Supnik, S. Thierauf, and R. Witek, "A 32b Microprocessor with On-Chip Virtual Memory Management," *31st International Solid States Circuit Conference*, San Francisco, February 23-25, 1984.

25. D.W. Clark, B.W. Lampson, and K.A. Pier, "The Memory System of a High-Performance Personal Computer," *IEEE Transactions on Computers*, vol. C-30, no. 10, pp. 715-733, October 1981.

26. S. Ballard and S. Shirron, "The Design and Implementation of VAX/Smalltalk-80," in *Smalltalk-80: Bits of History, Words of Advice*, ed. Glenn Krasner, pp. 127-150, Addison Wesley, September, 1983.

27. K. McCall, "The Smalltalk-80 Benchmarks," in *Smalltalk 80: Bits of History, Words of Advice*, ed. Glenn Krasner, pp. 151-173, Addison-Wesley, Reading, MA, 1983.

References 9 – 12 are available from the Publications Office, Computer Science Division, 573 Evans Hall, University of California, Berkeley, California 94720. If you would like copies, please send the report name and number plus a check (made out to the Regents of the University of California) to cover the following publication costs: Ponder (#122): $2.50, Peek (#135): $2.50, Katevenis (#141): $6.00, and Blomseth (#143): $4.00.

The Effect of Instruction Set Complexity on Program Size and Memory Performance†

Jack W. Davidson

Richard A. Vaughan‡

Department of Computer Science
University of Virginia
Charlottesville, VA 22903

ABSTRACT

One potential disadvantage of a machine with a reduced instruction set is that object programs may be substantially larger than those for a machine with a richer, more complex instruction set. The main reason is that a small instruction set will require more instructions to implement the same function. In addition, the tendency of RISC machines to use fixed length instructions with a few instruction formats also increases object program size. It has been conjectured that the resulting larger programs could adversely affect memory performance and bus traffic. In this paper we report the results of a set of experiments to isolate and determine the effect of instruction set complexity on cache memory performance and bus traffic. Three high-level language compilers were constructed for machines with instruction sets of varying degrees of complexity. Using a set of benchmark programs, we evaluated the effect of instruction set complexity had on program size. Five of the programs were used to perform a set of trace-driven simulations to study each machine's cache and bus performance. While we found that the miss ratio is affected by object program size, it appears that this can be corrected by simplying increasing the size of the cache. Our measurements of bus traffic, however, show that even with large caches, machines with simple instruction sets can expect substantially more main memory reads than machines with dense object programs.

1. INTRODUCTION

One of the primary goals of a computer architect is the design and construction of machines that support the efficient execution of the programs that will run on them. A number of new architecture design principles have evolved for guiding the design of machines to support the execution of high-level languages. The distinguishing characteristic of the machines constructed using these principles is the reduced number of operations contained in the instruction set. Consequently, these machines have been termed RISCs—*reduced instruction set computers* [8,12,14].

The simplicity of the instruction set provides for a number of implementation advantages that can substantially enhance the performance of the machine. For example, the restriction that arithmetic and logical operations be register-to-register may permit the

†This work was supported in part by the National Science Foundation under Grant CCR-8611653.

‡Current address: Department of Computer Science, Stanford University, Stanford, CA 94305.

number of pipeline stages and/or their duration to be reduced resulting in faster execution. The reduced number of operations and addressing modes may make it possible to produce a hardwired control unit. If the implementation is microprogrammed, silicon resources may be freed for the implementation of other features to enhance performance. Some possibilities are on-chip instruction and data caches, instruction buffers, and larger register sets. Finally, the use of fixed length instructions and a few formats permits simpler, faster instruction decoding.

A disadvantage of a RISC machine is that the memory requirements of programs may be substantially greater than those of programs on a complex instruction set machine (CISC). The number of instructions to implement a given function on a RISC machine will normally be greater than the number required for a CISC machine. In addition, CISC machines usually have densely encoded instructions and a variety of instruction formats that further reduces the size of object programs. It has been conjectured that the larger size of object programs on RISC machines may negatively affect memory performance [20].

Normally, comparisons between RISC machines and CISC machines are difficult because the architectures differ in more ways than just the complexity of their instruction sets. To perform fair experiments and so that no unseen architectural bias is introduced, we used a technique called architectural subsetting [14]. Three virtual machines with instruction sets of varying degrees of complexity were created and a high-level language compiler was constructed for each machine. The compilers were constructed using a state-of-the-art automatic code generation system. For each machine, a set of benchmark programs were compiled and the size of the resulting programs were compared across machines. Five of these programs were selected, and for each of the three machines, an address trace of their execution was obtained. We used the address traces to perform trace-driven simulations to evaluate the effect instruction set complexity had on cache memory performance and bus traffic.

This paper has the following organization. Section 2 describes the instruction sets used for the experiments. The programming language used and how the compilers were constructed are described in Section 3. The effects of instruction set complexity on object program size and on memory memory performance are reported in Section 4. Conclusions are presented in Section 5.

2. THREE INSTRUCTION SETS

Because of differences in implementation and software, designing and conducting experiments that fairly and without bias compare architectures is difficult. For example, measuring the execution speed of a high-level language program on different architectures may not reveal anything about the quality of the respective architectures. Differences in implementation, packaging, and software all affect the outcome of the measurements. This is not to say that such comparisons are not useful. It is, after all, the speed of the system (hardware and software) that counts. Often,

"Size and Memory Performance" by J.W. Davidson and R.A. Vaughn, *Proceedings of the 2nd International Conference on Architectural Support for Programming Languages and Operating Systems*, October 1987, pages 60–64.

however, such measurements are used erroneously as indicators of architectural quality.

To perform a set of experiments where such sources of bias are eliminated as much as possible, we used a technique called architectural subsetting [14]. In this technique, the instruction set of a virtual machine is created by selectively choosing instructions and addressing modes from an existing machine. The resulting virtual machine is a subset of the base architecture. For the experiments reported here, we created three subsets of the VAX instruction set with varying degrees of complexity. The richness of the VAX instruction set makes it ideal for architectural subsetting. The three machines are called MAXVAX, MIDVAX, and MINVAX. Because the machines are subsets of the same architecture and thus have the same underlying implementation, differences in instruction formats and operand and addressing mode encodings are eliminated. The major features of these machines are described in the following paragraphs. Appendix A contains a complete description of the instruction sets of all three machines.

The MAXVAX instruction set is the part of the full VAX instruction set necessary to support the compilation of Y programs. Y [7] is a high-level programming language that is similar in many respects to C. Section 3 contains a brief introduction to Y. The MAXVAX includes 16 addressing modes and most instructions can use any addressing mode as both a source and destination. Both two- and three-address forms of the arithmetic and logical operations are included. In addition, the instruction set contains special forms of common operations such as increment and decrement operations, a clear operation, and special instructions for pushing operands and addresses on the runtime stack. It also contains instructions that are designed to efficiently implement switch statements and loops.

In contrast to the MAXVAX instruction set, the MIDVAX instruction set contains only eight addressing modes. The instruction set is reduced further by allowing only two-address forms of arithmetic and logical instructions. While the source operand can be any of the MIDVAX addressing modes, the destination operand must be a register. All special case instructions such as increment, decrement, clear, as well as the special stack instructions and loop instructions are omitted.

The MINVAX instruction set was designed to represent an architecture as far as realistically possible from the MAXVAX on the machine spectrum. Consequently, its set of operations and addressing modes is quite small; possibly more so than many RISCs. The MINVAX instruction set contains only four simple addressing modes. All arithmetic and logical operations are two-address instructions and are register-to-register. Memory is accessed through load and store type instructions only.

3. THREE COMPILERS

Compilers for the Y programming language were constructed for the three machines. Y [7] is a structured, general-purpose programming language intended for use in systems programming applications, such as those described in *Software Tools* [10]. Syntactically and semantically, Y is similar to C. It supports separate compilation, recursive procedures, structured control flow constructs, and expressions involving scalars, and arrays of integers, characters, and reals. From a code generation point of view, Y is equivalent to C or Pascal.

The back ends of the Y compilers were constructed using PO, a retargetable peephole optimizer [4]. While PO can be used as a general-purpose peephole optimizer, it can also replace a conventional code generator found in a traditional compiler. Compilers developed using PO in this way use two pervasive strategies that lead to the generation of excellent code. The first strategy is to have the front-end generate naive but correct code for an abstract machine. The code expander translates the abstract machine code into straightforward code for the target machine. The code is

inefficient, but simple to produce. Both of these phases are concerned only with producing semantically correct code. Efficiency is *not* an issue. The second strategy is to perform all optimizations on object code. The guiding principle is more complete and thorough optimization is possible by operating on object code where knowledge of the target machine can be used. The above two strategies are similar to the approach taken in the PL.8 compiler for the IBM 801 [1,15].

PO is made up of three distinct phases called Cacher, Combiner, and Assigner. Each phase operates on register transfer lists ('RTLs') which describe an instruction's effect. For example, a PDP-11 instruction that adds two registers would be expressed in the RTL notation as:

$$r[2] = r[2] + r[3]; \; nz = r[2] + r[3] \; ? \; 0;$$

Any RTL is machine specific, but the form of the RTL is machine independent.

Briefly, Cacher performs common subexpression elimination, allocates registers, performs a limited type of flow analysis, and identifies dead variables. Combiner advances over Cacher's output seeking adjacent instructions that can be replaced with singletons. Combiner also performs targeting [11,17], evaluation order determination [18], and instruction scheduling if the machine includes a pipeline [16].

Once optimization is complete, Assigner does register assignment and translates the RTLs to assembly language. Both Combiner and Assigner are retargeted by supplying a description of the target machine's instruction set. Combiner uses the machine description (MD) to determine whether the combined effect of two instructions can be achieved by a single instruction. The MD is also used by Assigner to convert RTLs to assembly language. Other documents offer a more complete treatment of Cacher and Assigner [3], and PO [4,5].

PO is particularly well-suited to architectural experimentation for several reasons. It is quickly and easily retargeted to a new machine by supplying a description of the target machine's instruction set, and it is able to exploit any of the target machine's special operations and addressing modes. Finally, PO performs many of the optimizations that one would expect a production compiler to perform. Indeed, the code produced by PO compares favorably to the code produced by other state-of-the-art code generation systems [4,5]. PO has been used to create C compilers for the AT&T 3B5 and the VAX, as well as a validated commercial implementation of Ada. We point out that because the code selector of the compiler is constructed automatically by supplying a new machine description, the quality of the code emitted by the compiler has less dependence on the skill of the implementors than other code generation techniques.

4. RESULTS

A set of ten Y programs were selected to serve as benchmarks for evaluating the effect of instruction set complexity on object program size. The programs range in complexity from a simple solution to the eight queen's problem to a 3600-line compiler. The ten benchmark programs are:

1. 8q—a recursive solution to the eight queens problem,
2. find—searches for a regular expression in a file,
3. ypp—the Y preprocessor,
4. y—the Y front end,
5. wf—computes the frequency of word use in a file,
6. xd—a text editor,
7. ar—a file archiver,
8. roff—a text formatter,
9. spo—a simple peephole optimizer, and
10. od—a file dump utility.

4.1 Object Code Size

Table I shows the sizes of the object code for the ten programs on the three machines. The MINVAX machine required an average of 2.5 times more memory than the MAXVAX, while the MIDVAX machine required an average of 1.54 times more memory. We also measured the average instruction size for each machine. For the MAXVAX, MIDVAX, and MINVAX respectively, the average instruction size was 4.10 bytes, 3.71 bytes, and 3.61 bytes. Because MINVAX⊂MIDVAX⊂MAXVAX, the above numbers indicate the compiler was able to take advantage of the additional instruction set complexity. We note that Emer reported an average instruction size of 3.8 bytes for the complete VAX [6].

Program	Source Lines	MAXVAX Size	MAXVAX Relative	MIDVAX Size	MIDVAX Relative	MINVAX Size	MINVAX Relative
8q	40	1979	1.00	2271	1.14	2979	1.50
find	320	3625	1.00	4665	1.30	5801	1.61
ypp	898	10071	1.00	15931	1.58	25983	2.58
y	3599	37199	1.00	61219	1.65	100203	2.69
wf	169	3075	1.00	3779	1.22	5395	1.75
xd	1289	16349	1.00	23215	1.42	42671	2.61
ar	1403	14321	1.00	20336	1.42	31936	2.23
roff	2134	24025	1.00	40842	1.70	59103	2.46
spo	187	3246	1.00	4707	1.45	8147	2.51
od	723	9736	1.00	13631	1.40	25508	2.62
Average	1076	12363	1.00	19060	1.54	30773	2.48

Table I. Program Size (Bytes) and Ratio to MAXVAX.

There have been other studies that examined the effect of instruction set complexity on program size. In 1981, a group of researchers at the University of California at Berkeley compared the memory requirements of the VAX and RISC I [13]. For the eleven benchmark programs they used, they found that the RISC I programs required an average of 50% more memory than the VAX. In 1985, a group of researchers at Carnegie-Mellon compared the code size of 16 programs on the VAX and RISC II [2]. For those benchmarks, they found that the VAX required on average 3.5 times less memory than RISC II.

The results reported here fall between these two extremes. We believe that these results provide a more accurate characterization of the effect instruction set complexity has on program size. Most studies have compared different machines, and consequently do not serve to isolate the effect of instruction set complexity on program size. For example, the Berkeley experiments compared the VAX, a machine with 16 general-purpose registers, to RISC I, a machine with 32 registers. As was noted by the Carnegie-Mellon researchers, CISC machines can also benefit from additional registers.

A second possible source of bias is caused by the code generation technology used to build the compilers for the machines being compared. Many of the previous studies on program size used the Unix portable C compiler (PCC) to generate code for the machines being compared. The code generator for this compiler is retargeted by hand and as Johnson, the author of PCC, notes, retargeting parts of the compiler require hard intellectual effort [9]. The task of getting this compiler to produce "optimal" code for a machine with a large number of operations and many addressing modes is obviously going to be harder than getting it to generate "optimal" code for a machine with a simple instruction set. Consequently, the quality of the emitted code depends, to a large extent, on the ingenuity and perseverance of the person retargeting the compiler. In contrast, the three compilers used for the experiments described here were constructed using an automatic code generation technology. The compilers were retargeted by supplying a description of the target machine's instruction set†. Consequently, differences that

---

†Because of the strategy of producing naive code in the front end and because MINVAX⊂MIDVAX⊂MAXVAX, it was possible to use the same front end for all three compilers.

could be caused by the skill level of the persons retargeting the compiler are removed. In addition, this code generation system is specifically designed to exploit any special instructions or addressing modes the target machine may have.

The Carnegie-Mellon experiments, on the other hand, compared the size of 16 programs that were handcoded in assembly language. While the current generation of optimizing compilers produce excellent code, for small programs (like the benchmarks used), humans can still probably do a better job of generating code. Consequently, we believe that their measurements of the memory requirements of the VAX are too optimistic.

4.2 Cache Performance

To investigate the effect of program size on cache performance, we used the technique of trace-driven simulation [19]. Five of the benchmark programs were selected and address traces of their execution were obtained for the three machines. The traces were generated by modifying and instrumenting the UNIX debugger, *adb*, to record every address referenced by the program. The cache simulator measured the *miss ratio* and *bus traffic*. The miss ratio is the number of cache misses divided by the number of cache accesses. The bus traffic is the number of memory requests issued.

The five programs selected were wf, ypp, y, 8q, and xd. When compared to the MAXVAX, these programs required an average of 1.55 times more memory on the MIDVAX, and 2.5 times more memory on the MINVAX. The average size of these programs is similar to the average size of the complete set of benchmark programs. The simulations used all five traces to simulate multiprogramming. Scheduling of which trace to use next was done on a round-robin basis. A context switch was performed every 10,000 time units. A cache hit incremented the clock by one time unit, a cache miss incremented the clock by 10 time units. The traces were well over 250,000 references in length so the effects of cold start could be ignored.

In creating the three compilers a number of steps were taken to ensure that any differences in address traces were due to complexity of the instruction sets and not other factors. The register allocation and assignment phases of the three compilers were given the same number of registers to allocate (eight). In addition, because the MINVAX machine is a register-to-register architecture, one would expect it to use more registers than the other two machines. The normal VAX subroutine calling convention requires that a called program save and restore the registers it uses. This could mean that the MINVAX and MIDVAX would be penalized on subroutine calls. To be fair, the three compilers generated code to save and restore on procedure entry and exit all allocable registers regardless of usage. Finally, we instrumented the compilers to report when register spills occurred. The five programs used in these experiments had no register spills.

For the trace-driven simulations, the caches had the following parameters: a) two-way set-associative, b) LRU replacement, c) write-through and no write-allocate, and d) a line size of 16 bytes. The width of the data path between the CPU and the cache is 16 bytes and between the cache and memory is 8 bytes. Throughout the simulations described in this paper, the line size, the number of elements per set, and the replacement algorithm were held constant. Only the cache capacity was varied. In addition, we included the simulation of a simple instruction buffer (IB). The simulated IB issues requests to the cache when there is room for 4 bytes in the buffer. The simulation does not proceed until these bytes are placed in the buffer.

4.2.1 Miss Ratio

Figure 2 contains a plot comparing the miss ratios of the three machines using the address traces of the five programs. As one would expect, the MAXVAX had lower miss ratios than either the MIDVAX or MINVAX. For caches less than 32K bytes, the magnitude of the difference between the MAXVAX and the MIN-VAX, however, is surprising. For cache capacities of up to 32K bytes, the MINVAX would require a cache that is four times the size of the MAXVAX cache to obtain equivalent or better performance in terms of miss ratio. At cache size of 64k bytes or greater, the machines have essentially the same performance. One of the advantages often cited for a RISC is that the simplified implementation of the control unit may free silicon resources for other uses. Based on the results presented here, these resources may well be needed to compensate for higher miss ratios due to the increased working set size.

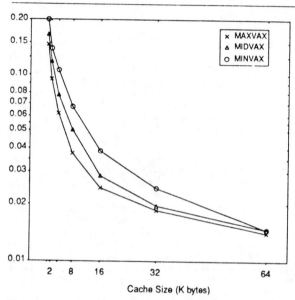

Figure 1. Miss Ratio vs. Cache Size for MAXVAX, MIDVAX, and MINVAX machines.

4.3 Memory Bus Traffic

An important factor in the design of a computer system is the amount of memory bus traffic. Because a machine with a simple instruction set requires more instructions to implement a given function, all other things being equal, we can expect such a machine to have higher memory bandwidth requirements than a machine with a complex, tightly encoded instruction set. Table II compares the number of main memory reads for the five benchmark programs running on the three machines with caches of various sizes†. Even for a cache size of 256k bytes, the MINVAX machine produces 1.85 times more main memory read requests than the MAXVAX machine.

Cache Capacity	MAXVAX		MIDVAX		MINVAX	
	Mem. Reads	Relative	Mem. Reads	Relative	Mem Reads	Relative
1k	174976	1.00	255860	1.46	471218	2.69
2k	116038	1.00	184108	1.58	331350	2.85
4k	73354	1.00	119340	1.62	253640	3.45
8k	42902	1.00	74848	1.74	159546	3.72
16k	25500	1.00	40198	1.57	88770	3.48
32k	17750	1.00	25574	1.44	51860	2.92
64k	13150	1.00	17024	1.29	28448	2.16
128k	12130	1.00	14556	1.20	24381	2.01
256k	11467	1.00	13416	1.17	21213	1.85

Table II. Bus Traffic and Ratio to MAXVAX.

†Because of the way the machines were constructed, the number of memory writes is the same for all machines.

5. DISCUSSION AND SUMMARY

This study has attempted to fairly evaluate the effect instruction set complexity has on program size and memory performance. By using subsets of the same machine to represent machines with instruction sets of varying complexity, machine differences that could have affected program size were eliminated. The machines had the same number of registers, they used the same calling sequence, and they used the same encodings for instructions and addressing modes they had in common. In addition, we used a state-of-the-art code generation system that is capable of exploiting a complex machine's instruction set and addressing modes. We expect that future compilers will be constructed with similar, if not better, code generation technology.

With all other factors constant, we found that simple instruction sets can result in programs that require two and a half times more memory than the same programs on a machine with a complex instruction set. Our evaluation of cache performance showed that for small cache sizes, instruction set complexity severely affected the miss ratio. Fortunately, this aspect of performance can be corrected through the use of large caches. Finally we examined the amount of bus traffic on the three machines. Even with a large caches (>64k), a machine with a simple instruction set can expect to generate twice as much bus traffic as a machine with a complex instruction set. Overcoming the potential performance bottleneck caused by the increased bus traffic will require innovative high-performance memory systems.

6. REFERENCES

1. Auslander, M. and Hopkins, M., An Overview of the PL.8 Compiler, *Proceedings of the ACM SIGPLAN Notices '82 Symposium on Compiler Construction*, Boston, MA, June 1982, 22-31.

2. Colwell, R. P., III, C. Y. H., Jensen, E. D., Sprunt, H. M. B. and Kollar, C. P., Computers, Complexity, and Controversy, *IEEE Computer 18*, 9 (September 1985), 8-19.

3. Davidson, J. W. and Fraser, C. W., Register Allocation and Exhaustive Peephole Optimization, *Software—Practice and Experience 14*, 9 (September 1984), 857-866.

4. Davidson, J. W. and Fraser, C. W., Code Selection through Object Code Optimization, *Transactions on Programming Languages and Systems 6*, 4 (October 1984), 7-32.

5. Davidson, J. W., A Retargetable Instruction Reorganizer, *Proceedings of the SIGPLAN Notices '86 Symposium on Compiler Construction*, Palo Alto, CA, June 1986, 234-241.

6. Emer, J. S. and Clark, D. W., A Characterization of Processor Performance in the VAX-11/780, *Proceedings of the 11th Annual Symposium on Computer Architecture*, Ann Arbor, June 1984, 301-310.

7. Hanson, D. R., The Y Programming Language, *SIGPLAN Notices 16*, 2 (February 1981), 59-68.

8. Hennessy, J. L., VLSI Processor Architecture, *IEEE Transactions on Computers 33*, 12 (December 1984), 1221-1246.

9. Johnson, S. C., A Tour Through the Portable C Compiler, *Unix Programmer's Manual, 7th Edition 2B*, (January 1979), Section 33.

10. Kernighan, B. W. and Plauger, P. J., *Software Tools*, Addison-Wesley, Reading, MA, 1976.

11. Leverett, B. W., Cattell, R. G. G., Hobbs, S. O., Newcomer, J. M., Reiner, A. H., Schatz, B. R. and Wulf, W. A., An Overview of the Production Quality Compiler-Compiler Project, CMU-CS-79-105, Carnegie-Mellon University, Pittsburg, PA, February 1979.

12. Patterson, D. A. and Ditzel, D. R., The Case for the Reduced Instruction Set Computer, *Computer Architecture News 8*, 6 (October 1980), 25-33.

13. Patterson, D. A. and Sequin, C. H., RISC I: A Reduced Instruction Set VLSI Computer, *Proceedings of the Eighth Annual Symposium on Computer Architecture*, Minneapolis, MN, May 1981, 443-457.

14. Patterson, D. A., Reduced Instruction Set Computers, *Communications of the ACM 28*, 1 (January 1985), 8-21.

15. Radin, G., The 801 Minicomputer, *Proceedings of the Symposium on Architectural Support for Programming Languages and Operating Systems*, Palo Alto, CA, March 1982, 39-47.

16. Rymarczyk, J. W., Coding Guidelines for Pipelined Processors, *Proceedings of the Symposium on Architectural Support for Programming Languages and Operating Systems*, Palo Alto, CA, March 1982, 12-19.

17. Schatz, B. R., Algorithms for Optimizing Transformations in a General Purpose Compiler: Propagation and Renaming, RC 6232, IBM Thomas J. Watson Research Center, Yorktown Heights, NY, October 1976.

18. Sethi, R. and Ullman, J. D., The Generation of Optimal Code for Arithmetic Expressions, *Journal of the ACM 17*, 6 (October 1970), 715-728.

19. Smith, A. J., Cache Memories, *Computing Surveys 14*, 3 (September 1982), 473-530.

20. Tanenbaum, A. S., Implications of Structured Programming for Machine Architecture, *Communications of the ACM 21*, 3 (March 1978), 237-246.

APPENDIX A

MINVAX Instruction Set
Addressing Modes

Mode	RTL Notation
register	r[N]
immediate	C
register deferred	m[r[N]]
displacement	m[r[N] + C]

Operations

Operation	RTL Notation
compare	nz = r[N] ? r[X];
bit test	nz = r[N] & r[X] ? 0;
load	r[N] = SRC; nz = SRC ? 0;
store	DST = r[N]; nz = r[N] ? 0;
arithmetic	r[N] = r[N] OP r[X]; nz = r[N] OP r[X] ? 0;
negate	r[N] = -r[N]; nz = -r[N] ? 0;
complement	r[N] = ~r[N]; nz = ~r[N] ? 0;
convert	r[N] = cvt(r[X]); nz = cvt(r[X]) ? 0;
bit set	r[N] = r[N] | r[X]; nz = r[N] | r[X] ? 0;
bit clear	r[N] = r[N] & ~r[X]; nz = r[N] & ~r[X] ? 0;
shift	r[N] = r[N] << r[X]; nz = r[N] << r[X] ? 0;
exclusive or	r[N] = r[N] ^ r[X]; nz = r[N] ^ r[X] ? 0;
jump	pc = LABEL;
conditional jumps	pc = nz REL 0 -> LABEL | pc;
call instruction	pc = calls(*numargs*, DST);

MIDVAX Instruction Set
Addressing Modes

Mode	RTL Notation
register	r[N]
immediate	C
register deferred	m[r[N]]
autoincrement	m[r[N]++]
autodecrement	m[--r[N]]
direct	m[A]
displacement	m[r[N] + C]
displacement deferred	m[l[r[N] + C]]

Operations

Operation	RTL Notation
compare	nz = DST ? SRC;
bit test	nz = DST & SRC ? 0;
load	r[N] = SRC; nz = SRC ? 0;
store	DST = r[N]; nz = r[N] ? 0;
arithmetic	r[N] = r[N] OP SRC; nz = r[N] OP SRC ? 0;
negate	r[N] = -r[N]; nz = -r[N] ? 0;
complement	r[N] = ~r[N]; nz = ~r[N] ? 0;
convert	r[N] = cvt(SRC); nz = cvt(SRC) ? 0;
bit set	r[N] = r[N] | SRC; nz = r[N] | SRC ? 0;
bit clear	r[N] = r[N] & ~SRC; nz = r[N] & ~SRC ? 0;
shift	r[N] = r[N] << SRC; nz = r[N] << SRC;
exclusive or	r[N] = r[N] ^ SRC; nz = r[N] ^ SRC;
jump	pc = LABEL;
conditional jumps	pc = nz REL 0 -> LABEL | pc;
call instruction	pc = calls(*numargs*, DST);

MAXVAX Instruction Set
Addressing Modes

Mode	RTL Notation
register	r[N]
register deferred	m[r[N]]
direct	m[A]
displacement	m[r[N] + C]
autoincrement	m[r[N]++]
autodecrement	m[--r[N]]
autoincrement deferred	m[l[r[N]++]]
displacement deferred	m[l[r[N] + C]]
immediate	C
indexed displacement	m[r[X] << SZ + C]
indexed register deferred	m[r[X] << SZ + r[N]]
indexed immediate displacement	m[r[X] << SZ + r[N] + C]
indexed autoincrement	m[r[X] << SZ + r[N]++]
indexed autodecrement	m[r[X] << SZ + --r[N]]
indexed autoincrement deferred	m[r[X] << SZ + m[r[N]++]]
indexed deferred displacement	m[r[X] << SZ + m[r[N] + C]]

Operations

Operation	RTL Notation
test	nz = DST ? 0;
compare	nz = DST ? SRC;
bit test	nz = DST & SRC ? 0;
clear	DST = 0; nz = 0;
push long	l[r[14]++] = SRC; nz = SRC ? 0;
move	DST = SRC; nz = SRC ? 0;
convert	DST = cvt(SRC); nz = cvt(SRC) ? 0;
move address	DST = addr(SRC); nz = addr(SRC) ? 0;
push address	l[r[14]++] = addr(SRC); nz = addr(SRC) ? 0;
increment	DST = DST + 1; nz = DST + 1 ? 0;
decrement	DST = DST - 1; nz = DST - 1 ? 0;
arithmetic	DST = SRC1 OP SRC2; nz = SRC1 OP SRC2 ? 0;
move negated	DST = -SRC; nz = -SRC ? 0;
move complemented	DST = ~SRC; nz = ~SRC ? 0;
bit set	DST = SRC1 | SRC2; nz = SRC1 | SRC2 ? 0;
bit clear	DST = SRC1 & ~SRC2; nz = SRC1 & ~SRC2 ? 0;
shift	DST = SRC1 << SRC2; nz = SRC1 << SRC2;
exclusive or	DST = SRC1 ^ SRC2; nz = SRC1 ^ SRC2;
jump	pc = LABEL;
conditional jumps	pc = nz REL 0 -> LABEL | pc;
add and jump	pc = DST + SRC <= SRC2 -> LABEL | pc;
increment and jump	pc = DST + 1 < SRC -> LABEL | pc;
increment and jump	pc = DST + 1 <= SRC -> LABEL | pc;
decrement and jump	pc = DST - 1 >= SRC -> LABEL | pc;
decrement and jump	pc = DST - 1 > SRC -> LABEL | pc;
case	pc = DST - SRC1 < SRC2 -> LABEL | pc;
call instruction	pc = calls(*numargs*, DST);

Notes: N and X denote register numbers. SZ indicates a shift count that depends of the size of datatype being accessed. DST and SRC denote any of the addressing modes. nz denotes the condition codes; pc is the program counter. OP denotes the arithmetic operators. REL denotes any of the six relational operations.

Reprinted from *IEEE Spectrum*, August 1985, pages 38–45. Copyright © 1985 by The Institute of Electrical and Electronics Engineers, Inc.

Toward simpler, faster computers

By omitting unnecessary functions, designers of reduced-instruction-set computers increase system speed and hold down equipment costs

An overriding direction taken by computer design over the last 30 years—packing more and more functions into computing hardware to handle more complex problems—is being challenged as self-defeating.

Proponents of reduced-instruction-set computers (RISCs) contend that the way to make computers solve problems faster is to pare down the number of built-in functions they perform. Leaving instructions out of a central processing unit, much like leaving the automatic transmission out of a sports car, RISC supporters say, may improve its overall performance. By leaving out seldom-used instructions, computer designers may improve supermini and mainframe performance by a factor of 2 or 3 while reducing costs by an equal proportion.

Increasing density and complexity have been the rule in computer design for years. Integrated-circuit technology has let computer designers pack more power into smaller packages, and they have done so with abandon: a dozen or so chips can now contain as many gates as the entire CPU of a leading-edge mainframe of the early 1980s. The vast bulk of these newly available gates have been used for implementing additional instructions to support high-level languages or operating systems.

But should they? Examinations, some of them made as far back as the late 1960s, of which instructions computers actually execute and how much time they spend executing them appear to indicate that complex, specialized instructions are so infrequent that they cost more to implement than they are worth. A computer designed according to RISC precepts—which its proponents see as the fundamental direction for computer architectures for the next decade—would jettison such instructions, allowing designers to concentrate on making the core instruction set run faster. About half a dozen RISC computers have been built so far, some of them research machines and others commercial products, and all claim significantly better performance than equivalent conventional computers.

Some computer engineers, on the other hand, question the validity of the RISC approach. Among their objections are the following:
• RISCs require larger programs than complex-instruction-set computers to do equivalent problems.
• RISC instruction sets have been pared down to the point where certain operations that might take only a few instructions on a conventional computer require complex subroutines.
• RISC principles make no use of the increasing density available with advances in integrated-circuit technology.

The current RISC movement germinated in the early 1970s, when studies at IBM Corp. revealed that the vast bulk of a computer's time was spent loading data from memory into registers and storing them back into memory. Program branches—loop instructions or transfers to different parts of a program—also oc-

curred relatively frequently, as did arithmetic operations, but many other instructions were used infrequently. Nonetheless most modern large computers have enormous instruction sets: the DEC VAX-11, for example, has 304, each of which can be used with one or more or the computer's 18 addressing modes to operate on one or more of its 20 data types.

The rationale behind such a proliferation of instructions is to make the computer's low-level instruction set as much as possible like the high-level language instructions that it will presumably be executing, thereby reducing what has been called "the semantic gap." In an extreme example, Honeywell Inc. offered an instruction set for one of its mainframe computers in the early 1970s that reduced every Cobol verb to a single corresponding machine instruction [see "Microcode: hiding the real computer," p. 40]. This approach has the following problems, RISC proponents claim:
• Large instruction sets require complex and potentially time-consuming hardware steps to decode and execute them.
• Complex machine instructions may not match high-level language instructions exactly, in which case they may be of little use.
• Rich instruction sets present an overwhelming choice to language-compiling programs, which may not be capable of finding the correct specialized instruction to carry out a particular high-level function.
• Since complex machine instructions often have intricate execution sequences and side effects, programs using them can be difficult to optimize.

Defining terms

Compiler: a program that translates high-level language programs in a series of machine-code instructions for a computer to execute.
Opcode: the binary code for a particular machine instruction.
Operand: a code specifying the data that an instruction operates on, or the data themselves. Operands can be part of an opcode, or they can be extensions of the opcode.
Procedure call: a program branch in which control is transferred to an essentially independent subprogram that accepts parameters from the main program and returns values to it. Because procedures act as independent units, the contents of registers must be saved before calling and restored after returning from it.
RISC: reduced-instruction-set computer. A RISC eliminates complex instructions in the interest of speed and simplicity. "Reusable independent storage computer" has also been suggested as an expansion of the acronym to imply that the RISC's power comes from optimizing the use of CPU registers and main memory. Some controversy has arisen over the exact definition of a RISC, with contention focusing on whether computers with variable-length instructions, microcoded control, or floating-point arithmetic should properly be called RISCs.

Paul Wallich   Associate Editor

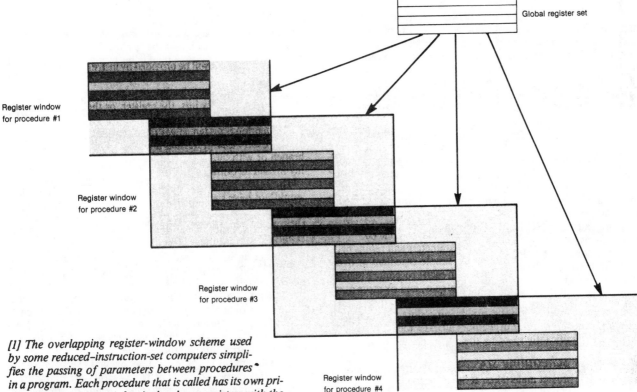

[1] The overlapping register-window scheme used by some reduced-instruction-set computers simplifies the passing of parameters between procedures in a program. Each procedure that is called has its own private register set (green), but it also shares registers with the procedure that called it and with the procedure it calls (red). Parameters are passed to a called procedure by placing them in the lower set of shared registers, and results are passed back by placing them in the upper set of shared registers. A computer with overlapped register windows will generally also have a global register set (blue) accessible to all procedures.

• Instruction sets designed with specialized instructions for several high-level languages will carry excess baggage when executing any one language.

Computers based on RISC principles, on the other hand, make choices simpler for compilers, since there will usually be only one way to perform a particular function. Moreover, since their instructions break operations down to the simplest possible level, it is relatively easy for optimizing programs to combine operations and make software faster.

Two approaches to RISC

Three pioneering RISC efforts were the 801 project at IBM's Thomas J. Watson Research Laboratory in Yorktown, N.Y.; the Microprocessor without Interlocked Pipeline Stages (MIPS) project at Stanford University in Palo Alto, Calif.; and the Reduced Instruction Set Computer project at the University of California at Berkeley, which produced both the RISC I and RISC II processors. Two slightly different approaches have been taken to building RISC computers: the register-window approach, which relies on a large number of registers to store variables that would otherwise have to be fetched from the slower main memory, and the single-register-set approach, which pares hardware down to a minimum and relies on a smart compiler to allocate variables most efficiently to registers.

Both approaches share what is called a load/store architecture, meaning that only load and store instructions can access memory. All calculation is done explicitly in registers, thus eliminating multistage instructions in which the addresses of operands in main memory are calculated, the operands are fetched and run through the CPU, and the results are stored again in memory. Because of this simple architecture, all instructions can be executed in a single clock cycle.

The 801 project—started in 1975 and completed in 1979, though not publicly reported until 1981—grew out of research that had been done into computers with special instruction sets for special applications like number crunching and telephone switching. It was also an effort to find potential alternatives to the ever-increasing complexity of IBM's 370-series machines. "There was a group of people who were dissatisfied with the complexity of newer computers," recalled one IBM researcher, Martin Hopkins.

One aim of the 801 project, Hopkins asserted, was to point the way to computers with improved reliability and maintainability as well as higher speed. Such considerations can be traded off against one another fairly straightforwardly, he said, and "engineers should not spend all that capital up front" on complex instruction sets when attention might more profitably be devoted to overall system performance.

The 801 project succeeded in making a faster computer with a simpler instruction set and simpler data path compared with conventional machines using similar technology. Partly because of the concurrent development of a high-quality optimizing compiler, program path lengths—the total number of instructions executed to perform a particular algorithm—were also shorter. The compiler used relatively well-understood techniques, Hopkins said, such as moving code segments, eliminating common subexpressions, and precalculating constants, but it brought them all together for the first time. The compiler also did break new ground in allocating variables to registers.

An interesting result was that this same compiler could be used to generate code for a conventional IBM 370, using mostly the simplest 370 instructions. A 370 computer running program code generated by the 801 compiler executed twice as many instructions per second as it did when running programs compiled with a standard 370 compiler. This measurement is somewhat misleading, since the 801 used mainly the simplest and fastest-executing 370 instructions, but, Hopkins said, the programs also solved problems considerably faster.

The RISC project at Berkeley emerged from a similar backlash against commercial computer architecture. David Patterson, a professor of computer science at Berkeley, started the project after spending a sabbatical at Digital Equipment Corp. in Maynard, Mass., working on the prodigiously complex microcode of the VAX-11/780 superminicomputer. RISC I, the first product of the Berkeley research, had 31 instructions, compared with the VAX's 304, and only one addressing mode: all arithmetic and logical instructions operated on registers, and only load and store instructions accessed memory. The RISC II had 39 instructions and was also a load-store machine.

Into the silicon area where the complex instruction-decoding hardware and microinstruction sequencer would have gone, Patterson put an enormous register array. On a conventional computer, every procedure call and return requires saving the CPU registers in memory, loading the procedure's parameters, performing a computation, placing the result in a register or in memory, and then reloading the saved registers to return to the main program. But the RISC I and II allocate a new set of registers from its register set to each new procedure that is called.

Furthermore, the two RISCs pass parameters and results back and forth between procedures by the simple expedient of overlapping their register sets: six registers in each procedure's register set overlap with those of a procedure it calls, and six more overlap with the register set of the procedure that called it [see Fig. 1]. This register-window scheme makes procedure calls virtually free, reducing the number of memory accesses the RISC I and II make and significantly speeding their operation.

Execution scheduling speeds programs

The MIPS project undertaken at Stanford took a different approach to increasing speed in a RISC—it simplified pipelining. In a conventional computer, pipelining is used to decode and partly execute several instructions at the same time [see Fig. 2], but a conventional pipeline can break down for a number of reasons,

among them the following:
• The program takes a branch, thus requiring the pipeline to be cleared and new instructions to be fetched.
• Instructions in the pipeline require information that is not yet available because it will be provided by instructions further ahead in the pipeline.
• Instructions in the pipeline require access to the same resource—the memory bus, the register, or the ALU—simultaneously.

Conventional design solves these pipeline problems with special hardware that prefetches instructions at the destination of a branch or with interlocks that prevent instructions from accessing invalid information or from trying to use the same resource.

The MIPS project was intended to produce a computer that would not have such pipeline conflicts. It used special compiler software to rearrange programs and schedule instructions so that they would not interfere with one another, according to John Hennessy, who led the project as an assistant professor of computer science at Stanford and is currently on sabbatical as chief scientist of MIPS Computers Inc. in Mountain View, Calif. The processor also uses a delayed branch instruction—as do the Berkeley RISCs—to simplify the problem of refilling the pipeline after a change of control: the instruction following the branch is executed before control is transferred to the branch destination, giving the CPU time to fetch the proper instruction from the destination and start it through the pipeline.

But what happens to the instruction that gets executed before the branch takes effect? Does it perform useful work? Filling the slot after the branch is particularly tricky because most branches are conditional instructions: they transfer control to another portion of the program only at certain times. Even though a compiler can predict whether the branch will most often be taken or not, only instructions that should be executed in either case can

Microcode: hiding the 'real' computer

Most modern computers, including microprocessors, execute their instructions by what is called microcode, which is yet another level of coding below the individual bits of the instructions fetched from memory. These microinstructions give individual and detailed control over the registers, data paths, and arithmetic-and-logic units of the processor [see fig.].

Microcode serves to simplify both the programming and design of a central processing unit. For example, the machine-level instruction "Add the contents of register A to those of register B and deposit the result in register C" requires routing the contents of the two registers somehow to the inputs of the arithmetic-and-logic unit, setting the ALU to do addition, and then routing the output to the third register. Some of these operations can be done in parallel, while others must be done serially. Microcode simplifies the programming task, since the programmer (or the compiler program) is not required to consider which operations can or cannot proceed in parallel or exactly what bits to set on the ALU. Because they control the CPU at a much greater level of detail, microinstructions are typically much wider than macroinstructions; 40 bits is a typical width, and 60 bits is not uncommon.

Microcoding also simplifies the hardware design because designers can compose many high-level operations from a small number of microinstructions rather than adding entirely new hardware for each new instruction. They can implement a multiplication instruction, for example, as a series of addition and bit-shifting microinstructions rather than build a hardware multiplier.

Instructions that are put into microcode can often run faster than if they had to be spelled out in machine code—or macroinstructions—because microinstructions have access to internal registers and other machine resources that are not visible at the higher level. Furthermore, because microcode is built into the CPU, the microinstructions can be fetched from the control store much faster than macroinstructions can be retrieved from main memory.

Because microinstructions can be used to build specialized high-level functions from simpler low-level ones, they are also often used to hide the low-level architecture of a computer from a

programmer. IBM Corp. has followed this path with great success in the 370 series, all members of which look almost identical at the instruction-set level, even though their underlying architectures are quite different. Microcode routines for each instruction match the "virtual machine" to the underlying hardware resources.

Microinstructions also have their problems, of course. The difficulty of writing them is an obvious one; wide-word microcode is particularly hard to write and debug because it involves many actions occurring in parallel with hard-to-follow interactions between them. So-called vertical microcode, which allows much less parallelism, is easier to write but less efficient.

Another difficulty with microcode is that it adds a level of indirection to the execution of instructions; unless hardware is added to decode instructions and fetch their microcode quickly, a microcoded computer will run more slowly than one that executes instructions directly. With the advent of very fast memories, this may no longer be a problem, especially with wide-word microcoding, where most instructions require only a single line of microcode. In such cases, microcoding is simply an alternative method of getting the correct data to the processor's internal control lines and is equivalent to a programmed logic array or any other control structure.   —P.W.

A microcoded central processor decodes an instruction into an address in a control store memory, which in turn directs the execution of a sequence of low-level steps. Operands must be fetched from registers, cache, or main memory, arithmetic or logical operations performed, condition flags set, results written back to registers or memory, and the program counter adjusted to point to the next instruction. In the example above (not corresponding to any particular microcoded processor), two fields of an instruction are used to find an address in a first-level control store, which in turn directs a sequencer and selects a series of microinstructions—a microroutine—in a second-level control store. Several different instructions may use the same microroutine.

safely be put in the slot immediately following a branch. A typical example of a predictable branch is a program loop, which executes many times—branching back to the beginning each time—but eventually exits.

About 70 percent of the time, Hennessy explained, the position can be filled with an instruction that will be required whether the branch is taken or not. Perhaps 20 percent of the time it is filled by an instruction that does not advance the state of the computation—if the branch behaves according to the compiler's prediction, then the instruction performs useful work; but if it is taken, then no incorrect operations are performed. Finally, 10 percent of the slots are filled with no-operation instructions, which is what would be happening all the time for a conventional computer that had to refill its pipeline after every branch.

Hennessy said that since about 20 percent of the instructions executed were branches, the delayed branch yields a gain of about 15 percent in overall execution speed. The MIPS group at Stanford is currently working on MIPS-X, a virtual-address version of its machine, and the company Hennessy helped found is working on a CMOS implementation of the processor intended to execute about 3 to 5 million instructions per second. Hennessy will return to Stanford in the fall to head the university's computer science laboratory.

Among those making commercial forays into RISC work are Ridge Computers Inc., which manufactures a RISC that includes floating-point mathematics instructions; Pyramid Technology Corp., whose 90x is a many-user superminicomputer optimized for the UNIX operating system; and Harris Corp, whose HCX-7 is also optimized for UNIX. Hewlett-Packard Co. has announced that it will be using RISC architectures for its future minicomputer lines, although it has not yet announced a product, and DEC and IBM are also both rumored to be working on RISCs as CPUs for high-performance personal workstations.

The RISC philosophy seems sensible, research projects have achieved impressive performance, and commercial RISCs show remarkable throughput figures. But some computer scientists have criticized the move toward reduced instruction sets, however, and have voiced the following objections:

• RISC programs take up too much space, which degrades performance, since more instructions must be fetched from slower main memory to perform a given operation.

• RISC computers have not been tested in enough real-world situations to judge their performance.

• Overlapped–register-set RISCs, such as RISC I and II, suffer dramatic performance losses when executing programs where the register stack overflows and must be copied to main memory.

• Although RISC computers have simpler hardware, their program compilers must be proportionally more complex to wring performance out of the bare-bones CPU.

• The performance gains that RISC machines show are based on features such as overlapped register sets, which have nothing to do with reduced instruction sets and could as easily be implemented on complex machines.

• To compete in the real world, RISC machines must be loaded down with additional instructions and hardware—such as floating-point arithmetic and memory management—that make them just as complex as the complex–instruction-set computers they are supposed to replace. "It takes a lot of work to turn a RISC into a real computer," said one critic.

A group of researchers at Carnegie-Mellon University in Pittsburgh, Pa., pointed out that a rating method for computers used by the U.S. Department of Defense in its search for a new standard computer architecture put RISCs very low on the scale, whereas the VAX—an archetypal complex instruction set computer—was rated near the top. In studies of the number of times the RISC II had to access memory to fetch instructions, or to

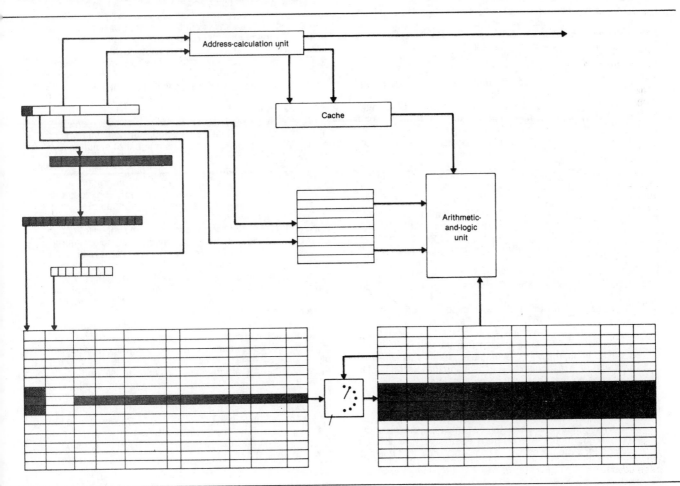

load and store data, it performed badly on programs that passed many parameters to their procedures, or that called huge numbers of procedures in succession. These cases were particularly difficult for the RISC II to handle because the overlapping register set could only handle a small number of procedure calls before overflowing to memory.

As soon as the RISC II had to make use of memory to save and restore its registers, the researchers found, its performance dropped precipitously, especially since it has no mechanism for saving or restoring only a few registers at a time—it must go through a software subroutine that saves or restores all 16 current registers, no matter how many are actually in use.

Two of the researchers, Charles Y. Hitchcock III and H.M. Brinkley Sprunt, also did studies in which they simulated the RISC, the MC68000, and the DEC VAX, adding or subtracting overlapping register sets to determine how much performance gain could be attributed to them when they did not overflow. They found that the RISC II's performance was largely dependent on its overlapping register set—without it, it ran about half as quickly on most problems. They also found that both the

MC68000 and the VAX could also benefit from having an overlapping register set added to their architectures, although the effect on them was less marked—only about a 30-percent difference.

RISC proponents counter that such an analysis is missing the point because overlapping register sets could not be added to the architecture of a 68000 or a VAX without reducing chip yield to unacceptable levels or increasing the number of boards in the CPU. "A VAX 780 has 27 boards in its CPU, and we have two," noted David Folger, president of Ridge Computers in Santa Clara, Calif. In applications such as integrated-circuit design, the Ridge outperforms a VAX 11/780 by a factor of 2 to 4.

On the other hand, one complex-microprocessor designer (whose company requested he not be named) said he believes that the RISC arguments "had their place at a certain point of technology," but that they have now been overtaken by the increasing density of semiconductor circuits. "Now we have eight times the density of RISC II," he noted. "So you put on a cache, and make addition and subtraction run faster, but what then?" He asserted that technological advances had made complex hard-

Compiler technology key to RISC success

Since what compilers do is break down high-level language programs into smaller actions, compiling for a reduced-instruction-set computer (RISC) simply requires a little more breaking down. A reduced instruction set provides fewer choices of instruction for the compiler, thus potentially leading to longer program code, but the reduced choice also simplifies the compiler, since it does not have to keep the complex accounting required to choose between several alternate ways of doing the same thing.

This simplification could have a salutary effect on compiler design. Martin Hopkins, a researcher at IBM Corp.'s Thomas J. Watson Research Center in Yorktown Heights, N.Y., for example, said he is a little disappointed with much recent university research on compilers because most of it has been aimed at "regularizing methods for making choices in special cases" rather than improving formal methods for global optimization and register allocation.

Simply generating machine code for a particular architecture is only the first stage in compilation. At least as significant for RISCs is the optimization stage, in which constants are precalculated, redundant subexpressions are eliminated, variables are shuffled among registers, and so forth.

And here the RISC shines: "It's almost undeniable that you can generate optimal code for a simple machine," said Robert Ragan-Kelley, vice president for computer architecture and planning at Pyramid Technology Corp. in Mountain View, Calif., "but it's difficult for a machine with lots of function." Complex-instruction-set computers present a difficult problem for optimization programs because there are too many choices for performing different operations, and even human experts may disagree on which is the best one.

In some RISCs, there is even a level below the compiler, called the assembler, which performs additional optimization and decoding of instructions. The assembler for the micro-Processor without Interlocking Pipeline Stage (MIPS) computer, built at Stanford University in Palo Alto, Calif., for example, translates such instructions as integer multiplication into the series of multiplication steps that the chip actually can do. In addition, the MIPS assembler contains a pipeline reorganizer that is responsible for scheduling the execution of instructions so that there will be no conflicts in the pipelined fetching of operands and no unused instruction slots due to branches that interrupt the pipeline.

The translation of a multiplication instruction into a series of smaller operations is exactly the same thing a microcoded complex-instruction-set computer does when it fetches the opcode for a multiplication, except, of course, that it is only

done once by the MIPS. John Hennessy, leader of the Stanford MIPS project and also chief scientist of MIPS Computers Inc. in Mountain View, said that this resemblance to traditional microcode is no mistake.

"Back in the 1960s and 1970s," he noted, "one of the big ideas was dynamic microcode"—an arrangement whereby the microcode that controlled the basic hardware of a computer would be changed on the fly to provide the most efficient execution sequence and machine instruction set at any given moment of program execution. Dynamic microcode ran into a host of problems, including the cost of reloading the high-speed memory of the control store and the difficulty of writing enormous amounts of microcode by hand.

Today, however, optimizing compilers can write the "microcode"—instructions for a RISC—and cheap CMOS memory chips can be built into large caches that are the equivalent of "a large writable control store," Hennessy said. Present compilers are up to the task of writing so-called vertical microcode, in which a relatively small number of operations take place in parallel, Hennessy asserted, but horizontal microcode, which controls an enormous number of simultaneous operations, is still some years in the future.

Because the compiler is an integral part of a RISC-based computer system, it is clear that most programming for RISCs will be done in high-level languages. But does this mean the end of assembly-language programming?

Certainly not, said IBM's Hopkins. For one thing, programming a RISC in assembly language is much simpler (although possibly more tedious) than programming a complex-instruction-set computer. And for another, there will always be a few applications where current compilers are not quite smart enough to recognize what tradeoffs they can make in the interests of speed. He cited such applications as interpreters for high-level languages as one area where human programmers have a edge in optimization.

"There are always going to be special-purpose routines for particular applications," said Hopkins, "and someone is going to have to code them in a high-level language or in assembly language." In fact, simple instruction sets may make it more feasible for programmers to write those routines in assembly language. Complex-instruction-set computers, Hopkins asserted, "take away power from individuals to solve their own performance problems and load the problems back onto some architectural group" of engineers who define the instruction set. RISC machines, on the other hand, give programmers direct access to the primitive operations required to do whatever they want. —P.W.

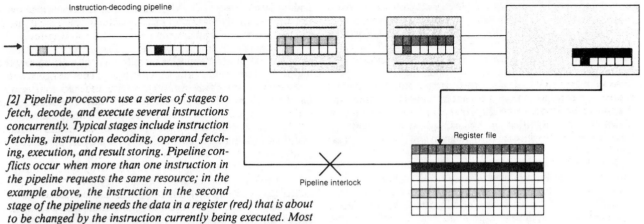

[2] *Pipeline processors use a series of stages to fetch, decode, and execute several instructions concurrently. Typical stages include instruction fetching, instruction decoding, operand fetching, execution, and result storing. Pipeline conflicts occur when more than one instruction in the pipeline requests the same resource; in the example above, the instruction in the second stage of the pipeline needs the data in a register (red) that is about to be changed by the instruction currently being executed. Most computers use special hardware to stop the pipeline until the register has been changed; others omit interlocks and use special techniques either to ensure that there will be no conflicts or to accelerate the delivery of new data to the pipe stage that needs it.*

Instruction-decoding pipeline

Instruction-execution unit

Register file

Pipeline interlock

ware configurations much more feasible than they were even a few years ago.

Smaller instruction sets make bigger programs

The argument that RISC programs take up more space than the corresponding programs for a complex–instruction-set computer would seem to make sense: after all, if the compiler for a RISC breaks down high-level language instructions into very simple actions, it should take more instructions to accomplish a task than the conventional computer, where a single instruction often sets off a long chain of actions. The Intel 432 microprocessor, for example, had a single machine-level instruction—which triggered a substantial series of microinstructions—to send a message from one process to another, a job usually handled by an operating-system software routine.

In this view, the high instruction-execution rates of a RISC machine do not lead to correspondingly short execution times—"If you make each instruction brain-damaged enough, you can get a very high clock rate," noted Stephen Johnson of AT&T Bell Laboratories, in Summit, N.J., author of the portable C-language compiler used to compile benchmark programs for the RISC I and II.

But, on the other hand, Hennessy of Stanford asserted that "the RISC machines tend to execute about the same number of instructions" as their complex–instruction-set counterparts for a given problem.

This seeming paradox is explained, he said, by the amount of optimization that compilers can perform on RISC programs. By carefully allocating variables to registers, for example, a RISC machine can reduce the number of times it has to access main memory and the total number of instructions it has to do. Furthermore, all the registers of a RISC are directly accessible to the compiler, whereas complex–instruction-set computers often have hidden registers accessible only to particular instructions—for example, those that move data from one memory location to another, or add the contents of two memory locations. Such features make the optimizing of programs more difficult.

The question of program size is important, not merely because of potentially misleading execution speeds, but also because the effects of program size can snowball throughout an entire computer system. Larger programs require more memory to store them, thus affecting program-loading time. They are also more likely to cause page faults—portions of the program not in main memory—in virtual memory systems, thus reducing performance, and in computers with caches larger programs will reduce cache hit rates, thus diminishing performance further.

RISC machines are particularly dependent on caches—small, high-speed memories—to feed them instructions at a rate fast enough that one instruction can be executed in each clock cycle. If a RISC has to wait for main memory to supply instructions and data, it can be slowed by a factor of 3 or more. Enhanced CPU performance can "get lost in the noise" in the face of such systemwide considerations, according to Robert Ragan-Kelley, vice president for architecture and planning at Pyramid. Overall evidence seems to indicate that program size is not a problem for RISCs so far, but it is certainly a pitfall to bear in mind when designing reduced instruction sets. "You can't just chop out instructions," he said. "The primitives must serve the application." If only a few crucial instructions are absent from its instruction set, a computer can take five or ten times as long to execute certain programs as it would if they were present.

Facing software questions

Because of their architectures, RISC machines may cross hardware thresholds and lose performance in a number of areas: not only in caches and main memory, but in registers as well. The two families of RISC machines face this problem differently. RISCs with a limited number of registers, such as the MIPS and the 801, may run out of registers because all calculations must be performed using them. Register-window RISCs, such as the RISC I and II and the Pyramid, may run out of registers for additional procedures, forcing an overflow to main memory.

The register-window RISCs face an additional problem when running multiple tasks at the same time, critics say: either they must allocate portions of the register set to each process, thus limiting how many tasks they can perform efficiently at the same time, or they must save and restore the entire register set when changing from one process to another, which represents a significant overhead penalty. (The RISC II has more than 100 registers, and the Pyramid has 528.)

Ragan-Kelley, on the other hand, contends that it is quite simple to implement a scheme whereby only a single register set is initially saved to make room for a new process and more are allocated as needed, thus reducing overhead substantially.

Much of the performance of RISC machines thus comes down to the technology of the compilers that convert high-level program code into the spare set of machine instructions the RISC will execute. If the compiler allocates variables to registers efficiently and eliminates redundant expressions, then all may be well, but if the compiler does not perform well, then code size can balloon and execution speed can plummet. Some critics assert that RISC designers have simply traded complexity in one place, hardware, for complexity in another, software.

But RISC proponents reply that writing compilers for a reduced-instruction set is at least as simple as writing a compiler for a complex–instruction-set computer—and potentially much easier, because the compiler usually has only one choice of instruction sequence for a particular operation. On a conventional computer, the same high-level language instruction could be executed in many different ways, each with its own specialized advantages and tradeoffs, but "on a RISC there's usually only one way to do things," said IBM's Hopkins.

Hennessy of Stanford contended that "the compiler issue has been exaggerated." For the most part, he pointed out, all a RISC compiler does is what typical complex–instruction-set computers do every time they execute an instruction: break an action down into smaller parts and execute these parts one by one. It stands to reason, he said, that efficiency is gained by paying the cost for that breakdown only once for each program and performing it as well as possible.

"We're not trying anything in our compilers that Fortran H doesn't do," said Ridge's Edwin Basart of his company's compiler technology. (Fortran H is a venerable optimizing compiler that has run on IBM mainframes for more than a decade.) Furthermore, he said, optimizing a program yields better and more predictable benefits on a RISC than on a complex–instruction-set computer, because eliminating an instruction always saves clock cycles, and the number of clock cycles saved by different alternatives is easy to calculate.

Compiler technology for RISCs has been attracting undue attention for two reasons, Basart contended. First, he said, "RISCs are new architectures, and so you have to build compilers for them; you can't just buy one off the shelf." Second, "Minicomputers haven't had good compilers—we're just doing what was done at Control Data 20 years ago."

Johnson, the compiler author at Bell Labs, agreed with this assessment of RISC compilers. After all, he points out, RISC instruction sets were designed after careful studies of exactly what instructions good compilers did generate.

IBM's Hopkins said, "Every trace tape ever run shows that nobody ever uses those fancy operations."

In a nutshell, according to Pyramid's Ragan-Kelley, "mature designers have always known that all computers do are loads and stores, procedure calls and returns, and so forth." Software complexity, he said, is not an issue.

Redefining a RISC

That major computer companies such as DEC, Hewlett–Packard, and IBM have either openly affirmed a commitment to RISC machines or sponsored extensive research and development efforts says something for the concept. But what of the three commercial RISCs already on the market? The Ridge, the Pyramid, and the Harris computers all stretch the definition of a RISC, and some critics question whether a computer like the Pyramid—with over 100 instructions, all implemented in microcode—should qualify as a RISC. Both the Ridge and the Pyramid are microcoded, and they also implement virtual memory, a technique usually reserved for complex computers.

Others, such as IBM's Hopkins, see elements of RISC philosophy being applied even in such complex machines as DEC's MicroVAX II, which achieves 80 percent of the performance of a VAX 11/780 even though it implements only about 60 percent of the VAX instruction set in hardware, relying on software for the rest.

The major reason to call the Ridge a RISC, said Folger, is the simplicity and regularity of its instruction set. The machine allows only load and store operations and operations that perform calculations on operands in registers. "The number of instructions isn't so important," he said. "For example, if you can do register-register addition, you get logical AND, OR, and exclusive-OR for free," because the same hardware is used for all these operations.

Because the Ridge instruction set is regular, the portion of the instruction specifying the operands can be sent to the register file to initiate the operand fetch, even while the instruction type is being decoded [Fig. 3]. Folger contrasted this with the VAX, where a series of extensions to the instruction opcode specify the kinds of operands, their locations, and their length. Because the oper-

ands can vary in length, the VAX cannot even determine the location of the second operand for an instruction until it has fully decoded the first, he pointed out.

Floating-point instructions, however, do appear to fall outside what is usually considered RISC architecture. "The IEEE floating-point standard has bells and whistles all over it," Johnson noted. Among these features are specifications for four different kinds of rounding, special extensions for very small numbers, and even a particular bit pattern to represent invalid numbers.

Both Ragan-Kelley and Folger pointed out, on the other hand, that floating-point calculations are an essential part of real computer applications, especially in science and engineering, so they must be included in a RISC manufactured for sale. Performance would be five to ten times worse without them, Ragan-Kelley asserted. In fact, since floating-point instructions do comprise such a large percentage of the instructions executed by scientific and engineering programs, including them in a commercial RISC is simply a reflection of the design principle that RISCs should include often-used instructions while leaving out those that are not used often or that can be efficiently emulated by subroutines.

RISCs that handle floating-point instructions are significantly more complex than RISCs that do not, but their complexity still does not approach that of conventional complex–instruction-set computers, Folger said. In fact, he asserted, one way of looking at the Ridge CPU would be as "a floating-point processor that also executes instructions on the side."

Another complex problem for RISCs is implementing virtual memory, a technique whereby programs can use far more space than is available in main memory by fetching "pages" from secondary storage as needed. Virtual memory requires a plethora of specialized hardware to translate between virtual and real addresses and to determine whether a page is in memory, as well as finely tuned software to decide which old page to swap out to make room for a new one. Nevertheless RISC machines have significant advantages in implementing virtual memory. Because RISCs perform all calculations in registers, only instruction fetches, loads, and stores can cause page faults that require swapping in a new page. And in any of these cases it is relatively easy to back up execution and restart the instruction after the required page has been brought in, because the instructions executed have no side-effect that must also be undone.

Since complex–instruction-set computers allow arithmetic and logical operations directly on memory, they run the risk of getting into states that are hard to untangle if a page fault occurs. For example, moving characters from one memory location to another on an IBM 370 could cause as many as eight page faults. Two page faults could occur fetching the portion of the instruction that sets the number of characters to be moved. Since instructions are allowed to straddle page boundaries, another two faults could occur fetching the move instruction itself, and four more page faults could occur in fetching the data from its source and storing it at its destination if each of those locations straddled a page boundary. The status of instruction execution and data movement would have to be saved when each page fault occurred and restored after the appropriate page was brought into memory. This problem would be significantly simplified by forcing instruction not to overlap page boundaries; some complex–instruction-set computers, on the other hand, do not even constrain instructions to begin and end at word boundaries.

RISCs change engineering tradeoffs

Complexities such as floating-point operations and virtual memory, however, are also fundamental to the problems that computers are being used to solve. "When you're doing a job that's inherently complicated, the complexity isn't going to go away," said Johnson. The point of designs like the RISCs is a willingness to trade off complexity across what were previously considered hard and fast system boundaries—making a little more work for the software so as to make a little less for the hardware. The present bias toward putting complexity in software

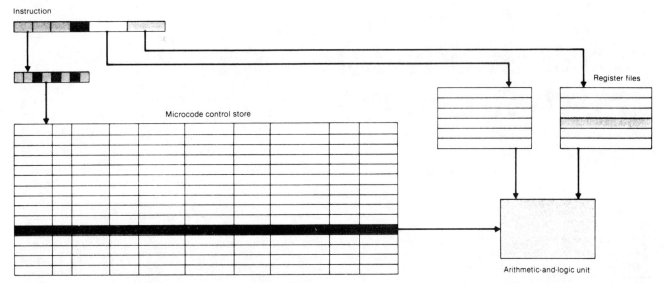

Instruction

Register files

Microcode control store

Arithmetic-and-logic unit

[3] A reduced–instruction-set computer uses a regular instruction format to speed execution. In this case, the first half of the instruction is decoded (red) whereas the second half is used to select operands from registers (green and blue). Complex-instruction-set computers often use several different instruction formats, so that the first part of the instruction must be fully decoded before the central processor can determine what to do with the rest of it. In extreme cases, each succeeding part of an instruction must be decoded for the processor to determine where the next part of the instruction begins.

arises because "bugs in the software are easier to fix," according to Johnson—certainly the turnaround time for compiling a piece of code is shorter than that for fabricating a piece of silicon.

"There's a wave of people now who are trained in the whole computer field from software to silicon," said Ridge's Basart, and these designers are better able to look at computers as systems consisting of many levels of hardware and software, rather than just at CPUs in isolation.

In addition, the rise of software standards has made it easier in the last half-decade to design new computer architectures. "UNIX is the unsung hero of all this," said Ragan-Kelley, "because without a retargetable operating system, there wouldn't have been a commercial environment for RISCs." With UNIX, a C language compiler, a few bright, dedicated programmers, and a great deal of hard work are about all that is needed to allow thousands of well-documented programs to be transported to a new computer.

If RISC concepts do point the way to a new design methodology for computers, what will be the result? Will conventional mainframes and minicomputers fade away? Probably not, since far too large an installed base of software would have to be converted. On the other hand, the increased speed of RISC architectures may place complex–instruction-set computers at an increasing disadvantage as time goes by.

"DEC has a terrible problem with the VAX, because you just can't build it to run fast," said one researcher who requested anonymity. "And, in the same way, IBM is stuck with the 370." One possibility for speeding such conventional machines is to apply some of the lessons learned from RISCs to their design. Although instruction sets and formats cannot be changed, their implementation can be, and it may be possible to emulate many instructions in software while maintaining performance. This kind of emulation, in fact, has been part of the designer's bag of trick for many years.

RISCs themselves will probably evolve as well. One possible direction is exemplified by the FRISC (fanatically reduced instruction set computer) in development at Schlumberger Palo Alto (Calif.) Research Center, which has no branch instructions in its CPU. Instead, in another example of tradeoffs across system boundaries, the processor relies on a special instruction-stream memory to feed it the correct next instruction to execute.

Another obvious direction for RISCs to take is toward added

complexity. The Smalltalk on a RISC project at Berkeley, for example, adds hardware support for the Smalltalk language to the basic structure developed by Patterson. The MIPS-X project at Stanford is intended to provide a uniform virtual-memory structure for a RISC, eliminating address translation as far as possible. Folger and others speculate that Hewlett–Packard's RISC will include hardware support for packed-decimal arithmetic or memory-to-memory operations, two requirements of the Cobol language used in the mainstream data-processing environments inhabited by HP's current minicomputers.

"Once you've cleared the decks, you can now put more baggage on them," commented Basart of Ridge.

Ragan-Kelley, on the other hand, suggested that RISCs would be used as a basis for more complex system architectures. "The next generation of baroqueness," he said, "will be not at the CPU level, but rather with topologies and interconnections of multiple processor systems." Pyramid only recently announced a multiple-processor version of its RISC minicomputer.

As more computers based on RISC ideas are developed and used, their benefits and drawbacks will become clearer. What is already clear, though, is that computer architecture is changing. Formerly hard-and-fast divisions between software and hardware appear to be giving way to a systems approach.

To probe further

RISC proponents have published a number of papers expounding their views. One of the first was "A VLSI RISC," by David Patterson and Carlo Sequin of the University of California at Berkeley, in *IEEE Computer*, September 1982. "The 801 minicomputer," by George Radin of IBM, appeared in the *IBM Journal of Research and Development* in May 1983. A review of existing RISC efforts is "Reduced Instruction Set Computers," also by Patterson, in *Communications of the ACM*, January 1985.

The most thorough critical examination of reduced-instruction-set concepts is "Computers, Complexity, and Controversy," by Robert P. Colwell, Charles Y. Hitchcock III, E. Douglas Jensen, H.M. Brinkley Sprunt, and Charles P. Kollar of Carnegie-Mellon University in Pittsburgh, Pa., to be published in the September 1985 issue of *IEEE Computer*. A number of additional articles comparing RISCs and complex-instruction-set computers have appeared in *Computer Architecture News*. ◆

Applications determine the choice of RISC or CISC

Ron Wilson
Senior Editor

Despite the publicity given to RISC CPUs, there are concrete architectural reasons why CISC machines will continue their dominance in 32-bit systems. But the contest is just starting.

Reduced-instruction-set computers are taking over the industry, according to much of the technical press in the last year. But facts don't support the claims. In 1989, the majority of 32-bit design wins will again go to complex-instruction-set microprocessors. And of the CPU chips slated for introduction this year, two of the most important—the 80486 from Intel (Santa Clara, CA) and the 68040 from Motorola (Austin, TX)—are very much CISC designs.

Why is there such a disparity between RISC promotion and RISC achievement? And why do CISC microprocessors, which have yet to approach the astronomical Mips ratings of the latest RISC chips, cling so stubbornly to design wins? There is no one answer—the dynamics of the 32-bit CPU market include a rich blend of technical issues, practical considerations and human foibles. But there are several key technical distinctions between RISC and CISC system architectures, and these differences give CISC machines a distinct advantage in some specific situations.

Consequently, we can expect that the existing CISC product families will be around for a long while, and

that they will continue to evolve aggressively. And we can expect the new RISC designs to begin evolving as well, often in some surprisingly complex ways.

■ The force of inertia

"The biggest single reason for the continued use of CISC machines is binary compatibility," claims Dave Ditzel, distinguished engineer and manager of advanced architectures at Sun Microsystems (Mountain View, CA). "When there are more than 2,000 codes out there for the 68000, cost/performance isn't always the driving issue in someone's decision process."

Tom Thawley, executive vice-president of Interphase (Dallas, TX), explains a further issue. "There's a strong motivation to stay with one processor just because of logistics: we have a huge investment in firmware, programmer experience and development tools. It's not with a light heart that you'd walk away from all that."

Yet even in applications in which no existing code libraries, tool, or prejudices preclude RISC chips from being considered, it's the CISC processors that are still winning the sockets. The reasons for this are

lodged deep within the RISC and CISC architectural concepts.

■ The code expansion factor

A typical algorithm coded for a RISC CPU will require between 25 and 45 percent more code than the same algorithm coded for a CISC CPU. In engineering workstations, such a difference in code density is more or less irrelevant—your program can probably be 30 percent larger and still fit in 7 Mbytes of main memory. But in space- or cost-constrained embedded systems, the difference in memory size can be important. "In embedded systems, cost/performance is the major issue but the most expensive component is usually memory," explains David Schanin, technical director for the 32000 program at National Semiconductor (Santa Clara, CA). "So if you can significantly reduce code size, you can significantly reduce system cost."

An important side effect of code density is memory bandwidth. If an instruction set can express a task in fewer instructions, then the CPU can execute the task with fewer instruction fetches. In practice, this means that CISC processors can be less demanding on memory bandwidth than RISC processors of equivalent throughput.

"We find that RISC machines will in fact run faster than CISC machines, but it's harder to keep them fed," reports Doug Johnson, workstation product marketing manager at Hewlett-Packard (Fort Collins, CO). "The RISC machines are more demanding on their caches, and on memory size as well: we see a 30 to 70 percent code growth between CISC and RISC."

■ The importance of cache

Cache memory subsystems are an important tool in the RISC designer's struggle against memory bottlenecks. This is also true for the architect of a CISC system, of course: most fast 32-bit CISC chips have, or soon will have, on-chip caches. But the problem for RISC designers is more acute because of the RISC CPU's insatiable one-instruction-per-clock appetite.

Consequently, well-tuned RISC systems need big caches. The three-chip Motorola 88000 processor, for example, starts out with 16 kbytes of cache for instructions and 16 kbytes for data, with the option to add further 16-kbyte increments to either side. In comparison, the 68030 provides 256 bytes of cache each for instructions and data.

This close link between large caches and speed keeps the system cost of current RISC implementations relatively high. The cache must be made from very fast SRAM, and current CMOS technology can't fit sufficient cache on-chip with even the most compact RISC cores. So where a mature CISC chip is running effectively with small, on-chip caches, its nearest RISC relative requires expensive external cache/memory-management unit (MMU) parts. The difference in cost might be negligible for a high-end workstation, but not in an embedded design.

There is a particular branch of the embedded control market where cache memory raises an entirely different issue. In real-time systems, designers must be able to guarantee the worst-case performance of a controller, rather than the average performance. But, as Intel 32-bit microprocessor marketing manager Bill Rash points out, "Cache doesn't help you with worst-case performance. In fact, it can actually hurt by causing some unnecessary prefetching. In the subset of embedded control applications that have real-time constraints—such as avionics, rather than something where the outside world can wait, such as a laser printer—cache may not be your friend."

■ Exploiting real estate

CISC processors may always be a better solution for real-time control, just because of the cache issue. But in the majority of control and even personal computing applications, the major difference between CISC and RISC machines comes down to a matter of system cost. Today, the RISC chips, with their higher initial prices and greater sensitivity to memory bandwidth, are more expensive to use.

But with the next generational improvement in silicon technology, the cost disparity will shrink. When both CISC and RISC vendors are working with hand-crafted cells in sub-micron geometries, there will be plenty of space left on an economically sized die even after a CISC core has been laid out. At this point, the RISC and CISC designers have to decide how to use that additional space.

For some of the RISC people, the answer will be caches. If the chip designers can pull adequate cache onto the CPU chip, they can eliminate the system cost disparity caused by RISC's higher bandwidth needs. And the availability of a fast, low-cost RISC CPU would give a vendor a shot at the personal computing market.

Cypress Semiconductor (San Jose, CA) has taken the first steps in this direction of Ross's ideal chip by implementing a set of support chips—a cache-controller/MMU and a floating-point-processor interface chip—for the 33-MHz 7C601 Integer Unit.

But while the RISC vendors are looking at the real estate on denser dice and thinking about caches and MMUs, the CISC vendors are having other ideas entirely. Unconstrained by the need for large caches, firms such as Intel and Motorola see an opportunity to start gathering in the control and peripheral elements of embedded designs.

Jeff Nutt, technical marketing manager at Motorola, holds a similar view for the increasing integration of 32-bit chips. "Today's 68030 CPU has about 300,000 transistors," he says. "When we introduce the 68040 this year, it will have about 1.2 million transistors. On that large a die, the core processor takes a relatively small portion of the space, whether it's RISC or CISC. So you have to decide how to use the extra area.

"You have two choices," Nutt continues. "Either you use the space to improve general-purpose performance, or you use it to increase on-chip functionality for some specific range of applications. For performance, you could increase cache size, add execution units, and so on. For functionality, you could add I/O devices." It's likely that Motorola is pursuing both alternatives.

■ Moving closer to applications

Some chip designers have seen those extra transistors as an opportunity to have their cake and eat it too. These architects reason that, in specific application areas such as graph-

The 33-MHz CY7C601 Sparc Integer Unit from Cypress Semiconductor exhibits two fundamental RISC characteristics: speed and hardware simplicity. The small CPU will eventually make possible the inclusion of support chips or even caches on the die.

The Sparc-based PC: the next standard in personal computing

In the next three years, a new personal computing standard will emerge. This open standard will drive a dramatic market-share wedge into the current 80X86- and 680X0-based personal computer standards. This will occur for largely the same reasons that CISC-based personal computers took market share away from minicomputers, and that minicomputers took market share away from mainframes.

Sparc-based personal computers, all running the same off-the-shelf binary applications software on top of Unix, will shatter the traditional price/performance levels of CISC-based personal computers and become the dominant desktop computing platform in the under-$10,000 systems market. These Sparc Unix PCs will be linked to Sparc-based file, compute and transaction server minicomputers and mainframes to provide an architecturally cohesive computing environment of unprecedented power.

Vendors of CISC machines claim that RISC architectures will find homes only in embedded-control systems and in computers priced above those based on existing CISC standards. By using RISC "design techniques," they claim, they can vastly improve the performance and price/performance of their CISC architectures. Nothing could be further from the truth.

The reality is that RISC architectures are as general-purpose as CISC architectures and yet are able to offer performance levels from three to five times those of CISC architectures implemented in the same technology. Because they're more efficient designs, RISC architectures can offer this superior performance at the same price points as CISC architectures and earlier in the technology life cycle.

■ RISC vs. CISC

RISC and CISC processors are dramatically different at the instruction-set architecture and microarchitectural levels. RISC architectures have a load/store model of execution; they can decouple the loading and storing operations from other instruction execution to obtain a high level of concurrency. CISC architectures can't do this because of their memory-/register-oriented instruction set.

RISC processors have nondestructive, three-address architectures. CISC processors, as a byproduct of normal instruction execution, destroy information existing in the machine due to their two-address architectures. The benefit of a nondestructive, three-address architecture is that instructions can be scheduled to allow for maximal concurrency.

The only limit to optimizing the scheduling of instructions is when data dependencies occur—that is, when one instruction depends on the results of the previous one. CISC architectures can't have their code scheduled for higher concurrency due to their destructive model of execution.

RISC processors have fixed-length, efficient instructions, whereas CISC processors have instructions of varying lengths. In fixed-length instructions, all op codes and operand fields are in the same location, allowing for parallelization of the instruction decode.

A further benefit is the simplicity of decode of fixed-length instructions. That is, RISC architectures have no microcode and devote a minimum of die area to control functions to maximize the amount of die area devoted to data processing. RISC architectures typically devote less than 10 percent of their die area to control circuitry, compared to 50 percent or more of die area consumed for control and microcode on CISC architectures.

This difference is the underlying reason why RISC architectures aren't just higher performance than CISC architectures, but are more silicon-efficient as well. RISC processors obtain their performance gains over CISC processors while using much less die area.

Sparc-based personal computers will become the dominant desktop computing platform in the under-$10,000 systems market.

■ ■ ■

Historically, a two-times price/performance advantage has caused migration of software to a new computer architecture. RISC architectures offer a three- to five-times gain over CISC designs. In fact, coupled with the trends toward distributed data processing, open systems, the use of high-level languages for application software development and the growing use of Unix, there's an unprecedented inertia for the emergence of a new personal computing standard. This computing standard will be based on the Sparc architecture.

■ Why Sparc?

The Sparc architecture is the only multiple-sourced RISC processor architecture in the world that is openly licensable. This open licensing policy has resulted in a Sparc gate array and custom CMOS, ECL and GaAs versions, available now or in the advanced stages of development.

All of the software and hardware products (Unix, optimizing compilers, debuggers, simulators and so forth) needed to make a computer that can run all the existing Sparc binary software are available and are priced to penetrate the PC market. One can design a system that can take advantage of all the existing applications software and have a full migration path for the future.

Well over 200 applications software packages are available now on Sparc. These applications software packages cover all aspects of computing, including office automation, financial services, artificial intelligence, computer-aided design and manufacturing and so on. In addition, Sparc is the only RISC architecture that has software allowing it to emulate both MS-DOS and VAX/VMS running all of the applications software from these environments. We estimate that Sparc has between 10,000 and 50,000 times the lines of application software source code running on it today compared to all other RISC microprocessors combined.

For these reasons, more than 80 companies—including Cypress Semiconductor (through its Ross Technology subsidiary), Unisys, Sun Microsystems, AT&T, Xerox, Fujitsu, Matsushita, Solborne, Tadpole Technology and Mizar—have all committed to Sparc.

Steve Goldstein, Director of Marketing, Ross Technology

It's easy to visualize the Texas Instruments 34020 graphics processor as a RISC CPU core with added hardware. In this case, TI has added some specialized execution hardware, including the barrel shifter, a small microcontrol unit, and some specialized memory control and peripheral logic.

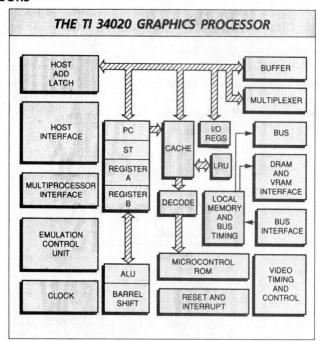

THE TI 34020 GRAPHICS PROCESSOR

ics or signal processing, a CPU still has to be general-purpose, but a few primitive operations make up the bulk of the computing load. In that environment, it can make sense to form a synthesis of RISC and CISC concepts.

In such a design, a compact RISC core handles most of the general-purpose computation, running very fast and taking little space. But the application's most computationally intensive parts are supported by complex instructions that are custom-tailored to minimize memory bandwidth and execution time. On paper at least, the result is a CPU with both the simplicity and speed of a RISC engine and the code density and cost advantages of a CISC machine.

The groundwork for such architectures was laid by the 801 project at IBM, which tried to identify and streamline the most frequently used instructions from the 360 architecture. But William Gimple, vice-president for systems technology at Pyramid Technology (Mountain View, CA), suggests that some RISC purists have lost sight of the goal. "A reduced instruction set should be the set of instructions you actually use, not some arbitrary small set," he argues. In illustration, Gimple points out that Pyramid's RISC machines have optional hardware support for string handling and even decimal arithmetic. "Just adding the hardware for those two functions can increase throughput 40 percent in a

Cobol environment," he observes.

One of the foremost adherents to this strategy is Texas Instruments (Dallas, TX), whose RISC-like CISC CPUs dominate the worlds of single-chip graphics and digital signal processing. "We developed our application-specific processors for the special environment of embedded computing, where a chip usually runs only one or two tasks, and these tasks have a high content of specialized operations," explains Jim Huffhines, microprocessor and microcomputer marketing manager at TI. In both the 320 line of DSP chips and the 340XX graphics processor family, TI built a specialized machine around a RISC-like core.

This approach can be powerful when the designer has a rough idea of the instruction mix in actual applications. But even then it must be used carefully. "You can always stick special functions in hardware," Sun's Ditzel cautions. "But there is a limited number of applications, such as graphics, for instance, where it makes sense. The application needs to have some complex operations that occur very frequently. Even then, if you put in complex instructions that slow the cycle time or mess up the pipeline, you may lose more than you gain, particularly if you don't use the complex instructions that often."

■ Advances in CISC compilers

One of the strongest arguments RISC proponents make against com-

plex instructions involves not the hardware required to execute them but the compilers required to generate them. "Special instructions can be useful in a controller, where you're going to be writing in assembly language," Ditzel says. "But compilers are only just starting to use complex instructions: it's a difficult problem for them, and there hasn't been much emphasis on it because the performance reward isn't usually very big."

But Craig Franklin, vice-president of marketing at Green Hills Software (Glendale, CA), is more optimistic about compiler technology for CISC machines. "If there's a major speed-up to be had, we can generate the code for it."

Franklin points out that today's compilers are capable of recognizing opportunities to use complex instructions in even highly ambiguous circumstances. "Even relatively simple-sounding things such as auto-increment addressing can be involved," he explains. "Before you can generate an auto-increment instruction, you need to identify a loop that uses subscript addressing, perform strength-reduction on the subscript computations, and recognize where all the computations and references are taking place—five or six steps in all. But now our compilers can fully utilize auto-increment and auto-decrement addressing modes in these circumstances."

Franklin cites other examples of complex instructions that can save considerable time and memory bandwidth if your compiler can figure out when to use them. Frequently a routine will require both the quotient and the remainder from a divide operation, for example: a sufficiently clever compiler will perform the divide only once, knowing that the single operation will yield both results. A more common situation is an opportunity to use the string operations available on many processors. The payoffs here can be substantial: not only does the single string-oriented instruction save an enormous amount of fetching, but on some processors the string move instructions run at the full bus bandwidth, actually faster than DMA hardware.

"The bottom line is that when you make an advanced computer, whether it uses complex instructions or not, you need a more sophisticated compiler," says Franklin. "There's always something new and difficult

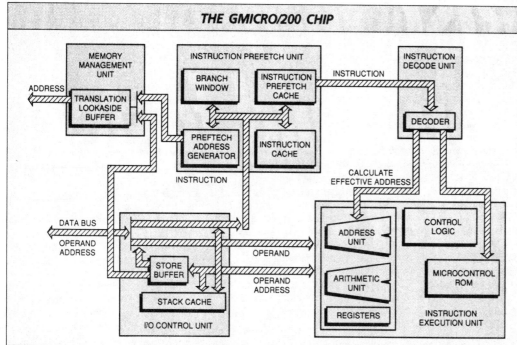

THE GMICRO/200 CHIP

MEMORY MANAGEMENT UNIT

TRANSLATION LOOKASIDE BUFFER

ADDRESS

INSTRUCTION PREFETCH UNIT

BRANCH WINDOW

INSTRUCTION PREFETCH CACHE

PREFTECH ADDRESS GENERATOR

INSTRUCTION CACHE

INSTRUCTION

INSTRUCTION

INSTRUCTION DECODE UNIT

DECODER

CALCULATE EFFECTIVE ADDRESS

DATA BUS

OPERAND ADDRESS

STORE BUFFER

OPERAND

OPERAND ADDRESS

ADDRESS UNIT

CONTROL LOGIC

ARITHMETIC UNIT

MICROCONTROL ROM

STACK CACHE

REGISTERS

INSTRUCTION EXECUTION UNIT

I/O CONTROL UNIT

The Gmicro/200, the fastest available implementation of the TRON specification, can be viewed as either the ultimate expression of a special-purpose RISC processor or the near-ultimate CISC processor. From either point of view, the Gmicro attempts to use hardware to accelerate the most frequent code sequences it's expected to encounter.

needed to get the performance out of the hardware."

■ The TRON story

Many designers accept the notion that you can add CISC instructions to a RISC core to accelerate a particular set of applications. It's even becoming credible that compiler technology is good enough to make use of the complex instructions. Now the Japanese, in a multivendor research project, are taking this concept to its logical extreme.

Called TRON (The Real-time Operating system Nucleus), it's an incredibly ambitious plan that defines an operating system, a human interface, a networking environment and a set of compilation tools for 32-bit computing. Then the project treats this complete software environment as if it were an application, and derives from it—you guessed it—a RISC-like core instruction set with complex extensions.

The resulting specification—and it's important to remember that TRON is a set of specifications, not a piece of silicon—may be the most challenging attempt ever to produce a CISC architecture. The instruction set does, in fact, have a variety of short, single-cycle instructions, but the number of specific additions to support operating system or compiler requirements dwarfs the RISC-ish core, resulting in a set with nearly 200 codes. Yet, as in the case of purely application-specific processors, the complex instructions are all there to meet a particular need in the TRON environment.

"One of the ideals of the specification was to spend as little time as possible running the operating system," explains Gary Wray, strategic marketing manager for microprocessors at Hitachi America (San Jose, CA). "So the TRON people specified a highly orthogonal instruction set with lots of data types, and a rich set of instructions for complicated operations like string, bit-field and queue manipulation."

Hitachi and Fujitsu Microelectronics (San Jose, CA) have both implemented the specification in the Gmicro/200, a chip that runs at about 6 to 10 Mips and includes onboard caches and an MMU. Future implementations of the TRON set will include the 20-Mips Gmicro/300 and the stripped-down Gmicro/100, which is intended for embedded or CPU core use.

None of the Gmicro vendors intends to take on RISC chips on their home turf of Unix workstations. As Charles Glenn, product line manager for 32-bit CISC microprocessors and peripherals at Fujitsu, explains, "We think RISC chips are outstanding in register-intensive, compute-intensive single-user scientific or engineering calculations. But for other tasks, such as for multitasking real-time kernels, where the bulk of the work isn't raw computation, CISC machines will outperform

RISC machines. And the TRON-compliant chips are the most advanced CISC machines around in terms of the instruction set's adaptation to the needs of operating systems and compilers."

So the TRON project neatly overcomes the problem of unused complex instructions by deriving the instructions from a predefined set of software requirements. Perhaps just as surprising to RISC adherents is that TRON exhibits two other characteristics that were supposed to be unique RISC features: scalability and an open architecture.

"Scalability is unique to RISC only if you don't have good enough design tools," claims Wray. "RISC CPU designs are intended to be simple enough to implement in gate array technology and turned around in one semester. But when Hitachi became involved in the TRON project, we recognized on the front end that the quality of our silicon design tools would be critical to the success of the product line. So we bit the bullet and worked on the tools first. The result is that we can offer a full range of Gmicro processors, from a CPU core to the Gmicro/300."

And TRON watchers expect the line to grow from there, because of the open-architecture approach the specification committee has chosen. There are already multiple vendors announced, including Hitachi, Fujitsu, Toshiba, Matsushita and Mitsubishi, some of whom will probably

CISC features bring balance and performance to RISC microprocessor

What's often lost in the marketing "noise" and in the positioning wars now going on between microprocessor vendors is the perspective that a microprocessor's purpose is system performance, not "RISC-ness." Achieving excellent system-level performance involves a balance between raw CPU performance, which is the hallmark of the RISC architectures, and system-level functionality, which is the domain of the CISC machines. In the Clipper microprocessor, Intergraph has built a foundation based on RISC architectural principles that have been around for many years in mainframes and supercomputers, and has added CISC-like elements violating "pure RISC" rules. But Intergraph's goal wasn't to build a RISC machine; it was to build a fast machine.

Clipper incorporates the essentials of RISC architectural design: a load/store architecture; hardwired rather than microcoded instructions, the majority of which execute in a single clock cycle; and a heavily pipelined, hardware scoreboarded integer execution unit to provide concurrent operation of fetch, decode and execution phases.

In many ways, however, the Clipper architecture departs from "pure" or "academic" RISC machines and incorporates some selected CISC features—much to the benefit of system designers, programmers and end-users.

■ Variable instruction length
One of Clipper's more traditional CISC features is its variable instruction length. The fixed, 32-bit instruction length of many RISC machines can often waste space and time. Clipper's most common instructions are 16 bits, or one parcel, long.

With Clipper's variable instruction length, more of these instructions can be fetched in a single memory reference than could be fetched in a fixed-instruction-length design, and more of them will fit into the CPU's internal instruction buffer. In addition, full 32-bit addresses or constants can be referenced or loaded in a single instruction in Clipper

instead of in the two or three instructions required by many fixed-length instruction machines.

Variable instruction lengths have to be implemented carefully, however. If implemented as in the VAX machines, for example, the entire instruction must be decoded before the hardware instruction decoder knows its length and operand types, which means you can't make any decisions early in the pipeline about what to do with the instruction. Clipper can tell in the first instruction parcel what the entire format is and decide what to do with the instruction. Hence, Clipper provides the benefits of variable-length instructions without the penalties usually associated with them.

■ Managing memory
The typical RISC approach to managing peripheral functions such as floating-point operations and cache memory is to implement them in the fastest possible discrete components. While this often gains speed, it also results in very low integration and high cost, which limits the kinds of applications that can take advantage of RISC performance. With the Clipper C300, the floating-point unit is integrated on the CPU chip. This has a number of advantages. First, the most important operations are close to the CPU; they don't require going off-chip and onto a slower bus. This eliminates the chip-to-chip delays and reduces CPU bus contention. What's more, the on-chip FPU gives Clipper excellent integration and permits it to address more space- and cost-sensitive applications than can less-integrated RISC architectures.

Clipper also provides support for virtual memory and cache management. The Clipper CPU/FPU chip lets designers build traditional, large, discrete caches and memory-management schemes as in other RISC engines. But one thing designers can do with Clipper that can't be done with other such chips is use its integrated, single-chip cache and memory-management units (CAMMUs) to create a compact design at essentially the same performance level as other, less-compact RISC machines.

Another significant benefit to using the CAMMUs and Clipper's implementa-

tion of virtual memory is that designers immediately have binary compatibility across all Clipper-based systems through a de facto application binary interface. Designers don't have to worry about multiple memory-management designs with different memory organizations and layouts that are visible even to the user mode, where it becomes difficult to move applications from machine to machine.

Clipper also differs from other RISC machines in how it supports multiprocessor applications. While many RISC machines relegate control to the operating system and additional discrete hardware, which increase system cost and design time, Clipper provides multiprocessor support in hardware. Clipper includes such critical multiprocessor-related instructions as test and set, and provides global translation lookaside buffer updates. And most important, Clipper implements bus watch in hardware. Bus watch is critical in multiprocessor designs for maintaining cache coherency, especially with copy-back caching.

A final CISC-like feature is Clipper's macro instruction set, which is stored in a special-function ROM on the CPU. These aren't microcoded instructions, but rather sequences of the regular hardwired Clipper instructions. This instruction set is used for commonly used operations such as string moves and floating-point conversions that, for either speed or space reasons, don't make sense to do hardwired in the machine.

The macro instruction ROM creates an instruction hierarchy between the hardwired instructions and standard software subroutines, somewhat analogous to the memory hierarchy that exists when cache memories buffer instructions and data between a high-speed CPU and slower memory. Each execution unit has a number of "hidden" registers that the macro ROM can use. These temporary registers minimize register saves and restores, providing higher performance and a superior user interface. The macro instructions also improve code density and efficiency. By implementing these instructions in the ROM, the entire cache is available to hold more of the program's code.

David Neff, Languages Manager, Advanced Processor Division, Intergraph

implement the spec beyond the current Gmicro product line. And, as Wray points out, "Any vendor that's interested can do its own implementation. The architecture is in the public domain."

Despite the advantages, it's still far from clear how great a role the TRON specification and its implementations will play in the United States. U.S. acceptance of Japanese architectures has been weak at best in previous cases. But it's already clear from design wins in the office automation and embedded control markets that TRON will be important in Japan, and perhaps even in all of Asia.

▪ What happens next?
One evolutionary path for 32-bit processors is clear: RISC cores that are augmented by additional complex-instruction hardware can be tailored to specific applications. The TRON project and future experiments will explore the limitations of this approach. But independently of this trend, another branch of architectural development is carrying RISC CPUs in a quite different direction: multiple execution units.

The first public discussion of chips with multiple execution units almost predates RISC microprocessors. The Clipper architecture from Intergraph (Palo Alto, CA) included both integer and floating-point execution units on its CPU chip. This practice was later adopted by Motorola's 88000 designers and Intel's 80960 designers.

The concept of having several independent execution units on a chip fits nicely into the RISC concept. Even a relatively simple compiler can arrange instructions so that integer-unit activity overlaps floating-point activity, so the chip can show a considerable increase in throughput for codes with a generous mixture of integer, logic and floating-point instructions. This of course is true only as long as the floating-point instructions are multicycle.

In fast systems with single-cycle floating-point, you can't fetch instructions fast enough over a conventional bus to keep both execution units running. The solution in the board-level Apollo DN 10000 architecture, and probably in the recently announced Fujitsu next-generation Sparc chip, is to double the bandwidth of the instruction bus, so you can fetch two instructions at once. In every cycle, for example, the DN

10000 fetches both an integer and a floating-point instruction.

As silicon technology advances, it makes room for more and more execution units on the chip. But adding more units quickly ceases to be an effective approach: it runs into a barrier known as the Flynn Bottleneck, a characteristic of the structure of programs that limits the amount of speedup from multiple execution units to between two and four times the speed of a single unit. Solving this problem required a fundamental software engineering breakthrough, and making it practical to include a large number of units on a chip required some rethinking of the concept of an instruction. Both of these milestones have been passed, not in the chip industry but in the supercomputing business, by Multiflow (Branford, CT).

"The company grew out of a compiler project at Yale," says John O'Donnell, Multiflow vice-president of engineering. "There, Josh Fisher had developed a technique called trace scheduling that could circumvent the Flynn bottleneck. By making assumptions about what would happen when the program came to a conditional branch instruction, we were able to compact long sections of code into a few very long instruction words. Each word would command the action of a large number of independent execution units. With hypothetical very-long-instruction-word

(VLIW) machines, we could get 20- to 80-times speed-ups on some programs.

The Yale compiler work moved to Multiflow, and led to several generations of compiler development. After the team was satisfied with the compiler, they began development of a hardware architecture to execute the compiled code. The result was the Trace family of multiple-execution-unit, VLIW computers.

The smallest member of the family, the Trace 7, contains seven independent functional units: two memory-reference units, two integer units, two floating-point units and a branch unit. The machine's instruction length is 256 bits, with each instruction word carrying a command for each of the seven execution units.

Each unit is essentially a little RISC processor: a single-cycle three-address machine with access to the Trace 7's register file. Because of this RISC-like characteristic, the internal operation of the Trace 7 is exposed to the compiler in just the way that the pipeline of a conventional RISC compiler is exposed to its compiler. The Multiflow compiler's job is to pack operations into the long instruction words to keep the execution units busy.

The concept seems to work. "We consistently get four or five operations per cycle on general-purpose programs," reports O'Donnell. He

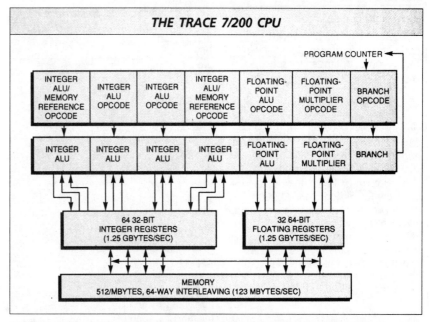

Multiflow's Trace 7/200 CPU contains seven independent execution units. Each is controlled by a section of the machine's 256-bit instruction word. This approach gives the compiler, not CPU control logic, the responsibility of analyzing the source code and figuring out how to keep all the execution units busy.

RISC plus CISC: the right mix for embedded systems

RISC architectures are one path to fast microprocessor performance, but they don't necessarily excel at every task. CISC features still hold benefits for many applications. The successful blending of RISC and CISC features adds up to better 32-bit processor architectures for embedded control applications.

Intel's RISC-based 80960 embedded processor is a case in point. The 80960 architecture contains features, such as on-chip floating-point math, debug support and bit-oriented operations, that would raise the eyebrows of a RISC purist but are embraced by designers of embedded systems.

Intel established at least three design goals for the 80960 architecture: high levels of functional integration, easy application development, and a growth path to compatible future processors. This almost guaranteed that the 80960 wouldn't be a pure RISC design. At the same time, Intel wanted to retain the high run-time performance of a RISC architecture.

Traditionally, RISC speed is gained by eliminating lesser-used, more complex instructions from a processor's instruction set. By using a large internal register set and a highly pipelined instruction queue, and by eliminating on-chip microcode, the performance of remaining instructions is optimized for speed, ideally achieving one instruction per clock cycle execution.

While this general approach is effective, there are some real-world applications and development considerations for which using a RISC architecture augmented by non-RISC features makes more sense, such as the on-chip floating-point unit and interrupt controller in the KB version of the 80960. These two features wouldn't be found on a typical RISC device, but high levels of integration pay off by providing a lower chip count in compute-intensive embedded applications. Reduced chip count means less power con-

sumption and circuit board real estate—both critical in the cost-conscious, embedded applications market.

■ The advantage of microcode

The 80960's most conspicuous departure from the academic principles of RISC design is the fact that it uses microcode. A pure RISC machine eschews microcode in favor of a complete hardwired implementation. The "most frequently" executed instructions are implemented in hardware, while all other functions are consigned to software.

Although Intel agrees that this rule is a useful design principle, blind adherence to it can be wasteful. Compact, cheap, and relatively efficient, microcode is an excellent compromise between the inefficiencies of software and the expense of hardware. Some functions, regardless of how frequently they're executed, aren't cost-effective to implement in hard logic because doing so would make the processor large and difficult to manufacture. Such functions include floating-point operations, interrupt handling, multiprocessing support, and software tracing. Yet these functions are much faster in microcode in the 80960 than they would be if implemented in software on another machine.

> *The 80960 architecture contains features that would raise the eyebrows of a RISC purist but are embraced by designers of embedded systems.*
>
> ■ ■ ■

There are several reasons for this. First, on-chip microcode isn't burdened with memory delays and procedural overhead. Second, unlike software, microcode can use private resources on-chip, such as extra registers or additional instructions, that aren't available to software programmers. Finally, functions that are microcoded in this generation of processor can be given faster, hardwired implementations in future versions when advances in silicon technology make them practical.

Other non-RISC features of the 80960 ease the development process. A built-in instruction pipeline manager operates transparently to software pro-

grammers and removes a major software development burden. Software trace instructions and built-in hardware breakpoints simplify software debugging. On-chip self-test features aid troubleshooting during development, and add to overall ease of system maintenance. And Boolean and bit-oriented instructions make control programming much easier. For designers of embedded systems, this adds up to benefits that are easily worth the trade-offs, if any, of not having a 100 percent RISC architecure.

■ Providing a growth path

The most notable constant in the embedded designer's world is change. Products evolve. New features are required. Competitive pressures mount, and higher performance components are required. Designers can no longer afford to design a completely new system from scratch with every new functional variation and performance requirement. Providing a future growth path for succeeding generations of compatible embedded processors was another critical factor in the 80960's design. In fact, Intel began working on second-generation, faster implementations of the 80960 architecture long before the first 80960KA and 80960KB products were released.

The 80960's internally managed pipeline shortens development time because it's transparent to the program. The pipeline is also a key to the architecture's future flexibility. The possibility of running multiple instructions per clock cycle—not just one instruction per clock cycle—exists because of the 80960's pipelined architecture.

Parallel execution will move the architecture's entire performance curve higher on the price/performance chart, achieving performance increases over and above the expected linear gains that come from faster clock rates. And designers who choose to use the 80960 in their applications will be able to make use of future parallel execution performance gains without rewriting their code.

Mike McGowan, Product Marketing Engineer, Intel

Silicon houses' focus on performance in RISC chips, combined with RISC's prodigious demand for bandwidth, make the chips inappropriate for embedded applications, claims Tom Thawley, executive vice-president of Interphase. "Right now, the cost/performance doesn't qualify RISC chips for use in a $1,000 embedded controller," he says.

claims that higher levels of parallelism occur with any frequency only in highly organized algorithms such as those found in some scientific calculations. For these, Multiflow offers larger machines with up to 28 execution units.

O'Donnell is careful to distinguish his company's machine from a multiprocessing system, pointing out that the execution units share an instruction word and a register file, and that they aren't identical: there are several types of units in each processor. Rather, the Trace machines represent something quite different—an extension of the fundamental concept of RISC systems. In the Multiflow design, the compiler has not only replaced the control logic between stages of the execution unit pipeline; it has also expanded to form the control logic linking independent execution units. A Multiflow machine, with its instructions scheduled by a sophisticated compiler, thus can use seven or 28 execution units at once without the geometric growth in control circuitry that would be required in a conventional architecture.

It's relatively certain that Multiflow's techniques will appear within two or three years at the chip level. By that time, designers' transistor budgets will be high enough to put several RISC-style units on a die, and package technology will provide enough pins to keep the chip fed. And the VLIW concept, with its ability to trade hard logic for compiler smarts, will keep the hardware de-

sign relatively simple. At that point, we'll have to find some better phrase than "RISC vs. CISC" to describe the contest of architectures in the 32-bit market. The emerging challenger will be firmly based in RISC concepts, but with very complex instructions indeed.

▮ A word to the wise

The opportunity for RISC architectures to evolve into VLIW architectures is exciting from a purist's point of view, but it carries a certain danger for chip designers. As O'Donnell points out, there may be a reason why RISC CPUs are having trouble adapting to some applications. "While the people who built RISC chips paid attention to Dhrystones, the people who built VAXes paid attention to what their customers did with computers."

This warning is coming with increasing urgency from the system designers who are evaluating the latest wave of CISC and RISC engines. "Silicon houses might claim they are targeting us in the embedded control business with their RISC chips," Interphase's Thawley says. "But they don't understand that we're a distinct class of customer." Thawley sees the RISC designers focusing on big Mips figures and big address spaces, neither of which is very useful in embedded control.

This focus on performance, and the difficulties RISC systems have with bandwidth, lead the chips astray in embedded applications. "Right now, the cost/performance

doesn't qualify RISC chips for use in a $1,000 embedded controller," Thawley argues. "We've learned to make up for some of the bandwidth and speed shortcomings of CISC chips by surrounding them with ASICs. So the comparison comes down to looking at $150 for the RISC chip or $15 for something from the 68000 family. And in low-priced products, there's just no place to hide any exceptional costs."

So the struggle goes on. RISC processors hold an acknowledged edge in the sort of register-intensive computation that characterizes engineering workstation use. CISC chips have some equally concrete advantages in the embedded and real-time processing areas. And each architectural family continues to evolve by incorporating good ideas from the other. Probably the best case for the design community would be the continuation of the rivalry. The worst case would be the market failure of some important RISC architecture because its vendor was unable, or unwilling, to meet the needs of a spectrum of users. □

"Computers, Complexity and Controversy" by R.P. Colwell, C.Y. Hitchcock III, E.D. Jensen, H.M. Brinkley Sprunt, and C.P. Kollar, September
1985, pages 8–19.

COMPUTER

Instruction Sets and Beyond:
Computers, Complexity, and Controversy

Robert P. Colwell, Charles Y. Hitchcock III,
E. Douglas Jensen, H. M. Brinkley Sprunt,
and Charles P. Kollar

Carnegie-Mellon University

Computer design should focus on the assignment of system functionality to implementation levels within an architecture, and not be guided by whether it is a RISC or CISC design.

The avalanche of publicity received by the reduced instruction set computer has swept away objectivity in the technical communities and obscured many important issues. RISC design seriously challenges some implicit assumptions that have guided computer design for years. A study of its principles should yield a deeper understanding of hardware/software tradeoffs, computer performance, the influence of VLSI on processor design, and many other topics. Articles on RISC research, however, often fail to explore these topics properly and can be misleading. Further, the few papers that present comparisons with complex instruction set computer design often do not address the same issues. As a result, even careful study of the literature is likely to give a distorted view of this area of research. This article offers a useful perspective of RISC/Complex Instruction Set Computer research, one that is supported by recent work at Carnegie-Mellon University.

Much RISC literature is devoted to discussions of the size and complexity of computer instruction sets. These discussions are extremely misleading.

Instruction set design is important, but it should not be driven solely by adherence to convictions about design style, RISC or CISC. The focus of discussion should be on the more general question of the assignment of system functionality to implementation levels within an architecture. This point of view encompasses the instruction set—CISCs tend to install functionality at lower system levels than RISCs—but also takes into account other design features such as register sets, coprocessors, and caches.

While the implications of RISC research extend beyond the instruction set, even within the instruction set domain, there are limitations that have not been identified. Typical RISC papers give few clues about where the RISC approach might break down. Claims are made for faster machines that are cheaper and easier to design and that "map" particularly well onto VLSI technology. It has been said, however, that "Every complex problem has a simple solution... and it is wrong." RISC ideas are not "wrong," but a simple-minded view of them would be. RISC theory has many implications that are not obvious. Research in this area has helped focus attention on some important issues in computer architecture whose resolutions have too often been determined by defaults; yet RISC proponents often fail to discuss the application, architecture, and implementation contexts in which their assertions seem justified.

While RISC advocates have been vocal concerning their design methods and theories, CISC advocates have been disturbingly mute. This is not a healthy state of affairs. Without substantive, reported CISC research, many RISC arguments are left uncountered and, hence, out of perspective. The lack of such reports is due partially to the proprietary nature of most commercial CISC designs and partially to the fact that industry designers do not generally publish as much as academics. Also, the CISC design style has no coherent statement of design principles, and CISC designers do not appear to be actively working on one. This lack of a manifesto differentiates the CISC and RISC design styles and is the result of their different historical developments.

Towards defining a RISC

Since the earliest digital electronic computers, instruction sets have tended to grow larger and more complex. The 1948 MARK-1 had only seven instructions of minimal complexity, such as adds and simple jumps, but a contemporary machine like the VAX has hundreds of instructions. Furthermore, its instructions can be rather complicated, like atomically inserting an element into a doubly linked list or evaluating a floating point polynomial of arbitrary degree. Any high performance implementation of the VAX, as a result, has to rely on complex implementation techniques such as pipelining, prefetching, and multi-cycle instruction execution.

This progression from small and simple to large and complex instruction sets is striking in the development of single-chip processors within the past decade. Motorola's 68020, for example, carries 11 more addressing modes than the 6800, more than twice as many instructions, and support for an instruction cache and coprocessors. Again, not only has the number of addressing modes and instructions increased, but so has their complexity.

This general trend toward CISC machines was fueled by many things, including the following:

- New models are often required to be upward-compatible with existing models in the same computer family, resulting in the supersetting and proliferation of features.
- Many computer designers tried to reduce the "semantic gap" between programs and computer instruction sets. By adding instructions semantically closer to those used by programmers, these designers hoped to reduce software costs by creating a more easily programmed machine. Such instructions tend to be more complex because of their higher semantic level. (It is often the case, however, that instructions with high semantic content do not exactly match those required for the language at hand.)
- In striving to develop faster machines, designers constantly moved functions from software to microcode and from microcode to hardware, often without concern for the adverse effects that an added architectural feature can have on an implementation. For example, addition of an instruction requiring an extra level of decoding logic can slow a machine's entire instruction set. (This is called the "$n+1$" phenomenon.[1])
- Tools and methodologies aid designers in handling the inherent

complexity of large architectures. Current CAD tools and microcoding support programs are examples.

Microcode is an interesting example of a technique that encourages complex designs in two ways. First, it provides a structured means of effectively creating and altering the algorithms that control execution of numerous operations and complex instructions in a computer. Second, the proliferation of CISC features is encouraged by the quantum nature of microcode memories; it is relatively easy to add another addressing mode or obscure instruction to a machine which has not yet used all of its microcode space.

Instruction traces from CISC machines consistently show that few of the available instructions are used in most computing environments. This situation led IBM's John Cocke, in the early 70's, to contemplate a departure from traditional computer styles. The result was a research project based on an ECL machine that used a very advanced compiler, creatively named "801" for the research group's building number. Little has been published about that project, but what has been released speaks for a principled and coherent research effort.

The 801's instruction set was based on three design principles. According to Radin,[2] the instruction set was to be that set of run-time operations that

- could not be moved to compile time,
- could not be more efficiently executed by object code produced by a compiler that understood the high-level intent of the program, and
- could be implemented in random logic more effectively than the equivalent sequence of software instructions.

The machine relied on a compiler that used many optimization strategies for much of its effectiveness, including a

powerful scheme of register allocation. The hardware implementation was guided by a desire for leanness and featured hardwired control and single-cycle instruction execution. The architecture was a 32-bit load/store machine (only load and store instructions accessed memory) with 32 registers and single-cycle instructions. It had separate instruction and data caches to allow simultaneous access to code and operands.

Some of the basic ideas from the 801 research reached the West Coast in the mid 70's. At the University of California at Berkeley, these ideas grew into a series of graduate courses that produced the RISC I* (followed later by the RISC II) and the numerous CAD tools that facilitated its design. These courses laid the foundation for related research efforts in performance evaluation, computer-aided design, and computer implementation.

The RISC I processor,[3] like the 801, is a load/store machine that executes most of its instructions in a single cycle. It has only 31 instructions, each of which fits in a single 32-bit word and uses practically the same encoding format. A special feature of the RISC I is its large number of registers, well over a hundred, which are used to form a series of overlapping register sets. This feature makes procedure calls on the RISC I less expensive in terms of processor-memory bus traffic.

Soon after the first RISC I project at Berkeley, a processor named MIPS (Microprocessor without Interlocked Pipe Stages) took shape at Stanford. MIPS[1] is a pipelined, single-chip processor that relies on innovative software to ensure that its pipeline resources are properly managed. (In machines such as the IBM System/360 Model 91, pipeline interstage interlocking is per-

formed at run-time by special hardware). By trading hardware for compile-time software, the Stanford researchers were able to expose and use the inherent internal parallelism of their fast computing engine.

These three machines, the 801, RISCI, and MIPS, form the core of RISC research machines, and share a set of common features. We propose the following elements as a working definition of a RISC:

(1) *Single-cycle operation* facilitates the rapid execution of simple functions that dominate a computer's instruction stream and promotes a low interpretive overhead.

(2) *Load/store design* follows from a desire for single-cycle operation.

(3) *Hardwired control* provides for the fastest possible single-cycle operation. Microcode leads to slower control paths and adds to interpretive overhead.

(4) *Relatively few instructions and addressing modes* facilitate a fast, simple interpretation by the control engine.

(5) *Fixed instruction format* with consistent use, eases the hardwired decoding of instructions, which again speeds control paths.

(6) *More compile-time effort* offers an opportunity to explicitly move static run-time complexity into the compiler. A good example of this is the software pipeline reorganizer used by MIPS.[1]

A consideration of the two companies that claim to have created the first commercial "RISC" computer, Ridge Computers and Pyramid Technology, illustrates why a definition is needed. Machines of each firm have restricted instruction formats, a feature they share with RISC machines.

Pyramid's machine is not a load/store computer, however, and both Ridge and Pyramid machines have variable length instructions and use multiple-cycle interpretation and microcoded control engines. Further, while their instruction counts might seem reduced when compared to a VAX, the Pyramid has almost 90 instructions and the Ridge has over 100. The use of microcoding in these machines is for price and performance reasons. The Pyramid machine also has a system of multiple register sets derived from the Berkeley RISC I, but this feature is orthogonal to RISC theory. These may be successful machines, from both technological and marketing standpoints, but they are not RISCs.

The six RISC features enumerated above can be used to weed out misleading claims and provide a springboard for points of debate. Although some aspects of this list may be arguable, it is useful as a working definition.

Points of attention and contention

There are two prevalent misconceptions about RISC and CISC. The first is due to the RISC and CISC acronyms, which seem to imply that the domain for discussion should be restricted to selecting candidates for a machine's instruction set. Although specification format and number of instructions are the primary issues in most RISC literature, the best generalization of RISC theory goes well beyond them. It connotes a willingness to make design tradeoffs freely and consciously across architecture/implementation, hardware/software, and compile-time/run-time boundaries in order to maximize performance as measured in some specific context.

The RISC and CISC acronyms also seem to imply that any machine can be classified as one or the other and that

---

* Please note that the term "RISC" is used throughout this article to refer to all research efforts concerning Reduced Instruction Set Computers, while the term "RISC I" refers specifically to the Berkeley research project.

the primary task confronting an architect is to choose the most appropriate design style for a particular application. But the classification is not a dichotomy. RISCs and CISCs are at different corners of a continous multidimensional design space. The need is not for an algorithm by which one can be chosen: rather, the goal should be the formulation of a set of techniques, drawn from CISC experiences and RISC tenets, which can be used by a designer in creating new systems. [4-6]

One consequence of the us-or-them attitude evinced by most RISC publications is that the reported performance of a particular machine (e.g., RISC I) can be hard to interpret if the contributions made by the various design decisions are not presented individually. A designer faced with a large array of choices needs guidance more specific than a monolithic, all-or-nothing performance measurement.

An example of how the issue of scope can be confused is found in a recent article. [7] By creating a machine with only one instruction, its authors claim to have delimited the RISC design space to their machine at one end of the space and the RISC I (with 31 instructions) at the other end. This model is far too simplistic to be useful; an absolute number of instructions cannot be the sole criterion for categorizing an architecture as to RISC or CISC. It ignores aspects of addressing modes and their associated complexity, fails to deal with compiler/architecture coupling, and provides no way to evaluate the implementation of other non-instruction set design decisions such as register files, caches, memory management, floating point operations, and co-processors.

Another fallacy is that the total system is composed of hardware, software, and application code. This leaves out the operating system, and the overhead and the needs of the operating system cannot be ignored in most systems. This area has received

far too little attention from RISC research efforts, in contrast to the CISC efforts focused on this area. [8,9]

An early argument in favor of RISC design was that simpler designs could be realized more quickly, giving them a performance advantage over complex machines. In addition to the economic advantages of getting to market first, the simple design was supposed to

> *The insinuation that the Micro-VAX-32 follows in a RISC tradition is unreasonable. It does not follow our definition of a RISC; it violates all six RISC criteria.*

avoid the performance disadvantages of introducing a new machine based on relatively old implementation technology. In light of these arguments, DEC's MicroVAX-32 [10] is especially interesting.

The VAX easily qualifies as a CISC. According to published reports, the MicroVAX-32, a VLSI implementation of the preponderance of the VAX instruction set, was designed, realized, and tested in a period of several months. One might speculate that this very short gestation period was made possible in large part by DEC's considerable expertise in implementing the VAX architecture (existing products included the 11/780, 11/750, 11/730, and VLSI-VAX). This shortened design time would not have been possible had DEC had not first created a standard instruction set. Standardization at this level, however, is precisely what RISC theory argues against. Such standards constrain the unconventional RISC hardware/software tradeoffs. From a commercial standpoint, it is significant that the MicroVAX-32 was born into a world where compatible assemblers, compilers, and operating systems abound, something that would certainly not be the case for a RISC design.

Such problems with RISC system designs may encourage commercial RISC designers to define a new level of standardization in order to achieve some of the advantages of multiple implementations supporting one standard interface. A possible choice for such an interface would be to define an intermediate language as the target for all compilation. The intermediate language would then be translated into optimal machine code for each implementation. This translation process would simply be performing resource scheduling at a very low level (e.g., pipeline management and register allocation).

It should be noted that the Micro-VAX-32 does not directly implement all VAX architecture. The suggestion has been made that this implementation somehow supports the RISC inclination toward emulating complex functions in software. In a recent publication, David Patterson observed:

> Although I doubt DEC is calling them RISCs, I certainly found it interesting that DEC's single chip VAXs do not implement the whole VAX instruction set. A MicroVAX traps when it tries to execute some infrequent but complicated operations, and invokes transparent software routines that simulate those complicated instructions. [11]

The insinuation that the Micro-VAX-32 follows in a RISC tradition is unreasonable. It does not come close to fitting our definition of a RISC; it violates all six RISC criteria. To begin with, any VAX by definition has a variable-length instruction format and is not a load/store machine. Further, the MicroVAX-32 has multicycle instruction execution, relies on a microcoded control engine, and interprets the whole array of VAX addressing modes. Finally, the MicroVAX-32 executes 175 instructions on-chip, hardly a reduced number.

A better perspective in the Micro VAX-32 shows that there are indeed cost/performance ranges where microcoded implementation of certain functions is inappropriate and software emulation is better. The importance of carefully making this assignment of function to implementation level—software, microcode, or hardware—has been amply demonstrated in many RISC papers. Yet this basic concern is also evidenced in many CISC machines. In the case of the MicroVAX-32, floating point instructions are migrated either to a coprocessor chip or to software emulation routines. The numerous floating-point chips currently available attest to the market reception for this partitioning. Also migrated to emulation are the console, decimal, and string instructions. Since many of these instructions are infrequent, not time-critical, or are not generated by many compilers, it

would be difficult to fault this approach to the design of an inexpensive VAX. The MicroVAX-32 also shows that it is still possible for intelligent, competent computer designers who understand the notion of correct function-to-level mapping to find microcoding a valuable technique. Published RISC work, however, does not accommodate this possibility.

The application environment is also of crucial importance in system design. The RISC I instruction set was designed specifically to run the C language efficiently, and it appears reasonably successful. The RISC I researchers have also investigated the Smalltalk-80 computing environment. [12] Rather than evaluate RISC I as a Smalltalk engine, however, the RISC I researchers designed a new RISC and report encouraging performance results from simulations. Still, designing a processor to run a single

language well is different from creating a single machine such as the VAX that must exhibit at least acceptable performance for a wide range of languages. While RISC research offers valuable insights on a per-language basis, more emphasis on cross-language anomalies, commonalities, and tradeoffs is badly needed.

Especially misleading are RISC claims concerning the amount of design time saved by creating a simple machine instead of a complex one. Such claims sound reasonable. Nevertheless, there are substantial differences in the design environments for an academic one-of-a-kind project (such as MIPS or RISC I) and a machine with lifetime measured in years that will require substantial software and support investments. As was pointed out in a recent *Electronics Week* article, R. D. Lowry, market development manager for Denelcor,

Risc II and the MCF evaluation

In the mid 70's, a committee was created by the Department of Defense to "evaluate the efficiency of several computer architectures independently of their implementations."[1,2] This committee developed the Military Computer Family studies based on the premise that the "architectural efficiency" of a computer corresponds to its life-cycle cost, given some standard of implementation technology. The MCF committee developed a means of evaluating architectural efficiency that consisted of two parts: (1) an initial screening to determine the "reasonableness" of an architecture based on several qualitative and quantitative factors (described later) and (2) a methodical application of benchmarks for machines that successfully passed this screening.

The MCF evaluations have been considered by many to be an important milestone in the systematic evaluation of computer architectures. The published evaluations of RISC ma-

chines have indicated performance advantages large enough to merit attention and analysis. To learn about RISC architecture and the usefulness of the MCF evaluation procedure, we applied the complete MCF evaluation to the Berkeley RISC II since it posed the fewest obstacles.

The MCF program evaluates architectures standardized at the instruction set level, since, according to Burr, it "is the only [way to ensure] complete software transportability across a wide range of computer implementations.[1] This view is contrary to a fundamental RISC tenet that one should zealously pursue unconventional tradeoffs across the architecture/implementation boundary that can produce higher performance.

In addition, the architecture that was judged the best by the MCF evaluation criteria was the VAX, a particularly intriguing judgement considering the uniformly bad reviews given the VAX in RISC performance studies.

Furthermore many of these RISC performance studies used variations and carefully chosen subsets of the MCF benchmarks.[3] Evaluating the RISC II with a full MCF analysis sheds new light on this seeming discrepancy.

MCF evaluation criteria. The first part of the MCF evaluation is an initial screening to ensure that the candidate architecture contains features deemed essential to a successful military computer: virtual memory, protection, floating point, interrupts and traps, subsetability, multiprocessor support, I/O controllability, extensibility, and the ability to execute out of read-only memory. Current RISC II systems have not provided many of these features, but most of these requirements could be met with additional resources.

The initial screening also analyzes quantitative factors. Since this

noted that "commercial-product development teams generally start off a project by weighing the profit and loss impacts of design decisions."[13] Lowry is quoted as saying, "A university doesn't have to worry about that, so there are often many built-in deadends in projects. This is not to say the value of their research is diminished. It does, however, make it very difficult for someone to reinvent the system to make it a commercial product." For a product to remain viable, a great deal of documentation, user training, coordination with fabrication or production facilities, and future upgrades must all be provided. It is not known how these factors might skew a design-time comparison, so all such comparisons should be viewed with suspicion.

Even performance claims, perhaps the most interesting of all RISC assertions, are ambiguous. Performance as measured by narrowly compute-bound, low-level benchmarks that have been used by RISC researchers (e.g., calculating a Fibonacci series recursively) is not the only metric in a computer system. In some, it is not even one of the most interesting. For many current computers, the only useful performance index is the number of transactions per second, which has no direct or simple correlation to the time it takes to calculate Ackermann's function. While millions of instructions per second might be a meaningful metric in some computing environments, reliability, availability, and response time are of much more concern in others, such as *space* and *aviation* computing. The extensive error checking incorporated into these machines at every level may slow the basic clock time and substantially diminish performance. Reduced performance is tolerable; but downtime may not be. In the extreme, naive application of the RISC rules for designing an instruction set might result in a missile guidance computer optimized for running its most common task—diagnostics. In terms of instruction frequencies, of course, flight control applications constitute a trivial special case and would not be given much attention. It is worth emphasizing that in efforts to quantify performance and apply those measurements to system design, one must pay attention not just to instruction execution frequencies, but also to cycles consumed per instruction execution. Levy and Clark make this point regarding the VAX instruction set,[14] but it has yet to appear in any papers on RISC.

When performance, such as throughput or transactions per second, is a first-order concern, one is faced with the task of quantifying it. The Berkeley RISC I efforts to establish the machine's throughput are laudable, but

screening includes such practicalities as the manufacturer's current customer base and the amount of existing software, the RISC II would compare unfavorably to the VAX in this part of the evaluation. While these factors were important in military computer standards, they are clearly irrelevant here.

After the initial screening, a series of test programs was executed on a simulator of the candidate architecture. To avoid compiler ambiguities, the benchmarks were programmed in the assembly language of the test system. The MCF committee was interested solely in compiled code performance, yet the members recognized that varying levels of compiler technology should not be allowed to affect the outcome of the study; compiler sophistication has nothing to do with inherent "architectural efficiency." At the time of the MCF evaluations, it was believed that even the best compilers would be unlikely to generate better code than expert programmers.

Sixteen benchmark programs were developed: they were representative of the tasks performed by military computers and were small enough for humans to write in a highly optimized form.

None of the sixteen benchmarks tests methods of subroutine linkage (although one of the benchmarks considered, but rejected, for the MCF study was the highly recursive Ackermann's function). Failure to test call efficiency was not an oversight by the MCF committee; two measures of subroutine efficiency are included in the quantitative factors section of the initial screening.

Rather than rely on combined architecture/implementation measurements such as execution throughput, the MCF measures of computer architecture efficiency were defined to be program size (S), memory bus traffic (M), and canonical processor cycles (R). The S measure includes the local data and stack space used by the benchmark, as well as its program space. (The benchmarks reflect a circa-1970 assumption that code and data each occupy about half of the available memory space.) The M measure for a benchmark is the number of bytes that the processor reads and writes to memory (no transparent caching scheme is used). To compute the R measure, the architecture being evaluated is emulated on a canonical processor. The R measure is the sum of the internal data register-to-register transfers required by the canonical processor. Thus, this measure is supposed to model the data traffic of the processor's internal activities during benchmark execution. To evaluate different architectures, these measures are used as dimensions of comparison.

RISC theory asserts that simple instructions can be made to execute very quickly if their implementations are unencumbered by the large con-

before sweeping conclusions are drawn one must carefully examine the benchmark programs used. As Patterson noted:

> The performance predictions for [RISC I and RISC II] were based on small programs. This small size was dictated by the reliability of the simulator and compiler, the available simulation time, and the inability of the first simulators to handle UNIX system calls. [11]

Some of these "small" programs actually execute millions of instructions, yet they are very narrow programs in terms of the scope of function. For example, the Towers of Hanoi program, when executing on the 68000, spends over 90 percent of its memory accesses in procedure calls and returns. The RISC I and II researchers recently reported results from a large benchmark, [11] but the importance of large, heterogenous benchmarks in performance measurement is still lost on many commercial and academic computer evaluators who have succumbed to the misconception that "microbenchmarks" represent a useful measurement in isolation.

Multiple register sets

Probably the most publicized RISC-style processor is the Berkeley RISC I. The best-known feature of this chip is its large register file, organized as a series of overlapping register sets. This is ironic, since the register file is a performance feature independent of any RISC (as defined earlier) aspect of the processor. Multiple register sets could be included in any general-purpose register machine.

It is easy to believe that MRSs can yield performance benefits, since procedure-based, high-level languages typically use registers for information specific to a procedure. When a procedure call is performed, the information must be saved, usually on a memory stack, and restored on a procedure return. These operations are typically very time consuming due to the intrinsic data transfer requirements. RISC I uses its multiple register sets to reduce the frequency of this register saving and restoring. It also takes advantage of an overlap between register sets for parameter passing, reducing even further the memory reads and writes necessary. [15]

RISC I has a register file of 138 32-bit registers organized into eight overlapping "windows." In each window, six registers overlap the next window (for outgoing parameters and incoming results). During any procedure, only one of these windows is actually accessible. A procedure call changes the current window to the next

trol engine normally required for complex instructions. Consequently, since the MCF evaluation avoids measuring implementation features, any performance gains realized by such simplified control engines are ignored, while penalties, such as the increased processor-memory traffic of these load/store machines, are still taken into account. This effect has been noted before in applying the MCF evaluation to real machines. [4]

Results and interpretation. The RISC II architecture was evaluated by simulating assembly language versions of the 16 benchmarks. To gauge the results, its performance was compared to that of the VAX, rated "best" by the MCF measures. The VAX had a significantly lower S measure (memory space requirements) in 14 of the 16 benchmarks, requiring an average of three and a half times less memory than RISC II. This result seems inconsistent with published RISC reports which found that the RISC I took an average of only 50 percent more memory. This difference is dramatic. Much of it may be due to the fact that previous studies used a compiler that produces reasonable code for the RISC II, but produces suboptimal code for the VAX (since it may not have been sophisticated enough to exploit the available complex instructions as a human would). If the latest compilers were used for both machines, the space difference between the machines would likely be reduced to that of handcoding in assembly language, which we used.

The RISC II had a much higher M (memory traffic measure) for 11 of the benchmarks, averaging over two and a half times more processor-memory traffic than the VAX. This MCF criterion shows the large penalty paid by RISC II because of its load/store architecture. It is accentuated by the generic RISC need to fetch more instructions per program, since RISC instructions have low semantic content.

The VAX also had a lower (better) R measure for 10 of the benchmarks, and it was substantially lower on five of them. Again, much of this difference was due to the increased number of instruction fetches required by RISCs. One of the ten benchmarks modelled the cost of a context swap, which is high on RISC II because of the amount of state information in the register file. On average, about half of the register file (approximately 64 registers) must be saved and restored in each process swap.

These benchmarks showed the RISC II to disadvantage on floating point,[5] integer multiplication, bit test and set operations, variable-sized block moves, and character string searches—operations for which RISC II has no primitive instructions. As a result, numerous instructions are required to emulate on a RISC

window by incrementing a pointer, and the six outgoing parameter registers become the incoming parameters of the called procedure. Similarly, a procedure return changes the current window to the previous window, and the outgoing result registers become the incoming result registers of the calling procedure. If we assume that six 32-bit registers are enough to contain the parameters, a procedure call involves no actual movement of information (only the window pointer is adjusted). The finite on-chip resources limit the actual savings due to register window overflows and underflows.[3]

It has been claimed that the small control area needed to implement the simple instruction set of a VLSI RISC leaves enough chip area for the large register file.[3] The relatively small amount of control logic used by a RISC does free resources for other uses, but a large register file is not the only way to use them, nor even necessarily the best. For example, designers of the 801 and MIPS chose other ways to use their available hardware; these RISCs have only a single, conventionally sized register set. Caches, floating-point hardware, and interprocess communication support are a few of the many possible uses for those resources "freed" by a RISC's simple instruction set. Moreover, as chip technology improves, the tradeoffs between instruction set complexity and architecture/implementation features become less constrained. Computer designers will always have to decide how to best use available resources and, in doing so, should realize which relations are intrinsic and which are not.

The Berkeley papers describing the RISC I and RISC II processors claimed their resource decisions produced large performance improvements, two to four times over CISC machines like the VAX and the 68000.[3,11] There are many problems with these results and the methods used to obtain them. Foremost, the performance effects of the reduced instruction set were not decoupled from those of the overlapped register windows. Consequently, these reports shed little light on the RISC-related performance of the machine, as shown below.

Some performance comparisons between different machines, especially early ones, were based on simulated benchmark execution times. While absolute speed is always interesting, other metrics less implementation-dependent can provide design information more useful to computer architects, such as data concerning the processor-memory traffic necessary to execute a series of benchmarks. It is difficult to draw firm conclusions from comparisons of vastly different machines unless some effort has been

what other machines provide in their instruction set; the MCF study provides a quantitative evaluation of this effect. The RISC II was comparable to the VAX on benchmarks that involved simple arithmetic and one-level array indexing.

Conclusions. Although the VAX achieves a better score on every aspect of the MCF evaluation than does the RISC II, it would be dangerous to conclude that the VAX is a "better" machine. The MCF study characterizes the life-cycle costs of various architectures based on a set of weighting factors culled from the military environment. The VAX can be said to be better only in the sense that the MCF life-cycle cost models clearly favor it.

Since RISC research explicitly gives up the possible benefits of the traditional architecture/implementation dichotomy to increase execution throughput, the most basic MCF tenet does not hold for RISCs. The MCF life-cycle cost models did not include execution throughput, so the RISC II performance-related features were ignored, yet the price paid for these features is clear.

The MCF study's S, M, and R measures of architectural efficiency are open to question. For example, the R measure of internal processor overhead is of dubious utility when the architectures being compared are dissimilar. It is hard to see what canonical processor could be devised to serve as a common implementation of the RISC II and the Intel 432, for example.

The MCF study remains, however, the only large-scale evaluation of computer systems that includes as a primary figure of merit system life-cycle costs instead of easy throughput comparisons based on many arbitrary and implicit assumptions. The care taken by MCF in factoring out the myr-iad interrelated elements of a computer system leaves it an excellent model for future evaluation efforts.

References

1. W.E. Burr, A.H. Coleman, and W.R. Smith, "Overview of the Military Computer Family Architecture Selection," *NCC Conference Proceedings* AFIPS, Montvale, N.J., 1977, pp. 131-137.

2. S.H. Fuller and W.E. Burr, "Measurement and Evaluation of Alternative Computer Architectures," *Computer*, Vol. 10, No. 10, Oct. 1977, pp. 24-35.

3. David A. Patterson, Richard S. Piepho, "RISC Assessment: A High-Level Language Experiment," *Proc. Ninth Ann. Symp. Computer Architecture*, 1982, pp. 3-8.

4. J.B. Mountain and P.H. Enslow Jr., "Application of the Military Computer Family Architecture Selection Criteria to the PRIME P400," *Computer Architecture News*, Vol. 6, No. 6, Feb. 1978.

5. D. Patterson, "RISC Watch," *Computer Architecture News*, Vol. 12, No. 1, Mar. 1984, pp. 11-19.

made to factor out implementation-dependent features not being compared (e.g., caches and floating point accelerators).

Experiments structured to accommodate these reservations were conducted at CMU to test the hypothesis that the effects of multiple register sets are orthogonal to instruction set complexity.[16] Specifically, the goal was to see if the performance effects of MRSs were comparable for RISCs and CISCs. Simulators were written for two CISCs (the VAX and the 68000) without MRSs, with non-overlapping MRSs and with overlapping MRSs. Simulators were also written for the RISC I, RISC I with non-overlapping register sets, and RISC I with only a single register set. In each of the simulators, care was taken not to change the initial architectures any more than absolutely necessary to add or remove MRSs. Instead of simulating execution time, the total amount of processor-memory traffic (bytes read and written) for each benchmark was recorded for comparison. To use this data fairly, only different register set versions of the same architecture were compared so the ambiguities that arise from comparing different architectures like the RISC I and the VAX were avoided. The benchmarks used were the same ones originally used to evaluate RISC I. A summary of the experiments and their results are presented by Hitchcock and Sprunt.[17]

As expected, the results show a substantial difference in processor-memory traffic for an architecture with and without MRSs. The MRS versions of both the VAX and 68000 show marked decreases in processor-memory traffic for procedure-intensive benchmarks, shown in Figures 1 and 2. Similarly, the single register set version of RISC I requires many more memory reads and writes than RISC I with overlapped register sets (Figure 3). This result is due in part to the method used for

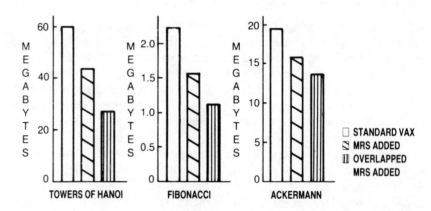

Figure 1. Total processor-memory traffic for benchmarks on the standard VAX and two modified VAX computers, one with multiple register sets and one with overlapped multiple register sets.

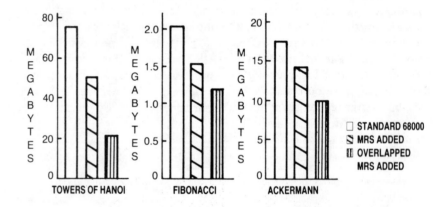

Figure 2. Total processor-memory traffic for benchmarks on the standard 68000 and two modified 68000s, one with multiple register sets and one with overlapped multiple register sets.

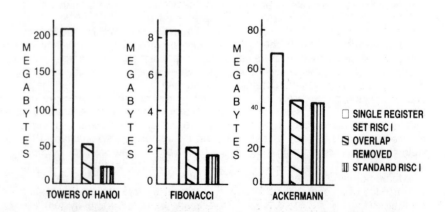

Figure 3. Total processor-memory traffic for benchmarks on the standard RISC I and two modified RISC I's, one with no overlap between register sets and one with only one register set.

handling register set overflow and underflow, which was kept the same for all three variations. With a more intelligent scheme, the single register set RISC I actually required fewer bytes of memory traffic on Ackermann's function than its multiple register set counterparts. For benchmarks with very few procedure calls (e.g., the sieve of Eratosthenes), the single register set version has the same amount of processor-memory traffic as the MRS version of the same architecture. [17]

Clearly, MRSs can affect the amount of processor-memory traffic necessary to execute a program. A significant amount of the performance of RISC I for procedure-intensive environments has been shown to be attributable to its scheme of overlapped register sets, a feature independent of instruction-set complexity. Thus, any performance claims for reduced instruction set computers that do not remove effects due to multiple register sets are inconclusive, at best.

These CMU experiments used benchmarks drawn from other RISC research efforts for the sake of continuity and consistency. Some of the benchmarks, such as Ackermann, Fibonacci, and Hanoi, actually spend most of their time performing procedure calls. The percentage of the total processor-memory traffic due to "C" procedure calls for these three benchmarks on the single register set version of the 68000 ranges from 66 to 92 percent. As was expected, RISC I, with its overlapped register structure that allows procedure calls to be almost free in terms of processor-memory bus traffic, did extremely well on these highly recursive benchmarks when compared to machines with only a single register set. It has not been established, however, that these benchmarks are representative of any computing environment.

The 432

The Intel 432 is a classic example of a CISC. It is an object-oriented VLSI microprocessor chip-set designed expressly to provide a productive Ada programming environment for large scale, multiple-process, multiple-processor systems. Its architecture supports object orientation such that every object is protected uniformly without regard to traditional distinctions such as "supervisor/user mode" or "system/user data structures." The 432 has a very complex instruction set. Its instructions are bit-encoded and range in length from six to 321 bits. The 432 incorporates a significant degree of functional migration from software to on-chip microcode. The interprocess communication SEND primitive is a 432 machine instruction, for instance.

Published studies of the performance of the Intel 432 on low-level benchmarks (e.g., towers of Hanoi[18]) show that it is very slow, taking 10 to 20 times as long as the VAX 11/780. Such a design, then, invites scrutiny in the RISC/CISC controversy.

One is tempted to blame the machine's object-oriented runtime environment for imposing too much overhead. Every memory reference is checked to ensure that it lies within the boundaries of the referenced object, and the read/write protocols of the executing context are verified. RISC proponents argue that the complexity of the 432 architecture, and the additional decoding required for a bit-encoded instruction stream contribute to its poor performance. To address these and other issues, a detailed study of the 432 was undertaken to evaluate the effectiveness of the architectural mechanisms provided in support of its intended runtime environment. The study concentrated on one of the central differences in the RISC and CISC design styles: RISC designs avoid hardware/microcode structures in-

tended to support the runtime environment, attempting instead to place equivalent functionality into the compiler or software. This is contrary to the mainstream of instruction set design, which reflects a steady migration of such functionality from higher levels (software) to lower ones (microcode or hardware) in the expectation of improved performance.

This investigation should include an analysis of the 432's efficiency in executing large-system code, since executing such code well was the primary design goal of the 432. Investigators used the Intel 432 microsimulator, which yields cycle-by-cycle traces of the machine's execution. While this microsimulator is well-suited to simulating small programs, it is quite unwieldy for large ones. As a result, the concentration here is on the low-level benchmarks that first pointed out the poor 432 performance.

Simulations of these benchmarks revealed several performance problems with the 432 and its compiler:

(1) The 432's Ada compiler performs almost no optimization. The machine is frequently forced to make unnecessary changes to its complex addressing environment, and it often recomputes costly, redundant subexpressions. This recomputation seriously skews many results from benchmark comparisons. Such benchmarks reflect the performance of the present version of the 432 but show very little about the efficacy of the architectural trade-offs made in that machine.

(2) The bandwidth of 432 memory is limited by several factors. The 432 has no on-chip data caching, no instruction stream literals, and no local data registers. Consequently, it makes far more memory references than it would otherwise have to. These reference requirements also make the code size much larger, since many more bits are required to reference data within an object than within a local register.

And because of pin limitations, the 432 must multiplex both data and address information over only 16 pins. Also, the standard Intel 432/600 development system, which supports shared-memory multiprocessing, uses a slow asynchronous bus that was designed more for reliability than throughput. These implementation factors combine to make wait states consume 25 to 40 percent of the processor's time on the benchmarks.

(3) On highly recursive benchmarks, the object-oriented overhead in the 432 does indeed appear in the form of a slow procedure call. Even here, though, the performance problems should not be attributed to object orientation or to the machine's intrinsic complexity. Designers of the 432 made a decision to provide a new, protected context for every procedure call; the user has no option in this respect. If an unprotected call mechanism were used where appropriate, the Dhrystone benchmark [19] would run 20 percent faster.

(4) Instructions are bit-aligned, so the 432 must almost of necessity decode the various fields of an instruction sequentially. Since such decoding often overlaps with instruction execution, the 432 stalls three percent of the time while waiting for the instruction decoder. This percentage will get worse, however, once other problems above are eliminated.

Colwell provides a detailed treatment of this experiment and its results. [20]

This 432 experiment is evidence that RISC's renewed emphasis on the importance of fast instruction decoding and fast local storage (such as caches or registers) is substantiated, at least for low-level compute-bound benchmarks. Still, the 432 does not provide compelling evidence that large-scale migration of function to microcode and hardware is ineffective. On the contrary, Cox et al. [21] demonstrated

that the 432 microcode implementation of interprocess communication is much faster than an equivalent software version. On these low-level benchmarks, the 432 could have much higher performance with only a better compiler and minor changes to its implementation. Thus, it is wrong to conclude that the 432 supports the general RISC point of view.

In spite of—and sometimes because of—the wide publicity given to current RISC and CISC research, it is not easy to gain a thorough appreciation of the important issues. Articles on RISC research are often oversimplified, overstated, and misleading, and papers on CISC design offer no coherent design principles for comparison. RISC/CISC issues are best considered in light of their function-to-implementation level assignment. Strictly limiting the focus to instruction counts or other oversimplifications can be misleading or meaningless.

Some of the more subtle issues have not been brought out in current literature. Many of these are design considerations that do not lend themselves to the benchmark level analysis used in RISC research. Nor are they always properly evaluated by CISC designers, guided so frequently by tradition and corporate economics.

RISC/CISC research has a great deal to offer computer designers. These contributions must not be lost due to an illusory and artificial dichotomy. Lessons learned studying RISC machines are not incompatible with or mutually exclusive of the rich tradition of computer design that preceded them. Treating RISC ideas as perspectives and techniques rather than dogma and understanding their domains of applicability can add important new tools to a computer designer's repertoire. □

Acknowledgements

We would like to thank the innumerable individuals, from industry and academia, who have shared their thoughts on this matter with us and stimulated many of our ideas. In particular, we are grateful to George Cox and Konrad Lai of Intel for their help with the 432 microsimulator.

This research was sponsored in part by the Department of the Army under contract DAA B07-82-C-J164.

References

1. J. Hennessy et al., "Hardware/Software Tradeoffs for Increased Performance," *Proc. Symp. Architectural Support for Programming Languages and Operating Systems*, 1982, pp. 2-11.

2. G. Radin, "The 801 Minicomputer," *Proc. Symp. Architectural Support for Programming Languages and Operating Systems*, 1982, pp. 39-47.

3. D. A. Patterson and C. H. Sequin, "A VLSI RISC," *Computer*, Vol. 15, No. 9, Sept. 1982, pp. 8-21.

4. R. P. Colwell, C. Y. Hitchcock III, and E. D. Jensen, " A Perspective on the Processor Complexity Controversy," *Proc. Int. Conf. Computer Design: VLSI in Computers*, 1983, pp. 613-616.

5. D. Hammerstrom, "Tutorial: The Migration of Function into Silicon," *10th Ann. Int'l Symp. Computer Architecture*, 1983.

6. J. C. Browne, "Understanding Execution Behavior of Software Systems," *Computer*, Vol. 17, No. 7, July 1984, pp. 83-87.

7. H. Azaria and D. Tabak, "The MODHEL Microcomputer for RISCs Study", *Microprocessing and Microprogramming*, Vol. 12, No. 3-4, Oct.-Nov. 1983, pp. 199-206.

8. G. C. Barton "Sentry: A Novel Hardware Implementation of Classic Operating System Mechanisms," *Proc. Ninth Ann. Int'l Symp. Computer Architecture*, 1982, pp. 140-147.

9. A. D. Berenbaum, M. W. Condry, and P. M. Lu, "The Operating System and Language Support Features of the BELLMAC-32 Microprocessor,"

Proc. Symp. Architectural Support for Programming Languages and Operating Systems, 1982, pp. 30-38.

10. J. Hennessy, "VLSI Processor Architecture," *IEEE Transactions on Computers*, Vol. C-33, No. 12, Dec. 1984, pp. 1221-1246.

11. D. Patterson, "RISC Watch," *Computer Architecture News*, Vol. 12, No. 1, Mar. 1984, pp. 11-19.

12. David Ungar et al., "Architecture of SOAR: Smalltalk on a RISC," *11th Ann. Int'l Symp. Computer Architecture,* 1984, pp. 188-197.

13. W. R. Iversen, "Money Starting to Flow As Parallel Processing Gets Hot," *Electronics Week,* Apr. 22, 1985, pp. 36-38.

14. H. M. Levy and D. W. Clark, "On the Use of Benchmarks for Measuring System Performance" *Computer Architecture News,* Vol. 10, No. 6, 1982, pp. 5-8.

15. D. C. Halbert and P. B. Kessler, "Windows of Overlapping Register Frames", CS292R Final Reports, University of California, Berkeley, June 9, 1980.

16. R. P. Colwell, C. Y. Hitchcock III, and E. D. Jensen, "Peering Through the RISC/CISC Fog: An Outline of Research," *Computer Architecture News*, Vol. 11, No. 1, Mar. 1983, pp. 44-50.

17. C. Y. Hitchcock III and H. M. B. Sprunt, "Analyzing Multiple Register Sets," *12th Ann. Int'l Symp. Computer Architecture*, 1985, in press.

18. P. M. Hansen et al., "A Performance Evaluation of the Intel iAPX 432," *Computer Architecture News*, Vol. 10, No. 4, June 1982, pp. 17-27.

19. R. P. Weicker, "Dhrystone: A Synthetic Systems Programming Benchmark," *Comm. ACM*, Vol. 27, No. 10, Oct. 1984, pp. 1013-1030.

20. R. P. Colwell, "The Performance Effects of Functional Migration and Architectural Complexity in Object—Oriented Systems," PhD. thesis, Carnegie-Mellon University, Pittsburgh, PA. Expected completion in June, 1985.

21. G. W. Cox et al., "Interprocess Communication and Processor Dispatching on the Intel 432," *ACM Trans. Computer Systems*, Vol. 1, No. 1, Feb. 1983, pp. 45-66.

Robert P. Colwell recently completed his doctoral dissertation on the performance effects of migrating functions into silicon, using the Intel 432 as a case study. His industrial experience includes design of a color graphics workstation for Perq Systems, and work on Bell Labs' microprocessors. He received the PhD and MSEE degrees from Carnegie-Mellon University in 1985 and 1978, and the BSEE degree from the University of Pittsburgh in 1977. He is a member of the IEEE and ACM.

Charles Y. Hitchcock III is a doctoral candidate in Carnegie-Mellon University's Department of Electrical and Computer Engineering. He is currently pursuing research in computer architecture and is a member of the IEEE and ACM. He graduated with honors in 1981 from Princeton University with a BSE in electrical engineering and computer science. His MSEE from CMU in 1983 followed research he did in design automation.

E. Douglas Jensen has been on the faculties of both the Computer Science and Electrical and Computer Engineering Departments of Carnegie-Mellon University for six years. For the previous 14 years he performed industrial R/D on computer systems, hardware, and software. He consults and lectures extensively throughout the world and has participated widely in professional society activities.

H. M. Brinkley Sprunt is a doctoral candidate in the Department of Electrical and Computer Engineering of Carnegie-Mellon University. He received a BSEE degree in electrical engineering from Rice University in 1983. His research interests include computer architecture evaluation and design. He is a member of the IEEE and ACM.

Charles P. Kollar is a senior research staff member in Carnegie-Mellon University's computer Science Department. He is currently pursuing research in decentralized asynchronous computing systems. He has been associated with the MCF and NEBULA project at Carnegie-Mellon University since 1978. Previous research has been in the area of computer architecture validation and computer architecture description languages. He holds a BS in computer science from the University of Pittsburgh.

Questions about this article can be directed to Colwell at the Computer Science Department, Carnegie-Mellon University, Pittsburgh, PA 15213.

Reprinted from *Computer*, November 1985, pages 142–143. Copyright ©
1985 by The Institute of Electrical and Electronics Engineers, Inc.

Response to "Computers, Complexity, and Controversy"

The causal reader of "Computers, Complexity, and Controversy" (September 1985, pp. 8-19) might erroneously conclude that the performance benefits of RISCs stem solely from multiple register sets, or MRSs, rather than from a wide range of benefits from the RISC approach. Furthermore, the authors suggest that architectural metrics—metrics we deny are of proven validity—show that RISCs are not good computers. They also declare that the 432 and MicroVAX 32 do not constitute evidence for the RISC approach, while the data suggest the opposite conclusion. While we welcome a scientific evaluation of the RISC approach, we feel most of the opinions in the article are not supported by evidence or by scientific reasoning.

The quantitative part of the article is the study on MRSs. A careful analysis of MRSs is worthwhile, but the relevance of the benchmarks used in such a study determine the relevance of its results. The authors mistakenly say that the "benchmarks used were the same ones originally used to evaluate RISC I." Table 1 shows the programs compiled, simulated, and published in papers about Berkeley RISCs. (We at Berkeley, by the way, supplied the authors with our compiler and simulator to run these programs.)

Table 1. RISC programs ordered by size in lines of code.			
SIZE (lines)	BENCHMARKS	SUBJECT	PUBLICATION (year)
29095	PCC	C compiler	1984
1608	SED	Text editor	1982
219	MCF #l	Iterative sort	1982
201	Whetstone	Floating point benchmark	1984
177	Puzzle	Bin-packing (pointer)	1982
136	Quicksort	Recursive sort	1981
133	Puzzle	Bin-packing (array)	1981
89	MCF #K	Bit matrix	1982
77	MCF #H	Linked list	1982
61	MCF #E	String search	1982
60	MCF #F	Bit test	1982
16	Towers	Recursive benchmark	1982
13	Ackerman	Recursive benchmark	1982

From this list, the authors chose the two smallest and most recursive programs, Ackerman and Towers of Hanoi, and added Fibonacci, a highly recursive two-line Lisp program. Since MRSs have major impact on procedure calls, their importance can be artificially inflated by programs with unusual procedure call patterns. Why did the authors choose the smallest programs with the largest number of recursive procedure calls to test their hypothesis that the effects of

MRSs are orthogonal to instruction set complexity? We asked this question at the June '84 International Conference on Computer Architecture in Boston, where they reported their results. Their only explanation was that some of the other programs were not used because they did not have enough procedure calls to support their hypothesis.

In concluding their discussion here of MRSs, the authors acknowledge the pathological nature of the programs ("It has not been established, however, that these benchmarks are representative of any computing environment."), yet they claim that the performance of RISC I "has been shown to be attributable to (MRSs)" and that "performance claims for RISCs that do not remove effects due to MRSs are inconclusive at best." Furthermore, these remarks ignore the benefits of RISCs on average instruction execution time, obviously a key to performance. And even if the authors could apply their study to nonrecursive programs larger than 16 lines, they overlook that both the 801 and MIPS have the same significant benefits in cost and performance—and neither of these designs use MRSs. If, as the authors suggest, MRS is the "real secret" behind RISCs, we wonder why MRS wasn't included in their list of RISCs characteristics.

The authors report that architecture metrics show that the VAX outperforms RISCs. We believe the emphasis on architecture metrics over implementation issues is in part responsible for a generation of machines with good metrics but poor cost/performance and long development cycles. The measurement of those metrics by assembly language programs exacerbates the gap between abstract metrics and the real implementation, which will be measured by applications that use high-level languages and compilers. The RISC approach advocates a methodology that balances the needs of compilers with the implementation efficiency of the architecture.

The illusion created by measuring architectural metrics in isolation from the implementation is illustrated by the history of the VAX-like Nebula architecture, which has the best MCF metrics. Although the architecture was completed in 1980 and was reported in the February 1981 *Computer* (pp. 35-41), there are no commercial versions of this machine, and even though the Air Force funded this effort as a new standard computer, the government has yet to put out requests for bids to build Nebula machines. In sharp contrast, RISC architectures have been vigorously pursued by both startups and established computer manufacturers. Even though RISCs were not funded to be a standard, the government recently put out requests for bids to build both gallium arsenide and CMOS versions of the MIPS RISC architecture. If the validity of the MCF architecture metrics was widely endorsed, we would expect industry and government to have rushed to build Nebula and ignored RISCs, not vice versa.

The section of the article on the 432 inadvertently provides further support for RISC ideas. The authors start by citing papers that report the 432 is 10 to 20 times slower than the VAX-11/780. They then hypothesize the 432 would be faster if it were redesigned: if it had more pins, a wider bus, and a faster memory system, it would be 25 to 40 percent faster; if it had a less complicated and faster procedure call, it would be 20 percent faster; and if it didn't have variable bit length instructions, it would be three percent faster. According to their own numbers, the

new hypothetical 432 is still six to 12 times slower than the VAX, and likely three to six times slower than the 16-bit Motorola 68000 microprocessor. By concentrating on microcoding high-level functions, the 432 architects apparently sacrificed the performance of the more frequently occurring simple functions. Contrary to the authors' statement that "it is wrong to conclude that the 432 supports the general RISC point of view," we believe that the performance data and the authors' suggested simplifications—to increase the 432's performance—both provide evidence indeed for the value of the RISC approach.

Contrary to their conclusion, we think that the history of VLSI implementations of VAX supports the RISC approach.

Again contrary to their conclusion, we think that the history of VLSI implementations of the VAX, reported in the October 1984 *IEEE Journal of Solid-State Circuits* (pages 663-681), supports the RISC approach. The VLSI VAX is an eight-chip implementation of the full VAX architecture. During the course of the VLSI VAX project, DEC found that 20 percent of the instructions required 60 percent of the microcode, yet were only 0.2 percent of the executed instructions. Several years after the beginning of the project, DEC decided to modify the layout and microcode of the main CPU chip and then subset the architecture to fit the microcode memory and data path into a single chip, thus creating the MicroVAX-32. (The authors do not mention the VLSI VAX and mistakenly say that the MicroVAX-32 "was designed, realized, and tested in a period of several months." The paper by the MicroVAX designers reports that it took 20 months from the start of the project to produce the first pass of the descriptions of the circuit masks. Chip fabrication, testing, and redesign lengthens the design cycle.) Although this subset project started later, it finished first and is now a product. Furthermore, the performance degradation of the MicroVAX-32 for the omitted instructions is just 4 percent while the fivefold reduction in control store size cuts the active chip area almost in half. DEC's decision to subset its complex architecture to exploit VLSI—plus the reduced design effort of the simpler machine—is certainly some indirect support for the RISC approach.

The reader should note that this last year has been good for RISCs. John Cocke of IBM won the ACM-IEEE Eckert-Mauchly Award for Computer Architecture in part for his work on RISCs, and Manolis Katevenis' dissertation on VLSI RISCs won the ACM Doctoral Dissertation Award. Gordon Bell, another winner of the Eckert-Mauchly award and one of the designers of the PDP-11 and the VAX, cited the Berkeley and Stanford RISC research on VLSI computers last October in this magazine (pp. 14-30) and said that given "the current speed of logic relative to memory, it is time again to return to direct (versus microprogrammed) execution of the instruction set."

Without identifying a specific publication or quotation, the authors of "Computers, Complexity, and Controversy" claim that some RISC publications are "oversimplified, overstated, and misleading." Fortunately, disagreements in computer design are not resolved on the pages of a magazine; hardware is the final judge of architecture. Many computer scientists and commercial computer designers have been convinced by the research presented in the RISC papers and dissertations, so we encourage readers to investigate the issue carefully.

David Patterson
University of California, Berkeley
John Hennessy
Stanford University

Suggested reading

M. Hopkins, "A Perspective on Microcode," Proc. 21st Ann. Computer Conf., San Francisco, Calif., Feb. 1983, pp. 108-110.

M. Katevenis, "Reduced Instruction Set Computer Architecture for VLSI," ACM Doctoral Dissertation Award Series, MIT Press, Cambridge, Mass., 1985.

D. Patterson, "Reduced Instruction Set Computers," Comm. ACM, Vol. 28, No. 1, Jan. 1985, pp. 8-21.

S. Przybylski et al., "Organization and VLSI Implementation of MIPS," J. VLSI and Computer Systems, Vol. 1, No. 2, Fall 1984, pp. 170-208.

R. Sherburne et al., "A 32-bit NMOS Microprocessor with a Large Register File," IEEE J. Solid-State Circuits, Vol. 19, No. 5, Oct. 1984, pp. 682-689.

THE OPEN CHANNEL

More controversy about "Computers, Complexity, and Controversy"

David Patterson and John Hennessy's response to our article, "Computers, Complexity, and Controversy," seems to indicate that they have misunderstood many important points that we tried to make. In this brief space we can only highlight their most serious misunderstandings. [1,2]

In our section on multiple register sets (MRS) we did not claim that RISC I's performance "has been shown to be attributable to (MRSs)." [1] Nor did we state that "MRS is the 'real secret' behind RISCs." [1] Our report was much different. To quote ourselves in context, we stated that "a significant amount of the performance of RISC I for procedure-intensive environments has been shown to be attributable to" [2] MRSs. Our experiments showed that the performance effects due to MRS are comparable for RISCs and CISCs. Consequently, we urge RISC researchers who incorporate this mechanism to factor out its performance effects when attempting to gauge performance due to the reduced nature of their machines. Similarly, one should do the same for any other mechanism which affects performance and is independent of instruction set complexity. In summary, it also seems necessary to restate that the goal of our MRS study was to evaluate the performance effects of MRS, *not* to re-evaluate the RISC I, the VAX-11 or the 68000. We simulated (using our own simulators) only procedure-intensive C benchmarks (all of which were supplied to us by Patterson) because MRS mechanisms are not exercised when procedure calls are not used. These benchmarks were appropriate for this study because they expose the performance effects of MRS, the focus of the study.

The tendency of many RISC supporters to emphasize throughput at the expense of architectural and other metrics is once again evident in the sentence, "The authors report that architectural metrics show that the VAX outperforms RISCs." [1] This is an incorrect paraphrase: we never said that "the VAX outperforms RISCs." In fact, we very clearly stated that throughput per se is *not* being measured by the MCF architecture evaluation scheme, and that this is arguably a shortcoming of the MCF model that unfairly penalizes machines which attempt to optimize throughput by making tradeoffs across the architecture/implementation boundary, as do RISCs: "The MCF life-cycle cost models did not include execution throughput, so the RISC II performance related features were ignored." [2] MCF was not designed to be a 100-yard dash for computer systems (as RISC performance studies usually are)—it was intended as a decathlon, reflecting our perception that actual systems in use need far more than large numbers of cycles-per-unit time in order to meet their goals.

In their response, Patterson and Hennessy have missed the most important point about performance comparisons with regard to the Intel 432. The 432's object orientation exacts an intrinsic performance cost, since it is manifested as a set of runtime checks and a large amount of additional information to be manipulated. Patterson and Hennessy state that an improved, "hypothetical 432 is still . . . three to six times slower than the 16-bit Motorola 68000." [1] This comparison, which we did not make, is meaningless because the two machines are not doing the same "work." To make a fair comparison, one would need either to migrate the object orientation of the 432 to the 68000 or to remove such support from the 432 (an enormous task in either case). Perhaps Patterson and Hennessy's comparison addresses the throughput costs of supporting the 432's style of object orientation, but it does not "provide evidence . . . for the value of the RISC approach." [2]

As history shows, there is not necessarily any correspondence between technical merit and success in the senses of awards, salesmanship, and commercial products. Researchers should be willing to let their work stand or fall on the basis of its own scientific worth. While it may be that many computer scientists and commercial computer designers have been convinced by the research presented in the RISC papers and dissertations, it has been our experience that a significant number have not (and for very good reasons, as we have argued in our article).

Robert P. Colwell
Charles Y. Hitchcock III
E. Douglas Jensen
H.M. Brinkley Sprunt
Carnegie-Mellon University

References

1. David Patterson and John Hennessy, "Response to 'Computers, Complexity, and Controversy,'" in "Open Channel," *Computer*, Vol. 18, No. 11, November 1985, pp. 142-143.

2. Robert C. Colwell, Charles Y. Hitchcock III, H. M. Brinkley Sprunt, E. Douglas Jensen, and Charles P. Kollar, "Computers, Complexity, and Controversy," *Computer*, Vol. 18, No. 9, September 1985, pp. 8-19.

Reprinted from *Computer*, December 1985, page 93. Copyright © 1985 by The Institute of Electrical and Electronics Engineers, Inc.

And Now a Case for More Complex Instruction Sets

Michael J. Flynn, Chad L. Mitchell, and Johannes M. Mulder

Stanford University

Reprinted from *Computer*, September 1987, pages 71–83. Copyright © 1987
by The Institute of Electrical and Electronics Engineers, Inc.

With the spate of recent papers and product announcements,[1,2] it might seem that the reduced instruction set computer, or RISC, approach to instruction set design has been universally accepted as superior. These RISC designs[3] have been characterized as having few simple instruction types with fixed instruction size and formats. The antithesis of RISC designs have been designated CISC, for complex instruction set computer, and characterized as having large instruction vocabularies with multiple sizes, formats, and addressing modes.[4]

RISC performance estimates, when compared to alternative conventional CISC (such as VAX, S/360, etc.) approaches, seem impressive. While there have been critical appraisals of the RISC approach,[5] the comparative performance evaluations provide formidable, although qualified, evidence in its favor.

Our purpose here is to evaluate and compare RISC-type designs with non-RISC instruction-set extensions using a level playing field: with similar compiler strategies, without compatibility considerations, and with similar implementation constraints. We also deal with instruction set evaluation. The data presented is based on five benchmark programs discussed later.

Using a computer architecture simulation platform, we can perform instruction set tradeoffs with a common optimizing compiler and workload.

Instruction sets have many attributes as well as constraints. The key to careful instruction set evaluation is to consider key attributes and the tradeoffs possible among them in light of implementation constraints.

Modeling performance in instruction set design

It is difficult to create a truly fair basis for comparing instruction set designs[6] because of the myriad of considerations and compromises in achieving the final design. Broadly, these factors fall into two classes: those concerned with functional requirements and those directly related to performance.

The former class includes issues such as compatibility, design time, and technology selection. We will discuss it briefly in a later section.

Performance-oriented considerations. Quantitative evaluation certainly makes for interesting comparisons, especially when driven by a common and representative workload. Typical runtime measurements include both static and dynamic characteristics of processor execution:

(1) Static measures. They simply represent the static size of program representation. In the absence of other considerations, smaller size is better, as more concise code should have better locality in a memory hierarchy and requires less memory bandwidth.

(2) Dynamic measures. They include the number and type of instructions executed, number of data references required for reads and writes, and memory traffic as measured in number of bytes transferred.

(3) Compilation time. An item frequently overlooked in comparisons is the time it takes to create a program represen-

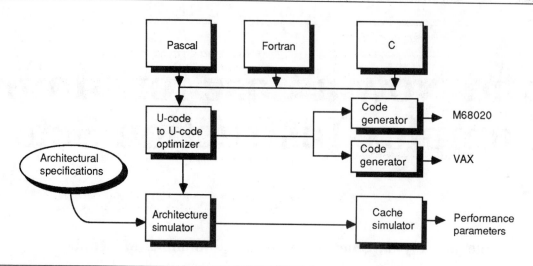

Figure 1. Computer architect's workbench.

tation. It has been variously estimated that half of mainframe problem-state activity involves compiling programs.

(4) Operating system execution time. Depending on the system and the application, a significant fraction of machine execution time is spent in the operating system. A good instruction set must support system functions.

A basis for comparison. In the creation of a new instruction set design, the evaluation of expected runtime parameters is an important facet in understanding the required tradeoffs. While it is imperative to compare a projected design against existing designs, it is just as important to understand the limitations of such comparisons. To achieve a small runtime advantage, for example over a VAX model, is necessary but not conclusive evidence of design validity. Similarly, comparing a design and technology which will be available to customers in future years with designs done several years ago and currently in production may give a misleading impression of the role of the instruction set in determining performance.

A further problem is that comparisons are made not simply across processors, but usually across processor-compiler pairs. Processor-instruction-set variations can become lost in the noise of differences in compilers. We need to create a level playing field for the evaluation of instruction set alternatives using a common compile-time strategy.

In the remainder of this article we assume

- a common workload (benchmarks),
- a simple register-oriented base instruction set,
- a fixed implementation technology,
- similar compiler optimizations for all instruction set variations, and
- the same arithmetic logic unit (ALU), data paths, and instruction vocabulary for operations for all instruction set variants (thus, the same ALU cost). Instruction count differences will arise *only* due to format and register differences.

We will use a simple base design to evaluate the usefulness of several possible additions.

A computer architect's workbench

The computer architect's workbench[7] is a set of tools developed at Stanford which allows the evaluation of architectural and memory system parameters for a variety of different instruction sets using a common compiler front end. As shown in Figure 1, applications written in Pascal, Fortran, or C compile into an intermedi-

ate code called U-code. If desired, we can optimize the U-code representation of the application by means of the global U-code to U-code global optimizer.

The actual simulation consists of a static and a dynamic part. During the static part, the simulator extracts static information per *basic block* (a code segment with a single entry and exit point). The information includes the code size of the basic block for the target architecture and data-reference information. The architectural specification drives this stage and determines the code size. To examine the relative performance of different instruction sets on an application, an architect simply parameterizes an architecture or instruction set family.

During the dynamic part, the benchmark executes and passes dynamic information to the simulator. Information includes the currently executing basic block and dynamic data references. The simulator associates the dynamic basic-block trace with the static basic-block information; generates simple architectural characteristics such as program size, number of executed instructions, number of memory references, and so forth; and generates an address trace to drive a subsequent cache simulator.

The architect's workbench allows rapid evaluation of multiple architectural and memory system designs. Among the instruction sets currently available are

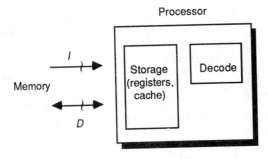

Tradeoff #1
Within limits, more complex instruction decode
(More formats, operations, etc.)
→ reduces memory traffic for instruction (without cache)
or → reduces instruction-cache size for constant memory traffic.

Tradeoff #2
Within limits, increasing register-set size (and/or complexity)
→reduces memory traffic for data (without cache)
or → reduces data-cache size for constant memory traffic.

Tradeoff #3
More complex instruction decode and/or increased register-set
size may increase cycle time and decode area.

Figure 2. Basic tradeoffs.

- stack machines, including fixed-size stack machines, byte-encoded stack machines, and B6700-type stack machines;
- register-set machines, including load-store architectures and System/360-type architectures; and
- direct-correspondence architectures.[8]

Using the architect's workbench to evaluate architectures. With the workbench we normalize the effects of compiler optimization. The optimizer can be turned on or off, but all architectures receive the same degree of optimization. With a program trace we can view the effect of register allocation and create perfect allocation by reallocating after initial program execution.

The workbench was developed to allow top-down evaluation of a variety of architectures for a particular workload. The designer uses the workbench to select an instruction set customized to the particular application. The system is easy to use since in the initial evaluation only the basic instruction set parameters need to be specified. Unless explicitly added, the system will default to (assume that)

(1) All architectures have the same functional (ALU-type) operations and these operations correspond to the actions defined by the high-level source language

of the benchmarks (Pascal, for our benchmarks).

(2) All architectures have the same data paths (32 bits for this study).

(3) All instructions execute in unit time. We do not evaluate the effects of pipelining, but we do calculate the processor cycles spent in the data buffer and memory.

The system is designed to allow basic high-level tradeoffs, such as in instruction format selection, instruction encoding, register-set size and organization, and cache size and organization. After making an initial evaluation to select several promising candidate architectures, the designer would supply the additional information specifying ALU vocabulary and timing, pipeline timing templates, pipeline interlocks, etc., for a complete behavioral simulation.

Currently our system does not include facilities for pipeline timing evaluation, although it is being extended to include all of the above mentioned features.

For this article we based our tradeoff measurements on memory traffic; they do not directly include pipeline-cycle counts. Where differences arise, we will estimate the effect on cycle count.

An instruction set consists of a tradeoff between memory bandwidth and processor storage, as well as processor-decode requirements (see Figure 2). There are

several basic tradeoffs based on instruction encoding and available processor storage. The amount of complexity associated with instruction decode (the conciseness of the encoding) determines both the number of instructions fetched and the number of bits required from memory to interpret a program. The number of registers available for the allocator, together with the allocation strategy, determine the data traffic. Both instruction and data references to memory can be diminished by the presence of cache, either separate caches for the instruction and data stream or an integrated cache for both.

If we use care in evaluating relatively close architectural alternatives, we can get a good idea as to which architectural strategies are better than others, even though we may not be able to determine an exact optimum. In dealing with two similar designs, we can invoke a principle of marginal utility: Enhance a base design by an alternative that provides the maximum performance per unit cost. In order to use this in our analysis, we make the assumption that all processor variants under study have the same operational instruction set—they execute the same data transformational instructions (add, shift, etc.), even though they may differ in architectural instructions required by their instruction set (number of loads and stores in a register architecture, or number of pushes and pops in a stack architecture). By

Table 1. Benchmark sizes for stack architecture.

Benchmark	Static Size (bytes)	% Actually Referenced	Dynamic Size (bytes)	Instructions (Dynamic)
CCAL	12,980	63%	4,391,864	1,058,262
Compare	8,948	60%	35,113,324	8,538,373
PCOMP	71,276	69%	22,084,724	5,323,939
PASM	15,424	80%	17,814,260	4,352,798
Macro	73,980	53%	2,538,512	617,765

Table 2. Four instruction sets studied.

Type	Formats	Encoding	Addressability
Fix32	Two basic types: (1) Load R_1, with Mem [addr] or (2) $R_1 \leftarrow R_2$ op R3 (all operands in registers)	All instructions occupy 32^b	Word (32^b)
OBI360	As with Fix32 plus RX type,* $R_1 \leftarrow R_1$ op Mem [Addr]	Memory refr instr use 32^b; register refr instr use 16^b and 32^b	Half word (16^b)
Stack	Stack formats	Instructions with op-code only 8^b; memory refr instr use 32^b	Byte
B6700	Stack formats with special encoding of constants and pointer-referenced memory	Instr with opcode only 8^b; memory refr instr use 16^b	Byte

*Register set machine operations take two independent source operands (R1 and R2) and place the result in either an independent register (R3) or one of the source operands (say, R1). Most RISC machines as well as our Fix32 use the former convention, while the IBM System/360 uses the latter. For our code generator there is little advantage for the independent R3 specification, i.e., the OBI360 data is approximately the same (within 1%) for either convention.

assuming the same operational (ALU) vocabulary, the same data path size, and the same arithmetic performance, we create a standard cost for that part of the processor. We are left with the comparison of only those parts of the architecture directly affected by the instruction set tradeoffs. These include the decoder, the register set size, instruction cache size, and data cache size. We assume that small tradeoffs in register set size and decoder size will not materially influence the cycle time itself. We will comment on this assumption later before drawing general conclusions.

The result of enhancing a base design with various alternatives provides insight into a *local* optimum; it does not find a *global* optimum. While we are able to comment on RISC and register-set-based instruction set variations, we will not comment here on significantly different instruction sets (such as complex stack machines).

The benchmarks. We selected the benchmarks used in this study as representative of workstation applications. They consist of five Pascal programs originally used by Alpert.[9] Some static and dynamic

measures for the benchmarks are given in Table 1. All data is for a stack machine with fixed 32-bit instructions (similar to P-code). The static measure is the program size in bytes as compiled without linkage overhead; it includes only executable code and constants as allowed in the stack machine architecture.[7] The percentage of code actually used, for the given input files, is between 53 percent and 80 percent. Since all stack instructions are 32 bits, the difference between dynamic size (divided by four) and instructions is the occurrence of pointers, especially those associated with procedure calls.

The CCAL benchmark emulates a desk calculator. It reads a script of calculations from a text file and produces results in another text file. As with the other benchmarks, any input files required are specified as part of the benchmark, thus defining a standard execution. The Compare benchmark compares two text files, producing a description of their differences (similar to the Unix Diff command). The PCOMP benchmark compiles a Pascal program by recursive descent and produces P-code output. The PASM benchmark assembles the P-code output from the P-code compiler. The Macro benchmark is a macro processor for the SCALD computer-aided design system.

The chosen benchmarks are representative Pascal programs of medium size. They represent program generation, file processing, and calculation. CCAL also represents an interactive (as opposed to batch) program, although it is driven from a script file to keep its execution standard.

Each of these benchmarks was executed once for each target architecture after analysis of its basic blocks. Subsequently the address trace of that execution was fed into the cache simulator. The results presented are for the mean of the (equally weighted) benchmarks.

RISC-CISC code analysis

In the following analysis we define the RISC-type architecture[3] as follows:

(1) Load-store architecture. It does not allow memory operands for ALU operations.
(2) Register-file oriented.
(3) Pipelined execution with short cycle time, delayed branch, and a few register-oriented instructions.
(4) Fixed 32-bit instruction size.

COMPUTER

The base RISC we simulate is called Fix32. It is a load-store architecture with a 32-bit fixed instruction size with a register-set size of 16. (We examine other register set sizes in later sections.) Because delayed branching can be applied to our base architecture and its extensions, the effect of delayed branching is not simulated. This does not influence the results, however, because delayed branching affects the extensions of our base architecture exactly the same way as it affects the base architecture itself.

While we present some data on a number of architectural possibilities (see Table 2), one is particularly interesting: OBI360 (Only-Binary IBM 360). This variation is generally similar to IBM System 360 with the storage-to-storage instruction format excluded. OBI360 makes two modifications to the RISC strategy:

1. It adds the "RX" format (32 bits), allowing one instruction operand to reside in memory:

$R_1 := R_1$ op Mem$[R_2 + \text{offset}]$

2. It adds half-size instructions (16-bit) register-to-register instructions:

$R_1 := R_1$ op R_2

Starting off with the minimum Fix32 architecture, we perturb this design in various ways, such as

(1) by increasing the complexity of the instruction encoding (using OBI360 instruction formats), or

(2) by increasing the number of registers available to the data stream.

We make the assumption that other things remain constant—the base instruction set operational vocabulary, cycle time (discussed later), etc. We first consider the effect of instruction set selection on memory traffic in the presence of various-sized caches, then we consider the issue of register set size, organization, and allocation policy on memory traffic, again in the presence of various-sized caches.

The instruction set

The instruction set itself is largely a compromise between the complexity of the decoder (and thus the ensuing size of the microcode, cycle-time, etc.) and the required memory traffic to support execution (and thus the number of memory references). The RISC approach has opted for minimum decode complexity and accepted a relatively high bandwidth requirement for the instruction execution.

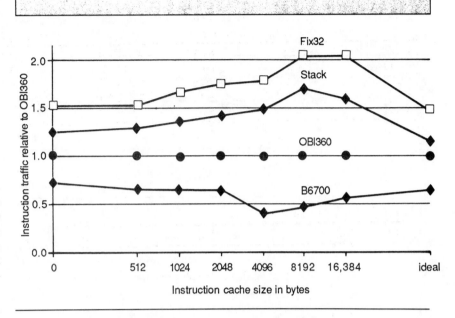

Figure 3. All architecture families (two-way associative 16-byte lines).

We can see the effects of instruction set selection on instruction traffic in Figure 3, which shows several instruction set families (see Table 2) relative to the memory traffic generated by OBI360 (with 16 general-purpose registers). The memory traffic is plotted for various cache sizes from no cache (zero bytes) to an infinite cache (ideal). A common cache policy of two-way associativity with a line size of 8 bytes has been selected across all caches and instruction sets. The relatively small line size tends to reduce the absolute amount of memory traffic required to support program execution and to diminish the difference among the instruction set families. Keeping the line size constant normalizes the cost for instruction caches for all of the families.

Figure 3 is interesting in a number of ways. Without a cache, the difference among architectures concerning the number of instruction bytes required to execute a program is about two to one (from the least dense architecture, the Fix32 with 16 registers, to the most dense architecture, the B6700).

Because an instruction cache benefits all architectures, it is difficult to see the relative benefit unless we normalize the traffic, as we have done in Figure 3. In the absence of a cache, the Fix32 architecture has 50 percent more instruction traffic than OBI360; this figure rises to 100 per-

cent for certain intermediate cache sizes (8K and 16K bytes). For these intermediate sizes, the OBI360 architecture has captured its working set, while the Fix32 has not yet done so. Ultimately, as all caches capture their working sets, the original relationship is restored, representing simply the number of references required to initially bring a program into the cache. Notice that for certain intermediate size caches, we can see relative differences of greater than five to one between the most dense and least dense architectures (B6700 to Fix32 in the 4K- to 8K-byte range).

Figure 4 shows the effect of marginal increases in the instruction decoder on overall dynamic program size and the resultant effect on cache performance. In Fix32-RX the RX format is added to Fix32. The RX format simply combines a load with a register-register operation. Since the RX format is the conjunction of two existing instruction types, its implementation cost can be minimal, depending on pipeline organization. About 10 percent fewer instructions will be executed with 10 percent fewer instruction-decode cycles. One might expect the pipelined program execution to improve by the same amount. It does not, because the RX instruction requires an extra cycle of interpretation, which may or may not be overlapped. Thus, in addition to a 10 percent reduction in instruction traffic, the

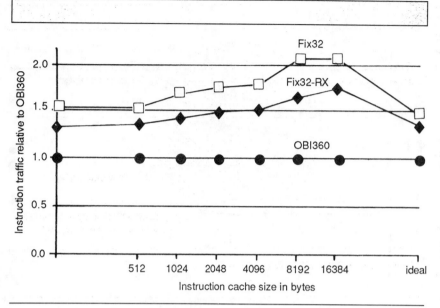

Figure 4. Memory referencing characteristics of register set architectures.

number of execution cycles also reduces, but less than 10 percent (see the sidebar, "The effects of memory-to-register (RX) instructions").

Adding the RX format and a half-sized (16-bit) RR format to Fix32 results in OBI360 with one-third improvement in instruction bandwidth requirements for the no-cache case. The addition of half-size instructions to the format, however, does require additional decoder complexity to realize the alignment of instructions for proper decoding (see the sidebar, "The cost of half-size instructions"). Whether the two modifications to Fix32 to obtain OBI360 extend the cycle time we will discuss later.

OBI360 provides a striking improvement over Fix32 in the effectiveness of an instruction cache. Table 3 shows that OBI360 realizes the same miss rate as Fix32 with an instruction cache of exactly half the size of Fix32. Thus, by moving to OBI360 and adding decoder hardware, the resultant design would require fewer instruction cycles and would realize the same memory traffic with half of the Fix32 cache.

The effects of memory-to-register (RX) instructions

If no change is made to the pipeline, there is no reduction in the number of cycles executed, only reduction in instruction bandwidth. Basically, the sequence

    Load R₁,R₂, Mem Disp; R₁ ← Mem [[R₂] + Mem Disp]
    Add R₃,R₁   ; R₃ ← R₃ + R₁

is replaced by
    Add R₃, R₂, Mem Disp; R₃ ← R₃ + Mem [[R₂] + Disp]

In both cases above, the sum is placed in R₃ in the same cycle. With the RX format, the pipeline is available one cycle early to admit a new instruction. However, if the pipeline uses the ALU for both address generation and execution, an RX instruction sequence will be limited to the same performance as before due to ALU contention.

If the processor is extended to include a separate adder for address generation and appropriate pipeline control, much (but not all) of this contention is avoided and performance enhancement can be realized.

As a rough estimate, suppose conditional branches represented 20 percent of instructions executed (and Fix32 load instructions, 30 percent). Now Fix32-RX reduces the frequency of load instructions to 20 percent (combining the load with an operation). However, the RX operation completes execution at the same time as the load-operate instruction pair. Thus, when the RX instruction immediately precedes a branch instruction that tests its result, no time is saved; otherwise a cycle is saved. Thus, if a branch is occupied every fifth position, a cycle is saved when the RX is located in any but the fourth position, or immediately preceding the branch. In the other three cases, the cycle is saved, giving a performance improvement potential (without register/ALU usage conflicts) of 7.5 percent rather than 10 percent.

The data stream

What is the value of large register sets? What is the value of register windows? How effective is a data cache in the presence of a register set? These are some of the questions that the architect must address in creating a balanced instruction set design.

Registers have many roles. They hold: temporary values in expression evaluation, variables from statement to statement within a procedure, constants and pointers. Figure 5 shows types of references to data memory for variable and temporary accesses for source (Pascal and C) programs. If one had an architecture without registers (an all-memory architecture), 47 percent of the data references would be for temporary storage of intermediate results within the evaluation of expressions. The addition of two or three registers, whether through use of a stack or a register-instruction format, basically eliminates these references. When we ignore expression evaluation, the resultant traffic is for *extended source variables*— variables whose values are to be carried statement to statement within a procedure because of high probability of use.

The register allocator is responsible for

predicting the optimum assignment of variables to registers. Let us define this data traffic as the unity data traffic (thus excluding expression evaluation). Unity data traffic is not exactly the same as the variable traffic seen in a source program, however. The difference includes accesses for dynamic links, static links (the runtime organization), the fact that source variables may have arbitrary lengths but the physical system has a fixed-length bus (assumed to be 4 bytes), and finally that the compiler must create variables to control, for example, With and For statements.

Given different instruction sets with the same register set size and same compiler optimizer, the resultant data traffic will be the same for all instruction sets. How does data traffic compare to instruction traffic? Without data or instruction cache, the instruction traffic dominates the data traffic, but this quickly decreases when even a small instruction cache is added.

Figure 6 shows the instruction traffic for Fix32 and OBI360 instruction sets relative to unity data traffic. Both Fix32 and OBI360 include 16 general-purpose registers. For OBI360, the figure shows 10 percent more traffic for instructions than for data, while for Fix32, this difference is 60 percent. The addition of an instruction cache reduces the instruction traffic well below the unity data traffic for all architectures; thus, we need to rebalance the data traffic when considering a small instruction cache for the processor. The following four sections present different ways to rebalance the total memory traffic between instructions and data.

Single register set. Figure 7 shows the allocation of registers within a typical register set. Unity data traffic requires about eight registers in the set; they are allocated for constants, the evaluation stack, and state variables. The marginal value of adding eight registers to the initial eight depends upon register allocation. Figure 8 presents two allocation strategies: a very simple strategy wherein registers are allocated only among variables within a basic block, and a more elaborate strategy which allocates variables within a procedure. Global register allocation is by means of priority-based coloring. Notice that with or without optimization, the marginal value of more than eight additional registers is moot, and that a reduction from unity data traffic down to 0.65 can be achieved with straightforward global register allocation.

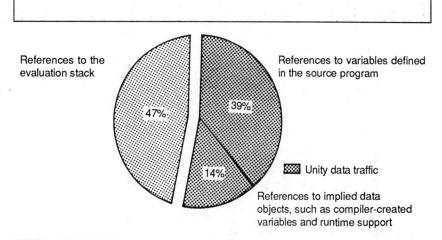

Figure 5. Distribution of data reference types.

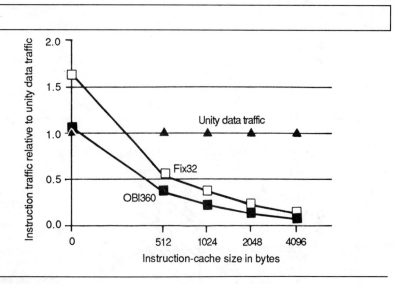

Figure 6. Instruction and data traffic as a function of architecture and instruction cache size.

The cost of half-size instructions

If a base processor design were intended to include 16^b instructions the following hardware might be added:

(1) A two-word instruction buffer (IB) 2×32^b
(2) Multiplexors from the IB into the instruction decoder
(3) Finite-state machine for IB control
(4) Modified program counter to allow both 16^b increment (for instruction control) and 32^b increment (for IB control)

Table 3. Relative traffic or miss rates. All traffic is relative to OBI360 without a cache and with 32^b-wide paths to memory.

For cache* size:	0	512	1^K	2^K	4^K
Fix32	1.52	.44	.30	.19	.11
Fix32-RX	1.33	.37	.24	.17	.09
OBI360	1.0	.28	.17	.11	.05

*Two-way set-associative, 8-byte lines

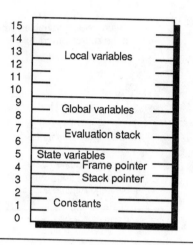

15	
14	
13	Local variables
12	
11	
10	
9	Global variables
8	
7	Evaluation stack
6	
5	State variables
4	Frame pointer
3	Stack pointer
2	
1	Constants
0	

Figure 7. A possible register set usage outline.

Figure 8. Single-register-set performance relative to unity data traffic.

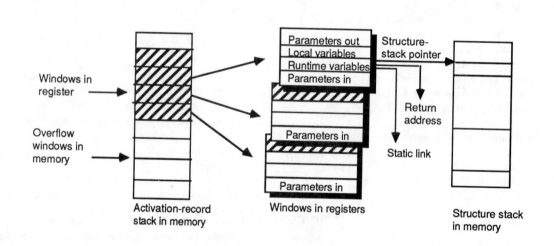

Figure 9. Multiple overlapping register windows.

To improve traffic beyond this requires allocation of registers across procedures. This can be done either in software, by interprocedural register allocation, or in hardware, through register windows.

Interprocedural register allocation. An interprocedural register allocator reduces the penalty of saving and restoring registers around procedure calls by allocating some registers as private to a particu-lar procedure. Because procedures which mutually exclude each other from being in the call chain at the same time can share private registers, the number of registers required is reasonably small. Inter-procedural register allocation has the additional advantage that runtime management variables, such as dynamic links, static links, and procedure-return addresses, can be allocated to registers using a method similar to that used for procedure variables.

A simple and efficient interprocedural allocation scheme[10] assigns private registers depth first in the call tree. Leaf procedures come first, callers of leaf procedures second, and so forth. This scheme treats recursion paths as single nodes and does not allocate private registers to procedures in such a path. Fig-ure 10 shows the performance of an allo-cator based on this scheme, but extended with an extra pass to detect variables potentially accessed through pointers[11]; these variables cannot be allocated to private registers. The figure shows a traffic ratio of 0.5 with 8 registers and 0.4 with 32 registers available to the allocator.

Interprocedural allocation also has its drawbacks:

- procedures called recursively cannot have private registers,
- separately compiled modules must have knowledge of the register usage of all intra-module calls, or require register allocation during link time, and
- incremental compilation without an explicit linking stage such as Lisp environments can profit only partially from this scheme.

Interprocedural register allocation may turn single register sets into the most efficient local memory. Because of the drawbacks, however, unless explicitly stated otherwise we use only global (procedural) allocation in comparing different data buffers in the following sections.

Multiple overlapping register windows. Register windows allow a new set of registers to be made available for each procedure, with an overlap of registers between the caller and the called procedure to allow for passing of parameters. When a procedure call exhausts the number of windows, a window is freed by saving its data in memory. Whenever the data is needed again, it is restored from memory. The conditions which require a window save and restore are called overflow and underflow, respectively.

The hardware windows are organized as a circular buffer always covering the top part of the runtime stack. The outgoing parameters of the top window are the same as the incoming parameters of the bottom window. The hardware windows can be envisioned as rolling back (returns) and forth (calls) over the window stack in memory. Every activation record in the runtime stack has a fixed size, the window size. A second runtime stack, called the *structure stack*, keeps additional procedure variables which do not fit in the window stack. Every record in the window stack maintains a pointer to that part of the second stack which holds these variables.

Figure 9 shows the facets of a multiple-overlapping-window organization: the hardware windows covering the top of the window stack; the overlapping windows, holding parameters, local and runtime

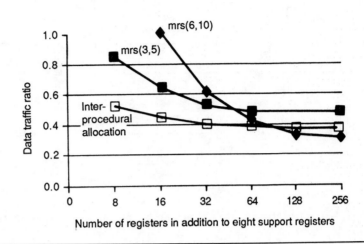

Figure 10. Performance of multiple overlapping register windows as a function of the total number of registers (relative to unity data traffic).

management variables; and the structure stack. An additional facility, which improves the performance of overlapping windows, allows pointer access to windows other than the one on top of the stack. This allows variables accessed through *var* parameters, the static-link, or pointers to be allocated in a window. For this article, we assume that overlapping windows include this facility.

We designate a window organization with N shared registers and M local registers by mrs(N, M). The effectiveness of register windows depends mainly on two parameters: the size of the window and the number of windows. Figure 10 shows that a large window size, mrs(6, 10), has a detrimental effect on performance for organizations with few windows. Few windows imply frequent under- and overflow conditions, and therefore a high penalty for large sets. However, a small window, mrs(3, 5), has a negative effect on performance for an organization that has many windows. A small window captures fewer local variables and parameters, and therefore is less efficient compared with a large window when the over- and underflow traffic stops dominating total traffic.

To achieve the best of both large and small windows, global register allocation can be combined with small windows. This combination on the average outperforms both mrs(3, 5) and mrs(6, 10) for our benchmarks. In this article, however, we are concerned with the utility of large reg-

ister sets and especially those organizations actually implemented in general-purpose microprocessors. The buffer comparison in the following section, therefore, does not take small-window buffers into account. The performance of small-window buffers with and without register allocation and additional caching is presented elsewhere.[11]

Single register set and cache combination. An argument in favor of larger register sets is that they will reduce the number of accesses to memory. Of course, a cache will do the same thing, and an interesting tradeoff occurs between increasing register set size and introducing or enlarging a data cache. Viewed from the memory system, enlarging either the register-set size or the cache size reduces the required memory traffic.

Using the traffic ratio as a function of provided storage for buffer comparison is not fair for two reasons: first, the storage provided does not accurately reflect the usage of chip area; and second, the traffic ratio does not completely determine processor performance.

To present buffer performance as a function of occupied area instead of the number of bits of storage, we define a simple storage-to-area mapping. The key points in this mapping are the inclusion of tag and status bits for caches, the distinction between the size of a cache RAM cell and a multiport register RAM cell, and the

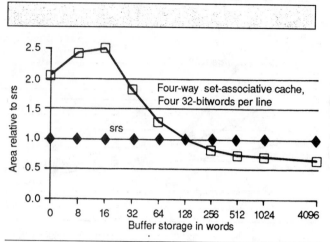
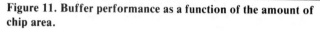

Figure 11. Buffer performance as a function of the amount of chip area.

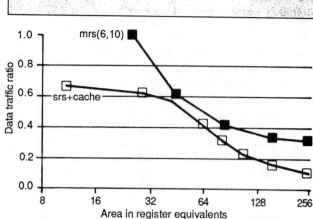

Figure 12. Data traffic ratio as a function of chip area.

inclusion of area for drivers, sense amplifiers, and tag comparators. The intent of this model is to penalize small register sets and caches for their inherent area overhead and to penalize register sets for their relatively large RAM cells, which they need to supply the high bandwidth required for pipelined processors. The main assumption underlying this model is that the RAM-cell size of a particular buffer is independent of the size of the buffer. Figure 11 shows the area of the cache* relative to the area of a register set as a function of the provided storage. The initial area disparity between the two buffers is mainly due to the tag comparators, and the state machine needed to control the cache. When the cache becomes larger than 32 lines, or 128 words, it actually takes less area than the register set, because the cache RAM cell is significantly smaller than the register RAM cell. Mulder gives a complete description and a validity assessment of the area model elsewhere.[11] The model parameters are all based on actual CMOS register set and cache designs.[12,13]

The traffic ratio depicts the effectiveness of the data buffer viewed from the memory, but the situation is not quite the same when viewed from the processor. Access to a cache is usually a one- or two-

cycle operation, whereas access to a register set can be included within a cycle. Very large register sets may add a cycle or extend the cycle (see next section), but caches invariably add additional cycles to total program execution. A more accurate measure than the traffic ratio would be the ratio of the processor cycles spent in the buffer and main-memory combination and the cycles spent in the memory system without the presence of a buffer. Mulder describes this measure, the *cycle ratio*, in detail.[11]

In a highly pipelined organization which keeps its buffer and memory system busy all the time, the cycle ratio describes the exact performance of the processor. Note that pipeline breaks, not caused by the memory and buffer system, may cause the real performance to deviate from the cycle ratio. Nonetheless, it is a good measure for evaluating different buffer organizations and their timing parameters.

Figure 12 summarizes the traffic ratio, and Figures 13 and 14 the cycle ratio of two buffering strategies. All three figures show their ratios as a function of occupied area in register equivalents; one register equivalent is the area occupied by 32 register bit cells. Figures 13 and 14 show the cycle ratio for a main memory access time of two and three cycles, respectively.* The figures show the ratios for a multiple-register-window organization, mrs(6,10), and a

single-register-set and cache combination, srs + cache. The register allocator only uses four registers for allocation, but the architecture is assumed to have an additional eight as described before.

Both Figures 12 and 14 show a slight advantage for srs + cache over mrs(6,10) between 40 and 80 register equivalents. Before and after this interval, srs + cache performs significantly better than mrs(6,10). Reducing the memory access time from three to two cycles, however, undoes the srs + cache advantage. Now mrs(6,10) is slightly better than srs + cache for the 40- to 80-register interval, and performs approximately the same for larger buffers. Nonetheless, an increase in average memory access time is always an advantage of the srs + cache organization. The case for multiple register sets with relatively large sets is slight, at best, and occurs only in the region of 32 to 128 registers for one- or two-cycle main memory access time. An important advantage for the srs + cache organization is its relative independence from the reference distribution. A smaller percentage of references to the window stack immediately degrades mrs(6,10) performance, while this is not necessarily the case for srs + cache.

Several buffer characteristics are not taken into account in this comparison because they lie outside the scope of the article or because insufficient data was available. These include the effect of system functions (interrupts, I/O, and context switches) and data-consistency

---

*The cache is four-way set associative with four one-word transfer units per line. The first data point, however, is a direct mapped one-line cache, and the second data point is a two-way set associative two-line cache.

---

*A cache hit takes one cycle, while a cache miss takes one cycle plus a memory access.

COMPUTER

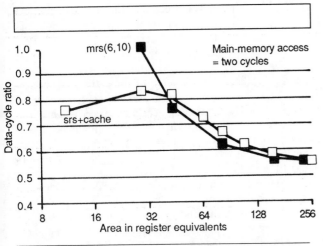

Figure 13. Cycle ratio as a function of chip area (two-cycle memory).

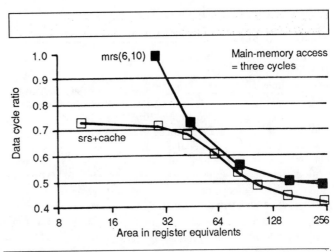

Figure 14. Cycle ratio as a function of chip area (three-cycle memory).

requirements in the case of multiprocessing.

Trading instruction traffic for data traffic

Memory traffic is the sum of the instruction traffic plus the data traffic. Assume that a processor with a Fix32 instruction set has eight general-purpose registers. Is it better to add registers, or to increase instruction complexity? Table 4 gives insight into these tradeoffs. Note that the table presents total traffic relative to the total instruction and data traffic of Fix32 with eight registers. If we increase the Fix32 register set size from eight registers to 16, we reduce the relative traffic from 1.00 to 0.76. However, if we increase the instruction complexity and retain a register set size of eight by moving from Fix32 to OBI360, the relative traffic also reduces from 1.00 to 0.76. Clearly it is desirable to do both, which would reduce the relative traffic to 0.56.

If we assume a Fix32 base design with a register set size of 16, there is almost no saving in increasing the size to 32 (unless coupled with interprocedural register allocation. The instruction traffic and the data traffic remain essentially constant. By adding eight register windows, mrs(6,10), for a total of 128 registers, we reduce data traffic to 0.12 and instruction traffic to 0.52—a net savings of 0.12 references from Fix32 with 16 general-purpose

Table 4. Instruction and data traffic measured relative to the total traffic of our initial architecture, the Fix32 with eight registers.

Architecture	Register Set Size	I-traffic	D-traffic	Total
Fix32	8	0.68	0.32	1.00
Fix32	16	0.55	0.21	0.76
Fix32	32	0.55	0.21	0.76
Fix32-MRS	128	0.52	0.12	0.64
OBI360	8	0.44	0.32	0.76
OBI360	16	0.35	0.21	0.56
OBI360	32	0.35	0.21	0.56
OBI360-MRS	128	0.32	0.12	0.44

registers. On the other hand, if we simply retain the 16 general-purpose registers and modify the instruction set from Fix32 to OBI360, we realize a savings of 0.20 references. Thus, the addition of 112 registers and window control results in only 60 percent of the traffic reduction we can achieve with better instruction encoding (the change from Fix32 to OBI360).

Cycles and cycle time

So far we have dealt with design alternatives assuming that the processor execution (independent of memory traffic) was

unaffected. In this section we review the alternatives examined and assess the possible impact on either the number of cycles required to execute a program, or the cycle time itself.

The cycle count. Concerning the cycle count, consider the principal design alternatives presented.

(1) We first considered Fix32 compared with Fix32 plus a memory-to-register instruction format (Fix32-RX). This change will either leave cycle count unaffected or it will allow a modest (less than 10 percent) decrease in the number of cycles (see the sidebar, "The effects of memory-to-register (RX) instructions")

when hardware is added to the pipeline.

(2) We next considered the change from Fix32-RX to OBI360. This change adds the 16[b] (or "half size") instruction; it should have no effect on cycle count (also see the sidebar, "The cost of half-size instructions").

(3) Finally we considered adding either additional registers or a data cache to a 16-register design. Additional registers may increase cycle time (discussed below), while a cache may require either more or fewer cycles than a large register set, depending on the memory access time.

Without interprocedural allocation, there is obviously no marginal utility, in terms of traffic ratio or cycle count, in enlarging a single register set beyond 16 registers. With interprocedural register allocation, we see an improvement in memory traffic by increasing the total register set to 32, after which again there is little or no marginal utility. The cycle count will decrease as memory traffic decreases.

Part of the effect on cycle count of moving from a base 16-register design to multiple register set versus the move to register set and cache combination was discussed in "The data stream" and shown in Figures 13 and 14. The design with a cache clearly expends fewer cycles accessing objects not in the register set. On the other hand, when we call a new procedure, the multiple register set has an advantage because it requires fewer cycles to save and restore register values. However, many parameters are involved (frequency of calls, number of parameters, cache miss penalty, etc.), and a specific situation may find one approach significantly superior.

The cycle time. Concerning cycle time, we have considered two design extensions that could adversely affect the internal processor cycle time:

(1) The extension of Fix32 to OBI360 increases the instruction decoder complexity.

(2) Increasing the number of registers may increase register access time.

Cycle time is typically determined by one of four paths:

(1) Instruction decode
(2) Register access
(3) Cache access
(4) ALU operation and condition-code set

The designer usually is confronted with physical limitations which determine the longest path from one of the above considerations. Once that is determined, the

other paths can be increased to roughly the same duration so as to minimize costs. A review of several recent RISC designs (RISC II[14] and SOAR[15]) indicates that register access time has been a primary determinant of cycle time, not instruction decode. In MIPS,[16] a pipelined RISC with 16 general-purpose registers, the main cycle time determinant was pipeline and exception control circuitry. It seems in some cases that the use of smaller register sets could improve the cycle time, while the use of OBI360 should have a negligible effect on cycle time.

Other considerations in instruction set design

So far in this article, we have examined such aspects of performance as the basic criteria in instruction set selection and design. Many important functional considerations are not performance related, or are related to performance only in a secondary way. In this section we briefly remind the reader of several of these considerations.

Compatibility. The primary level of transportability of programs is the instruction set, not the higher-level language. The reason that the VAX series from Digital Equipment Corporation and the 68000 series from Motorola Corporation resemble their antecedents is not simply an issue of designer's preference, but of customer preference. The VAX instruction set is a good case in point. It is derived from (built upon) the PDP-11, a 16-bit architecture noted for its flexible use of addressing modes. Rather than abandon the addressing modes, the VAX designers enhanced them, preserving subset compatibility with the PDP-11 yet achieving generous functionality in the 32-bit arena. The resultant design provides for relatively concise encoding of programs. Unfortunately, the flexible object identification introduces extra cycles into instruction interpretation and makes instruction pipelining more difficult. Still, the VAX series has become an industry standard because of compatibility, connectivity (I/O capabilities), and availability of software, not simply performance.

Technology. In the context of microprocessors, chip area constraints force a design to fit in a fixed area. Performance may be severely limited where an instruction set has been selected without consideration of these area constraints. Pins as well as area may constrain designs, restricting access to memory. This provides a premium for those architectures which make the best use of memory bandwidth.

Most instruction sets are children of their technological times. Assumptions concerning memory size, access time, and the relative cost of registers, as well as the ability of a compiler to use those registers, determine the tradeoffs that go into a resultant instruction set specification.

Life cycle costs. Compatibility, technology, performance, software and hardware development effort, maintenance costs, and hardware reliability are ingredients in determining the total system cost (and profitability) for the product over its lifetime. Life cycle cost is clearly an ultimate measure, and our performance discussion is simply one factor of it.

While instruction set design involves many considerations, performance data is an important component. Indeed, performance may well be a primary consideration in certain custom application-specific designs.

In evaluating design tradeoffs, the architecture-simulation platform described above provides valuable relative performance data and greatly assists in optimizing design choices from the top down. The workbench provides an early assessment of the relative merits of different design options and facilitates the selection of the option with the greatest marginal utility.

In this article we limited the data presented to five benchmarks selected from a Pascal-type environment similar to that reported on by other researchers in the area. Different environments might produce significantly different results.

The principal design alternatives we have examined are Fix32 and OBI360:

(1) Fix32 is RISC-like in formats and encoding, but *does not reduce* the ALU instruction vocabulary. The functional instruction set is the same for all architectures studied, so as to keep the ALU cost relatively constant. RISC implementation with fewer instruction types may require additional instruction memory traffic and exaggerate the difference between

architectures (see Figure 3).

(2) OBI360 is Fix32 with the addition of both the RX and half-size instruction formats. OBI360 is not System 360 or System 370. Typical S/370 code includes the operating system interface, calling conventions, and runtime prolog/epilog, which significantly distorts the locality and cache results presented here. However, to evaluate System 370 code is to evaluate an evolution of software, not simply instruction set technology. The relatively good results of OBI360, however, are a compliment to the basic tradeoffs made by System 360 instruction set designers over twenty years ago.

Concerning the various alternatives:

(1) Fix32 (a simple load-store architecture) with 16 or fewer registers and *without cache* represents a reasonable design point for a minimum cost processor. Note that the minimum processor cost was achieved with a 50 percent to 100 percent increase in instruction traffic (Figure 3), compared with more complex designs.

(2) If Fix32 is extended to reduce memory traffic, instruction encoding and formats should receive priority attention over the expansion of an instruction cache. By adding modest decode hardware to Fix32, we create OBI360, which achieves the same memory performance as Fix32, but uses an instruction cache of only half the Fix32 cache size (Table 3).

(3) From data traffic considerations alone, it seems that OBI360 with a register set of about size 16 plus a small data cache is preferable to multiple register sets for most area combinations (Figures 12 and 13).

More generally, instruction set designers cannot afford to ignore issues of code density in favor of instruction simplicity or decoding ease. Instruction bandwidth can be a significant component of memory traffic and, ultimately, processor performance. Using larger register sets to reduce data traffic from memory makes sense only when efficient instruction encoding is used to make a corresponding reduction in instruction traffic. *Balanced optimization* is the key to overall instruction set efficiency.□

Acknowledgments

Several basic ideas used in the computer architecture simulator were based on the work of our colleague Don Alpert. We also used his benchmark programs. The U-code system included in our platform was the work of John Hennessy and Gio Wiederhold and their students here at Stanford.

This research was supported by NASA under contracts NAG2 248 and NAGW 419, and by an IBM graduate fellowship.

References

1. Also see product announcements for Fairchild Clipper, Hewlett-Packard Spectrum, Advanced Micro Devices AM29000, and MIPS Corp.

2. Mark Hill et al., "Design Decisions in SPUR," *Computer*, Nov. 1986, pp. 8-22.

3. John Hennessy, "VLSI Processor Architecture," *IEEE Trans. Computers*, Dec. 1984, pp. 1221-1246.

4. David A. Patterson and Carlo H. Sequin, "RISC I: A Reduced Instruction Set VLSI Computer," *Proc. 8th Ann. Symp. Computer Architecture*, May 1981, pp. 443-458.

5. R.P. Colwell et al., "Computers, Complexity, and Controversy," *Computer*, Sept. 1985, pp. 8-19.

6. Michael J. Flynn, "Towards Better Instruction Sets," *Proc. 16th Ann. Microprogramming Workshop*, Oct. 1983, IEEE Computer Society Press, pp. 3-8.

7. Chad L. Mitchell, *Processor Architecture and Cache Performance*, Tech. Report CSL-TR-86-296, Computer Systems Laboratory, June 1986.

8. Scott Wakefield, *Studies in Execution Architectures*, PhD thesis, Stanford University, Jan. 1983.

9. Donald Alpert, *Memory Hierarchies for Directly Executed Language Microprocessors*, PhD thesis, Stanford University, June 1984.

10. Peter A. Steenkiste, *LISP on a Reduced-Instruction-Set Processor: Characterization and Optimization*, PhD thesis, Stanford University, Mar. 1987.

11. Johannes M. Mulder, *Tradeoffs in Data-Buffer and Processor-Architecture Design*, PhD thesis, Stanford University, 1987. In preparation.

12. M. Horowitz and P. Chow, "The MIPS-X Microprocessor," *Proc. Wescon 1985*, Stanford University, 1985.

13. Anant Agarwal et al., "On-chip Instruction Caches for High Performance Processors," *Proc. Advanced Research in VLSI*, Stanford University, Mar. 1987.

14. M.G.H. Katevenis, *Reduced Instruction Set Computer Architectures for VLSI*, PhD thesis, UC Berkeley, Oct. 1983.

15. David Ungar et al., "Architecture of SOAR: Smalltalk on a RISC," *11th Ann. Symp. Computer Architecture*, Ann Arbor, Mich., June 1984, pp. 188-197.

16. Steven A. Przybylski et al., *Organization and VLSI Implementation of MIPS*, Tech. Report 84-259, Computer Systems Laboratory, Apr. 1984.

Michael J. Flynn is a professor of electrical engineering at Stanford University, where he served as director of the Computer Systems Laboratory from 1977 to 1983. He is also a senior consultant at Palyn Associates, a computer design firm in San Jose, California. He was a cofounder and vice president of Palyn in 1973 while on leave from Johns Hopkins University.

Flynn worked at IBM for ten years in the areas of computer organization and design. He was design manager of prototype versions of the IBM 7090 and 7094/II, and later for the System 360 Model 91 CPU.

Flynn received his PhD from Purdue University in 1961.

Chad L. Mitchell is currently Chief Technical Officer at Great Wave Software, which he helped found in 1984. He has written several programs for personal computers, including the award-winning Concertware music system.

Mitchell received a BA in mathematics in 1979 and a BS in computer science in 1980 from the University of Utah, both Magna Cum Laude. He received an MS in computer engineering in 1982 and a PhD in computer science in 1986 from Stanford University. While there, he coauthored the Gambit prototyping language.

Johannes M. Mulder is currently completing the requirements for the PhD degree at Stanford University. His primary research interests are in computer architecture, VLSI, and computer and memory system design and evaluation.

Mulder received the MS degree in electrical engineering in 1982 from Delft University of Technology in the Netherlands.

Readers may write to Flynn at Electrical Engineering Dept., ERL 452, Stanford University, Stanford, CA 94305-4055.

Section 7: GaAs RISC

7.1 Background

The long-awaited commercial feasibility of GaAs for integrated circuits has arrived, and the marriage of this technology with RISC is a natural one. Although GaAs provides very high speed, it is difficult to achieve the dense packing normally required for VLSI. The simpler, more regular layout of a RISC chip (compared to CISC) lends itself to implementation in GaAs. The following subsections provide a brief introduction to GaAs, with a comparison to more widely-used logic families.

7.2 Logic Families

Gates are the fundamental elements of digital logic, and these elements are in turn constructed of transistor circuits. In most cases, the transistor circuits are themselves fabricated in silicon. Various techniques may be used in this fabrication, which affect the cost, size, and performance of the circuits. Each such technique is referred to as a *logic family*. The most important logic families are:

- Transistor-transistor logic (TTL)
- Emitter-coupled logic (ECL)
- n-channel metal-oxide silicon (NMOS)
- Complementary metal-oxide silicon (CMOS)
- Gallium Arsenide (GaAs)

Table 7.1 summarizes these families.

7.3 Circuit Characteristics

Each of these families represents a tradeoff among a number of factors. The most important of these are speed, power consumption, packing density, and cost. The *speed* of digital circuits is measured in terms of the signal propagation delay through a single gate. When the input to a gate is changed, there is a delay while the electrical impulses propagate through the components (flip-flops) of the gate and a stable output is produced. The gate delay will determine the speed with which the various components of the computer (e.g., ALU, main memory) can operate. A second key characteristic of digital circuits is *power consumption*. Power consumption in the circuits produces heat, which must be dissipated. The higher the power consumption, the more complex and costly is the circuit packaging to allow adequate dissipation. The cost of the power supply is also increased. These problems become more acute in the case of very-large scale integration (VLSI), in which large number of gates are concentrated on a single chip. Thus, power consumption limits the number of gates that can be placed on a given chip, limiting packing density. In general, the greater the speed of a circuit, the greater the power consumption.

Figure 7.1 shows the speed/power characteristics of the major logic families.

In addition to power consumption, other factors influence *packing density*, which is simply the number of gates-per-

Table 7-1: Integrated Circuit Logic Families

Name	Acronym	Transistor Type	Strengths	Weaknesses
Transistor-transistor logic	TTL	Bipolar	Easy to interconnect; fast, wide selection of circuits available; inexpensive	Generates noise spikes; relatively high power dissipation; modest packing density
Emitter-coupled logic	ECL	Bipolar	Highest-speed silicon IC; generates little noise internally	Difficult to interconnect; low packing density; difficult to cool
n-channel metal-oxide silicon	NMOS	Unipolar	Good speed; relatively low power; good packing density; inexpensive; relatively easy to manufacture	Has limited ability to drive lines and to interface with other circuits
Complementary metal-oxide silicon	CMOS	Unipolar	Very low standby power required; modest speed and packing density; reasonably priced; good noise resistance	Power consumption increases when switched at high speeds.
Gallium arsenide	GaAs	Unipolar	Very high speed; relatively low power requirements; good resistance to radiation; can convert electrical signals to optical signals	More expensive than silicon ICs; difficult to fabricate

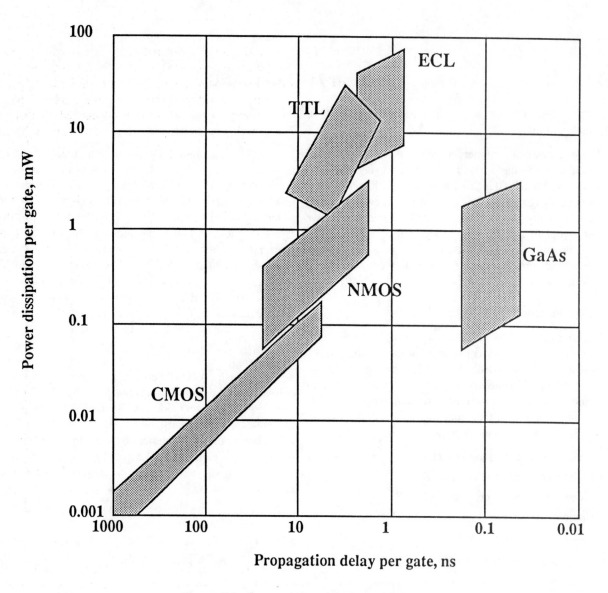

Figure 7-1: Comparison of GaAs and Silicon

unit area that can be accommodated on a chip. These other factors include the shape and size of the basic circuit components, and the manufacturing technique used. Packing density affects overall speed: With more gates on a single chip, the propagation delays between gates are reduced.

7.4 Transistor Types

All integrated circuits are based on the use of the transistor as the basic switching element from which flip-flops and gates are constructed. Two types of transistors are in use: bipolar and unipolar. These types differ in the polarities of the charges that flow through the transistor.

Bipolar transistors, which might be referred to as conventional transistors, are the solid-state equivalent of vacuum tubes. Each transistor consists of three regions arranged in a linear fashion. The three regions are either n-p-n or p-n-p, where p and n refer to positive (holes) and negative (elec-

trons) charges, respectively. With the bipolar transistor, both positive and negative charges flow through the transistor. The TTL and ECL logic families use bipolar transistors.

Unipolar transistors, also referred to as field-effect transistors (FET), use only one type of charge, positive or negative. Both n-type and p-type unipolar transistors can be fabricated. The silicon-based integrated circuits that are fabricated with unipolar transistors are metal-oxide silicon (MOS) circuits. Unipolar transistors are also used in GaAs integrated circuits.

7.5 Characteristics of Logic Families

The most popular logic family for special-purpose circuits and for the smaller-scale SSI and MSI circuits is the *transistor-transistor logic (TTL)* family. TTL is quite economical and provides good speed. Compared to some of the other families, TTL is comparatively easy to fabricate. TTL makes use of bipolar transistors.

The other type of bipolar circuit in use is the *emitter-coupled logic (ECL)* family. ECL achieves the highest speed of any silicon-based circuit by preventing the individual transistor from ever turning completely "on." This gives high speed, but unfortunately also produces greater power dissipation. In addition, ECL is particularly susceptible to noise.

The other popular silicon-based integrated circuits use *metal-oxide silicon (MOS)* and unipolar transistors. MOS has three important advantages over bipolar circuits:

- MOS achieves higher packing density, allowing more gates on a single chip.
- MOS employs simpler fabrication techniques; therefore MOS integrated circuits are more economical to manufacture.
- Power consumption is much less than for bipolar gates. Thus the MOS circuits are more economical to operate.

The disadvantage of MOS is speed. The propagation delay is high because the act of turning unipolar transistors on and off requires moving a considerable amount of charge through some fairly high resistances.

In general, the advantages of MOS outweigh the disadvantages in making larger-scale integrated circuits. Thus, MOS is the most widely used approach for LSI and VLSI integrated circuits. Two types have found wide favor for these chips: NMOS and CMOS.

The *n-channel metal-oxide silicon (NMOS)* family is characterized by the use of only n-type unipolar transistors. It provides good speed at relatively low power consumption and good packing density. In contrast, the *complementary metal-oxide silicon (CMOS)* family uses both types of unipolar transistors to limit current flow and therefore power consumption. It provides very good noise resistance. On the other hand, CMOS circuits are larger than NMOS and are more complex to fabricate.

The most exciting recent development in integrated circuits makes use of a material other than silicon: the compound *gallium arsenide (GaAs)*. Although GaAs has been around for some time, it is only recently that it has begun to gain noticeable market share. GaAs has a number of potential advantages over silicon-based integrated circuits, including greater speed and lower power consumption. Unfortunately, GaAs is also expensive, fragile, and difficult to manufacture.

The speed advantage of GaAs has been tempting to integrated-circuit makers for a long time. High cost and low packing density have held back its acceptance. Gradually, costs are coming down and packing densities are going up. Furthermore, GaAs is particularly attractive for RISC processors, which have a simpler circuit layout than ordinary CPUs.

7.6 Article Summary

"The Aging Young Pretender" is a brief introduction to GaAs and its potential role in integrated circuits. "An Introduction to GaAs Microprocessor Architecture for VLSI" specifically looks at the use of GaAs for implementing VLSI RISC processor chips. GaAs technology is examined in detail.

The next three articles look at specific GaAs RISC projects. "A DCFL E/D-MESFET GaAs Experimental RISC Machine" examines the design of a 32-bit RISC processor developed by RCA. "A 32-Bit, 200-MHz GaAs RISC" reports on a DARPA-sponsored project to develop a 100-MIPS, GaAs RISC processor chip. "Toward a GaAs Realization of a Production-System Machine" looks at the use of GaAs RISC to implement a machine for expert system applications.

SCIENCE AND TECHNOLOGY

The aging young pretender

GALLIUM arsenide (GaAs) is the gifted child of electronics. Silicon, its rival, seems dutiful but dull by contrast. A GaAs chip is born with many advantages: it can work five times faster than silicon; it uses less power; it is less affected by radiation; and it can convert electronic signals to light. Unfortunately, GaAs is also expensive, ill-trusted and troublesome. It accounts for a meagre 0.5% of the semiconductor market. Silicon, cheaper and better understood, triumphantly takes almost all the rest. Now many companies claim they have overcome GaAs's problems. Is the awkward child about to blossom?

Many of GaAs's strengths stem from one property: current-carrying electrons move more easily past arrays of GaAs atoms than they do past arrays of silicon atoms. So electronic signals can trigger and flow through a GaAs microchip faster, and waste less power. Also, the output of a GaAs chip is less distorted. Electronics engineers exploit these traits in circumstances where silicon does not come up to scratch.

Most of these are in defence and tele-communications. GaAs is useful for amplifying the weak signals received by radar and satellites. In space, its modest appetite for electrical power helps batteries last, and its resistance to radiation protects it. It also plays a part in telephony. In order to squeeze more traffic on to a line, telephone calls are often "multiplexed"—that is, cut up into little packages which are shuffled and then transmitted together. This job often gets too hectic for mere silicon.

Lucrative (and fast growing) as these niches are, GaAs needs to find its way into wider use in equipment like computers. Only then will it truly come of age. The makers of GaAs look hopefully to two trends: their improving ability to handle the material, and their customers' stringent demands for high performance. University research also promises to find new ways to bring gallium arsenide into the mainstream.

Take the producers first. Some 70% of the world's GaAs is made by the military and telecoms divisions of multinationals like America's McDonnell Douglas and Britain's Plessey (for their own use). The rest comes from specialist companies, like Vitesse Semiconductor and Gigabit Logic, both in California. All of them have struggled to find ways to get round GaAs's numerous problems. Many need a boost in demand: not long ago, Integrated Circuit Engineering of America found that GaAs producers were working at only 35% of their capacity.

Because gallium arsenide is made from two ingredients (whereas silicon is a simple material), it can be a tricky job to produce GaAs which is pure and neatly enough arranged to hold microscopic electronic circuits. What is more, GaAs is brittle. Some 7% of wafers (the discs of pure material on which circuits are imprinted) break during processing. Only 1% of silicon wafers break. Silicon's oxide, which is easily formed with oxygen, can act as one of the structural components of the transistors that are built upon its surface. GaAs, on the other hand, has no such convenient compound. Its transistors have to be built in more subtle ways. Also, since GaAs does not conduct heat well, transistors will overheat if they are too closely packed on a chip.

These problems are reflected in the cost of a three-inch wafer of GaAs: about $160, compared with $30-40 for a six-inch silicon wafer. A finished chip might cost three-five times as much in small quantities. When companies produce more GaAs, costs will fall. In the mean time new technology can push prices lower. Vitesse uses a highly automated production line and finds that fewer wafers are broken. And the companies have had enough experience fine-tuning these processes for total yields (the proportion of chips which are not duds) to be around 45% for some types of chip. Three years ago comparable gallium-arsenide yields were 5%.

They are also adapting processes from the silicon industry that sidestep the need for an oxide. Earlier this month Vitesse announced a process which it hopes will bring costs down to below 5 cents per logical step, or gate, on a chip's surface. Gates on high-speed silicon chips cost 2.5-5 cents.

Pushing down the cost of GaAs chips should help persuade computer makers to include them in their machines. But there are other reasons why GaAs might be used—at least in high-performance computers. Cray Research, a Minnesota company which builds some of the world's most powerful supercomputers, is using GaAs chips in the Cray-3, which will be launched next year. It wants the speed that GaAs can offer, whatever the cost. Other companies, including Sun Microsystems and Digital Equipment, have been sniffing around GaAs, partly because its low power consumption would give them more speed without liquid cooling. Chip materials are cheap compared to clanking great cooling systems.

A new fad in chip design, called reduced instruction set computing (RISC), works in GaAs's favour too. RISC computers build up complicated programs from a few, simple tasks etched into their chips. Although more steps are

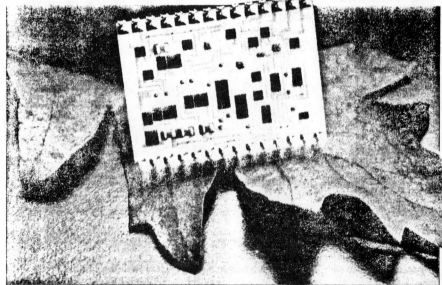

Autumn for silicon?

needed to run a given program than on a conventional chip, which has more complicated instructions etched beside the simple ones, RISC chips work fast enough to get through the job more quickly. Since RISC chips have fewer instructions, they also need fewer circuits built into them. This diminishes the advantage which silicon usually enjoys by being able to pack more circuits on to a chip.

The universities, too, are helping GaAs to grow up. One of the busiest areas of research is in semiconductor lasers. Lasers with GaAs chips inside are already used to convert the electronic signals of digital telephone calls into light, which is beamed down optical fibres. Adding impurities to tailor the optical behaviour of the material, and using some of GaAs's close relatives like indium phosphide, will help to make such lasers more versatile. Eventually they may be used to guide data between the computers in an office network or even through the insides of single computers.

Recent research at the University of Illinois suggests it might be possible to combine the qualities of GaAs and silicon in a single chip by placing a layer of gallium and arsenic atoms on a silicon base. At first sight this looks an unlikely prospect: the natural arrangements of atoms in silicon and in gallium and arsenic do not match. But the Illinois team, led by Dr Hadis Morkoç, have found that tilting the silicon base by four degrees creates atomic steps on which gallium and arsenic atoms can nestle comfortably. Hybrid chips may soon find applications in solar cells and charge-coupled devices (which turn light into electronic signals).

With so many opportunities at the high end of technology, GaAs is likely to increase its worldwide sales on the open market from the paltry $150m it will earn this year. But its share of that market may not increase. Silicon will find ever more to do at the high-volume, low-tech end of the street. And silicon research, now in its 30th year, has far from dried up. Plenty of current work aims at building fast and dense chips that might compete with GaAs. Gifted children do well to remember that as they grow wiser their plodding siblings grow wiser too.

Reprinted from *Computer*, March 1986, pages 30–42. Copyright © 1986 by
The Institute of Electrical and Electronics Engineers, Inc.

An Introduction to GaAs Microprocessor Architecture for VLSI

Veljko Milutinovic and David Fura, Purdue University

Walter Helbig, RCA

The implementation of GaAs processors is now feasible with their VLSI capability, their higher speed, and their greater tolerance of environmental variations.

allium arsenide, or GaAs, technology has recently shown rapid increases in maturity. In particular, the advances made in digital chip complexity have been enormous. This progress is especially evident in two types of chips: static RAMs and gate arrays. In 1983, static RAMs containing 1K bits were announced. One year later both a 4K-bit and a 16K-bit version were presented. Gate arrays have advanced from a 1000-gate design presented in 1984 to a 2000-gate design announced in 1985. With this enormous progress underway, it is now appropriate to consider the use of this new technology in the implementation of high-performance processors.

GaAs technology generates high levels of enthusiasm primarily because of two advantages it enjoys over silicon: higher speed and greater resistance to adverse environmental conditions.

GaAs gates switch faster than silicon transistor-transistor logic, or TTL, gates by nearly an order of magnitude. These switching speeds are even faster than those attained by the fastest silicon emitter-coupled logic, or ECL, but at power levels an order of magnitude lower.[1] For this reason, GaAs is seen to have applications in computer design within several computationally intensive areas. In fact, it has been reported that the Cray-3 will contain GaAs parts.

GaAs also enjoys greater resistance to radiation and temperature variations than does silicon. GaAs successfully operates in radiation levels of 10 to 100 million rads. Its operating temperature range extends from −200 to 200°C. Consequently, GaAs has created great excitement in the military and aerospace markets.

Unfortunately, GaAs is also characterized by some undesirable properties. Two significant areas where GaAs is inferior to silicon are cost and transistor count capability.

The higher cost of GaAs chips is largely the result of the higher cost of the GaAs material itself and the lower yield (typically 1 to 2 percent for VLSI in 1985) of GaAs chips. GaAs material is more expensive than silicon since gallium is relatively rare, whereas silicon is abundant. Also, since GaAs is a compound, additional processing is required to create it from its elements and to verify its composition. The lower GaAs yield is also due to multiple influences. First, although improvements are being made in this area, GaAs is characterized by a higher density of dislocations than silicon. Second, in order to achieve working devices with adequate noise margins, very fine control of circuit parameters is required, and this is not yet easily achieved. Finally, the high brittleness of the GaAs substrate (the gallium arsenide material itself) contributes to its high cost because of increased breakage of the finished product. Currently, GaAs chips are roughly two orders of magnitude more expensive than their silicon

This research, conducted at the Purdue University School of Electrical Engineering, has been sponsored by and conducted in collaboration with the RCA Advanced Technology Laboratories.

counterparts; however, this difference should narrow to possibly one order of magnitude by the end of this decade.

Transistor count limitations of GaAs are attributed to both yield and power considerations. The relatively low yield of GaAs chips forces designers to consider chips with a smaller area (therefore lower transistor count) in order to get more chips on each wafer. When operating at the same speeds as silicon gates, GaAs gates require less power. However, GaAs gates do consume considerably more power than slower silicon MOS gates. Because of the thermal management problem this creates, fast GaAs chips cannot match the transistor count potential of silicon chips.

It is believed that these four GaAs-silicon differences are not of a temporary nature, but instead result from inherent differences between GaAs and silicon materials. Conclusions that are based on these four fundamental characteristics will remain valid even as GaAs technology matures.

Because of these GaAs-silicon differences, it is not sufficient merely to copy existing silicon designs into GaAs in order to obtain optimal GaAs performance. The GaAs environment presents the computer architecture designer with a new set of challenges. However, the rewards of successfully exploiting this new environment are substantial. With the high speeds that characterize GaAs and the recent introduction of GaAs chips with VLSI levels of integration ($>$10,000 transistors), we are presently on the verge of achieving, with a single-chip processor, speeds for scalar operations typical of present-day supercomputers.

To explore the use of GaAs as a technology for high-speed processor design, an examination of GaAs technology and the identification of those of its characteristics that influence processor design should be made, as should where these characteristics differ from those found in silicon. This information is needed in order to discuss the trade-offs present in GaAs processor design. Design approaches that appear well-suited to this environment may then be presented.

Technology and IC design

To illustrate which GaAs device and logic families have shown the greatest potential

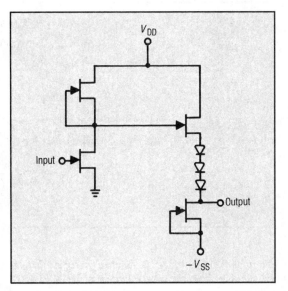

Figure 1. BFL D-MESFET inverter.

for near-term processor implementation it is best to select one family as representative GaAs technology and then present the characteristics that are relevant for processor design. These characteristics, when compared with those of silicon NMOS, will illuminate those traits of GaAs that introduce architectural design considerations different from those found with using silicon.

GaAs device families. Several different device families have been studied for GaAs implementation. However, because of the superior maturity of the metal semiconductor field effect transistor, or MESFET, device family, we will use it in all our comparisons with silicon. Some other devices show greater potential than MESFETs but just aren't expected to achieve VLSI complexity soon. These other devices include heterojunction bipolar transistors, or HJBTs, and modulation doped FETs, or MODFETs, also known as high electron mobility transistors or HEMTs.

GaAs MESFET logic families. MESFET logic circuits have been built in GaAs using both depletion-mode transistor drivers, or D-MESFETs, and enhancement-mode transistor drivers, or E-MESFETs. These two transistor designs have a number of important differences. D-MESFETs are better in that they are generally faster, have better noise immunity, are less sensitive to increases in fan-in and fan-out, and have fewer fabrication problems than E-MESFETs. However, D-MESFETs require two power supplies and extra logic to provide

voltage level shifting—neither of which is needed by E-MESFETs. D-MESFETs also require more power than E-MESFETs and use a more complex circuit design, which results in higher area requirements.[2]

There currently exist three principal GaAs MESFET logic families. They are Buffered FET Logic, or BFL, and Schottky Diode FET Logic, or SDFL, of the D-MESFET family, and Direct Coupled FET Logic, or DCFL, of the E-MESFET family.[3]

The earliest work in GaAs digital circuits was done with BFL D-MESFETs. This family is generally characterized by fast switching speeds and high power requirements. Early work produced BFL logic gates with propagation delays of 34 ps and a power dissipation of 41.0 mW per gate. More recently, however, there have been efforts to reduce the power requirements with the introduction of low-power, or lp, BFL circuits. An lp-BFL design for a 4-bit ripple-carry-adder containing about 40 gates with gate delays of 250 ps at 6.0 mW per gate has been presented. The highest integration obtained with BFL gates to date appears to be a 32-bit adder containing 420 gates with gate delays of 230 ps at 0.8 mW per gate.[4] An example of a BFL D-MESFET inverter is shown in Figure 1.

SDFL D-MESFET gates were proposed as an alternative to BFL logic gates. SDFL gates generally require less power and area than BFL gates. Consequently, this family has received considerable interest for LSI circuit applications. One of the first LSI

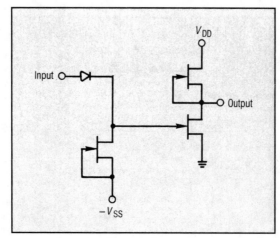

Figure 2. SDFL D-MESFET inverter.

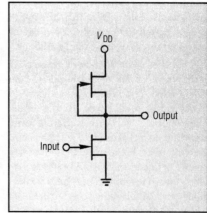

Figure 3. DCFL E/D-MESFET inverter.

GaAs applications was an 8×8-bit multiplier containing 1008 gates using SDFL logic. Gate delays were 150 ps and power dissipation was approximately 1.5 mW per gate. Recently an SDFL RAM-per-gate array chip has been presented. The chip contains 432 SDFL cells, 32 interface cells, and 64 bits of RAM totaling approximately 3000 FETs and 5000 diodes. The gate delays are 150 ps and power dissipation is 1.5 mW per gate. Simulations of low-power versions of this design indicate that gate delays of 300 ps at power levels below 0.2 mW per gate are possible. An example of an SDFL D-MESFET inverter is shown in Figure 2.

E-MESFETs were long considered to be more suitable for VLSI implementation than D-MESFETs because of lower power requirements and simpler circuit design. However, it has been only recently that advances in fabrication have allowed E-MESFETs to reach the VLSI level of complexity. A number of recent designs have been introduced using the DCFL E/D MESFET (enhancement-mode driver with depletion-mode load) approach. A 16×16-bit parallel multiplier containing 3000 gates with gate delays of 160 ps at 0.3 mW per gate has been reported. A gate array containing 2000 gates has been designed with a gate delay below 100 ps and a power dissipation of 0.4 mW per gate. The highest reported level of integration achieved to date with a GaAs process is a DCFL $16K \times 1K$ SRAM containing 102,300 FETs with an access time of 4.1 ns and power dissipation of 2.5 W. An example of a DCFL E/D-MESFET inverter is shown in Figure 3.

Characteristics of GaAs MESFET designs. Table 1 contains the published performance characteristics of some GaAs MESFET designs. As this table indicates

and the above discussion implies, it is clear that GaAs will soon provide a suitable vehicle for processor implementation. Currently the most promising MESFET solution is provided by the DCFL E/D-MESFET approach, based on its low power requirements. The presentation of a 102,300-FET chip certainly helps demonstrate the merits of DCFL. Currently, the major drawback to this approach is its fabrication complexity and resulting low yield and high cost. However, based on the present rate of fabrication technology improvement, the implementation of microprocessors in GaAs should be feasible within two or three years. Therefore, it is crucial that we now begin to understand the GaAs environment, and determine how the characteristics of GaAs will influence processor architecture design in that environment.

GaAs-silicon comparison. A GaAs-silicon comparison can be made using GaAs circuits based on the DCFL E/D-MESFET logic family.

Table 2 compares several characteristics of GaAs and silicon processes that are important for computer architecture design and optimization. Significant GaAs-silicon differences can be observed in the following areas: (1) transistor count, (2) on-chip gate delay, (3) the ratio of off-chip to on-chip memory access time, and (4) gate fan-in and fan-out.

Transistor count limitations were once primarily dictated by the poor yield of large GaAs chips. Recently, however, power dissipation has taken a more dominant role. If on-chip power requirements significantly exceed 2 W, special packaging techniques are required in order to remove heat from

Table 1. Performance characteristics of GaAs MESFETs.

Unit	Speed, ns	Power	Device count
Arithmetic			
32-bit adder (BFL)	2.9 total	1.2 W total	2.5K
8×8-bit multiplier (SDFL)	5.2 total	2.2 W total	6.0K
16×16-bit multiplier (DCFL)	10.5 total	1.0 W total	10K
Control			
Gate array/SRAM (SDFL)	0.15/gate	3.0 W total	8.0K
1000-gate gate array (DCFL)	0.10/gate	0.4 W total	3.0K
2000-gate gate array (DCFL)	0.08/gate	0.4 W total	8.2K
Memory			
1K-bit SRAM (DCFL)	2.0 total	0.5 W total	7.1K
4K-bit SRAM (DCFL)	4.1 total	2.5 W total	102.3K

the chip. With current GaAs processes characterized by power dissipations of 0.2 mW per gate, a 2-W chip will contain about only 30K transistors. In the silicon environment, the Motorola 68020 with a transistor count of close to 200K and power of 2 W is commercially available.

Small on-chip gate delays give GaAs an essential edge over silicon for high-performance digital systems. These speed advantages are derived from inherent properties of GaAs, such as higher electron mobility and lower parasitic capacitances. For this reason, GaAs will remain a potentially faster technology than silicon.

Unfortunately, the speed advantage that GaAs enjoys over silicon for the on-chip environment is reduced considerably for the off-chip environment because of propagation delays. Such sources of off-chip delay as capacitive loading and speed-of-light limitations (about 0.5 ns per foot propagation delay) affect GaAs and silicon equally. However, as these delays increase, they dominate the switching delays in GaAs and reduce the inherent GaAs advantage. Techniques utilized by microwave engineers are commonly used to help minimize these delays. Also, new interchip connection schemes are being investigated.[5] However, the ratio of off-chip to on-chip delays is still considerably higher than that found within silicon.

Low fan-in and fan-out of GaAs gates, although not believed to be a permanent characteristic, nevertheless currently introduce constraints not found in silicon. Gate fan-out can be generally be increased by using larger transistors, as is done in silicon. However, low gate fan-in is a serious problem, particularly for NAND gates. This is because an increase in the number of inputs to a NAND gate reduces the noise margin, and noise margins are very small in GaAs devices to begin with.

In addition, varying degrees of difficulty have been reported in the implementation of read only memories, or ROMs, tristate buffers, and pass transistors.

In conclusion, the differences between GaAs and silicon are substantial.

GaAs processor design

To discuss processor design in the GaAs environment it is best to present the characteristics of GaAs that heavily influence processor design and to outline techniques for overcoming some of the problems posed by GaAs. Such individual design issues as the choice of processor configuration, pipeline structure, register file, execution unit, and instruction set figure importantly in such a discussion.

Implications of GaAs characteristics on computer architecture design. Several of the characteristics of GaAs enumerated previously have a large influence on computer architecture design. As already indicated, these characteristics are a low transistor count, a high ratio of off-chip memory access delay to on-chip datapath delay, low gate fan-in and fan-out, and low yield.

A processor implemented in GaAs is limited to fewer transistors than if implemented in silicon; therefore, a premium is placed on simple designs in the GaAs environment. This has a large effect on the processor design philosophy in general, as well as on the design of the individual sections of the processor.

The advantage that GaAs enjoys over silicon for on-chip switching speed is, unfortunately, not accompanied by an equal advantage in off-chip memory access time. Thus a GaAs processor will generally have a very high ratio of off-chip memory access delay to on-chip datapath delay. The fundamental problem caused by this high ratio is that the information (instructions and data) requirement of a GaAs processor may not be satisfied, and lower-than-expected performance will result. Careful design techniques are needed so that the advantage in gate switching speed that GaAs enjoys can be maximally exploited, even though the off-chip to off-package speed advantage is much lower.

There are two approaches to solving the GaAs information bandwidth problem. The first one is to reduce the processor's requirements for off-chip information. This can be accomplished by either increasing the size of on-chip memory or by increasing the length of time that information is used by the on-chip execution unit. The second one is to increase the rate of information flow. There are two ways of accomplishing this. First, the information content of each transfer can be increased, either by increasing the number of bits per transfer or by reducing the redundancy in the information transferred. Reducing instructions falls in

Table 2. Performance comparison of typical GaAs (DCFL E/D MESFET) and silicon (NMOS) and silicon (CMO/SOS).

	GaAs	Silicon NMOS	Silicon CMOS/SOS
	Complexity		
Transistor count/chip	20-30K	300-450K	75-175K
Chip area (max.)	40,000 sq. mils	90,000 sq. mils.	120,000 sq. mils
	Speed		
Gate delay	50-150 ps	1-3 ns	1-1.25 ns
On-chip memory access	0.5-2.0 ns	10-20 ns	10-20 ns
Off-chip/on-package memory access	4-10 ns	40-80 ns	20-40 ns
Off-chip/off-package memory access*	20-80 ns	100-200 ns	100-200 ns
	IC design		
Transistors/single gate	1 + fan-in	1 + fan-in	2 × fan-in
Transistors/memory cell			
Static	6	6	6
Dynamic	1	1	—
Fan-in (max.)	5	5	5
Fan-out (max.)	3-5	10-20	10-20
Gate delay increase for each additional fan-out relative to gate delay with fan-out = 1	25-40%	25-40%	10-20%

*Subject to change.

In general, multichip
GaAs processor
configurations are less
desirable than
configurations
containing only
one chip.

the latter category. The second approach is to increase the effective transfer rate. This may be accomplished through sophisticated off-chip memory design techniques.

The lower on-chip fan-in and fan-out of GaAs circuits has important consequences for circuit design within the processor, especially within the execution unit. We will show the effects of this GaAs characteristic later in this section.

Lower GaAs yield encourages the computer architect to consider including features to improve this yield.

Choice of processor configuration. Several types of processor configurations have been used in the silicon environment. The Cray-1 was implemented with SSI, MSI, and LSI parts. The Univac 1100/60 was implemented using bit-slice parts. The Xerox PARC Dorado processor contains multiple VLSI chips. Several processors are available as a single VLSI chip, including the Intel iAPX 286.

In general, multichip GaAs processor configurations are less desirable than configurations containing only one chip. This is because the large amount of interchip communication typical for multichip configurations greatly diminishes the inherent GaAs switching speed advantage. A single-chip processor configuration minimizes this interchip communication and, therefore, offers the best potential performance.

Single-chip processor design methodology. Low transistor count severely limits the types of architecture we can consider for GaAs implementation of a single-chip processor. Today we cannot implement a GaAs design requiring considerably more than 30K transistors. Therefore, we must carefully examine what trade-offs may be necessary in adding certain hardware

features in a GaAs processor. Every transistor must be justified.

Fortunately, a product of modern design philosophy that is compatible with the close scrutiny of all design options has already been introduced: Reduced Instruction Set Computers, or RISCs. Examples of RISCs include the University of California at Berkeley RISC I & II, or UCB-RISC, and the Stanford University MIPS, or SU-MIPS,[7] with transistor counts of 41K and 25K, respectively. In contrast, some Complex Instruction Set Computers, or CISCs, contain over 100K transistors, such as the Motorola MC68020 and HP-FOCUS, with approximately 190K and 450K transistors, respectively. We wish to make an important distinction between the term *RISC*, which represents either the reduced instruction set philosophy or any processor design based on this philosophy, and *UCB-RISC*, which is a specific processor design based on the RISC philosophy.

The RISC design philosophy has been stated as follows:

1. First identify the machine instructions most frequently used by the target application.

2. Optimize the datapath and timing for these frequent instructions only.

3. Incorporate other frequent instructions into the instruction set only if they fit into the already elaborated VLSI scheme.[8]

Implicit in the RISC design philosophy is a constant examination of hardware/software trade-offs. A function is included in hardware only if justified by an acceptable increase in expected performance. Functions that are not directly supported by hardware must then be synthesized by the compiler out of more primitive functions.

Current silicon RISCs are characterized by several common traits. As their name implies, they have simplified instruction sets. The number of different instructions is low, instructions are of fixed length and execute in a single cycle, register-to-register operations are used, and data memory is accessed via loads and stores. Because of the simplicity of their instruction sets, RISCs use hardwired control logic instead of microcode. The control logic of the UCB-RISC requires only 10 percent of the total chip area, compared to the 68 percent required by the control logic of the MC68000. RISC designers try to move as much work as possible from execution time to compile time. In fact, the capabilities of a sophisti-

cated optimizing compiler are included in the architectural design trade-off analysis. The result is that RISCs are better targets for optimizing compilers and, consequently, execute programs written in high-level languages faster.

Performance comparisons between some RISCs and CISCs have been presented in reference 9, where it is shown that RISCs execute high-level language programs considerably faster. There are those who remain unconvinced of the superiority of RISCs, however, especially when system-level issues are considered. Examples of some strong counterarguments are presented in reference 10.

In the silicon environment the RISC-CISC debate rages on. However, in the GaAs environment there is no such dilemma. Because of the limited transistor count of a single-chip GaAs processor, the RISC philosophy is clearly the most appropriate approach.

Pipeline design and optimization in a GaAs environment. Pipeline design consideration for GaAs processors can be approached by describing a principal goal of pipelining. Example pipelines used in silicon processors and a demonstration of why these may be inappropriate for a GaAs implementation are integral parts of such an approach. The optimal design of a GaAs processor pipeline influences the design of the execution unit, register file, instruction set, and off-chip memory system.

Pipelining is frequently used in silicon processors to improve performance. This performance gain is primarily achieved through increased utilization of the processor's datapath. We define the datapath time as the time the processor takes to fetch the operand(s) from the register file, to propagate them through the execution unit, to write the result back into the register file, and to perform optional bus precharging. The goal of pipelining in the GaAs environment is the same as in the silicon environment. However, full datapath utilization is much harder to achieve in a GaAs processor because the ratio of instruction memory access time to datapath time is much higher. The reasons for this high ratio are evident from Table 2 and are

1. The ratio of off-chip memory access delay to both on-chip memory access delay and ALU delay is much higher in the GaAs environment than in the silicon environment.

2. The lower transistor count of GaAs chips precludes the use of an on-chip cache for memory access speedup.

In Table 3 we present typical ratios of the instruction memory access time to the datapath time for both GaAs and silicon. We assume that in all four of these cases an instruction cache is used. For reasons noted above, the ratios for GaAs are considerably higher than for silicon.

As Table 3 shows, in the silicon environment the instruction fetch delay is generally equal to or less than the datapath delay. This has a direct effect on the type of pipelines that are implemented in the silicon environment. In Figures 4 and 5 we show two such pipelines, which are from silicon RISCs: the UCB-RISC and the SU-MIPS, respectively.

In the GaAs environment, on the other hand, the instruction fetch delay is generally much greater than the datapath delay. If a silicon pipeline is used directly in a GaAs environment, severe datapath underutilization will occur. As an example, in Figure 6 we show the UCB-RISC pipeline implemented in a GaAs environment with an instruction fetch-to-datapath ratio of 3.

The reason for the ineffectiveness of silicon pipelines in a GaAs environment is apparent from the data in Table 2. As already indicated, although the GaAs on-chip switching speed is nearly 10 times faster than in silicon, the off-chip/off-package memory access delay is improved only by a much smaller amount. A critical design problem for computer architects is to exploit the much superior switching speed of GaAs, even though the GaAs off-chip/off-package memory access speed improvement is much lower.

The GaAs pipeline design problem is again primarily one of finding methods to ensure that the instruction bandwidth satisfies the processor's datapath requirements. Two such methods exist. One is to increase the instruction information bandwidth. Another is to increase the length of time the datapath is used in order to match the instruction fetch delay, hopefully in a way that yields benefits.

Increasing the instruction information bandwidth can be accomplished in several ways. The methods that we present here have implications on the off-chip memory system, processor pin count, and the instruction format.

One method is to include more levels in the instruction memory hierarchy than is typically found in memory systems for silicon processors. For a given hierarchical memory system, the difference in access times (in terms of instruction cycles) between the various levels will be greater for a GaAs processor than for a silicon processor. With such large differences, the addition of more levels will greatly reduce the average memory access time.

Another method is to use a pipelined memory system. This has been used on such high-performance silicon computers as the Amdahl 470V/6. The pipeline illustrated in Figure 7 reflects this approach.

A third method is to use an interleaved memory system. This technique has been used on such silicon computers as the IBM 3033. Here, multiple words are read from a relatively slow, but large memory into a faster, smaller memory, or possibly even into the processor.

The final method we will consider for increasing the effective instruction fetch rate is to fetch multiple instructions. This technique has been used in the silicon environment as well, in the SU-MIPS, although there are indications that the benefits of this approach were not great. In the GaAs environment, however, multiple-instruction fetches are potentially more valuable. Pipelines produced by this method resemble that in Figure 8. Multiple instruction fetching introduces requirements for increased package pin count, compact instruction formats, or both.

Table 3. Memory access to datapath delay ratios for silicon and GaAs.

Technology	Access type	Typical ratio
Silicon	On-chip	0.3—0.6
Silicon	Off-chip	0.8—1.2
GaAs	Off-chip/on package	1.6—3.2
GaAs	Off-chip/off-package	4.0—8.0

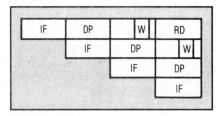

Figure 4. Pipeline structure used in the UCB-RISC. IF—Instruction Fetch Cycle; DP—Datapath Cycle; W—Register Write; RD—Data Load Cycle.

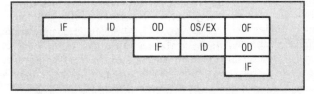

Figure 5. Pipeline structure used in SU-MIPS.

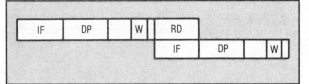

Figure 6. One possible GaAs implementation of the UCB-RISC pipeline.

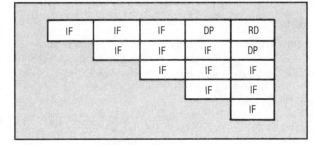

Figure 7. Example pipeline with a pipelined memory.

Key to cycles:
IF—Instruction Fetch
ID—Instruction Decode
OD—Operand Decode
DP—Datapath
OS/EX—Operand Store/Execute
W—Register Write
OF—Operand Fetch
RD—Data Load

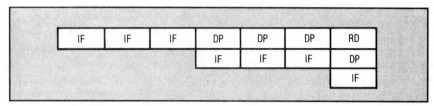

Figure 8. Example pipeline with instruction packing. IF—Instruction Fetch Cycles; DP—Datapath Cycles; RD—Data Load Cycle.

If the above methods cannot provide a sufficiently close match between the instruction fetch and datapath times, then increasing the time the datapath is used may yield some important benefits.

One method of increasing datapath delay is to remove resources, (transistors, chip area, etc.) from datapath functions and to reallocate them elsewhere. This is in keeping with the RISC philosophy in that hardware resources should be allocated only where they will provide benefits. The adder is one example of a datapath element where this technique may be used.

Another method is to use the execution unit more than once for each instruction fetch. Of course, this works only for complex operations that may be synthesized from multiple primitive operations, and it is also contrary to the design of many silicon RISCs. However, this technique may increase the average datapath utilization substantially. Another benefit of using multiple-cycle instructions is that application programs are more compact. An experimental GaAs processor design that uses this approach is the VM architecture.

Still another is to include within the execution unit the hardware to directly execute a complex operation. The comments made concerning the previous method apply here as well. An on-chip, off-datapath, bit-serial multiplier is one example of an application of this method.

Register file design and optimization in the GaAs environment. Registers provide a greater performance enhancement for GaAs processors than for silicon processors. Although there are some problems associated with register files, certain register file configurations can combat these problems. Moreover, using register file fault-tolerance techniques can also increase the yield of GaAs processors.

Performance enhancement of register files for GaAs processors. The benefits of a large on-chip register file for silicon processor performance enchancement have been well documented. Several of these benefits, presented reference 11, are even more important in the GaAs environment in the following ways:

1. Since the ratio of off-chip memory access delay to register access delay is larger for a GaAs processor, the improvement that registers provide in reduced operand access delay is more substantial.

2. The reduction in instruction size that results from shorter operand addresses is also more important for GaAs processors. This is because compact programs increase the effectiveness of the instruction cache and other elements of the memory hierarchy.

3. Since GaAs processors will likely have load/store architectures, accessing a value in the register file eliminates the execution of a load/store instruction. Not only are fewer load/store instructions executed, but they also need not be stored in instruction memory, again reducing the program size.

In conclusion, in a silicon environment, allocating leftover transistors to the register file may be acceptable. However, in a GaAs environment, because of the more severe performance penalties in accessing off-chip data, register file design is one of the most important design considerations. A large and well-designed register file is critical for superior performance in the GaAs environment.

Register cell design. Several register cell designs have been used in silicon processors. For high-performance designs, register cells with multiple read and/or write ports are commonly used. In Figures 9 and 10 are shown the register cells used in the SU-MIPS and HP-FOCUS respectively. Although these two register cells are fairly complex, they both allow two reads or two writes to be performed in parallel.

In the GaAs environment, simpler register cell designs are generally more appropriate because the off-chip instruction fetch time may exceed the datapath time, anyway. There is no performance loss in slowing the register access as long as the total datapath delay is less than the effective instruction fetch delay. Another reason for simple cell design is that in the transistor-scarce GaAs environment the chip resources not needed for register cells may be profitably used elsewhere.

An example of a register cell that deserves strong consideration for a GaAs implementation is shown in Figure 11. This cell was used in the UCB-RISC register file. Two reads may be performed in parallel, but the access speed is not as good as that in complex cells. Even though two buses are required, this cell design still requires far fewer chip resources than complex cells.

Thus the register cell that might be the most suitable for GaAs—one with only a single read bus—is one that sees increasingly less use in the silicon environment. If two operands are to be read from this type of cell, they must be fetched serially. This increases the time loss of this segment of the datapath, but even this will most likely not be the performance bottleneck (usually the adder carry chain is anyway). On the other hand, the area saved by eliminating the read bus may be profitably used for other purposes, especially in increasing the number of registers in the register file. There are indications that this approach yields benefits in the GaAs environment. This register cell is shown in Figure 12.

Register file configurations. Most modern silicon processors contain a monolithic (single window) register file containing 16 or 32 registers, for example, the National NS32032. There are a few exceptions, however, such as the UCB-RISC with 138 registers divided into eight windows. Perhaps a movement toward large, multiple-window register files for high-level language support is underway; however, currently single-window register files with 16 or 32 registers dominate the silicon environment.

There are, however, two disturbing characteristics of single-window register files that take increased importance in the GaAs environment. First, on context switches, data generally must be transferred between the register file and off-chip memory. Second, very few registers need to be allocated for subroutine variables and formal parameters in well-structured programs. Thus

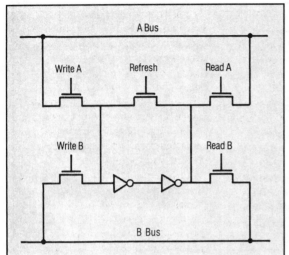

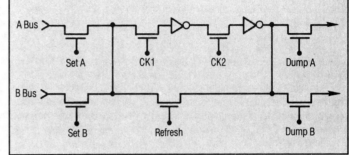

Figure 9. Register cell used in the SU-MIPS.

Figure 10. Register cell used in the HP-FOCUS.

the average register file utilization tends to be low. In the GaAs environment, which penalizes off-chip communication so severely, a more sophsicated register management policy is highly desirable.

With a single-window configuration, the main method of reducing the information bandwidth requirements during context switches is through sophisticated compilation techniques. What is required is the ability to preserve values in registers across procedure boundaries. One method of achieving this is through the use of "in-line procedures." With this technique the compiler replaces the machine code that implements the procedure call with the machine code of the called procedure itself. However, this technique is generally limited to very small procedures or to those called only once, otherwise large increases in program size are incurred. A substantial reduction in context switching overhead appears to be beyond the current state-of-the-art compiler technology.

It is because of the inherent limitations of single-window register files for reducing context switching overhead and register file underutilization that multiple-window techniques are promising alternatives for GaAs processors. In a multiple-window scheme, the register file is partitioned into windows and each window may be allocated to a separate procedure. On a context switch, instead of saving and restoring the register file, a new window is "made active," perhaps by moving a pointer as in the UCB-RISC. The only time that values need to be transferred is on an "overflow" or "underflow." An overflow occurs when

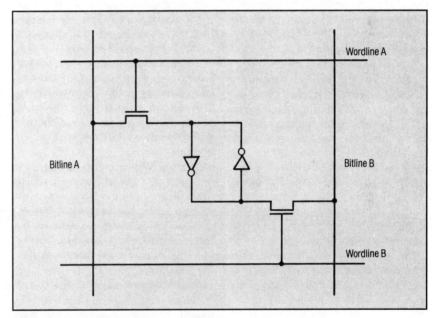

Figure 11. Register cell used in the UCB-RISC.

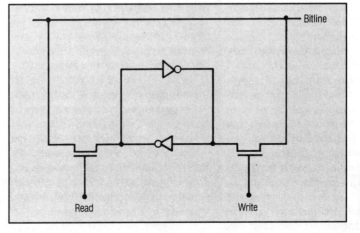

Figure 12. Single Read bus register cell.

On the cover

The 32-bit gallium arsenide E/D test circuit wafer shown on the cover was designed at RCA in conjunction with research done at Purdue University. RCA used its CADDAS automatic layout and routing system in its design. The wafer was fabricated at TriQuint Semiconductor, Inc. As shown in the accompanying photograph, the wafer consists of four quadrants that are repeated across the entire wafer. Quadrant 1 consists of a custom-crafted 16 × 32-bit register file containing 4780 devices; quadrant 2 contains a proprietary process control monitor used during wafer processing at Triquint; quadrant 3 contains a standard-cell-implemented adder with 1863 gates; and quadrant 4 contains a programmable logic array (PLA) and a number of test structures for verification of smaller elements contained within quadrants 1 and 3. The PLA in quadrant 4 was generated using an automatic PLA synthesis program to fabricate a 32-bit instruction decode unit (IDU). Quadrant 4 also contains the core standard cells used for the 32-bit adder in quadrant 3 and a single-bit register cell from the 16 × 32-bit register file in quadrant 1.

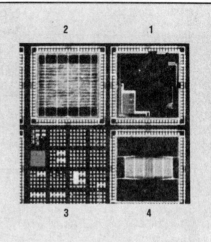

all the windows are full and a procedure call is required. As underflow occurs on returns when the values of the returned procedure were previously stored to off-chip memory because of an overflow.

The multiple-window schemes studied for silicon implementation are characterized by a large number of registers.[12] However, the large area and transistor requirements of these schemes make them unsuitable for GaAs. This warrants examining two schemes that have been presented for silicon: a multiple-window scheme with variable-size windows and a multiple-window scheme with background-mode loading and storing. Both attempt to achieve the performance level of a large register file with a much smaller register file.

The multiple-window scheme with variable-size windows is worthy of strong consideration for GaAs implementation because of its ability to achieve 100 percent register file utilization. Well-structured application programs have many procedures that contain few local scalars. With the ability to allocate exactly enough registers for each procedure, small register files can contain several windows.

The multiple-window scheme with background-mode loading and storing is also a candidate for further study. This scheme utilizes a very effective technique for combating high communication costs—communication is performed in parallel with computation. This technique allows a register file with few windows to perform as well as a register file with many more by reducing the frequency of overflows and underflows. This is achieved through selective preloading and prestoring of variables through one window of the register file, while another window is used for normal computations.

The selection of an appropriate register file configuration is, of course, dependent upon the application environment as well as technology. Multiple-window schemes perform best when procedures contain few local variables and formal parameters. They also do well when the "locality of nesting depth" is low, so that overflows and underflows aren't too frequent.

Multiple-window register files deserve much more attention in the GaAs environment than they currently seem to be getting from silicon designers. Their major advantage is their ability to reduce off-chip communication, which is a more serious problem in the GaAs environment. The implementation cost of a multiple-window scheme is higher, however. The effect is felt in possibly increased datapath delay, which is not as disastrous as in silicon, and increased transistor count, which is even more so. The variable-size window and background load/store approaches rate serious considerations. However, their advantages must be weighed against their contribution to hardware complexity. A careful study of design trade-offs is necessary to determine the appropriate configuration.

Fault tolerance for yield improvement. Fault-tolerant design features incorporated into the register file may provide important increases in the yield of GaAs processors. In a GaAs processor with fault-tolerance capabilities, a fault in a register cell will not disable the entire chip. The approach depends on the register file configuration. One approach is a single window register file; the other, a multiple window register file. Of course, many traditional approaches to fault tolerance can be applied to the GaAs environment as well.

In a single-window register file configuration, fault tolerance may be implemented through compilation techniques. The basic approach is to let the compiler locate only variables in registers that are known to be good. One disadvantage is that the smaller register file size will result in decreased performance. Also, a program compiled for one machine may not work on another. However, for dedicated applications this may not be an unreasonable approach.

In a multiple-window register file configuration, fault tolerance may be added with little runtime overhead. Initially, a self-test program is required to detect the presence of a bad register cell and to store the register cell somewhere within the processor. During execution, whenever the window pointer is moved, the register cell status is checked. If the new window contains a bad cell, then the window pointer is moved again.

The appropriateness of this approach depends on several factors. First, the runtime overhead involved with fault checking must be acceptable. Also, the loss of performance due to the reduced number of register windows must not be too severe. The hardware cost must be acceptable as well. A thorough analysis should be performed in order to determine the appropriateness of fault tolerance for yield improvement in GaAs processors.

Execution unit design and optimization in the GaAs environment. There are some particularly important GaAs properties that influence the goals of execution unit design. Execution unit design involves three major execution unit components: the adder, the multiplier/divider, and the shifter.

Execution unit design philosphy. The two prominent GaAs characteristics that have a direct influence on execution unit design are the high off-chip memory access delay and the low transistor count of GaAs chips. As a result, the goal of execution unit design in GaAs is not to utilize large amounts of chip resources to speed up primitive operations, as is often done in silicon designs. One reason is that chip resources are scarce. Also, because off-chip communications will likely be the performance bottleneck, speeding up the execution of primitive operations may yield no benefit anyway.

There are two promising approaches to execution unit design in the GaAs environment. The first is to decrease the resources allocated to execution unit members even if this slows down the execution of primitive operations. This will cause no loss in execution speed as long as off-chip communication costs remain dominant. The resources saved may then be used elsewhere, perhaps to increase the size of on-chip memory, as already pointed out. The second approach is to increase the resources dedicated to the execution unit, but only for the implementation of complex operations. Performance benefits may be realized because of the increased execution speed of the complex operations and because of the reduced redundancy of the instructions that implement the complex operations.

Adder design in the GaAs environment. Many different adder designs have been considered for use in silicon processors (Table 4). Four example adder designs, in order of increasing complexity, are ripple-carry, carry-select, conditional-sum, and carry-lookahead. For a silicon implementation, it is generally true that the designs requiring the larger transistor count also provide the faster addition times. This is certainly true for SSI/MSI implementations. For VLSI implementations, although there are indications that this may not be true, carry-lookahead adders are used in such high-performance silicon processors as the HP-FOCUS and BELLMAC-32.

In the GaAs environment, simple adder designs such as ripple-carry and carry-select are better candidates than carry-lookahead. The justification presented earlier for sim-

ple register cell designs is also appropriate here. Again, the reasoning is that the tradeoff of high speed for reduced resource requirements is advantageous for GaAs datapath designs. There is, however, another reason why simple adders are more attractive. The carry-lookahead design is plagued with very large gate fan-ins and fan-outs. As mentioned earlier, GaAs gates are now often characterized with low fan-in and fan-out capabilities. Therefore, additional gates must be used implement a carry-lookahead adder. Because carry-lookahead is an irregular adder design, it has a large area requirement. This combined with the need for additional gates may make carry-lookahead adders inappropriate for a GaAs processor.

The ripple-carry design is the simplest and most regular of the three and so is advantageous from the VLSI point of view. The carry-select approach is the next best. Because the limited fan-in of GaAs gates degrades the performance of the partial carry-lookahead approach so severely, the nonregularity and long wirelengths associated with this technique make it undesirable for a GaAs/VLSI implementation. The ripple-carry approach is nearly as fast as a parallel approach in a silicon VLSI environment for a word length of 32 bits. Because of the limited fan-in of GaAs gates, the ripple-carry approach may be faster for a GaAs VLSI implementation. Even if not the fastest, the ripple-carry approach may still be preferred because of its low layout area requirements.

Multiplier/divider design in the GaAs environment. Multiplication and division operations show a wide variation in frequency of use. For example, scientific applications require these operations much more often than general-purpose applications. Therefore, the application environment has a large influence on the selection of appropriate multiplication and division techniques.

Several multiplier designs have been used in silicon processors. Some processors, such as the UCB-RISC, utilize an adder and an iterative add-and-shift algorithm that requires n steps, where n is the word length. A variation of this method incorporates a recorded number system, such as a modified Booth algorithm used in the Fairchild F9450, which requires only n/2 steps. Alternatively, more hardware can be used, such as in the design used by the TMS320, which

Table 4. Comparison of three 32-bit adders.

Adder type	Transistor count	Gate delays
Ripple-carry	1.0K	66
Carry-lookahead	2.0K	20
Carry-select	2.2K	19

uses a modified Booth algorithm implemented in hardware. Parallel, array multipliers have also been used, such as in the NEC IPP. Also, bit-serial multipliers have been presented. A survey of the topic and some interesting novel solutions for GaAs can be found in reference 13.

Many different divider designs are also evident in silicon processors. Some designs, such as the SU-MIPS, utilize an iterative subtract-and-shift algorithm requiring n steps. Cellular array and bit-serial dividers have been studied. A division-by-repeated-multiplication technique has been used in several processors, including the IBM 360/91.

As is the case for adder design in the GaAs environment, the use of simple hardware is desirable for multiplier/divider design. The "cheapest" techniques in terms of hardware requirements require only one adder and little control logic. These are the add/subtract-and-shift methods mentioned above, and they are good candidates for GaAs implementation. Next in complexity is the add-and-shift multiplication technique with a modified Booth algorithm. This requires very little additional logic and is also a promising technique for GaAs implementation. Bit-serial hardware, parallel to the main datapath, is next in complexity and another promising method. The other techniques mentioned above require too much hardware for implementation into a general processor. However, these designs may be appropriate for implementation into a coprocessor.

The three multiplication techniques and two division techniques appropriate for a GaAs implementation show increasing performance with increasing hardware requirements. As already mentioned, the standard add/subtract-and-shift multiplication/division approaches require only the main datapath adder and require n steps. The modified Booth multiplication scheme requires only a small increase in hardware and reduces the number of steps by half, so this is a cost effective approach.

Both of the above approaches use an iterative algorithm and may be implemented in

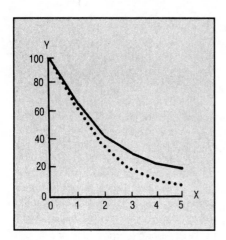

Figure 13. Effects of multiply fill-in. X— Number of NOOPs to eliminate; Y—Percentage of time that NOOPs are sucessfully eliminated.

several ways. For illustration purposes, consider the multiplication of two 32-bit numbers using the standard add-and-shift method.

In one approach, two add-and-shift instructions are used with a loop that must be executed 16 times. Because of the overhead associated with loop execution in a vertical architecture (calculating the branch address, etc.), this method is over twice as slow as some other methods.

In another approach, 32 different instructions are fetched from instruction memory. Each instruction implements a single add-and-shift. However, this method has features that lessen its appeal for a GaAs implementation. Since 32 instructions must be fetched, there is a higher likelihood that a cache miss will occur during the execution of the multiply than if just one instruction is fetched. Also, if 32 instructions must be located in memory for each multiply operation, then other instructions must be relegated to storage in slower memory.

A third approach is to include the 32 instructions in a runtime support routine where it need only be stored once. The disadvantage of this method is that a subroutine call and return must be performed for each multiply.

An alternative approach resembles the execution of silicon microcoded CISCs in that only one instruction (macroinstruction) is fetched from memory. This has the desirable effect of reducing the memory bandwidth and storage requirement, which is a major concern in the GaAs environment. However, it also complicates the control logic. In the GaAs environment this ap-

proach deserves strong consideration for implementation.

A third alternative design for GaAs processor implementation is the bit-serial approach off the main datapath. A multiplier may be implemented that executes in 2n steps. This method exploits a principal GaAs advantage—its high switching speed. Each step of the multiplication process requires only a full addition and flip-flop access, so a very high clock rate can be used. A multiply operation using this approach may be executed in the time needed to execute only five or so standard instructions.

Not only is the raw speed of the hardware multiplier better than the other two methods, but there is also a potential performance enhancement due to "multipler fill-in." Since multiplication occurs off the main datapath, other instructions requiring the datapath may be executed in parallel with multiplication. A sophisticated optimizing compiler like that used for branch fill-ins in the SU-MIPS is required here in order to find the instructions that may be executed in parallel with the multiplication. A preliminary investigation performed at Purdue University[14] indicates that for some applications a substantial performance gain may be realized if such a scheme were implemented. These results are presented in Figure 13.

Shifter design in the GaAs environment. Many modern microprocessors allow variable-length shifts on data from 0 to $n-1$ bits, where n is the word length. One example is the TMS 320. However, the inclusion of such a shifter may violate the RISC philosophy since the frequency of multiple-length shifts may not justify its inclusion, especially if an off-datapath multiplier/divider is incorporated. The designers of UCB-RISC indicate that the incorporation of a (0-31)-bit barrel shifter was a mistake.[8] Because of the large hardware requirements of such a variable-length shifter, a thorough analysis is required to determine if it is appropriate for a GaAs processor.

Some of the applications for a barrel shifter include data alignment for memory loads and stores, data alignment for immediate operands, multiplication/division support, and fast multiplication when either the multiplier or multiplicand is a power of two. Also, some high-level languages, such as C, have a shift statement that must be supported.

Typically, only a small subset of the shift distances are required for data alignments and multiplication/division support. For example, in the SU-MIPS, for data align-

ments for memory accesses the shift distance is a multiple of eight. In order to use the shifter directly for multiplication, the value that is a power of two must be known at compile time so that the appropriate shift operation can be used to replace the multiply operations. The frequency of these occurrences is probably low. The frequency of the shift statements in C programs should be determined in order to discover the shifter's value in this regard. It may be the case that it is used infrequently.

The number of gates needed to implement a barrel shifter is approximately 3n log n, where n is the word length. Therefore, significant hardware savings may be realized if a shifter design is used that provides only the functionality absolutely required, e.g., 1, 2, and 8, or a similar subset.

Instruction set design and optimization. The careful design of the processor instruction set is extremely important in a GaAs environment. There are two desirable and conflicting instruction set characteristics. First, the instruction set should be simple. There should be a small number of instruction formats, and the same instruction fields should be used in each format whenever possible. Also, the number of different operations should be kept small and the operations themselves should be kept primitive. Secondly, an effort should be made to design the instruction set so that program memory requirements are minimized. There exists a rationale for these goals as well as techniques for achieving compact instructions. However, the dual goals of instruction set simplicity and program compactness are conflicting.

Because of the relatively small number of transistors within a GaAs processor, the circuitry devoted to instruction decoding and control must be minimized. This is achieved primarily by keeping the instruction set simple. Such an approach is one of the primary reasons why the RISC design philosophy is appropriate for GaAs implementation study.

The high off-chip propagation delays characteristic of the GaAs environment make compact programs very beneficial. Compact programs are desirable for several reasons.

The difference in access times (in terms of instruction cycles) between the various levels of the instruction memory hierarchy will probably be large for a GaAs processor. Therefore, the ability to maximize the likelihood that a required instruction is in the higher levels of the hierarchy is important. It has been shown that the hit ratio of a cache depends primarily on the cache size. [15] Since a reduction in instruction size has the same effect as an increase in the size of the memory containing it, compact instructions have a very positive effect on hit ratios of the higher levels of the memory hierarchy and, consequently, on performance.

Instruction packing is a technique that was mentioned earlier as a method for increasing the information bandwidth between a GaAs processor and its external environment. However, because of the pin limitations of a single-chip processor, a short instruction format is necessary in order for packing to be possible. It is also necessary to implement the packing in a way that minimizes decoding and control complexity.

A primary disadvantage of using silicon RISC processors for GaAs implementations is the low information content of the instructions. Because of this, single-cycle instruction execution may be a less worthy goal for GaAs RISCs than for silicon RISCs. In order to maintain single-cycle execution, all complex operations must be synthesized from primitive operations. However, in some relatively frequent complex operations, such as multiply and divide, the same primitive operation is repeatedly executed. Therefore, the information content of each primitive instruction is very low, and this results in a potentially large increase in program size. In the GaAs environment, this has a more negative effect on performance than in the silicon environment; therefore, the addition of complex instructions to the instruction set may be justified for GaAs processors. Again, care must be taken to minimize the negative effects this has on control complexity.

Several techniques for reducing the instruction size have been studied; three techniques may be appropriate for a GaAs implementation. The first is based on Huffman-like variable-length encodings. [16] The second involves replacing common instruction sequences with a single instruction. The third approach consists of the selection of the optimal data addressing mechanism.

Huffman coding is a frequency-based technique that yields a minimum-sized encoding. A variation of this technique was utilized for the Intel iAPX 432. The essence of the algorithm is that the opcodes that appear most frequently receive the smallest encoding. In a related technique, referred to as "conditional coding," the encoding is also dependent on a number of prior in-

structions, as well as the current instruction. Although these techniques theoretically lead to the most compact instructions, the compactness is program-dependent since it relies on instruction frequencies. More importantly, complicated decoding logic is required and the decoding must be performed sequentially, which reduces execution speed. Because of these negative characteristics, Huffman-like coding is not desirable for a GaAs processor.

The second technique is to increase the level of opcode encoding by replacing frequently occurring instruction sequences with a single instruction. One example of this is the inclusion of multiply and divide instructions, which was mentioned earlier. This technique also results in increased instruction decoding complexity, but may be justified by the expected performance gains in the GaAs environment.

There has been much debate over the instruction compactness of stack, register, and memory-to-memory architectures. Although it appears that memory-to-memory addressing leads to more compact code than "traditional" register or stack architectures, this kind of addressing is probably not appropriate for a GaAs implementation because of the long off-chip memory access time. As mentioned earlier, it is very desirable to keep frequently accessed data on-chip. If a large, multiwindow register file can be accommodated, then this would result in faster execution than a memory-to-memory architecture. [17] Furthermore, it would probably lead to more compact code as well, since register accesses would be very frequent and only a small number of bits are needed to specify register addresses.

The implementation of microprocessor architectures in the GaAs environment is a very promising and challenging area of research. The characteristics of GaAs demand different architectural solutions than those found in silicon designs. With proper modifications, the reduced instruction set computer design philosophy is a good candidate for GaAs implementations. However, research is needed for the development of special computer architecture strategies optimized for the GaAs environment. □

Acknowledgments

The authors appreciate the assistance they received from W. Heagerty, W. Moyers, and S. Undy.

References

1. R. C. Eden, A. R. Livingston, and B. M. Welch, "Integrated Circuits: the Case for Gallium Arsenide," *IEEE Spectrum,* Vol. 9, No. 12, Dec. 1983, pp. 30-37.

2. R. C. Eden et al., "The Propsects for Ultrahigh-Speed VLSI GaAs Digital Logic," *IEEE J. Solid-State Circuits,* Vol. SC-14, No. 2, April 1979, pp. 221-239.

3. G. Nuzillat et al., "GaAs MESFET IC's for Gigabit Logic Applications," *IEEE J. Solid-State Circuits,* Vol. sc-17, No. 3, June 1982, pp. 569-584.

4. R. Yamamoto et al., "Design and Fabrication of a Depletion GaAs LSI Hi-Speed 32-Bit Adder," *IEEE J. Solid-State Circuits,* Vol. SC-18, No. 5, Oct. 1983, pp. 592-599.

5. G. Leopold, "New Approach Promises GaAs Interconnections," *Electronics Week,* Vol. 58, No. 22, June 3, 1985, p. 27.

6. D. A. Patterson and D. R. Ditzel, "The Case for the Reduced Instruction Set Computer," *ACM SIGARCH Computer Architecture News,* Vol. 8, No. 6, Oct. 1980, pp. 25-32.

7. J. Hennessy et al., "The MIPS Machine," *Digest of Papers*, Spring COMPCON 82, San Francisco, Feb. 1982, pp. 2-7.

8. M. G. H. Katevenis, *Reduced Instruction Set Computer Architectures for VLSI,* PhD thesis, UC, Berkeley, Oct. 1983.

9. D. A. Patterson and R. S. Piepho, "Assessing RISCs in High-Level Language Support," *IEEE Micro,* Vol. 15, No. 11, Nov. 1982, pp. 9-19.

10. D. W. Clark and W. D. Strecker, "Comments on 'The case for the reduced instruction set computer,' by Patterson and Ditzel," *ACM SIGARCH Computer Architecture News,* Vol. 8, No. 6, Oct. 1980, pp. 34-38.

11. D. R. Ditzel and H. R. McLellan, "Register Allocation for Free: The C Machine Stack Cache," *Proc. Symp. Architectural Support for Programming Languages and Operating Systems*, Palo Alto, Calif., March 1982, pp. 48-56.

12. B. W. Lampson, "Fast Procedure Calls," *Proc. Symp. Architectural Support for Programming Languages and Operating Systems*, Palo Alto, Calif., March 1982, pp. 66-76.

13. B. Hoefflinger, *Design of Very-High Throughput Rate GaAs Multipliers,* technical report, Purdue University, March 1984.

14. K. Keirn, *Studies of the RISC Architecture in GaAs,* internal report, Purdue University, 1984.

15. J. E. Smith and J. R. Goodman, "A Study of Instruction Cache Organizations and Replacement Policies," *Proc. Tenth Ann. Symp. Computer Architecture*, Stockholm, Sweden, June 1983, pp. 132-137.

16. D. A. Huffman, "A Method for the Construction of Minimum Redundancy Codes," *Proc. I.R.E.*, Vol. 40, No. 9, Sept. 1952, pp. 1098-1101.

17. G. J. Myers, "The Case Against Stack-Oriented Instruction Sets," *ACM SIGARCH Computer Architecture News*, Vol. 6, No. 3, Aug. 1977, pp. 7-10.

chair for panels on GaAs computers at the nation's leading conferences, including ICCD-85 (Port Chester, N.Y., October 1985) and HICSS-19 (Honolulu, Hawaii, January 1986). He has lectured in Europe and North and Latin America. His current interests include VLSI computer architectures for GaAs, high-level language computer architecture, distributed task allocation, artificial intelligence computer architectures, and multiprocessor systems for signal processing. He has been involved in consulting activities for a number of high-tech companies, including Aerospace Corporation, Intel, Honeywell, NASA, RCA, and others. He is currently involved in the industrial implementation of a 32-bit VLSI microprocessor in GaAs technology, with responsibilities in the microarchitecture domain. He is a member of the IEEE and is on the EUROMICRO board of directors.

Walter A. Helbig is a unit manager at RCA's Advanced Technology Laboratories heading the Advanced Computation Systems unit for the Systems Engineering Laboratory. He joined RCA in 1952 and has been involved in the design and application of computer systems and in the construction of support software programs since. He directed the architecture design of a GaAs 32-bit RISC and is presently a consulting architect for the design of a 32-bit silicon RISC and for the construction of an 8-bit GaAs RISC Technology Demonstration System. His recent background includes work in the area of CAD tool design, construction and evaluation. Previously, he directed the design of two versions of the RCA ATMAC microprocessor, all of their support software, and several single and multiboard systems using the ATMAC.

Helbig has had several years of recent experience in the area of design and construction of computer system hardware and software; communication security equipment design and construction; and system design, construction, and debug for an advanced passive autonomous sonar system, A. He has also developed video display systems and communication systems.

Helbig holds a BSEE degree from the Milwaukee School of Engineering. He has thirteen US patents and has authored and coauthored numerous papers. He was a senior member of the IEEE.

Veljko M. Milutinovic is on the faculty of the School of Electrical Engineering, Purdue University. He received the PhD degree from the University of Belgrade, Belgrade, Yugoslavia. He has published over 60 technical papers, two original books, and five edited books. His research has been published in *IEEE Transactions, IEEE Proceedings, IEEE Computer,* and other refereed journals. His book on microprocessor-based design has been published in several languages. He is the editor of the IEEE PRESS Tutorial on Advanced Microprocessors and High-Level Language Computer Architectures for VLSI. He is the coeditor of the IEEE PRESS Tutorial on Advanced Topics in Computer Architecture. He has been appointed to serve as a

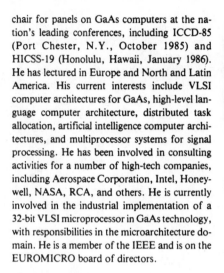

David A. Fura is a graduate student in the School of Electrical Engineering, Purdue University. He received dual BSE degrees in Electrical Engineering and Computer Engineering from the University of Michigan. Before entering Purdue, he spent three years as an electrical design engineer with Texas Instruments, Inc. His current research activity is in the area of computer architecture design for high-speed digital circuit technologies. His interests include reduced instruction set computer architectures and dataflow systems. He is currently involved in the industrial implementation of a 32-bit VLSI microprocessor in GaAs technology. He is a member of the IEEE Computer Society, ACM SIGARCH, and Eta Kappa Nu.

For more information about this article, contact Milutinovic at School of Electrical Engineering, Purdue University, West Lafayette, IN 47907.

Reprinted from *IEEE Transactions on Computers*, February 1989, pages 263–274. Copyright © 1989 by The Institute of Electrical and Electronics Engineers, Inc.

A DCFL E/D-MESFET GaAs Experimental RISC Machine

WALT HELBIG AND VELJKO MILUTINOVIĆ

Abstract—Design of RCA's 32-bit GaAs microprocessor is presented. We first discuss technology limitations and influences of the software environment. Then we describe the details of the ISA (instruction set architecture) and details of the IES (instruction execution sequence). We underline the essense of the original contributions of the research and the design. Finally, we present the simulated performance evaluation data.

Index Terms—ASIC, DCFL E/D-MESFET GaAs, RISC processor architecture, RISC processor design, 32-bit GaAs microprocessor.

I. INTRODUCTION

This paper describes one microprocessor architecture, the design prepared by RCA of a 32-bit machine intended for implementation using GaAs VLSI. The architecture was patterned along the lines of the basic RISC philosophy. It was designed to include the fundamental operations (to support all functions needed for the intended applications), but limited in VLSI area to what can be put onto a practical size GaAs VLSI chip. As will be seen later, design decisions that we had to make are different enough from typical silicon design decisions.

GaAs has definitely reached the VLSI level of complexity [1], and this work is a part of the effort which was to show that implementation of a 32-bit microprocessor on a GaAs chip is feasible. Still, GaAs chip densities are relatively small, and GaAs designs are characterized with a number of problems not present in silicon designs.

When one is using silicon VLSI, even the newest 1.25 μm technology, the on-chip gate delays are measured in the nanoseconds, and the machine clock cycle time is most often 20 or more times longer. Delays on the board are on the order of 1 percent of the machine clock cycle time per inch of conductor path, the result being that board transmission times are insignificant for planning of the design. In a GaAs design, this percentage is an order of magnitude higher, and must be factored into the architecture. This usually necessitates having interchip communications be pipelined. Furthermore, it means that the board layout must be critically controlled, both at the design level and the architecture level.

II. IMPACTS OF THE TECHNOLOGY

There are a number of computer design related problems with GaAs, as an integration medium, is the limitation on the logic functions that can be created with its devices. RCA chose to work with TriQuint, Inc's DCFL E/D-MESFET.[1] In the DCFL family, NOR gates of 2–5 inputs are present, but NAND gates do not exist. Furthermore, on each input to a NOR gate, a two-input AND gate may be included.

This limitation is the result of the circuit construction technique and the inherent properties of GaAs, one of these being that the

Manuscript received June 17, 1986; revised February 17, 1987 and September 10, 1987. This work was supported by RCA Corporation.

W. Helbig is with the Advanced Technology Laboratories, RCA Corporation, Morrestown, NJ 08057.

V. Milutinovic is with the School of Electrical Engineering, Purdue University, West Layfette, IN 47907.

IEEE Log Number 8718952.

voltage swing of the signal in a logic gate is relatively small (± 220 mV), and is centered around the intermediate value of the reference voltage ($+320$ mV). The important factor for the logic designer is that this characteristic causes the power dissipation in a given circuit to be high (since it is always drawing current), thus limiting, severely, the number of logic elements that one may put on a chip, before its internal power consumption becomes prohibitive. Of course, one may design all of the circuits' internal impedances so that they are high (by using small-sized devices). This results in the circuit that has a small fan-out (but permits a large fan-in), uses a small area on the chip, and requires only a small amount of power to operate. On the other hand, a circuit with a larger fan-out tends to permit a smaller number of inputs (smaller fan-in), uses a larger area on the chip, and dissipates more power internally.

The penalty that the logic designer pays by not being able to tie the outputs of two circuits together is even more severe [2]. In other words, one cannot design phantom functions into the logic. With no "off state" in the circuit, tying outputs together does not change the amount of power dissipated, but does decrease the operating noise margin of the resulting logic tree. For the logic designer, this translates into a need to design a system bus, with its many inputs and outputs, as a single entity with only one active load circuit. This means including, in the design, allowances for the function of "bus precharge," and time in each operating cycle to accomplish this precharge. The related loss of time could be substantial and, in the case of the DCFL E/D-MESFET GaAs logic family, is not justified. The reason is that the natural, and easily implemented, logic function AND–NOR is just what is needed to create a multiplexer—a perfect replacement for a bus.

With the above in mind, the choice that was used in the design of the RCA's 32-bit microprocessor was as follows. In those areas where the design was to be handcrafted anyway, and where the speed of operation was not penalized to the point of slowing the system, buses were used. (This occurred in two areas, the general register file and the barrel shifter.) In the remainder of the architecture, multiplexers were used, and this frequently resulted in including additional functional capabilities in the machine, simply because it was cheaper to keep them than to exclude them.

Still another technology-dependent choice made for this design was to use circuits of three different power levels. There was one set of logic gates that had a low power consumption, a low fan-out, and a small chip area requirement. There was also one set that had a high power consumption, a high fan-out, and a large (relatively speaking, of course) chip area requirement. In the third set of logic gates, everything was somewhere between the two extremes.

Interchip communications required very special attention. Because of the circuit limitations, buses could not be used. This decision was reaffirmed later, when it became obvious that the state of the "packaging art" would not allow control signals to be passed freely throughout the system. Furthermore, it was determined that passing signals from one IC to another would be done only with signal delays that are equal to a significant fraction of the CPU cycle time. With a required minimum CPU clock frequency of 200 mHz, and stripline construction on alumina substrates being used for controlled impedance and high-power handling capability, the delays are approximately equal to 5–10 percent of the clock period, per inch of conductor path length. Thus, with any significant amount of conductor length (which is almost a foregone conclusion for paths that go from one board to another), the IC at the sending end could

[1] Only DCFL E/D-MESFET GaAs is treated in this paper.

easily become involved in the clock cycle $n + 1$ before the signals sent during the clock cycle n reach the other IC. Furthermore, by the time the second IC reacts to the signals sent by the first IC, to perform the requested operation and to send the results of its operation back to the first IC, several clock cycles can have elapsed.

This problem is severe, and the designer must consider all of the latencies that might occur in order to construct a design that will operate, no matter how the IC's are placed on the board. Delays will occur in instruction fetch, data store and fetch, as well as in control and address signal distribution. Delays will occur in the distribution of the clock so the IC's will not necessarily be operating in phase with each other. The result may be that the latency in an operation may not be an integer number of clock periods. This phenomenon may also appear in fast silicon designs; however, its impacts are much greater in GaAs designs. On the other hand, the entire system may be designed to be pipelined, wherein the clock is distributed with the data, and at every junction point all signals are reclocked, to remove any variations in delay they might have undergone in making their transit. Then, by having signals distributed out from the CPU, through a series of these junction points, to wherever they are destined to go, and then going back through the same junction points to the CPU, the information will always arrive at the CPU in phase with its clock. Such an approach was chosen for the design of the RCA's 32-bit microprocessor system.

III. Impacts of the Support Software

RISC architecture philosophy is one of allowing the support software to, as much as it can, compensate for decisions made in designing the hardware [3].

The most notable examples of the RISC-type solution are the "branch latency fill-in" and the "load delay fill-in" operations, performed by code optimizer, to give the CPU something useful to do while waiting for its pipeline to complete the operations needed to perform a branch or a load. With respect to these issues, an important difference between silicon and GaAs is that GaAs designs are characterized with much deeper pipelines, and the fill-in algorithms have to be modified [4], [5].

Sometimes, however, there are features that can be added to the hardware to eliminate, from the required support software operation, a function that it can only do crudely at best. Two such features were added to the design of the RCA's 32-bit microprocessor, just for this purpose.

The *first* of these is to allow the system to handle immediate values efficiently. Immediate values typically have the same range of values as addresses and data—equal to the word length of the machine. This means that the machine must have the ability to express or create immediate values of length equal to the data word length, or in this case 32 bits. Creating full word length immediate operands can be done by loading partial length operands, and assembling these by instruction execution (requiring the allocation of at least two general registers for this function). They may also be handled by having an instruction format that includes, for some instructions, a field for an immediate value equal to the word length. Several problems arise here that the architect must handle. First, not all immediate values need to be the full 32 bits in width. In fact, most of the time 8 bits are sufficient [2]. Only a few percent of the time does one need the long immediate field.

Here are two possible ways to get around the problem. The Stanford MIPS machine [6] gets around the problem by including some instructions that have 16-bit immediate fields and some with 24-bit immediate fields but none with 32-bit immediate fields. This leaves the programmer/compiler with the problem of building, at run time, the full word length immediates, or storing all needed immediates in memory and fetching them at run time. An alternative approach was used in the RCA ATMAC [7] where the instruction word was longer (24 bits) than the data word length (16 bits). It worked quite efficiently for this 16-bit machine, because the nonimmediate instructions also required 24 bits to control the ATMAC's horizontal architecture. Other approaches include se-

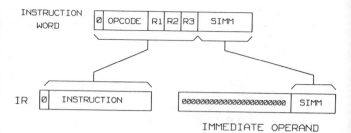

Fig. 1. One-word format (SIMM: 8-bit short immediate operand).

quences of load and shift instructions, or the special read–shift–OR–replace instruction. RCA's 32-bit GaAs machine handles the problem in a way which is not typical for early RISC machines [8]-[10]. However, we had good reasons for such an approach (see below), and also, we have noticed that some recent (independently generated) designs have employed a similar solution [11].

The instruction format chosen uses one- and two-word instructions. The first part of all instructions is of the same format, specifying the operation code, the three general register file addresses, an unsigned 8-bit immediate value, called SIMM in Figs. 1 and 2 (to take care of 95 percent of the cases where immediate data are needed), and a single bit to designate whether or not there is a second part to the instruction (see Fig. 1). The optional second part of the instruction carries only the 24 most significant (MS) bits of the immediate value, where the 8 bits in the first part of the instruction are the least significant (LS) bits. This arrangement greatly simplifies the instruction decoding logic (see Fig. 2), achieving very efficiently one of the principal goals of RISC machines: improved execution time for compiled HLL code [8]-[10]. As already indicated, a similar approach was used in the AT&T's CRISP microprocessor [11].

While AT&T's motivations behind choosing this solution are as given in [11], our motivations were somewhat different. In designing this microprocessor to fit within the technology limits of a GaAs VLSI circuit, we were looking for simplicity and speed; the two basic demands of a RISC system. We utilized simplicity in the design wherever possible to accomplish as great a gain in performance as possible, while leaving as many as we could of the available devices for other functions. With our approach we were able to inexpensively obtain the full word length immediate operand that we needed for applications that are logic and arithmetic oriented.

The *second* feature added to the architecture of the machine was a way to decrease the time between two executions of two load instructions. Normally, when a load instruction is executed, the data memory address is sent from the CPU, the data are read from the memory, sent back to the CPU, and the value is put into the general register file during the course of execution of the instruction. In a RISC machine, however, especially one made using GaAs IC's, the time available for these operations is too short for any practical memory system. Furthermore, with the interchip communication latency included, several of the machine's clock cycles can have passed between sending the address from the CPU and getting the result back to the CPU (storing the result into the general register file). Each of these clock cycles corresponds to another instruction execution period. In order to keep straight where the data are to go when they get back to the CPU, the normal approach is to hold the general register (GR) file address in the CPU, and have the program not execute another load operation until the first one is completed. The time elapsed is equal to the load latency.

An alternate approach, one that is built into this machine, is to send the destination address (the general register file address) out from the CPU, along with the memory address, to the memory and then have the destination address sent back with the data. When the data finally reach the CPU, the destination register address is with the data, and the data may be properly stored. Therefore, no matter what the interchip communication and the memory system latencies are, and no matter how many load requests are active (initiated but not

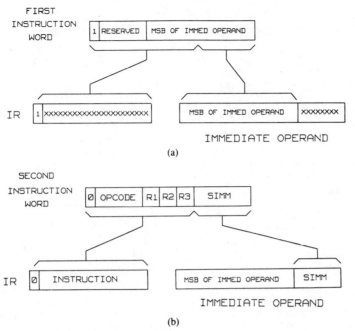

FIRST
INSTRUCTION
WORD

| 1 | RESERVED | MSB OF IMMED OPERAND |

IR | 1 | XXXXXXXXXXXXXXXXXXXXXX | | MSB OF IMMED OPERAND | XXXXXXXX |

IMMEDIATE OPERAND

(a)

SECOND
INSTRUCTION
WORD

| 0 | OPCODE | R1 | R2 | R3 | SIMM |

IR | 0 | INSTRUCTION | | MSB OF IMMED OPERAND | SIMM |

IMMEDIATE OPERAND

(b)

Fig. 2.   Two-word format. (a) First word. (b) Second word.

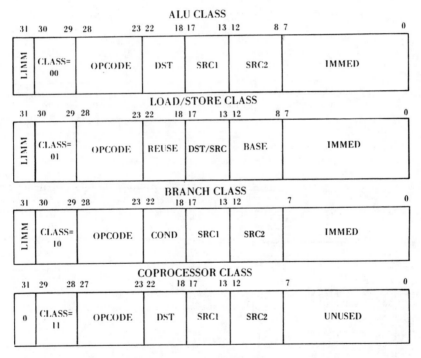

ALU CLASS

31	30 29	28 23	22 18	17 13	12 8	7 0
LIMM	CLASS= 00	OPCODE	DST	SRC1	SRC2	IMMED

LOAD/STORE CLASS

31	30 29	28 23	22 18	17 13	12 8	7 0
LIMM	CLASS= 01	OPCODE	REUSE	DST/SRC	BASE	IMMED

BRANCH CLASS

31	30 29	28 23	22 18	17 13	12 7	0
LIMM	CLASS= 10	OPCODE	COND	SRC1	SRC2	IMMED

COPROCESSOR CLASS

31	29 28	27 23	22 18	17 13	12 7	0
0	CLASS= 11	OPCODE	DST	SRC1	SRC2	UNUSED

Fig. 3.   Instruction format.

completed; we deal here with a relatively deep memory pipeline, as explained in a later section of this paper), at any time everything is kept straight. Consequently, requests for memory load may be issued at every instruction cycle, which would not be possible with standard pipeline organizations.

IV. CPU ARCHITECTURE

Once it is known what the technology and support software guidelines are, the CPU architecture has to be created so as to fit within these guidelines [12], [13]. We created the architecture by including, in the design, those features needed to make the system execute programs efficiently, in the conditions typical of the GaAs

technology [12], [13]. Instruction format details are given in Figs. 3–6. A block diagram of the CPU is shown in Figs. 7–10, for various execution phases of a typical instruction.

For this type of pipelined architecture, a stack of registers is required to be connected to the PC, so that the last N values of the instruction memory address can be remembered. These values will be used to restart those instructions that did not finish executing, when an interrupt occurred. Even though these N instructions were fetched, they may not have finished execution when they were stopped, in order for the CPU to execute the called sequence, i.e., the interrupt response program. We have found that the traditional approach to this problem will work well in the GaAs environment,

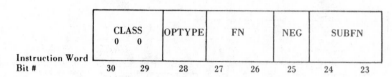

CLASS		OPTYPE	FN		NEG	SUBFN	
0	0						

Instruction Word Bit #

| 30 | 29 | 28 | 27 | 26 | 25 | 24 | 23 |

Fig. 4. ALU class op-code field assignments.

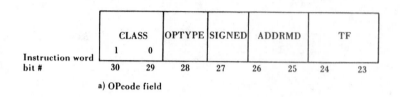

CLASS		OPTYPE	SIGNED	ADDRMD		TF	
1	0						

Instruction word bit #

| 30 | 29 | 28 | 27 | 26 | 25 | 24 | 23 |

a) OPcode field

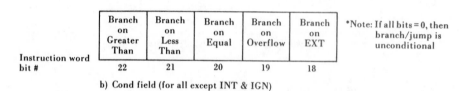

Branch on Greater Than	Branch on Less Than	Branch on Equal	Branch on Overflow	Branch on EXT

Instruction word bit #

| 22 | 21 | 20 | 19 | 18 |

*Note: If all bits = 0, then branch/jump is unconditional

b) Cond field (for all except INT & IGN)

Fig. 5. Branch/jump class op-code field assignments.

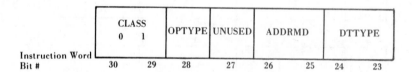

CLASS		OPTYPE	UNUSED	ADDRMD		DTTYPE	
0	1						

Instruction Word Bit #

| 30 | 29 | 28 | 27 | 26 | 25 | 24 | 23 |

Fig. 6. Load/store class op-code field assignments.

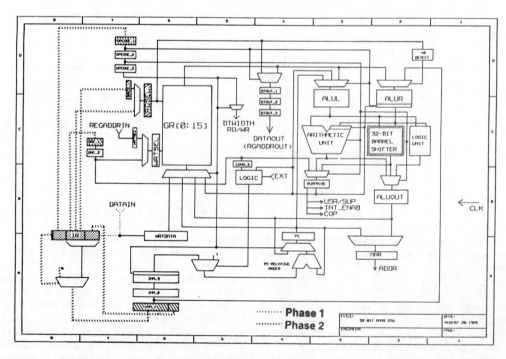

Fig. 7. Instruction read phase.

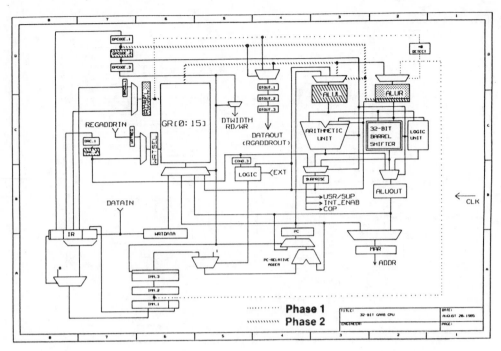

Fig. 8.   Register read phase.

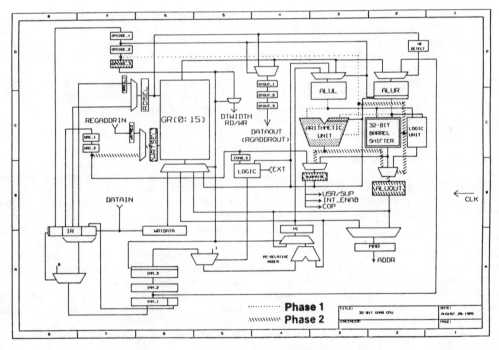

Fig. 9.   The ALU phase.

except for differences due to the fact that the value of N is larger [14]–[16].

As each instruction address is generated, it is simultaneously sent to the instruction memory to fetch the instruction, and is pushed onto the register stack containing the last N values. When an interrupt occurs, i.e., when the execution of the interrupt instruction begins, the operation of the stack ceases, while the PC continues to function, first branching to the called routine, and then going through the execution of the called routine. When the interrupt service routine is fully executed, execution of the interrupted routine is restarted, by retrieving the instruction memory addresses from the stack, and refetching the instructions from memory. By the time the execution of

the Nth instruction has begun, the CPU will have recovered from the interrupt, and will be back to the point in the interrupted routine where it was interrupted. The PC stack operation is then restarted, and program execution is allowed to proceed normally until another interrupt is received. In this machine, the PC stack is located in the memory controller system rather than in the CPU. This decreased the number of devices to be put on the CPU chip and improved the speed of the recovery process. It allowed the stack to be built with a depth equal to the largest expected N, and still operate efficiently with a small value for N.

One of the major design problems with GaAs microprocessors is the relatively high ratio of off-chip memory access time to on-chip

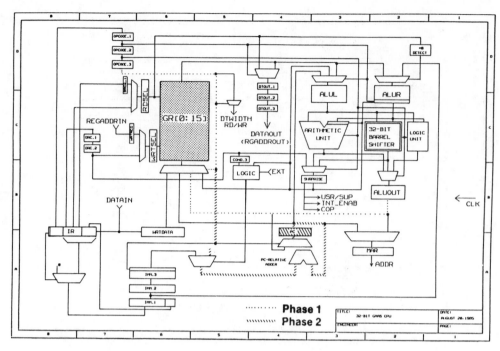

Fig. 10.   The write-back phase.

data path time. With the target execution rate being one instruction per CPU clock cycle, we have defined the system such that more than one instruction is in the process of being fetched.

The first phase of each instruction execution is instruction fetch (MAR loaded with the instruction's address from the PC). In this machine, a series of partial instruction decoders are included between a series of registers that hold the unused portions of the instruction at each stage of the execution cycle. The first of these registers is called the instruction register (IR) and holds the entire instruction. Its output is connected to multiplexers that sequentially use the general register file addresses to access the file, and fetch the two operands that are to be used in the course of the execution of the instruction. Input logic recognizes whether the incoming instruction is the MS bits of the immediate operand OR the following instruction. If that is the case, then the transfer path (to copy the contents of the appropriate bits of the instruction to the immediate operand register for the ALU) is activated (see Fig. 7).

When the next clock cycle of the CPU is completed, the next instruction is ready to be placed into the instruction register, so the present contents must be moved to the "next instruction register." This action occurs at the same time that the operands from the general register file are put into two registers at the input of the ALU, and the immediate operand is put into a third register at the ALU's input (see Fig. 8). At this time, the immediate operand is assembled (using 8 bits from the "second instruction register" and 24 bits from the input to the "first instruction register," if the continuation bit is set), and put into the third ALU input register. If the continuation bit is not set (in the word at the input to the first instruction register), then the 8 bits from the "second instruction register" are put into the third ALU input register, with the 24 most significant bits of this register set to zero. Note the essential difference between this scheme and the "shifted control" scheme used in some other machines.

In order to accomplish all this successfully, with the logic family available, this machine was designed with a two-phase CPU clock system, and two levels of registers for each stage. It also uses a general register file that has one read port and one write port [17], but is fast enough that two pairs of read and write operations may be accomplished during a single CPU clock cycle. In reality, then, the system, on the first clock phase after the instruction is put into the instruction register, reads the first operand out of the general register file, puts it into a temporary holding register, and puts all of the

remaining bits of the instruction into another instruction register. On the second clock phase, the first operand is put into the first ALU input register, the second operand is fetched from the general register file, and put into the second ALU input register. Here, two decisions had to be made.

First, the ALU will only accept two operands, but we have assembled three. So two must be selected from the three. In many machines, the selection is based on the op-code, with some instructions being designed for immediate operands only, and others designed to use two variables only. These machines include an extra bit in the instruction format to specify which operands are to be used: the first and second operands fetched from the register file, or the first operand fetched from the register file, plus the immediate operand. This machine, instead, uses an arrangement to achieve more flexibility (without adding any bits to the instruction format), and to achieve a convenience that is needed later on in the instruction execution cycle. It does this through the implementation of the general register file such that "register zero" does not exist and the file, when register zero is addressed, always puts out a value of zero. Furthermore, the ALU operand selection logic is designed to select the immediate operand, if the second source register address is zero, and select the content read from the general register file, if this address is nonzero. This solution adds a little to the overall complexity of the decoding circuitry, but improves the code density, which is especially important in GaAs machines which have a relatively small instruction cache (located off-CPU-chip/on-CPU-package).

Second, for ALU operations, the first operand is always sent to the ALU unmodified, and the second one may be sent unmodified or complemented, depending on the instruction op-code. However, destinations of operands are determined by the type of operation to be performed. For example, for arithmetic, logic, and shift instructions, the appropriate contents of the ALU input registers are sent to the adder, the logic unit, or the shifter. For coprocessor instructions, the CPU operation is meaningless; so any operation is allowed, as long as the result does not disturb a register whose content is to be kept valid from one instruction to the next. For branch instructions, the selected operands are sent to the ALU, but the value in the $R1$ field is used as an extension to the op-code, to specify the test to be performed on the result of the adder operation (to determine if the branch should be taken). In this case, the value in the "immediate operand register" is

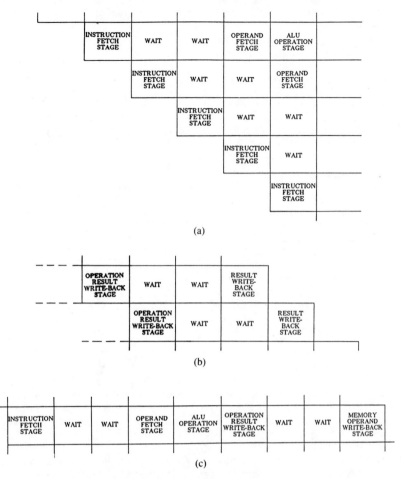

Fig. 11. (a) Instruction execution sequence through the ALU operation
phase. (b) The operation result write-back phase of instruction execution.
(c) Complete instruction execution cycle.

sent to the PC adder, so that it may be conditionally added to, or subtracted from, the present PC value, for a PC-relative branch. For jump instructions, the values normally selected for the ALU input are sent to the adder, and the adder output is sent later on to the PC, to execute the jump.

The execution of the subtract operation, for the interval when the operands are sent to the ALU, during the next two phases of the CPU clock is illustrated in Fig. 9. Note that, during this cycle, the inputs to the ALU are available at the beginning of the first phase of the clock, and that the selected output of the ALU goes into the ALU "output register" and the "surprise register," at the end of the second phase of the clock. Fig. 11(a) illustrates the phases of the instruction execution sequence through the ALU operation stage. The last stage of the execution of an instruction in the CPU is the stage in which the output of the ALU is sent to its ultimate destination: either to the data memory system as an address, or to the general register file as the result of the computation. In the case of the memory reference, the address goes out, but the result is not sent back immediately, so the information requested by load operation cannot be put into the general register file during the next cycle of the CPU clock. This value will come back later, and will be put into the file then. In the case of the ALU operation, the result is written into the general register file on the first of the two clock phases of this last instruction execution stage (see Fig. 10). The alternate phase of operation is used to handle the storage of any data that come from the data memory (from some previously executed load operation). This part of the operation of the machine is illustrated in Fig. 11(b). It shows how the destination address has been delayed during the instruction execution, so that it arrives at the general register file at the same time when the

result arrives. The complete instruction execution cycle is shown in Fig. 11(c). Shown also are the two latency periods, the first one related to the instruction fetch, and the second one related to the operand fetch for a load operation.

A number of unique features were added to solve problems caused by the operation of the architecture at a rate of 200 MIPS, a cycle time so short that any interchip communication would use up much of this time (about 0.5 ns per inch of conductor length). This fact mandates the use of memory pipelines, in conjunction with the small number of devices on each related GaAs chip. The first of these added features is the "ignore instruction," to help reclaim some of the instruction memory space lost due to the long branch latency.

In a pipelined machine, following a branch instruction, there are several instructions that will have entered the pipeline, and will be executed, whether the branch is taken or not. For these types of machines it is the job of the code optimizer to find things for the CPU to do, either those that need to be done all the time, or those that are useful sometimes (say when the branch is taken), and harmless the other times (when the branch is not taken). Unfortunately, for the current state of the art compiler technology, code optimizer efficiency is not very high for relatively deep pipelines. Consequently, branch fill-in of one or two instructions being about all that can be accomplished [3]. Therefore, the remainder of the instruction slots in the branch latency area have to be filled in with NoOp instructions. This results in wasting a relatively large part of the memory space.

This space can be reclaimed through the use of the ignore instruction. This is accomplished by having the code optimizer put the ignore instruction following the last useful instruction migrated into the branch latency area. The count in the ignore instruction is

TABLE I
(a) PERCENTAGE OF BRANCH FILLS WITH/WITHOUT THE SQUASH MECHANISM (STATIC NUMBERS). (b) PERCENTAGE OF NoOp's (TOTAL NUMBER OF NoOp's/TOTAL NUMBER OF INSTRUCTIONS). (c) PERCENTAGE OF NoOp's (TOTAL NUMBER OF NoOp's ELIMINATED/TOTAL NUMBER OF NoOp's BEFORE ORGANIZATION). (d) PERCENTAGE OF CODE REDUCTION (NUMBER OF INSTRUCTION WORDS REDUCED/TOTAL NUMBER OF INSTRUCTIONS BEFORE REORGANIZATION

benchmarks		total branches	% 3-fills	% 2-fills	% 1-fills	% 0-fills	% fills
REALMM	(without)	29	31.0%	20.7%	13.8%	34.5%	49.4%
	(with)		42.9%	35.7%	3.6%	17.9%	67.9%
PUZZLE	(without)	84	8.3%	9.5%	8.3%	73.8%	17.5%
	(with)		33.7%	44.2%	9.3%	12.8%	66.3%
BUBBLE	(without)	23	26.1%	17.4%	13.4%	43.5%	42.0%
	(with)		29.2%	16.7%	1.3%	41.7%	44.4%
WEIGHT	(without)	131	37.4%	17.6%	25.2%	19.1%	57.5%
	(with)		40.8%	21.5%	23.1%	14.6%	62.8%

(a)

without coprocessor				
benchmarks	static		dynamic	
	non-reorg'd	reorganized	non-reorg'd	reorganized
REALMM	66.6%	16.8%	54.2%	17.0%
PUZZLE	39.4%	18.9%	40.0%	10.7%
BUBBLE	48.3%	23.4%	47.4%	20.3%
WEIGHT				
with coprocessor				
REALMM	48.5%	29.1%	44.2%	26.5%

(b)

	without coprocessor							
	static				dynamic			
	by intrablock reorganztn	by branch optimiztn	by squash	total	by intrablock reorganztn	by branch optimiztn	by squash	total
REALMM	83.3%	5.1%	1.6%	90.0%	68.3%	11.2%	4.5%	84.0%
PUZZLE	68.7%	2.9%	7.4%	79.0%	65.3%	7.9%	11.2%	84.4%
BUBBLE	56.8%	11.1%	1.3%	69.2%	65.2%	5.2%	1.9%	72.3%
WEIGHT								
with coprocessor								
REALMM	44.4%	9.0%	2.9%	56.3%	43.5%	7.8%	3.1%	54.5%

(c)

without coprocessor		
	static	dynamic
REALMM	60.2%	49.1%
PUZZLE	45.6%	46.3%
BUBBLE	36.3%	35.3%
WEIGHT		
with coprocessor		
REALMM	30.5%	24.0%

(d)

then set to cause the CPU to ignore execution of the number of instructions specified, no matter what they are. The memory space following the ignore instruction can be used to hold other instructions.

Most of the decisions made for this processor's design were verified by simulating the execution of compiler-generated code sequences on the alternative architectures, and choosing the best [14]-[16]. In our design, the ignore count was integrated with the branch instruction, putting a count and a control bit in an unused portion of the instruction word. The control bit specified whether the execution of the following N instructions (count field value) should be performed, if the branch is taken or not.

This version of the design, quite similar to the branch squashing technique (e.g., [18]), was simulated for several programs [see Table I]. Two types of statistics were gathered to evaluate the usefulness of this approach. The first statistic showed that, through the use of this technique, the amount of filling of the branch latency area with useful instructions increased on the average about 10 percent (with the best being an improvement from about 17 percent to about 66 percent). It also showed that the number of NoOp instructions in the program memory decreased by an average of about 5 percent (see Table I).

Another place where this technique showed its usefulness was in the area of the elimination of NoOp instructions in the CPU's instruction memory following a coprocessor instruction, and in the execution of NoOp instructions by the CPU while it is waiting for the coprocessor to finish the execution of its instruction. In this case, an average of about 3 percent of the NoOps were eliminated in both the static count of these instructions and about 3 percent in the dynamic execution of the NoOp instructions. These figures could be improved if the count field were larger. Furthermore, the separate instruction is less expensive in terms of device count than the branch squashing approach (see Table I).

A crucial problem in a pipelined machine is that of interrupts. These may be handled totally by hardware on the CPU chip, if there is no external memory pipeline. If a memory pipeline exists in the system, however, no hardware control on the CPU alone can solve the problem conveniently, because of the same reason that necessitated the presence of the memory pipeline in the first place. The problem was solved in this machine by having the interrupt handler logic insert an "interrupt instruction" in the instruction stream (when an interrupt request is placed by the external logic) in place of one of the instructions already fetched from memory. The INT was to be used by the hardware with the base register specified as zero. An appropriate ignore field count is also included with this instruction, so that the proper number of instructions already in the memory pipeline (ones that immediately follow the interrupt instruction) are ignored. Note that the PC stack contents mentioned earlier will be used to refetch the instructions which were fetched but not executed, when the interrupt occurred. This will permit their execution upon return from the interrupt.

The two other problem areas found in machines of this type are associated with the implementation of the multiply and divide operations. In the Stanford MIPS computer, these operations were augmented by the inclusion (in the hardware) of special shift registers, called the Hi and Lo registers, and by putting the barrel shifter in series with the adder. This allowed the MIPS to process two multiplier bits and one quotient bit per instruction cycle.

This solution is not applicable in the case of GaAs-oriented design. First, the barrel shifter could not be put in series with the adder. Unlike the MIPS which executed instructions at the rate of one every other machine cycle, this machine was designed to execute instructions at the rate of one every clock cycle, requiring that the critical path be very short. Second, the cost of the Hi and Lo registers was too large for what gain could be achieved in the throughput. Since GaAs chips have to be small, this was felt to be one thing that could be omitted. And finally, the machine was designed to support double precision arithmetic (on a coprocessor), including multiply and divide, and these would make the Hi–Lo register approach even more expensive. As a result, the machine was designed to perform the multiply and divide operations by reading the operands from the general register file, operating on them, and putting them back into the same file. This resulted in a very inexpensive approach that permitted the system to handle single, double, or higher precision operations, without having any ALU or branch latency problems. The result is that multiply is executed at the rate of two multiplier bits for every three machine cycles, for single precision, and every six machine cycles for double precision. Divide is executed at the rate of one quotient bit for every three machine cycles for single precision, and every six machine cycles for double precision.

When it came time to make a decision as to how to do multiply in this machine, we were faced with several ground rules and a difficult choice to make. Without a multiply operation or a barrel shifter, the computer implementation took up all but about 700 of the allowable active devices that could be put on a GaAs VLSI (to assure a "nonzero" fabrication yield). The question that faced us was what to use these remaining devices for. We needed an extendable length multiply and divide operation because the processor had to perform the same operations without the floating point coprocessor, as it did with it. Thus, we had to be able to program both 24 × 24 bit multiplies and 53 × 53 bit multiplies, to provide both the short and the long floating point operations.

We did not want the shifter in series with the adder, because this would double the critical path delay time and, therefore, cut the throughput. We have also performed some preliminary designs and have found out that we could add either the barrel shifter, or the single-length Hi-Lo register combination [10], or a serial multiplier in parallel with the adder, but we could not have more than one of these items without exceeding the device count limit.

Simulations were run on designs of machines that had one of these three items but not the others, to find out which one was the most valuable [16]. The barrel shifter was by far the best choice. Combining it with the designs for the multiplier and divide operation explained before, the average throughput for the machine design was clearly better in almost all benchmark programs tested.

Additionally, it was found that the long divide operations, while simple to program with the chosen approach, would have been costly to implement with the Hi–Lo register approach [10]. Not only did the design permit long divide to be achieved, but multiword multiplies were easy to get as well.

V. Experimenting

Design of the CPU was preceeded by a number of experiments designed to quantify the value of alternate design approaches. Of about one dozen different experiments done at Purdue University

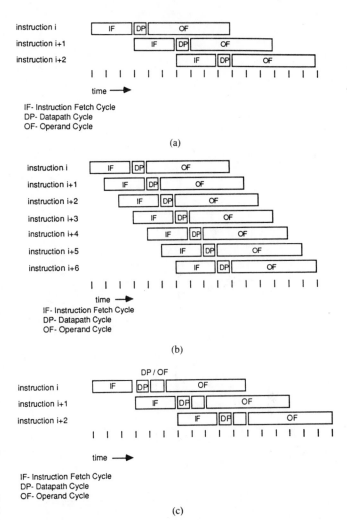

(a)

IF- Instruction Fetch Cycle
DP- Datapath Cycle
OF- Operand Cycle

(b)

IF- Instruction Fetch Cycle
DP- Datapath Cycle
OF- Operand Cycle

(c)

IF- Instruction Fetch Cycle
DP- Datapath Cycle
OF- Operand Cycle

Fig. 12. (a) Silicon-type pipeline, with an on-package instruction cache, and an off-package data cache [14]. (b) Pipelined-memory pipeline, with an on-package instruction cache, and and off-package data cache [14]. (c) Packed pipeline, with an on-package instruction cache, and an off-package data cache [14].

[14]–[16] and RCA Corporation, one which was crucial for many of the decisions was the one related to the design of the pipeline and the evaluation of its efficiency.

The major goal of the pipeline design experiment was to compare the three alternative approaches discussed in [12]. These three approaches are referred to as 1) silicon-type pipeline, 2) pipelined-memory pipeline, and 3) packing-oriented pipeline [14]. The first approach is similar to the Stanford MIPS pipeline implemented in conditions typical of GaAs (large ratio of off/chip to on/chip delays). The second approach is characterized by the branch delay latency equal to the ratio of the off-chip memory access time and the on-chip data-path time (time to read from the general register file, to propagate the signal through the ALU, and to write the result back into the general register file). That is, the approach is characterized by the maximum reasonable depth of the memory pipeline. The third approach is based on the concurrent fetch of more than one operation, and their sequential execution on the single ALU [14]. More details on the three schemes could be found in Fig. 12(a), (b), and (c) and in [14]. The three schemes imply an off-CPU-chip/on-CPU-package instruction cache and an off-CPU-package/on-CPU-board data cache of limited size.

A flexible simulator of all three candidate pipelines was implemented at RCA, and selected benchmarks (described below) were run on each of the candidate pipelines. The results depend on the probability of instruction and data cache hit, as well as on the branch and load fill-in probability.

Note the essential difference between data in Fig. 13 and data in

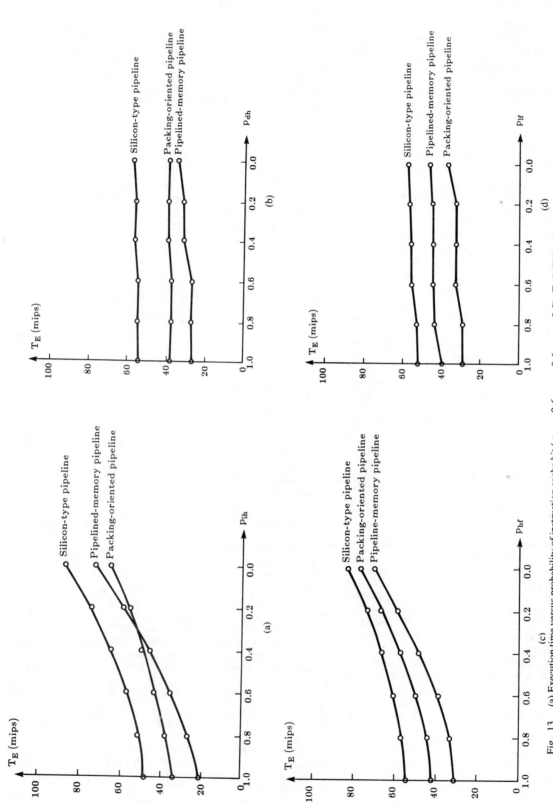

Fig. 13. (a) Execution time versus probability of instruction cache hit ($p_{bf} \simeq 0.6$, $p_{lf} \simeq 0.6$, $p_{dh} \simeq 0.8$). T_E (MIPS)—Execution time expressed in millions of instructions per second. p_{ih}—Probability of instruction cache hit. p_{bf}—Probability of branch fill-in. T_{ic}—Instruction cache miss delay ($T_{ic} = 3$). T_{dc}—Data cache miss delay ($T_{dc} = 3$). (b) Execution time versus probability of data cache hit ($p_{bf} \simeq 0.6$, $p_{lf} \simeq 0.6$, $p_{ih} \simeq 0.8$). T_E (MIPS)—Execution time expressed in millions of instructions per second. p_{dh}—Probability of data cache hit. p_{ih}—Probability of instruction cache hit. p_{bf}—Probability of branch fill-in. T_{ic}—Instruction cache miss delay ($T_{ic} = 3$). T_{dc}—Data cache miss delay ($T_{dc} = 3$). (c) Execution time versus probability of branch-delay fill-in ($p_{lf} \simeq 0.6$, $p_{ih} \simeq 0.8$, $p_{dh} \simeq 0.8$). T_E (MIPS)—Execution time expressed in millions of instructions per second. p_{bf}—Probability of branch fill-in. p_{lf}—Probability of load fill-in. T_{ic}—Instruction cache miss delay ($T_{ic} = 3$). T_{dc}—Data cache miss delay ($T_{dc} = 3$). T_E (MIPS)—Execution time expressed in millions of instructions per second. p_{bf}—Probability of data cache hit. T_{ic}—Instruction cache miss delay ($T_{ic} = 3$). (d) Execution time versus probability of load-delay fill-in ($p_{bf} \simeq 0.6$, $p_{ih} \simeq 0.8$, $p_{dh} \simeq 0.8$). T_E (MIPS)—Execution time expressed in millions of instructions per second. p_{bf}—Probability of branch fill-in. p_{lf}—Probability of load fill-in. p_{ih}—Probability of instruction cache hit. T_{ic}—Instruction cache miss delay ($T_{ic} = 3$). T_{dc}—Data cache miss delay ($T_{dc} = 3$).

392

[14]. The former was obtained through an empirical method from an ENDOT, Inc. simulator [19] and an operational compiler, while the later was obtained via a combined analytical/empirical method, through the SU-MIPS simulator [3], and the precalculation of results to reflect the differences in the pipeline depth of the SU-MIPS machine and the RCA GaAs machine.

Fig. 13(a) gives the performance of three pipelines versus probability of instruction cache hit, for the benchmark mix from Table I, and for the selected values of other relevant parameters. Fig. 13(b) compares the three pipelines from the point of view of their sensitivity to the data cache miss. Fig. 13(c) plots the execution time versus the probability of the branch-delay fill-in. Fig. 13(d) plots the execution time versus the probability of the load-delay fill-in.

Conclusions from the experiments are as follows. In conditions where the probability of fill-in for load and branch delays is relatively high (above 60 percent), the pipelined-memory pipeline performs the best, the packing-oriented pipeline is the next in performance, while the silicon-type pipeline is characterized with a very modest performance. On the other hand, when the probability of the instruction cache hit drops down to below 40 percent, which may happen for extremely small caches, the performance of the pipelined-memory pipeline rapidly decreases. In an extreme case, its performance degrades to being comparable to the performance of the silicon-type pipeline. Also, if one compares results from Fig. 13 and [14], one can conclude that two different methods (one based on the detailed direct-correspondence simulator and an operational optimizer/compiler, the other based on the SU-MIPS simulator/optimizer and precalculation of results to reflect a deeper pipeline) applied to two different but similar benchmark mixes (both oriented to numerical processing with elements of signal processing, data processing, and symbolic processing) have generated very similar results.

With all the above in mind, it was decided to invest maximally into the compiler technology [4], and based on this experiment, a pipelined-memory structure (described previously) was chosen.

Finally, the efficiency of the chosen pipeline was evaluated using the ENDOT, Inc. simulation package, and the related ISP' language [19]. In Table I, some of the benchmarks from [3] are used in their modified form. Realmm(8*8) computes a product of two real matrices of the size eight. Bubblesort(20) performs a bubblesort of twenty integers. Weight (1024) is a computation-heavy program which performs an FFT-based signal transform on a 1024-element signal vector. Puzzle(3) is an iteration-heavy program to solve a three-dimensional cube packing problem. Extrapolated execution speed is given in terms of mega-instructions-per-second (MIPS).

Note that the results from Table I are somewhat different than results from [4], due to the most recent compiler improvements at RCA. Table I(a) presents the percentage of branch fills with and without the squashing mechanism. Table I(b) presents the percentage of NoOp's, for the cases with and without an arithmetic coprocessor [13]. Table I(c) presents the percentage of NoOp's eliminated through the code optimization process, while Table I(d) presents the percentage of code reduction.

One of the main conclusions from Table I is that a major effort is needed to improve the efficiency of delayed branches in deep memory pipelines (which are typical for GaAs microprocessors [20]).

VI. Conclusions

A project is not undertaken properly if all that is accomplished is that something is built. For any project to be truly successful something should be learned. With this project being one of the first that was to design a computer for construction in GaAs VLSI, a computer that would be patterned after the Stanford MIPS architecture, and like that machine, would have a support software system to make optimum use of the architecture, several lessons were learned in each of the three major areas: technology, architecture, and software.

One was that any significant differences in the lengths of conductors among the lines of parallel paths to carry the bits of a single word would necessitate the use of deskewing buffers at the receiving end. This approach is very inconvenient because of the small amount of logic that can be put on a GaAs VLSI chip today.

Another was that handling one instruction per machine clock cycle increases the problems related to designing the logic for the CPU. All critical paths between registers (such as through the adder and the shifter) must be very short, and typically no more than 20 gate delays long. Furthermore, it was found that the faster the machine operates, the longer the memory pipeline will be. The increasing pipeline length increases the latency that the code optimizer must compensate for: the branch latency, the load latency, and perhaps even the ALU latency. It lengthens the stack that must accompany the program counter to enable the handling of interrupts. It also increases the number of CPU resources that must be "shut down" and then "restarted" properly, during the process of interrupt handling.

Finally, it was proven that in GaAs RISC systems, more than in any silicon RISC systems, the compiler should be considered as an integral part of the architecture. (This is partially due to the deeper memory pipelines of GaAs systems, and partially due to the fact that designers tend to move many traditional hardware functions into the compiler.) However, compiler technology (code optimization technology), not being ready for code optimization in the presence of deep pipelines, caused the execution rate for many benchmarks to be well below the peak execution rate of 200 MIPS.

Acknowledgment

The authors are thankful to B. Heagerty, T. Geigel, and N. Chen for their help.

References

[1] S. Karp and S. Roosilv, "DARPA, SDI, and GaAs," *IEEE Computer*, pp. 17–19, Oct. 1986.

[2] R. Wedig and T. Lehr, "The GaAs realization of a production system machine," in *Proc. HICSS-19*, Honolulu, Hawaii, Jan. 1986.

[3] T. Gross, "Code optimization of pipeline constraints," Stanford Univ. Tech. Rep. 83-255, Dec. 1983.

[4] V. Milutinović, D. Fura, W. Helbig, and J. Linn, "Architecture/compiler synergism in GaAs computer systems," *IEEE Computer*, May 1987.

[5] J. Linn, "Horizontal microcode compaction," *Microprogramming and Firmware Engineering Methods*. S. Habib, Ed. New York: Van Nostrand Reinhold, 1987.

[6] J. Gill *et. al.*, "Summary of MIPS instructions," Stanford Univ. Tech. Rep. 83-237, Nov. 1983.

[7] W. Helbig and J. Stringer, "A VLSI microprocessor: The RCA ATMAC," *IEEE Computer*, vol. 10, pp. 22–29, Sept. 1977.

[8] R. Colwell *et al.*, "Computers, complexity, and controversy," *IEEE Computer*, pp. 8–20, Sept. 1985.

[9] D. Patterson and C. Sequin, "A VLSI RISC," *IEEE Computer*, pp. 39–47, Sept. 1982.

[10] J. Hennessy *et al.*, "The MIPS machine," in *Dig. Papers, Spring COMPCON 82*, San Francisco, CA, Feb. 1982, pp. 2–7.

[11] D. R. Ditzel, H. R. McLellan, and A. D. Berenbaum, "The hardware architecture of the CRISP microprocessor," in *Proc. ACM/IEEE Int. Symp. Comput. Architecture*, Pittsburgh, PA, June 1987, pp. 309–319.

[12] V. Milutinović *et al.*, "An introduction to GaAs microprocessor architecture for VLSI," *IEEE Computer*, pp. 30–42, Mar. 1986.

[13] V. Milutinović *et al.*, "Issues of importance in designing GaAs computer systems," *IEEE Computer*, pp. 45–57, Oct. 1986.

[14] D. Fura, "Architectural approaches for GaAs exploitation in high-speed computer design," Purdue Univ. Tech. Rep., TR-EE 85-17, Dec. 1985.

[15] M. Bettinger, "Comparison of CMOS silicon and E/D-MESFET GaAs for VLSI processor design," Purdue Univ. Tech. Rep., TR-EE 85-18, Dec. 1985.

[16] V. Milutinović and D. Fura, *Gallium Arsenide Computer Design*. Washington, DC: Computer Society Press, 1988.

[17] W. Helbig, R. Schellack, and R. Zieger, "The design and construction of a GaAs technology demonstration microprocessor," in *Proc. MIDCON 85*, Professional Program Session Rec. 23, Chicago, IL, Sept. 1985, pp. 1–6.

[18] P. Chow and M. Horowitz, ''Architectural tradeoffs in the design of MIPS-X,'' in *Proc. 14th Annu. Int. Symp. Comput. Architecture*, Pittsburgh, PA, June 1987.

[19] C. W. Rose, G. M. Ordy, and P. J. Drongowski, ''M.mPc: A study in university–industry technology transfer,'' *IEEE Design Test*, pp. 44–56, Feb. 1982.

[20] V. Milutinović Ed., Special Issue on GaAs Microprocessor Technology, *IEEE Computer*, Oct. 1986.

A 32-Bit, 200-MHz GaAs RISC

Reprinted from *IEEE Micro*, December 1987, pages 8–20. Copyright © 1987 by The Institute of Electrical and Electronics Engineers, Inc.

for High-Throughput Signal Processing Environments

Barbara A. Naused and Barry K. Gilbert
Mayo Foundation

> GaAs technology has matured sufficiently to allow fabrication of an entire RISC on one chip. GaAs also supports 200-MHz clock rates and 100-MIPS instruction rates.

The first complex single-component microprocessor fabricated in gallium arsenide (GaAs) is now being developed as a major core element in a project known as the Advanced Onboard Signal Processor. Funded jointly by the Defense Advanced Research Projects Agency (DARPA) and the US Air Force, the AOSP will be assembled by 1990 entirely with GaAs components as a demonstration that digital GaAs technology will be sufficiently mature to be used in signal processing systems.

In the early 1980's, DARPA asked the Special Purpose Processor Development Group of the Mayo Foundation to identify a microprocessor architecture suitable for implementation as a custom-designed monolithic GaAs IC by the late 1980's. A number of commercial, aerospace, and Department of Defense microprocessor architectures were reviewed for their suitability. Here, we compare their strengths and deficiencies in the AOSP application context and discuss the selection of a RISC architecture for GaAs implementation.

The AOSP

The AOSP is a general-purpose, distributed signal processor presently under development in silicon technology by Raytheon Corporation for use in several DoD signal processing applications. The architecture of the AOSP is based on a network of processing elements, called array computing elements (ACEs), which can all be identical, or can be a variety of types to perform several different functions. A distributed operating system controls the network, which is specialized for signal processing. The ACEs communicate through an efficient interconnection network which also allows spare ACEs to be substituted for faulty ones in real time (Figure 1). Each ACE contains two sections:

- *the Network Control Unit* (NCU), which is responsible for communication with the network and control of the ACE, and
- *the Application Processing Unit* (APU), which is optimized for execution of signal processing applications and also interfaces directly with the outside world.

Each NCU consists of an interelement bus interface and a control processor. The APU contains a

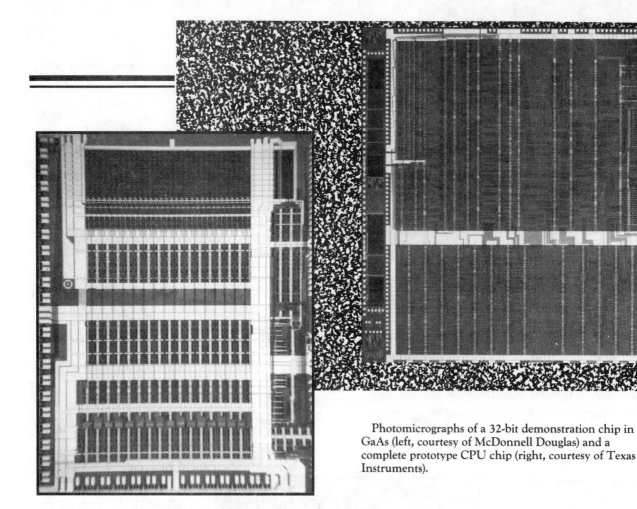

Photomicrographs of a 32-bit demonstration chip in GaAs (left, courtesy of McDonnell Douglas) and a complete prototype CPU chip (right, courtesy of Texas Instruments).

signal processor, referred to as the Macro Function Signal Processor (MFSP), a system I/O unit, and a data processor for scalar operations. A Motorola 68010 microprocessor functions as the control processor in the NCU and the data processor in the APU, as illustrated in Figure 2.

As the design of the AOSP progressed in silicon, DARPA management realized that certain applications would require very high clock rates, extreme radiation hardening, and/or very low power dissipation and that a GaAs implementation of the AOSP might achieve these combined features.[1]

Several studies conducted during 1981 and 1982 assessed the level of technology required to achieve a radiation-hardened, low-power signal processor by the end of the decade. These studies used the AOSP architecture as a baseline. Results indicated that GaAs IC technology would have to be sufficiently sophisticated to permit fabrication of configurable cell or gate arrays in the size range of 4000 to 6000 equivalent gates, as well as static RAMs (SRAMs) of at least 16K bits.

Assessments of the AOSP architecture indicated that—with one exception—an entire AOSP ACE could be fabricated using only the gate arrays and SRAMs. To assure that these technologies would be in place by the mid-1980's, DARPA embarked upon an ambitious plan to fund the creation of three pilot fabrication line facilities for GaAs chips. The products of the first two pilot lines were to be gate arrays

of at least 6000-equivalent-gate complexity, and SRAMs of 16K-bit complexity. These projects are doing well. A Rockwell/Honeywell team demonstrated 5500 gate arrays in late 1985, and both Rockwell and McDonnell Douglas demonstrated 4K-bit SRAMs in early 1986. Rockwell demonstrated fully functional 7000 gate arrays in mid-1987 and fully functional 16K-bit SRAMs in September 1987.

A single exception to the assembly of an entire AOSP ACE based upon GaAs gate arrays and SRAMs remained: the requirement for a microprocessor to serve as the control and data processor elements of the AOSP ACE, as we earlier discussed. In order to achieve the full benefits of digital GaAs technology, the entire AOSP ACE had to be fabricated with GaAs components, including the microprocessors. However, further studies indicated that no modern microprocessor could be assembled efficiently with gate arrays. A custom IC was necessary to achieve optimum performance. Because GaAs IC technology was then, and remains, relatively immature in comparison to silicon technology, the device densities of GaAs gate arrays and custom components are considerably less than in silicon. As a result, a major constraint was placed on the design of a GaAs microprocessor. It would have to require less than 10,000 equivalent gates to allow its placement on a single custom chip.

The AOSP application placed additional constraints on the design of a microprocessor:

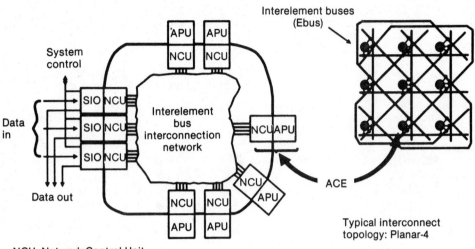

Figure 1. The AOSP system architecture developed by Raytheon Corp.

NCU: Network Control Unit
APU: Application Processor Unit

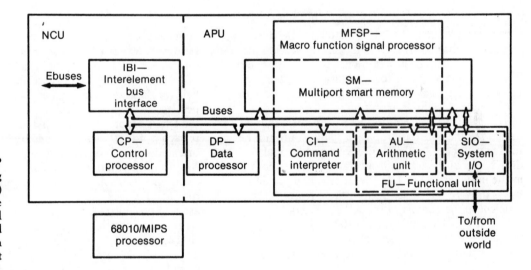

Figure 2. AOSP Array Computing Element (ACE) showing both the Network Control Unit (NCU) and the Application Processor Unit (APU).

- a 32-bit architecture;
- a 24- to 32-bit address bus to support at least 16M bytes of direct memory access (DMA);
- an efficient I/O handler;
- an efficient interrupt handler;
- a high-instruction execution rate; and
- the capability of floating-point operations in hardware.

If necessary, the floating-point hardware could be a separate coprocessor chip. Accordingly, DARPA tasked us to identify a 32-bit microprocessor architecture for full implementation in GaAs in time to achieve an all-GaAs AOSP brassboard demonstration in 1990.

Microprocessor architectures

Although a microprocessor could have been designed specifically for GaAs implementation, we did not consider this type of approach attractive without guaranteed software support. The possible use of an existing architecture therefore added another constraint to the GaAs microprocessor selection process. A microprocessor design that was nonproprietary, readily available, and well-documented was required. These constraints formed the basis of our study.

Commercial architectures. We first investigated commercially available microprocessor architec-

Table 1.
Possible architectures for use in a GaAs microprocessor.

	Gate count <10K	32-bit architecture	Non-proprietary	DMA ≥ 16M bytes	Execution >1 MIPS
Standard architectures					
Mil-Std 1750A (TI)			●		●
TI 9900					
MC68010 (12 MHz)		●		●	●
NS16032		●		●	
Nebula		●	●		
Intel iAPX432		●		●	
Rockwell AAMP				●	
RISC architectures					
RISC II - Berkeley		●	●	●	
IBM 801	?	●		●	●
Inmos transputer		●			●
MIPS - Stanford	●	●	●	●	●

tures—in particular, the Motorola 68010. Because this microprocessor is used in the silicon version of the AOSP under construction by Raytheon, it would have provided a straightforward target architecture. However, the gate count of this processor is too large for a single-chip implementation in GaAs at projected late-1980's integration levels. Further, the design for the 68010 is proprietary and would not be made available. Raytheon discovered additional drawbacks of the 68010. Wait states are incorporated in the initialization of I/O operations, and the data bus is only 16 bits wide. Both of these features are inefficient in the context of the AOSP. We did not consider it a drawback that the 68010 requires a coprocessor for floating-point operations, provided that the coprocessor could be made to operate at sufficiently high speed.

We also examined and rejected the following commercial and aerospace industry architectures on the basis of one or more of the criteria previously described: the National Semiconductor 16032, the Texas Instruments 9900 series, the Rockwell International AAMP (Advanced Architecture Microprocessor), and the Intel iAPX 432 (Table 1). These microprocessors shared a principal drawback—their large gate counts.

Military architectures. We also considered a GaAs implementation of the Mil-Std-1750A[2] architecture because of the large amount of software written for this processor. Because this design is a DoD standard, there was considerable initial enthusiasm within the DARPA community for its selection as the target

architecture for the GaAs microprocessor project. However, Mil-Std-1750A specifies a 16-bit architecture with a single 16-bit bus, yielding only 128K bytes of DMA, half of which is used for instructions and half for data. A memory management unit can be appended to the processor in most versions to expand the DMA capability to 2M bytes. However, this approach is not efficient for the large number of array-oriented and I/O operations required in the AOSP. Most implementations do support on-chip floating-point operations and also contain an efficient interrupt handler. Sixteen general-purpose, 16-bit registers are also provided. A very large number of instructions and addressing types are available in this architecture, yielding a variety of instruction formats and lengths. Control logic for the 1750A is implemented with microcode. One implementation of Mil-Std-1750A by Texas Instruments[3] requires two chips, each containing over 16,000 gates and 110K bits of microcode ROM.

We rapidly concluded that Mil-Std-1750A could not provide a suitable GaAs microprocessor architecture for the AOSP project. The processor architecture is too complex and yet does not implement a 32-bit machine. Computation with 64-bit operands is not supported, and the direct address space is considered too small, given the trends toward ever-increasing direct memory capacity.

We also examined the Nebula machine (Mil-Std-1862B), a DoD 32-bit architecture, for implementation in GaAs (Table 1). However, this architecture is not necessarily a single-chip microprocessor, even in silicon VLSI. One of the multichip implementations

The major strengths of a RISC include a small number of simplified instructions, a reduced gate count, and faster instruction execution time.

attempted to date by Raytheon Corporation requires approximately 44,000 gates, which is much too large for a GaAs version, at least through the end of the decade. The instruction execution rate of this machine is also comparatively slow at 500 KIPS. Therefore, we also eliminated this architecture from further consideration.

RISC architectures. The family of reduced instruction set computers (RISCs) appeared to match the constraints of a GaAs microprocessor more closely than the machines described previously. This type of computer, developed independently by several universities and corporations, was considered a novel approach in the early 1980's. Only recently has it become commercially available in silicon. The family of RISC architectures was developed after it was recognized[4] that a large number of complex instructions normally implemented in hardware on a microprocessor are rarely used in compiled or manually prepared assembly-language code. These infrequently used instructions could therefore be more efficiently implemented in software, reducing the hardware support to a small set of simple instructions.

This design approach can reduce the gate count of the processor considerably, especially in the control section, and can permit the remaining simple instructions to execute much more rapidly. The simplified hardware instruction set complicates the low-level software required for the microprocessor, but this price is paid only once at compile time, rather than every time an instruction is executed. Compile-time penalties are not a major concern if overall performance is improved and the simplified microprocessor exhibits a considerably reduced gate count. Several versions of RISCs had been introduced at the time we performed this architecture study, including the RISC II processor design by the University of California at Berkeley, the 801 minicomputer design by IBM, the transputer design by Inmos Ltd., and the MIPS (Microprocessor without Interlocked Pipeline Stages) design by Stanford University (Table 1). As we will discuss, this last architecture appears to be best suited for implementation in GaAs.

The major strengths of a RISC include a small number of simplified instructions, a reduced gate count, and faster instruction execution time. Several

other architectural aspects naturally lend themselves to straightforward hardware implementation on this type of machine (although not every RISC employs all of these features). These features include:

• a load/store architecture (only load and store instructions access memory, while all others operate on registers);
• single-cycle execution of most instructions;
• a short critical path;
• a hardwired control section (rather than microcode);
• a Harvard architecture (separate memories and buses for data and instructions);
• a fixed-instruction format (all instructions are the same size and structure);
• preprocessing of pipeline interlocks in software; and
• the ability to keep major resources of the machine (the ALU, the data memory, and the instruction memory) fully occupied most of the time.

The RISC II. The RISC II[4] contains a large on-chip register file used for storing instructions, local variables, and constants. The register file consists of eight overlapping windows of 32 words each (a powerful support structure for procedure calls). However, the file must be loaded one word at a time. When this machine is interrupted, the contents of the entire register file must be stored in off-chip memory—a very time-consuming operation. The machine supports only 31 instructions in hardware, each of which is one word (32 bits) in length. All instructions execute in one clock cycle, except load or store operations, which require two cycles. The RISC II contains a three-stage pipeline. The compiler targeted for this machine rearranges the instructions to allow useful operations to be executed during pipeline conflicts. The RISC II designers intended that users would almost always program in high-level languages (HLLs), thereby allowing this associated compiler to optimize the code before execution.

Because only a small portion of the chip area is devoted to control, the floor plan of the device is very regular. The addresses and data words are multiplexed to reduce the total I/O count for the chip to 50 pins, but the multiplexing degrades I/O operation speed. Programs written for the RISC II are approximately 50 percent larger, but typically run faster, than programs written for the more conventional machines we described earlier. Floating-point operations are handled off chip, and integer multiply and divide operations are executed in software. Interrupts are supported only with an external interrupt flag; all other interrupt operations must be processed off chip. The inability of the RISC II to process interrupts on chip is a significant limitation in the AOSP application environment.

The complexity of the RISC II is 12,000 gates, which could have been reduced somewhat in a GaAs version by decreasing the size of the register file at the cost of a severe performance degradation. Although the RISC II offered many attractive features, it did not appear to be efficient for the type of application typical of the AOSP environment, and therefore we did not recommend it for implementation in GaAs.

The IBM 801 machine. The 801 minicomputer designed by IBM[5] is a RISC in which the most recently used instructions are stored in an instruction cache which has an access time of one machine cycle. A data cache is also provided. Data from the two caches are fetched asynchronously to one another, and it is possible to overlap access to the two caches. A software I/O manager synchronizes the caches when required, minimizing the execution of unnecessary load and store operations. A compiler reorders the code to allow useful instructions to be executed during branch and load delays. This processor was also intended to be an HLL-computer, using a very efficient compiler to produce object code nearly as efficiently as the best hand-generated code.

Thirty-two general-purpose, globally allocated registers are available in the 801 machine, so that data needed again within a short duration is available immediately. Instructions are 32 bits in length and have been optimized for microcode. Complex instructions are executed in software. Addresses and data values are also 32 bits in length. A fixed-precision multiplication can be completed in 16 cycles, while a division can be completed in 32 cycles. Floating-point operations are executed off chip with the 801. This machine averages 1.1 cycles per instruction, exhibits cache hit ratios close to 100 percent, and contains a two-stage pipeline. The number of instructions required for a program varies considerably. In some cases, instruction streams are equivalent in length to those found in a more complex processor. In other cases, a 50 percent increase in the number of lines of code is required, particularly for applications requiring many floating-point operations. The information to determine if this machine has an acceptable gate count for a GaAs implementation was not available. The architecture is proprietary to IBM, and additional information is not accessible by the public. This machine appears to match the AOSP environment and might be applicable to a variety of tasks in GaAs if the design were made available.

The Inmos transputer. The transputer is a very high speed 32-bit microprocessor executing a reduced-instruction set of 59 instructions.[6] The current implementation requires approximately 62,500 gates, including 4K bytes of SRAM, a memory interface, a peripheral interface, and on-chip serial links to other transputers, as well as the main processor. A

> **The MIPS machine was the only architecture which satisfied all constraints of a GaAs microprocessor for the AOSP.**

transputer can be used alone, although the intention as stated by Inmos is to employ networks of transputers to increase the performance of an entire system. The same software can be used regardless of the number of processors used. The transputer, which responds very quickly to external interrupts and supports simultaneous block transfers, was designed to implement concurrent processes. Instruction sequences are executed with no wait states.

The transputer can be programmed in most high-level languages, but is intended to perform most efficiently when programmed in Occam, a language specifically developed by Inmos to exploit concurrency. Occam eliminates the need for assembly-language programming and is the lowest level language supported by the transputer. Floating-point operations are executed in software in the early versions of the transputer, and, we believe, are to be executed in hardware in the later versions. The transputer supports a single 32-bit bus, which must be multiplexed for data and addresses. The transputer employs an internal microengine to execute its assembly-level instructions, and possesses no completely general-purpose registers in the hardware. These features are unusual in a RISC. The transputer is also a proprietary architecture. If this design had been available, we might have considered it as a replacement for the entire NCU portion of an AOSP ACE (implemented with multiple chips), rather than merely as the control processor in the NCU.

The MIPS machine. Stanford University originally developed the MIPS machine[7-10] in 1981 as a RISC-architecture project under DARPA sponsorship. After examination, the MIPS machine was the only architecture which satisfied all constraints of a GaAs microprocessor for AOSP. The philosophy behind the MIPS project was to implement in hardware only the most frequently executed and time-consuming instructions and to implement infrequently used instructions in software. This implementation of the instructions increased the overall speed of operation of the processor. The MIPS machine architecture and supporting software were available for government-supported projects. The MIPS is a very high speed 32-bit architecture, primarily due to an efficient match between its architecture and its supporting software.

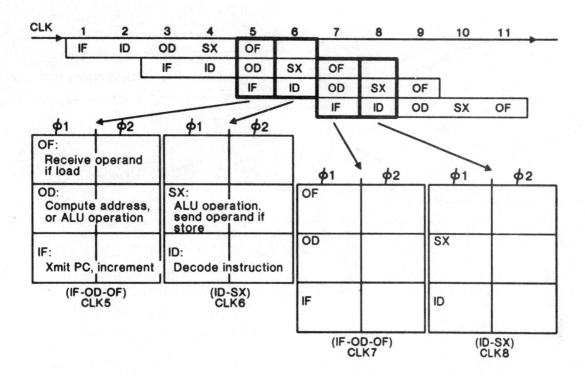

Figure 3. Stanford MIPS five-stage pipeline with active pipe states for each clock cycle. Reproduced in part from Hennessy et al.[9]

The Stanford MIPS machine contains a five-stage pipeline, with a new instruction entering the pipe every other cycle, yielding three active instructions per cycle. Each pipestage executes in the same amount of time, and every machine instruction passes through each stage. The five stages are called

• *IF* (instruction fetch), which transmits and increments the program counter for fetching the instruction;
• *ID* (instruction decode), which decodes the instruction;
• *OD* (operand decode), which either computes the memory address for a load or store instruction, computes the program counter for a branch instruction, or performs an arithmetic operation;
• *SX* (store and execute), which transmits the operand for a store instruction, and, in addition, either performs an arithmetic operation or performs the compare for a conditional instruction; and
• *OF* (operand fetch), which receives the operand for a load instruction.

The machine alternates between the IF-OD-OF cycle and the ID-SX cycle, as long as no interrupts occur, as shown in Figure 3. This pipeline implementation enables 100 percent utilization of the major hardware resources of the processor, which include the instruction memory (by the IF and ID pipestages), the ALU (by the OD and SX pipestages), and the data memory (by the OF and SX pipestages), as depicted in Figure 4. Because two pipestages are able

to execute arithmetic operations, two adds can be packed into one machine instruction and executed within one machine cycle. A 32-bit fixed-precision multiply can thus be executed in eight cycles, with a 2-bit Booth's algorithm executed at 4 bits per cycle. An ALU operation can also be packed with a load into one machine instruction in this architecture.

Interlocks are necessary in pipelined microprocessor architectures to prevent instructions from interfering with one another as they traverse the pipeline. The MIPS machine implements its pipeline interlocks in software, rather than in hardware as is customary in other microprocessor designs. This implementation eliminates a significant amount of complex control logic from the processor. Interlock arbitration can be accomplished in software because the information necessary to generate the interlocks is known at assembly time. By moving this function from execution time to compile time, execution time becomes much faster. The MIPS uses a sophisticated reorganizing assembler which is tightly coupled with the simpler hardware. This "reorganizer" assembles the code into executable machine code, packs two independent instructions into one instruction where possible, and reorganizes the code. Code reorganization accomplishes pipeline interlocking by substituting useful instructions from elsewhere in the code stream where No-op instructions would otherwise have to be inserted to avoid pipeline conflicts, as shown in Table 2. Reordering of instructions improves code execution speed an average of 20 per-

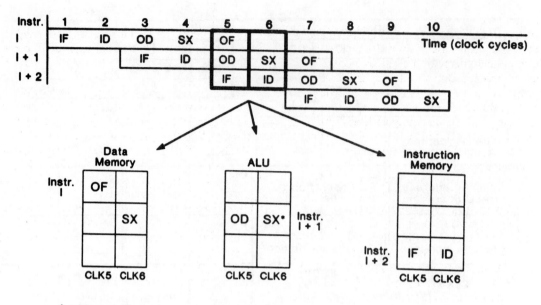

* Denotes ALU reserved for use of OD and SX of instruction I + 1

Figure 4. Stanford MIPS five-stage pipeline showing hardware resource utilization by each pipestage. Reproduced from Przbylski et al. [7]

Table 2.
Example of MIPS code before and after reorganization and packing by the sophisticated assembler.*

	Source code	Correct code with No-ops	Reorganized code
(For Loop)	Begin		
	A[i]:=B[i]+C[i]	L20: ld (r4, r1), r6	L100: ld (r4, r1), r6
		ld (r5, r1), r7	ld (r5, r1), r7; add r6, r8
		No-op	
		add r7, r6, r9	add r7, r6, r9; add r7, r10
		st r9, (r3, r1)	st r9, (r3, r1); add #1, r1
	R:=R+B[i]	add r6, r8	
	S=S+C[i]	add r7, r10	
		add #1, r1	
		ble r1, r2, L20	ble r1, r2, L100
		No-op	st r8, R(sp)
		No-op	st r10, S(sp)
	End	st r8, R(sp)	
		st r10, S(sp)	

*Note that the code length has been reduced by almost half. Reproduced from Hennessy et al. [10]

cent.[7] Instruction packing increases code density, and reduces the execution time of an instruction stream by an additional 30 percent. This gives a combined improvement in execution speed of over 50 percent, when compared to the execution speed of code produced by traditional assemblers. Because the reorganizer accepts MIPS assembly code as input and produces machine-executable code as output, this software module must be unique to each hardware implementation.

The Stanford MIPS machine implements conditional control flow with software by using a compare and branch instruction, which executes in a single machine cycle. The MIPS does not use condition codes—the typical method of implementing conditional control flow—because the structure of the hardware typically employed for condition codes is irregular, both in design and in physical layout. Thus, condition codes are an inefficient use of space on the chip. A total of 16 comparisons, both signed and unsigned, are available in the ALU for this purpose. The MIPS also implements a "set conditional" instruction with the same 16 comparisons.

The Stanford MIPS machine employs a Harvard architecture, having separate data and instruction memories which are accessed on alternating phases of the two-phase clock. Only load and store instructions access memory; all other instructions operate on registers (thus referred to as a load/store architecture). Five addressing modes are available: long-immediate, absolute, based, indexed, and base-shifted by n (where $0 < n < 5$). Although the Stanford MIPS is a word-addressed machine for both instructions and data, it has special instructions to support byte operations on data. Data is accessed with a 24-bit physical address, expandable to a 32-bit virtual address. This yields 16M words of directly addressable memory, with one level of optional page mapping off chip. In addition, if an instruction is *not* a load or store (approximately 50 percent of the instructions), a memory cycle may be used for cache write-back or prefetch.[7]

The Stanford architecture supports vectored interrupts with a 12-bit address concatenated to the current machine status for a jump to the proper interrupt routine. When any type of exception is detected, instructions that are currently in the pipeline are completed, if possible. The state of the processor is stored in the "surprise register." Execution is transferred to memory location zero, where the registers and three return addresses are saved for return to the code sequence that was in progress, and the interrupt handling routine is invoked.

The original MIPS chip was fabricated in NMOS and requires 8000 gates and 84 I/O pins. The chip layout is very regular, containing six major hardware sections. The control of the microprocessor is divided into two functional units implemented as PLAs: (a)

the instruction decode unit, and (b) the master pipeline control. These occupy about 20 percent of the chip area. The data path is interconnected through a pair of 32-bit buses. It consists of the ALU, a barrel shifter, a register file (including 16 general-purpose registers), and the program counter and address mask unit. A control bus interfaces the data path to the control sections.

These chips have an average throughput rate of two million instructions per second and a power dissipation of 1.6W, at a clock rate of 4 MHz.[9] The Stanford MIPS was benchmarked against a Motorola 68000 and a VAX 11/780 by executing several computation-intensive programs written in Pascal. The results of these benchmarks demonstrated that the average throughput of the MIPS was five times faster than that of the Motorola 68000 and twice as fast as that of the VAX 11/780[8] (Table 3).

The MIPS instruction set originally defined at Stanford[7] contains 32 instructions. All of these instructions are 32 bits in length, have the same instruction format, and execute in a single machine cycle. The Stanford MIPS machine requires a coprocessor for high-speed execution of floating-point operations. However, if one is not attached, these instructions can be executed in software on the main processor.

Current projects in GaAs based on the MIPS architecture

After completing our 1983-84 studies, we felt that an entire MIPS-type microprocessor might be implemented as a custom-designed GaAs IC containing approximately 10,000 equivalent gates, because of the relatively low complexity of such a microprocessor. We also felt that a custom-designed floating-point coprocessor might be implemented in an additional 10,000 gates on a second chip.

Based on these results, in 1984 DARPA initiated a five-year program to develop a full 32-bit architecture microprocessor and floating-point coprocessor in gallium arsenide using the Stanford MIPS machine as the baseline. Three contractors—McDonnell Douglas, Texas Instruments teamed with Control Data Corporation, and RCA Corporation teamed with TriQuint Semiconductor—completed a one-year architecture study phase. A four-year, two-phase project to fabricate a 32-bit GaAs microprocessor is currently under way, both at McDonnell Douglas and at Texas Instruments. The goals for these GaAs microprocessors are

• a custom main processor chip and a custom floating-point coprocessor chip,
• a chip complexity of 10,000 gates,
• operation of both chips at a 200-MHz clock rate, and

Table 3.
Results of Pascal benchmarks in seconds.*

	MIPS	M68000	VAX 780 (appr.)	DEC 20/60
Clock speed	(4 MHz)	(8 MHz)	(5 MHz)	
Si transistor count	(25,000)	(65,000)		
Puzzle	2.40	6.1	5.2	2.6
Queen	0.44	1.9	1.0	0.5
Perm	0.56	3.0	1.2	0.6
Towers	0.64	2.9	1.4	0.7
Intmm	0.80	5.0	1.0	0.5
Bubble	0.58	3.7	1.4	0.7
Quick	0.41	2.6	0.8	0.4
Tree	1.01	9.9	2.0	1.0
Avg. (relative to MIPS)	1.00	5.1	2.0	1.0

*Reproduced in part from Przbylski et al.[7]

• a sustained throughput rate of at least 100 million instructions per second.

The first phase ended in March of 1987 with each of the companies producing

• the assembler, linker, and reorganizer software;
• stand-alone demonstration chips containing large portions of the microprocessor; and
• a more detailed system-level specification.

During the second phase, the actual chips and boards will be fabricated by the two contractors, and the systems will be integrated into single-board computers. DARPA plans to receive the first prototype GaAs RISC CPU chips and floating-point coprocessor chips by early 1988. DARPA then expects completion of the first GaAs single-board computers for the GaAs AOSP project in early 1989.

A computer operating at a 200-MHz clock rate presents a serious design problem: data starvation. The main memory currently cannot supply instructions and data operands to the processor at a sufficiently high rate to keep it occupied. The provision of fast cache memory helps alleviate this problem. Both GaAs RISC development projects plan to use two off-chip cache memories (one for instructions and one for operands) and two cache controllers or memory manager chips.[11,12] The caches will be necessary in both the autonomous single-board computer system and the GaAs AOSP. These caches will be 1K words each, with an optimum access time of one nanosecond and a worst case access time of 2.5 ns. The complete computer system will contain

• the RISC CPU,
• two floating-point coprocessors,

• two cache memories,
• two memory management units,
• a system controller for low-speed I/O and external exceptions, and
• main memory.

The CPU chip may also function as an embedded controller for a system which supplies its own memory and does not require the floating-point coprocessor.

We believe that there is also considerable growth potential in the GaAs version of a MIPS processor chip set, which could be explored as follow-ons to the present projects. For example, with more available real estate on the chips, a cache memory or additional registers could be placed on chip. The addition of on-chip cache would provide a significant performance gain, since in current GaAs RISC designs a transfer bottleneck occurs between the microprocessor and its off-chip caches. Alternately, some of the floating-point functions now performed on the coprocessor chip could be incorporated into the microprocessor itself.

In addition, Rockwell International preliminary studies indicate the possibility of a MIPS-based machine operating at a 500-MHz clock rate and executing more than 200 million instructions per second. This version of the MIPS machine would require second-generation GaAs transistors, such as HEMTs or HBTs.

Silicon versions of the DoD MIPS machine. The GaAs RISC project has had an impact on concepts within DARPA, the US Air Force, and the Strategic Defense Initiative Office regarding optimum architectures for next-generation processors. In order to gain additional benefits from GaAs RISC developments in architecture, hardware, and software (see discussion on software), DARPA has initiated a parallel development in silicon. These microprocessors will be fabricated using bulk CMOS and CMOS/SOS to exploit the higher complexity levels available in silicon. Three contractors—Sperry, General Electric, and RCA—completed a one-year architecture study phase in 1986. Two of these contractors are now conducting a two-year phase to fabricate a silicon MIPS-type chip containing on-chip cache, and a floating-point coprocessor chip, with the target clock rate of 40 MHz. Silicon chip prototypes were successfully demonstrated by the two contractors in the late fall of 1987.

Establishment of a standard ISA and transportable software. The government agencies involved with these projects decided to establish a standard Instruction Set Architecture (ISA) for all MIPS-based machines. This standard provides software compatibility for all MIPS-based processors presently under development while still allowing flexibility at the hardware design level. An ISA is a list of attributes visible to an assembly-language programmer or to an HLL compiler. In general, an ISA description includes lists of data formats, instruction formats and mnemonics, addressing modes, available registers, memory and interrupt control structures, I/O operations, and detailed instruction-set requirements. However, an ISA does not include specific details for a given hardware implementation of a processor.

Carnegie Mellon University, Stanford University, Mayo Foundation, and the contractors currently implementing MIPS-based hardware collaborated to develop an ISA document for the DoD MIPS machines.[13] Their goal was to ensure that all versions of the MIPS processor will execute the same software on an interchangeable basis. This MIPS-based ISA currently serves as the baseline document for HLL compilers (in Pascal and Ada) under development through DoD sponsorship for the MIPS processors. Translators, or cross-assemblers, are also being written for the Motorola 68000 and for the Mil-Std-1750A microprocessors. Assembly-language programs previously written for these processors can then be used directly on any of the DoD-sponsored MIPS processors. This software is now available, with the exception of the Ada compiler. The Software Engineering Institute associated with Carnegie Mellon University is maintaining this software.

We now briefly describe several features required by the DoD-standard ISA for all current and future MIPS-based processors. The ISA increased the number of assembly-level instructions from 32 to 69. The additional instructions support

- unsigned arithmetic operations;
- byte, half-word, and word operations; and
- floating-point operations.

Most of these added instructions should still execute within a single machine cycle. Floating-point operations are executed in hardware on the coprocessor, or—in the absence of a coprocessor in applications not requiring high-speed floating-point operations—in software on the main processor. Single-precision integer and floating-point data operands are 32 bits wide, while double-precision data operands are 64 bits wide. At least 16 general-purpose, 32-bit registers and at least four 64-bit, floating-point registers must be available on these processors to satisfy the ISA. All data memory access is by explicit load and store instructions. Instructions continue to be addressed on word boundaries. However, addressing of data operands has been changed to a byte-addressed format. As a result of this change, data can be loaded and stored as byte, half-word, and word-sized operands. Only two addressing modes have been specified in this ISA: *absolute*, in which the address is specified directly; and *based*, in which the address is obtained by adding an offset to a base register.

Several changes not specified in the standard ISA have also been made, which appear to improve the efficiency of the GaAs implementations of MIPS in comparison to the original Stanford MIPS architecture. These changes include

- modification of the number of pipestages from five to three in one implementation and to six in the other;
- initiation of a new instruction every machine cycle, rather than every other cycle; and
- elimination of the capability of packing two assembly-language instructions into one machine instruction.

(Instruction packing unnecessarily complicates the design of the processor control section.)

An additional feature of the GaAs RISC implementations is that up to eight coprocessors can be attached to a single microprocessor chip. These coprocessors do not necessarily have to be floating-point coprocessors.

Coprocessor implementations. Because the coprocessor architectures currently being implemented with the GaAs RISC processors vary considerably, we present only one of the coprocessor implementations under development.[11] The microprocessor and its coprocessor operate synchronously from a common clock and have common instruction address, instruction data, and operand data buses. The microprocessor calculates memory addresses and initiates memory references and then continues executing its own instructions. The coprocessor accepts its own instructions and data and outputs its values either to memory or to the processor. The system presently is designed to operate with two floating-point coprocessors attached to a single processor. All three operate concurrently. The design also allows for the addition of up to six additional coprocessors. Each of the two coprocessors has a separate operation code field in the instruction word. The coprocessor interrupts the processor on a floating-point exception. The microprocessor then determines the cause of the exception by reading the coprocessor status register, and the appropriate software handler is executed by the microprocessor. The coprocessor monitors the processor's status bits and uses this information to track the pipeline-stage sequencing in the processor to detect wait states and exceptions that may affect the operations within the coprocessor.

All coprocessor instructions have a fixed execution time with no operand dependencies. This simplifies the reorganizer's scheduling task. The predictability of coprocessor operations and the presence of instruction prefetching simplify pipelining. Instruction prefetching means that a new instruction word is fetched on the last cycle of the previous instruction. Two arithmetic instructions are loaded into the coprocessor with one instruction word, so that the second instruction can be initiated immediately upon completion of the first. The control signals for the operating cycles of each coprocessor are decoded one cycle ahead, eliminating control decode time and making the cycle time dependent only on the data path.

This coprocessor design is divided into two sections—the bus interface unit and the arithmetic unit—each with separate control. The chip area devoted to control of the coprocessor is very small, consisting of two small PLAs and using only 20 percent of the transistors on the coprocessor. The bus interface unit performs conditional branching and testing and monitors the instruction bus while the arithmetic unit is processing data. This architectural approach allows the CPU to execute a "branch on coprocessor busy" operation rather than executing No-op instructions. This approach also enables a branch based upon the results of the first arithmetic instruction while the second instruction is executing in the coprocessor.

The arithmetic unit is optimized for floating-point operations and provides full double-precision data paths. Eight double-precision operand registers are also available. Operands are converted to single-

precision values only during load and store operations. The exponent and significant processors of the arithmetic unit are separate and operate in parallel. A single- or double-precision add or subtract operation requires four clock cycles to complete, plus two additional clock cycles if normalization is required. The multiply operation is performed 2 bits at a time, requiring 15 cycles to complete a single-precision multiplication and 30 cycles to execute a double-precision multiplication. The coprocessor hardware supports four rounding modes from the *ANSI/IEEE Standard 754-1985 for Binary Floating-Point Arithmetic*, as well as six exceptions.

This coprocessor implementation appears to be very efficient and should demonstrate a substantial execution rate.

Silicon microprocessor designers have capitalized on the availability of large numbers of gates on VLSI chips to create complicated architectures based on parallelism and a complex set of assembly-language instructions. A gallium arsenide implementation of a microprocessor requires an alternate design approach with the availability of a limited number of gates and very fast transistors. Our study of microprocessor architectures demonstrated that a simple design, implementing in hardware only a small set of frequently used assembly-language instructions, is better suited to a GaAs fabrication technology than is a more complex design. More complicated functions are implemented in software tightly coupled to the hardware. Several computer architectures with these characteristics, known as RISCs, have been developed in the past few years. A review of these architectures indicated that one of them, the MIPS machine developed by Stanford University, could be fabricated in GaAs with approximately 10,000 gates and may operate at a clock rate of 200 MHz with a sustained throughput of 100 million instructions per second. Digital GaAs technology can take advantage of the fact that the MIPS architecture is very simple and relies heavily upon an instruction pipeline and a sophisticated assembler.

The original goal of our microprocessor evaluation project was the identification of a 32-bit microprocessor architecture that could not only execute at high speed but could also be entirely implemented on a single GaAs chip (with the exclusion of the floating-point coprocessor) in the near future. Because the MIPS architecture appeared to offer this possibility, two GaAs implementations of this architecture are presently under development,[11,12] as is the required software support. The DoD-sponsored MIPS will be able to function both as a stand-alone computer and also as a microprocessor embedded within more complex processors fabricated either in silicon or GaAs, as in the DARPA/Air Force AOSP. ▓

Acknowledgments

This research was supported in part by contracts MDA-903-84-C-0324, N66001-85-C-0337, and F29601-84-C0016 from the Defense Advanced Research Projects Agency. The authors wish to thank C.L. Bates, D.D. Endry, S.M. Karwoski, L.M. Krueger, J.M. Ryan, M.L. Samson, D.J. Schwab, B.R. Shamblin, R.L. Thompson, C.R. Treder, T.L. Volkman, and S.K. Zahn of the Mayo Foundation for technical assistance; S. Roosild of DARPA and S. Karp for helpful discussions; and E.M. Doherty and S.J. Richardson of the Mayo Foundation for preparation of text and figures.

References

1. B.K. Gilbert et al., "Signal Processors Based Upon GaAs ICs: The Need for a Wholistic Design Approach," *Computer*, Oct. 1986, pp. 29-43.

2. *Military Standard Sixteen-Bit Computer Instruction Set Architecture*, MIL-STD-1750A (USAF), US Gov't Printing Office: 1980-603-121/3202, Department of Defense, Washington, DC, May 21, 1982.

3. *VHSIC Data Processor Unit Integrated Circuit Specification*, Preliminary Draft, Revision C, Texas Instruments, Dallas, Tex., Feb. 21, 1985.

4. M.G.H. Katevinis, *Reduced Instruction Set Computer Architectures for VLSI,* doctoral dissertation, Univ. of California, Berkeley, Calif., Report No. UCB/CSD 83/141, Oct. 1983.

5. G. Radin, "The 801 Minicomputer," *IBM Journal of Research and Development,* May 1983, p. 237.

6. I. Barron et al., "Transputer Does 5 or More Mips Even When Not Used in Parallel," *Electronics,* Nov. 17, 1983, p. 109.

7. S.A. Przbylski et al., "Organization and VLSI Implementation of MIPS," Tech. Report No. 84-259, Computer Systems Laboratory, Stanford Univ., Stanford, Calif., April 1984.

8. J.L. Hennessy et al., 'Hardware/Software Tradeoffs for Increased Performance," Tech. Report No. 228, Computer Systems Laboratory, Stanford Univ., Feb. 1983.

9. J.L. Hennessy et al., "Design of a High Performance VLSI Processor," Tech. Report No. 236, Computer Systems Laboratory, Stanford Univ., Feb. 1983.

10. J.L. Hennessy et al., "MIPS: A VLSI Processor Architecture," Tech. Report No. 223, Computer Systems Laboratory, Stanford Univ., June 1983.

11. T.L. Rasset et al.,"A 32-Bit RISC Implemented in Enhancement-Mode JFET GaAs," *Computer*, Oct. 1986, pp. 60-68.

12. E.R. Fox et al., "Reduced Instruction Set Architecture for a GaAs Microprocessor System," *Computer*, Oct. 1986, pp. 71-80.

13. T. Gross and R. Firth, *Core Set of Assembly Language Instructions for MIPS-based Microprocessors*, Version 3.2, Software Eng. Inst., Pittsburgh, Pa., Nov. 18, 1986.

Barbara A. Naused has been a computer design engineer at the Mayo Foundation's special-purpose processor development group since 1981. Her experience includes signal processor architecture systems and GaAs integrated circuit design, comparative reviews of microprocessor architectures, and hardware and software design.

Barbara Naused received her BS degree in applied mathematics from the University of Wisconsin in 1981 and is currently completing an MS degree in electrical engineering from the University of Minnesota.

Barry K. Gilbert is staff scientist and director of the special purpose processor development group at the Mayo Foundation. He is currently responsible for the design and development of computer-aided engineering tools and hardware design methods to exploit the speed performance of GaAs digital ICs in the next generation of high-performance signal processors. His interests include the development of algorithms for the real-time analysis of wide-bandwidth image and signal data and the design of specialized computers to execute these tasks.

Barry Gilbert received his BS degree in electrical engineering from Purdue University in 1965 and his PhD in physiology/biophysics from the University of Minnesota, Minneapolis, in 1972.

Questions about this article may be directed to Barbara Naused at the Department of Physiology and Biophysics, Mayo Foundation, Rochester, MN 55905.

Toward a GaAs Realization of a Production-System Machine

Theodore F. Lehr and Robert G. Wedig

Carnegie Mellon University

The computation and memory demands of OPS5 production systems suggest that the underlying production-system machine architecture can take advantage of a high-speed realization technology.

Production systems are a special class of expert systems. *Expert systems* are tailored programs or system environments that are designed to handle problems whose solution normally requires human expertise in a particular area. In this article, we attempt to demonstrate the issues involved in realizing a GaAs processor designed for efficient execution of the OPS5 production-system language. [1-3] We review the state of GaAs D-MESFET technology, which is a mature technology, and discuss how its capacities can be exploited by a reduced instruction set computer (RISC) called RISCF.* RISCF was designed at Carnegie Mellon University.

A *production-system machine* is a machine whose architecture and implementation are optimized for the execution of production-system languages. The OPS5 production-system language is currently being researched and used at Carnegie Mellon University, as well as at a number of industrial sites.

OPS5 has several advantages over other production-system languages. It is generally easier to encode rules in OPS5 than in other types of expert-system languages. Unfortunately, OPS5 suffers from the same problem that plagues all production-system languages—insufficient execution performance.

Research on improving the execution speed of production systems has been conducted at Carnegie Mellon on three basic fronts:

- investigation of the maximum amount of parallelism that can be built into a production system,
- the evaluation and development of special-purpose architectures for production-system execution, and
- investigation of alternative implementation technologies for production-system machines.

Only through the combination of parallelism, architecture, and technology can the highest system performance be achieved.

Investigation of parallelism in production systems was performed by Anoop Gupta and Lanny Forgy, both of Carnegie Mellon. Their work has been reported by Gupta [3,5] and will not be discussed here except to note that they determined that a small number of processors connected by means of a tightly coupled network can at-

---

An earlier version of this article appeared on pp. 246-252 of the *Proceedings of the 19th Hawaii International Conference on System Sciences* under the title "The GaAs Realization of a Production-System Machine." © 1986 IEEE.

*RISCF conforms to the definition of a RISC given by Cowell et al. [4]

tain a significant amount of the parallelism available in OPS5 production-system programs.

Jim Quinlan of Carnegie Mellon performed a study[6] of the suitability of different architectures for production-system machines. In this study, he compared a number of commercial computers that run production-system programs with each other and with two proposed special-purpose machines. The results of the architectural analysis indicate that when a custom RISC processor is given the same cycle time as a complex microcoded architecture designed solely for the execution of production-system programs, it can perform as well as the microcoded architecture, or better.

Our work is to investigate the issues involved in realizing a RISC processor in gallium arsenide to obtain estimates of parameters like the cycle time and the basic system requirements of such a processor. The work reported in this article is a feasibility study of a GaAs implementation of RISCF. This study, which was performed with the cooperation of the Honeywell Corporate Systems Development Division near Minneapolis, Minnesota, focuses on the feasibility, design, and layout of, and performance estimates for, a D-MESFET implementation of a customized processor for the execution of production-system languages. It was carried out by the authors from the fall of 1983 until December of 1985. The work was performed solely by the authors, although Honeywell provided the packaging, density, and technology specifications and the CAD facilities for verifying the accuracy of the design. Ours was a feasibility study, and the design has not been implemented; however, through this work, we have been better able to determine the feasibility of GaAs as a system-realization technology, and we have helped to push back the limits of the execution speed of production-system programs.

Quinlan's study of five architectures[6] suggests that two proposed architectures—a microcoded machine with long, semantically complex instructions and a specially designed RISC processor (RISCF)—are best suited for executing production systems. Since these architectures are markedly dissimilar, it may seem odd that microcoded and RISC processors have comparable performance for OPS5 applications. Quinlan points out, however, that computer-system issues, such as available processor-memory bandwidth, are critical factors affecting the relative

R1: IF light blue exhaust smoke AND
     low compression THEN check piston rings

R2: IF unburned gas in exhaust AND
     low compression THEN check valves and valve seats

R3: IF compression ratio < 6.5:1 THEN low compression

Figure 1. Some rules from a hypothetical production system.

performance of both these machines.

In this article, we assume that each serves a host machine as either a dedicated accelerator or a coprocessor. The systems issues that arise when they are dedicated processors or coprocessors that execute only OPS5 are different from those that arise when they are machines of more general utility. In the case of RISCF, we also assume that we have access to high memory bandwidth. By "realization," we mean roughly the semiconductor technologies on which a machine is built. "Implementation" refers to the machine's register-transfer-level description, and "architecture" usually refers to its instruction-set design, although the boundary between "implementation" and "architecture" is not constant across all machines. We are indebted for our use of the terms to an unpublished manuscript by Blaauw and Brooks.[7]

For purposes of illuminating the issues that arise when one attempts to realize a processor in GaAs, we have made the GaAs realization of the RISCF production-system machine our principal thrust in this article. Given the complexity of the microcoded architecture, any reasonable implementation would be quite large, and hence we do not consider that a feasible realization in GaAs is possible with today's technology. RISCF, however, has single-cycle instruction execution, is predominantly load/store in design, and is composed of relatively few instructions. It also has a regular instruction format and a fixed 32-bit instruction width. In Lehr,[8] the implementation of this architecture is discussed, and a number of its interesting features are presented.

Every semiconductor technology—whether it be NMOS, ECL, or MESFET—has fabrication and design rules that uniquely affect the implementation of a system. In our researches, we used GaAs D-MESFET logic because it is one of the most established GaAs technologies. (Companies like Honeywell and Rockwell offer product lines based on D-MESFET technology.)

OPS5 and the Rete algorithm

OPS5 is an efficient production-system language in which rules are codified in the form of a search tree called the *Rete tree*.[1,2]

The less efficient production systems typically store a list of rules in one memory space and a formal description of the problem in another. Searching for a match between the LHS of the rules and the elements of the problem is performed in these systems by indexing through the two memories in such a way that each entry in one is compared with every entry in the other. Although the inefficiency of this method can be mitigated with techniques like hashing the lists by means of certain keys, these are frequently just *ad hoc* improvements because they seldom take advantage of behavior indigenous to production systems.

In contrast, the OPS5 search tree is constructed to take advantage of the propensity in production systems for parts of conditionals to exist in the LHS of more than one rule. For example, in Figure 1, R1, R2, and R3 represent three rules in a hypothetical production system for auto-engine diagnostics. (Of course, in actual OPS5 code, these rules would be formally specified.) Since R1 and R2 share the condition "low compression" in their LHSs, the tree guarantees that when this condition is found in the problem space, each rule will simultaneously instantiate the "low compression" part of its LHS. That is, both rules concurrently get their LHSs partially satisfied. Despite the prevalence of such shared conditions, previous production-system languages did not exploit them.

The Rete tree is part of the more general *Rete matching algorithm*. As we just noted, the tree takes advantage of structural similarities between the LHSs of rules in OPS5 production systems. In addition to exploiting this property, Rete also capitalizes on temporal similarities between the elements in the problem. As we noted earlier, production systems make several passes through a problem, updating it each time rules are satisfied. The Rete algorithm recognizes that it does not need to look for a match in the entire updated problem, only in the part of the problem that has just changed. Consequently, Rete records those aspects of the problem that have been altered and applies the rules to only those altered parts. For example, should a 5:1 compression ratio be one of the problem elements in the hypothetical engine-diagnostic system mentioned earlier, rule R3 would add the element "low compression" to the problem description. Then, in the next pass through the problem, the Rete algorithm would attempt to match only "low compression" to the LHSs of the rules, since any partial matches from the first pass would still exist. In this case, rules R1 and R2 would be partially instantiated. If the element "light blue exhaust smoke" had been found in the first pass, R1 would be fully instantiated in the second pass, which would indicate that the rings should be examined.

A study of the Rete algorithm's implementation demands shows that where conventional processors are involved, the kinds of computations it performs after a memory access are usually simple. Once data is resident in a conventional processor, only simple arithmetic instructions are needed to perform the matching tests. Heavy memory traffic and a preponderance of simple instructions are two key run-time characteristics of the Rete algorithm. They are also characteristic of matching algorithms for less efficient production systems, since the computation most often done in production systems is the comparison of two operands.

A third characteristic of the Rete algorithm is the prevalence of branch instructions over other types. One of the reasons for this is that part of the Rete algorithm consists of the Rete tree, which is built upon the antecedent parts of all the rules in the production system. The Rete tree is a complex structure that implements not only the sharing of parts of antecedents, but also implements a number of other features of the Rete algorithm. It must be traversed while the algorithm tests for matches. The tree, however, is mapped onto the sequential code of a uniprocessor. Consequently, when moving among the branches of the Rete tree, the processor is frequently forced to jump to noncontiguous localities in the instruction stream. The jump frequency is heightened further because the processor is usually

executing iterative loops when it is at branch nodes in the tree.

These three characteristics—high memory traffic, the simplicity of instructions in OPS5, and frequent branching—drive designs for the architecture and implementation of the processor for executing OPS5. We do not know if a preponderance of branching instructions is a property of other production systems, although the simple, repetitive nature of searching for matches makes this likely.

The architecture and implementation of RISCF

When compiled into assembly-language instructions, the Rete algorithm consists of many Load-Jump and Compare-Jump sequences. It does not need complex instructions, but requires only a few simple Load, Compare, and Jump types. A sequential processor dedicated exclusively to executing OPS5 can be based on a small core of simple instructions that have the potential for being executed in a single cycle. Other Rete characteristics favor a processor that can efficiently support both (a) heavy data traffic in and out of memory and (b) frequent branching.

An OPS5-executing processor that is built on a set of simple instructions and optimized to support all these Rete characteristics can achieve a speedup over an uncustomized OPS5-executing processor that supports numerous complex instructions. This is so because the overhead of supporting instructions superfluous to OPS5 execution is eliminated. Such a processor architecture—one built primarily of simple Load-Store instructions, each of which executes in one machine cycle—suggests a RISC-like architecture. John Cock of IBM initiated the seminal work on RISC architectures with the 801 minicomputer.[9] This machine inspired work done at Berkeley[10] and Stanford[11] and has affected the design of some recently introduced commercial machines.

The instruction set of RISCF, the RISC we developed for executing OPS5, is streamlined to accommodate the properties of the Rete algorithm. (The "F" in "RISCF" refers to Charles L. Forgy of Carnegie Mellon, the developer of the Rete algorithm.) Compare-and-branch and Load-and-branch instruction sequences are implemented under a static branch-prediction strategy. Memory-

reference instructions use simple addressing techniques, and Arithmetic-logic instructions are decoded and executed in a single machine cycle. All of RISCF's instructions are 32 bits long. The main data type is the 32-bit integer, and the only arithmetic operations are Add and Subtract. RISCF has four addressing modes: absolute, immediate, base register plus displacement, and register. The functional integrity of all RISCF subsystems except the caches has been verified in a simulation done on the MIMOLA Software System.[12,13]

The RISCF branch-prediction strategy is integrated into a three-stage data pipeline. Ordinarily, a heavily pipelined machine suffers performance degradation when it runs programs with incessant branching. The degradation occurs because a branch to a different program location usually requires that the pipe be flushed, which reduces the concurrency available on the machine. The degradation is most serious when it frequently happens that the data in the pipeline is dependent on previous or subsequent data, or when there are frequent cache misses. Both the simplicity of RISCF's single-cycle instructions and its branch-addressing mode, however, curtail such data dependencies. We applied statistics on the runtimes of typical OPS5 programs[14] to RISCF instruction sequences that were generated by James Quinlan.[6] The results show that a static branch-prediction scheme speeds up RISCF's execution of the Rete algorithm by 15 percent over RISCF execution of the algorithm without branch prediction.

In developing a processor's pipeline, the types of instructions, the instruction sequences, and the frequency of cache misses are important design parameters. The simplicity of the RISCF instruction set and the regularity of RISCF operations allow for uncomplicated pipelining. The only data dependencies that exist between instructions and can cause pipe breaks are those between Branch-prediction instructions and Branch instructions. An internal forwarding mechanism handles any dependencies that arise between instructions requiring common registers. Despite the value of the pipeline, the high number of branch instructions used in the Rete algorithm might indicate incessant pipe breaks and recurrent cache misses. However, the RISCF pipeline is structured to permit the decoder to decode all instruction sequences without pipe breaks except when those sequences harbor incorrectly predicted branches. These isolated sequences are slower than straight line code by one machine cycle.

The efficiency of the pipeline is also enhanced by the structure of RISCF's register file. The register file is a large, 128-bit × 32-bit structure consisting of two read ports and a single write port. It is meant to hold critical elements from the problem space and pointers to various matching tests in the Rete tree. The register file's ports are essential components in establishing RISCF's three-stage pipeline. If the processor-control state asks for parallel reading and writing of the same register, the write data is forwarded internally, which guarantees that the most up-to-date data is sent to the ALU. RISCF does not require an ALU with complex functionality because the predominant operation performed by the processor is the comparing of an operand from data memory with a register operand. Consequently, the ALU is a simple structure with only 10 functions.

RISCF derives some of its performance from logically separate instruction and data caches. For a RISC processor, especially one realized in GaAs, memory bandwidth is a critical performance factor. Executing an instruction every machine cycle requires memory fast enough to supply the instructions. The dual RISC caches permit simultaneous fetching of one instruction while the operand of another is retrieved. Without the additional cache, the processor would need to delay the instruction fetch each time data was fetched from memory. Lehr[8] suggests that a large data cache (32K bytes × 32 bytes or larger) can hold over 90 percent of all data references. It is not likely, however, that such a large cache would operate fast enough for a GaAs RISC. Fortunately, data references in OPS5 frequently exhibit a high degree of locality, so a smaller cache is probably sufficient. The architecture of the memory interface is an important area for further research.

RISCF is a superior uniprocessor architecture for production systems—and for OPS5 production systems in particular—because its instruction set is tailored to executing the Rete algorithm and because the size and simplicity of its instruction set permit the machine to fetch an instruction every machine cycle. The RISCF instructions are basically a modified subset of the instruction sets found on larger, more complex machines (there are Compare-and-predict-to-branch instructions, for example). RISCF instructions are basically those that are usually used to

implement the Rete algorithm on these larger machines. The computational requirements of the Rete algorithm, including those for making control-flow decisions, are simple enough that an instruction set designed to support the algorithm can be implemented on a machine that offers single-cycle execution. Such a machine—RISCF is an example—takes maximum advantage of the available memory bandwidth, since *with respect to the Rete algorithm*, RISCF has a very high ratio of useful computations per memory reference. This high ratio is usually not a characteristic of RISC machines designed

---

RISCF is a superior uniprocessor architecture for production systems.

---

for a broader range of applications, but RISCF is intended for a single application.

The notion of useful computations per memory reference is a complex and subtle one. The ratio depends on the meaning assigned to "useful," and therefore on the application being executed. The microcoded machine proposed by Quinlan[6] tries to maximize the ratio of useful computations per memory reference, but does so by raising the architectural level of the machine above typical assembly-language instructions to that of an instruction set that more directly executes the primitive operations of the Rete algorithm. Quinlan carefully discusses the assumptions behind RISCF and the microcoded machine, and he analyzes the performance that results when OPS5 is executed on architectures like the VAX/780. With its shorter cycle times, RISCF is superior to the microcoded machine when the problem of increased processor-memory bandwidth (a problem inherent in RISC machines) is mitigated.

It is difficult to compare machines as dissimilar as a VAX/780 and RISCF, for the VAX is a computer *system* designed for a multiprogramming environment, while RISCF is a dedicated *processor* designed for executing OPS5. How well the processor architectures of the 780 and RISCF execute production systems depends on their implementations and on the systems in which they are placed. In addition, while the 780 is a successful commercial product on which physical experiments can be made directly, RISCF is

a set of architecture and implementation specifications whose performance has been verified through computer simulations. In his study, Quinlan[6] derives performance estimates for the architectures by means of such metrics as instruction/data traffic and the number of machine cycles required to execute OPS5 programs. One of the metrics attempts to base the estimate of the execution times on more of a *processor-to-processor* analysis by decoupling the VAX architecture from its memory-management system. This decoupling is done by packing the Rete code in tight loops, which enables the 780 to obtain nearly a 100 percent hit ratio in cache memory. In such a case, the match time of OPS5 running on a VAX/780 that accesses cache every 200 ns is approximately two to four times longer than the match time of RISCF that is realized in NMOS VLSI and has a 300-ns cycle time.

As a RISC machine, however, RISCF can take greater advantage than a VAX can of the higher speeds that come from reduced chip counts. Consequently, a high-speed realization of RISCF in GaAs is likely to widen the performance gap. Because of RISCF's architectural simplicity, a silicon realization would require a relatively small amount of real estate. This simplicity means that it is worth considering whether a GaAs realization is viable. In considering this, one must first analyze those characteristics of GaAs devices that affect system-design issues.

Factors affecting the performance of GaAs ICs

Questions of the viability of realizing RISCF in GaAs and of the advantages RISCF might obtain from such a realization suggest that one should examine how GaAs differs from silicon with respect to the logic structures, scale of integration, and signal-propagation behavior.

Available logic structures. Designing digital circuits in GaAs D-MESFET technology is attended by two major constraints not encountered when one designs with silicon technology in mind.

The first constraint arises because only depletion-mode transistors are used. This constraint means that at least two voltage sources must be used. If a depletion-mode transistor has its source tied to ground and its drain connected to some positive potential, it can only turn off if a potential less than or equal to its pinch-off voltage is applied to its gate. Consequently, unless two or more sources are available, or unless elaborate charge-pump circuits are used, D-MESFETs will always be on.

The second constraint is a consequence of the small pinch-off voltage usually found in depletion mode MESFETs (the usual pinch-off voltage is $V_p \approx -1$ volt) and of the range of the output-voltage swings ($\Delta V_{out} \approx 1.0$ volt).[15] At a fixed gate potential, small V_p (that is, when V_p is close to zero) do not permit channels to conduct as strongly as they conduct for larger V_p. Since the channels are less conductive, there is a comparatively large drop in the drain-source voltage (V_{ds}) across the transistor. This relationship between V_p and V_{ds} removes basic NAND gates and most pass transistors from the set of viable design alternatives.[16] The large voltage drop across each of the NAND pull-down transistors when they are off raises the low-voltage logic levels of GaAs chips dangerously high. This prevents the gate from driving load transistors. Although NAND gates and pass transistors can be fabricated, the designer must either accept reduced switching speeds or have access to very fine process control to produce circuits of the quality necessary to prescribe the device parameters accurately. Typically, however, the low logic levels and diminished noise margins obtained by placing two MESFETs in the usual pull-down configuration of an NMOS NAND gate are unacceptable. Pass transistors suffer the same effects from that configuration: large drain-source voltage drops and diminished noise margins.

To the integrated circuit designer accustomed to the variety offered by silicon MOSFETs, the absence of NAND gates and pass transistors imposes onerous constraints on the complexity and functionality that can be packed into a given chip area. The designer can no longer implement a simple multiplexer that incorporates an array of pass transistors selected by inverted and noninverted control signals, but must instead derive the canonical expressions for the multiplexer and coax them into a form generally consisting of NOR gates. Consequently, a GaAs multiplexer and some other integrated structures require more transistors than their silicon MOSFET alternatives. If the GaAs version of a structure uses more gate stages than a functionally identical silicon circuit, the effect of the structure on the speed advantage enjoyed by in-

dividual GaAs devices is diminished. The inability to map silicon gate structures directly onto functionally similar structures in GaAs also affects comparisons of the achievable scales of integration in the two technologies.

The scale of integration in GaAs. In order for large digital systems to benefit from the intrachip speeds of GaAs, the scale of integration must increase so that greater functionality can be placed on a single chip. The number of transistors that can be placed on a single GaAs chip with acceptable yield has recently tipped 25,000 in the implementation of highly regular structures like static RAMs. Less densely packed systems include gate arrays and parallel multipliers that contain between 1000 and 10,000 transistors.[17-19] Each of the integrated circuits exhibits the high-speed, low-power characteristics usually associated with GaAs, but usually also endures weak fan-out performance. For example, the Honeywell HGAS-500 gate array is a fast (~ 0.25 ns per logic gate) aggregate of NOR/OR-NAND gates, but it has maximum dc fan-outs of only two for unbuffered NOR and OR-NAND gates and of five for buffered NOR gates.[20] The low fan-out of GaAs buffers is a stumbling block to designers: It will force them to confront dismal interchip propagation delays for large systems until GaAs advances from LSI to VLSI.

The move to VLSI and the advantages that may be derived from it hinge on process-control improvements and the kinds of gates that may be fabricated. As was noted in the section on "Available logic structures," the circuit geometries of transistors in silicon MOSFET structures and those in functionally equivalent GaAs MESFET structures are not mirror images of one another. Since D-MESFET circuits cannot use NAND gates and pass transistors, they typically require more transistors for implementation of a digital system than a MOSFET circuit would. This discrepancy may disappear, however, as decreases in feature sizes, in voltage swings, and in tolerances for threshold-voltage variations cause difficulties in implementing NAND gates and pass transistors in future silicon VLSI technology. In addition, the advent of reliable heterojunction bipolar transistors (HJBTs) will eventually introduce NAND gates and pass transistors to GaAs, but this technology is still years away from being a viable VLSI alternative. Although larger chip areas are required for circuits limited

to NOR and compound-logic gates, this is not the principal obstacle impeding successful VLSI fabrication in GaAs.

The major impediment to reducing both the sizes of features and the voltage swings of GaAs integrated circuits is that chip yield is very poor.[16,21] As integration scales increase, the swing of gate voltages must decrease so that manageable power-dissipation levels can be maintained. Decreasing gate-voltage swings necessitates the reduction of threshold-voltage deviations across a wafer. Threshold voltages are not constant over a wafer, but deviate from an ideal threshold voltage according to some statistical distribution. In order to ensure that many of the chips on the wafer function correctly, the range of gate-voltage swings must be adjusted to accommodate the worst-case threshold values. This is required so that one can be certain that the transistors having those values will be forced to turn on and off. In light of this, it can be seen that the poor control over threshold voltages in GaAs technology forces voltage swings in the logic to widen. As was just noted, the larger voltage swings cause the typical transistor to dissipate more power, and if the power dissipation is too large, it must be countered by increasing device sizes—which means lower circuit-integration scales. Once GaAs performance parameters achieve the sensitivity necessary for VLSI circuits, the advantages of the faster device speeds will be realized more easily. Off-chip delays will then be less critical, since the logic that used to be distributed over several chips will be present on one. Long intrachip paths, however, might occur more frequently. Since only SSI, MSI, and LSI circuits are currently available in GaAs, any timing studies of systems as large as RISCF must look at both on- and off-chip signal propagations.

Propagation delays. Interchip signal propagation comprises a significant part of the circuit delays in both GaAs and silicon systems. Although intrachip signals propagate faster than interchip broadcasts, the geometry of an integrated circuit can pose difficult problems in timing subcircuits for harmonious operation. Long intrachip buses occasionally confiscate substantial chip area for routing, and they usually diminish the effects of fast device speeds by loading driver transistors. Though delays resulting from the length of intrachip buses are not endemic to gallium arsenide, integrated circuits in GaAs are more vulnerable to them than their silicon cousins in that as bus lengths increase, the speed advantage that GaAs has over silicon begins to decrease.[18] However, since GaAs integrated circuits have not yet reached the VLSI level, the predominant propagation delays continue to be at interchip interfaces.

The advantage RISCF would obtain from a GaAs technology that has not matured to the VLSI level would depend on how well RISCF could be modularized to reduce the effects of interchip delays. The decomposition of RISCF into modules depends on transistor counts, communication paths, and the number of I/O pins permitted on each chip module.

Modularizing RISCF for gallium arsenide

The modularization of RISCF that we discuss below is based on conservative estimates of the numbers of gates for different structures and on an upper pin-out bound of around 80.

Since D-MESFET systems can be scaled no further than the LSI level, RISCF must be decomposed into modularized chips if it is to be realized in this GaAs technology. Dissecting RISCF requires determining the approximate number of gates needed for each substructure, the shared communication paths, and the maximum pin-out allowed for a GaAs chip. An estimate of the speed of the modularized processor requires that one know approximate intrachip delays and the nature of interchip loading. Our modularization of RISCF is contrived in part from the performance-affecting factors (available logic structures, integration scale, and propagation delays) that were discussed in the section on "Factors affecting GaAs performance," and in part from information acquired from the Honeywell, Inc., Physical Sciences Center located outside of Minneapolis, Minnesota.[20] (We used the Honeywell data in our analysis of the main substructures of the processor—the analysis is given below—and we used the analysis, in turn, to arrive at an estimate of the machine-cycle time.)

We have selected the logic of each of the substructures primarily for its simplicity, not for gate conservation or for attractive performance characteristics. By limiting each substructure of the processor to configurations of NOR and NOT gates and by using rudimentary logic implementations, we have established a conservative upper

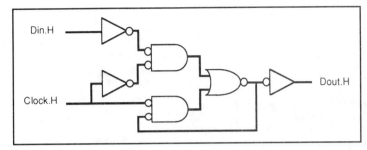

Figure 2. A single static-latch bit.

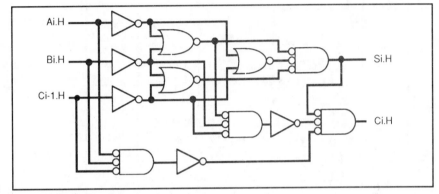

Figure 3. A ripple-carry adder.

bound on the number of gates needed by each major substructure. For example, though a parallel adder will most likely outperform a simple ripple-carry type, the implementation considerations for a parallel adder are more complex and its logic structure is more elaborate. Since the modularization of RISCF makes intermodule communication the major source of performance degradation, it would be premature to select elaborate logic implementations for their potential performance gains before the modularity is established. More significantly, the purpose of selecting gate configurations is not to ascertain the optimal modularity of RISCF, but to help realize a modularization that has the advantage of simplicity.

Gate geometries of RISCF substructures. The substructures of RISCF include register-transfer-level (RTL) units like registers, incrementers, the ALU, multiplexers, and other structures of similar complexity. In assigning the gate geometry to these structures, we have used only NOR and NOT gates and we have paid no attention to the different transistor configurations used in GaAs to implement these gates.

We assume that the inputs and outputs of the structures described below are asserted high.

Register. Since reliable pass transistors cannot be implemented in GaAs MESFET

technology, a GaAs static register cell consists only of standard NOR and NOT gates. Figure 2 depicts a single static-latch bit. A latch contains six gates per bit.

Multiplexer. The absence of pass transistors most strongly affects the implementation of multiplexers. Instead of being implemented as an array of pass transistors that are all controlled by a single input-select unit, a GaAs multiplexer is implemented with an armada of combinational logic. A GaAs multiplexer requires $2n + 1$ gates per bit, where n is the number of inputs.

Adder. The number of gates in the single adder cell shown in Figure 3 also reflects the absence of pass transistors. The central goal in synthesizing a modularization scheme is to arrive at a rough estimate of processor-cycle time. Consequently, we have made no special efforts to implement a fast adder, since it would not contribute to the accuracy of the estimates. The adder is a simple ripple-carry type. It contains 10 gates per bit.

Incrementer. In GaAs, an incrementer is a simplified adder in which one of the summands is a single bit equal to one. Consequently, we have constructed the incrementer out of half-adders that add the carry of the previous bit to the current bit. An incrementer has seven gates.

Decrementer. The logic construction of a GaAs decrementer is similar to that of the incrementer. Like the incrementer, it

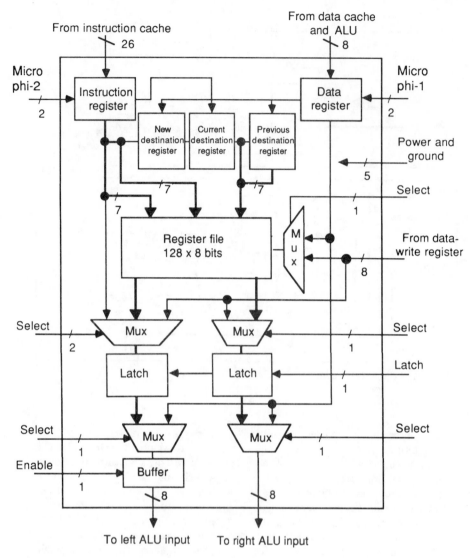

Figure 4. A register-file module.

has seven gates per bit.

ALU. The arithmetic-logic unit of RISCF can perform one of six operations each machine cycle. The operations are

• *Addition.* The geometry of the logic of the ALU's addition function can be much like that of the adder structure shown in Figure 3, but the geometry is somewhat constrained because of the other ALU operations.

• *Subtraction.* This operation is implemented in the form of the gate geometry of the addition function; however, it includes the simple twos-complement converter on one of the inputs.

•*Signextend.* The first 19 bits of input *a* are passed directly to the output. The nineteenth bit's value is passed to each of the succeeding bits and is transferred to their output. Passing the bit value on to the succeeding bits is easily achieved if a two-gate drive is placed every three bits or so.

•*Hiload.* The values of the lower 16 bits of input *a* are passed to the upper 16 bits of input *b* and are concatenated with the lower 16 bits of input *b*. The modified *b* value is sent to the output. The bit values to be passed can simply be gated into their proper locations.

•*Passleft* and *Passright.* In Passleft, the left input is selected to be passed to the ALU output. (In Passright, it's the right input.) The gating is relatively trivial.

•*Or, And, Xor,* and *Not.* These logic instructions can be implemented simply, and their gating is trivial.

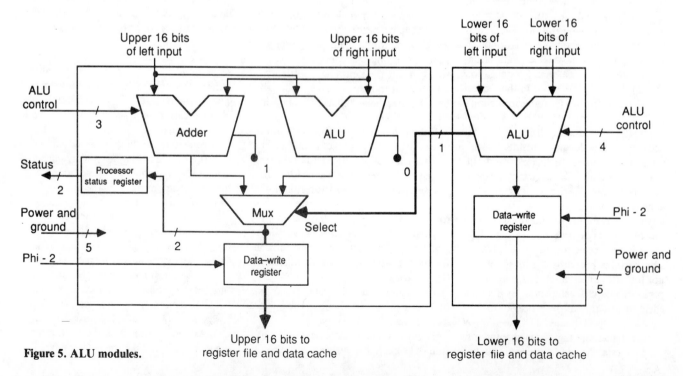

Figure 5. ALU modules.

We do not discuss in this article the gate geometries of the *Select* logic for the ALU and multiplexer, since these geometries are not complex. They have physically large realizations, however, so that they can drive control signals across the structures, but these large realizations are only significant if the gate counts per module approach LSI limitations.

In addition, there are several logic structures in the control section of RISCF that check for equality, inequality, and other relationships, but these are typically not very wide and occur infrequently.

A possible modularization scheme. The gate geometries just discussed permit approximations of the number of gates belonging to the individual modules of a given modularization scheme. A good modularization scheme attempts to decompose RISCF in such a way that critical paths and closely related substructures are kept within individual modules. Figures 4, 5, 6, and 7 depict our RISCF decomposition scheme, which attempts to satisfy the demands of pin-out, of requirements concerning numbers of gates, and of communication paths. The pin-out and communication-path requirements relegate the problem of gates per module to insignificance, since even in the case of large, highly regular structures like the register file modules, the number of gates is below 10,000. Figure 4 shows one of four register files, together with the multiplexers and the supporting latches. The four-module

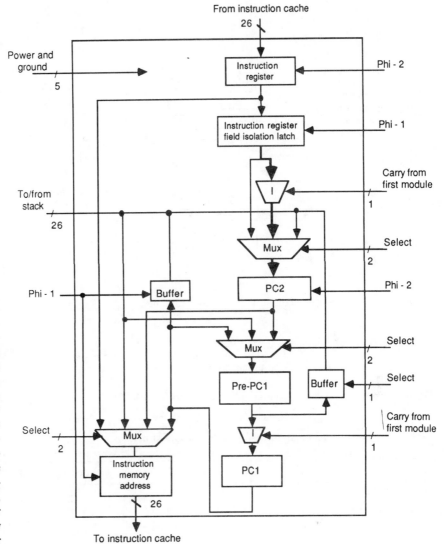

Figure 6. The instruction-fetch module.

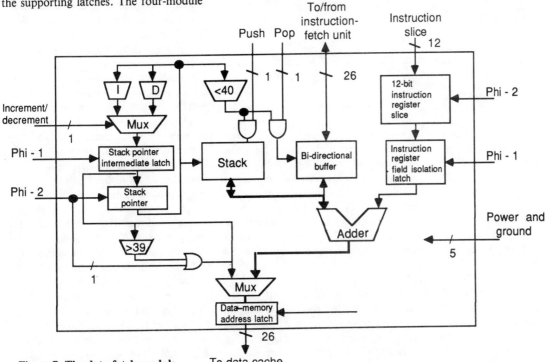

Figure 7. The data-fetch module.

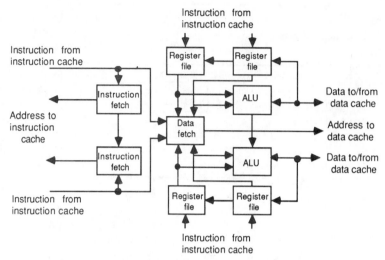

Figure 8. A layout showing juxtaposition of RISCF modules.

Total delay = 15 (gate delay) + 65 x (unit fan-outs)
+ 0.16/micron x (unit fan-outs) (first metal)
+ 0.14/micron x (unit fan-outs) (second metal)

Figure 9. The typical delay, in picoseconds, for a 10μ-wide MESFET.

Table 1. Propagation delays, in picoseconds, for various structures.

Structure	Data Paths	Select Logic	Worst Case
Register (write)	320	—	320
Multiplexer (2:1)	320	110/bit	3500 (32 bits)
Adder[1]	600/bit	—	8960 (16 bits)
Incrementer	390 + 290/bit	—	7540 + drivers
Decrementer	390 + 290/bit	—	7540 + drivers
Register file (write)	3000	4500	4500
Register file (read)	2800	4500	4500
ALU (32 bit)[2]	12,500	400	12,500
Driver	250/stage	—	1500 (6 stage)

1. Delay for the ripple-carry adder shown in Figure 3.
2. Delay for dual, carry-selected adders in the highest 16 bits.

macrostructure of which it is a part contains more gates than any other macrostructure and has the widest data path of them all (approximately 37,000 gates, of which those in the multiport register file make up over 95 percent).

The ALU and the status and data-write registers, shown in Figure 5, are combined into two modules of about 60 pins each. The most significant slice of the ALU contains two adders—with carry-input values of zero and one, respectively—and a multiplexer for selecting between them. A design like this permits the two modules to work concurrently and to arrive at three separate 16-bit results simultaneously. The carry of the lower 16-bit result selects the

appropriate upper 16-bit result, an operation that incurs only the extra delay associated with the multiplexer instead of the delay that would result from another 16-bit computation. A 16-bit ripple-carry adder needs less than 180 gates, and a 16-bit multiplexer uses only about 120. This split-adder feature does not force the module's total gate count over 1000, and it cuts the adder's execution time nearly in half.

The more significant half of the instruction-fetch macrostructure is shown in Figure 6, and the entire data-fetch macrostructure is shown in Figure 7. The instruction-fetch macrostructure consists of 62 pins and is composed of less than

2500 gates. The instruction-address stack and the stack pointer reside in the data-fetch macrostructure, a module with 74 pins and about 2000 gates.

The PLA controller, which is not shown in any of the figures in this article, comprises comparatively few gates, and can be subsumed into either the instruction-fetch module or the data-fetch module. The approximate module-gate totals are computed by identifying the principal substructures, which include the input/output buffers in the applicable module, and summing their respective subtotals.

Juxtaposition and timing. There is some overlap of functionality among the nine modules (chips). For example, slices of the instruction latch are contained in both of the instruction-fetch modules and in each of the four register-file modules. The replication of shared structures in the different modules reduces the penalties of interchip delays. As we have discussed, interchip signal propagation among both GaAs and silicon circuits is a principal source of performance degradation. Since GaAs circuits are low in power, the problems associated with driving off-chip signals are relatively greater than they are for silicon technologies like NMOS or bipolar logic, and the degradation suffered is more profound because of the high intrachip speeds of GaAs circuits. Consequently, until VLSI GaAs circuits appear, the problems of interchip signal propagation will continue to haunt the designer who wishes to build in gallium arsenide. Honeywell, Inc., is investigating a form of wafer scale integration called hybrid wafer-scale integration (HWSI), in which previously fabricated chips are deposited onto a substrate wafer and the interconnect is laid down subsequently. Such a scheme, though difficult, takes advantage of both the lower capacitances resulting from the common substrate and the absence of highly capacitive DIP pins. It also has potential for higher yields than would be obtained through general wafer-scale integration. Both our discussion of the juxtaposition of the RISCF modules and our timing analysis of these modules, which follow, assume a HWSI implementation.

Figure 8 shows a possible RISCF-module layout. In this layout, we have not attempted to find an optimal arrangement of modules, but we did note that keeping the communication distances between modules short is an important layout concern. An actual wafer might space the modules by as much as a centimeter.

COMPUTER

Honeywell is researching special, low-dielectric chip interconnects that reduce interchip delays if sufficiently powerful off-chip drivers that are compatible with the interconnect medium are used. The typical on-chip delay for a 10μ-wide MESFET is shown in Figure 9.

As can be seen from Figure 9, unless a gate is driving a long bus ($> 500~\mu m$), the most significant loads on the gate come from the devices connected to the gate's output. Since we have not established the circuit layout of each module, our timing estimates use only the intrinsic gate delay and the delay arising from load devices that is explained by the expression in Figure 9. Although delays owing to bus length are excluded from these estimates, the fact that the implementations of the structures that we discussed earlier are not optimal helps to compensate for the absence of bus-length-related delays in the estimates. The values in Table 1 and other calculations described below assume that unit-sized gates (10-μm-wide FETs) are used for all on-chip functions except those performed by the off-chip drivers, and the off-chip drivers are scaled appropriately. We use the approximate delay in picoseconds for each of the major intrachip structures discussed above to analyze the critical paths through each of the modules and to ascertain an approximate machine-cycle time.

We have obtained a measure of the delay for each of the Table 1 structures except the register file by applying the expression for gate delay (the expression does not include the delays resulting from bus length) to a logic representation like that shown in Figure 2. The estimates of the read/write and access times of the register file were drawn from comparisons of available GaAs SRAM circuits. [22] We assume that the register file consists of parallel 128-bit × 32-bit SRAMs and that each SRAM pair supports parallel read/write operations. The delay time for the multiplexer is based on an analysis of the logic multiplexer described previously. The driver delay takes on a successor stage, or a load three times larger than the load it presents to the preceding driver.

The critical paths in each of the four macromodules—the register-file, ALU, instruction-fetch, and data-fetch modules—are shown by the dark, heavy lines in Figures 4, 5, 6, and 7. The choice of path is based on the propagation delays of the structures the paths contain. These delays determine the maximum time to be allotted to the machine for intrachip opera-

tions. Every RISCF module latches a state during at least one of the two phases of the machine cycle. That is, each module contains a minimum of one latch between its inputs and outputs, and therefore requires that the processor bridge the interchip media only once during a clock phase. Consequently, an estimate of the period of the machine cycle is derived by summing the longest intrachip delay incurred during the first phase with the longest such delay incurred during the second, then adding the result to the approximate interchip delay.

Estimated machine-cycle time. The longest intramodule delay for Φ_1 operations is about 11 nanoseconds, and the longest for Φ_2 is about 15 nanoseconds. We have not yet ascertained the effect of the drivers except in the special case of ALU operations. If, as Table 1 indicates, the delay from a six-stage driver is 1.5 nanoseconds, then a more accurate estimate of the phase periods is 13 nanoseconds for Φ_1 and about 17 nanoseconds for Φ_2, which makes for a total machine-cycle time of roughly 30 nanoseconds.

The GaAs alternative

Although the previous calculations are approximate (they leave out delays that result from bus length), they give a ballpark estimate of the RISCF machine-cycle time. More precise estimates would require both detailed layouts for each of the modules and more information on the advantages of HWSI. The six-stage drivers used in our analysis may be larger than we need for GaAs implementation of RISCF, since, according to one text [23] on MOS VLSI design, a six-stage driver in which each successive stage is three times larger than its predecessor should efficiently drive loads more than 700 times larger than that of a minimum-sized driver. Of course, the drive capability of the six-stage driver is actually less, since larger drivers require longer buses, which places a greater load on the drivers. Investigations of a more detailed kind that are conducted about possible layouts and gate organizations will yield more precise estimates, but given the conservatism of the estimates discussed here, any estimates relying on more intricate evaluations of a RISCF realization in GaAs will probably come up with an even faster machine cycle.

The appeal of such a fast processor should not overshadow the difficulties

impeding its realization. A 30-ns cycle time is of little value unless caches with compatible access times are available. In fact, with the recent success of alternative device and packaging technologies for GaAs, RISCF's cycle time could be even shorter. The question still remains, however, of how a machine of single-cycle instructions with, say, a 10-ns cycle time will maintain an unbroken supply of instructions. It is feasible that small (4K-byte × 32-byte) memories could be used to achieve a 30-ns memory-access time. A

> Recent successes in alternative device and packaging technologies for GaAs may mean that RISCF's cycle time will be shorter than 30 ns.

small cache, however, might not provide sufficient support for the memory demands of Rete. Consequently, designing for GaAs-related speedups brings tradeoffs into the design of an integrated-processor system for executing OPS5; indeed, it brings tradeoffs into all processor-architecture design.

According to simulations and physical experiments, if RISCF is designed with a 300-ns cycle time, it executes OPS5 code two to four times faster than a VAX/780 that accesses memory exclusively from the cache. If a RISCF with a 30-ns cycle time had access to memory that supplied an instruction every 30 nanoseconds, it would increase this performance by almost a factor of 10. Of course, if the performance of the 780 processor is improved by implementation and realization enhancements, RISCF's performance advantage decreases.

Although gallium arsenide devices promise high speed, they have substantial fabrication and implementation problems. Currently, the GaAs systems that have been realized consist of SRAMs, gate arrays, and multipliers. Recently, some experimental GaAs RISC-like machines have been developed that are addressing the system issues we have alluded to in this article. [24,25]

We have illustrated some of the problems that arise when one attempts to realize a RISC machine in GaAs D-MESFET technology, which is a mature gallium arsenide technology. Owing to the comparatively low levels of integration and the poor fanout characteristics of D-MESFET logic, systems as complex as a RISC machine cannot yet enjoy the full advantages of the speed of gallium arsenide. To compound the difficulties, there is the question of whether caches and other supporting subsystems can accommodate the speed of a GaAs processor at reasonable costs. However, given the progress that researchers have made in improving the GaAs integrated circuit, the future holds some promise for RISC processors and other systems that display a similar type of complexity. Improving alternative GaAs technologies, such as HEMT, HBJT, and enhancement/depletion logic, may eliminate some of the logic-design constraints and fan-out problems endemic to D-MESFETs.

At Carnegie Mellon, current research into improving the speed of production systems concentrates on algorithm design and investigations of appropriate parallel-processor architectures. Although the speedup of a processor such as RISCF over machines that are more general-purpose in nature is not insignificant, the importance of actually realizing a physical GaAs RISCF is mitigated by the as yet unanswered higher level issues currently under investigation. For example, the prevalence of new multiprocessors on the market has created an environment in which very fruitful investigations can be performed on how to exploit parallelism in production systems.

Our investigation of a customized GaAs processor design provides a means to approximate an upper bound for the execution speed that can be expected from a single processor for OPS5 or other production-system languages. Our research goals, however, do not make the actual building of a GaAs RISCF a high priority because experimental GaAs RISC machines are being investigated by others and because Quinlan's comparison [6] has suggested to us that though RISCF has a performance advantage over a particular uncustomized RISC architecture when it is built with similar technologies, this small advantage is not significant enough to outweigh the costs we would incur in building a RISCF machine.

As a result of efforts by researchers to produce GaAs systems, the viability of realizing a GaAs production-system machine will likely improve.

We anticipate that subsequent investigations of GaAs RISC processors are likely to yield promising results if alternative technologies are pursued. □

Section 8: Glossary*

Some of the terms in this glossary are from the *American National Dictionary for Information Processing Systems*, developed by the American National Standards Committee X3, Information Processing Systems, or from the *Vocabulary for Data Processing, Telecommunications, and Office Systems*, IBM Report GC20-1699-5. These are indicated in the text by ANS and IBM, respectively.

ABSOLUTE ADDRESS (ANS) An address in a computer language that identifies a storage location or a device without the use of any intermediate reference.

ACCUMULATOR The name of the CPU register in a single-address instruction format. The accumulator, or AC, is implicitly one of the two operands for the instruction.

ADDRESS A number that uniquely identifies a memory location, register, or I/O port.

ADDRESS SPACE The range of addresses (memory, I/O) that can be referenced.

ADDRESSING MODE Technique used to determine the address of an operand based on the bits of the address field of the instruction.

ARITHMETIC AND LOGIC UNIT (ANS) A part of a computer that performs arithmetic operations, logic operations, and related operations.

ASSEMBLY LANGUAGE (ANS) A computer-oriented language whose instructions are usually in one-to-one correspondence with computer instructions and that may provide facilities such as the use of macroinstructions.

BASE ADDRESS (ANS) A numeric value that is used as a reference in the calculation of addresses in the execution of a computer program.

CACHE MEMORY A memory that is smaller and faster than main memory and that is interposed between the CPU and main memory. The cache acts as a buffer for recently used memory locations.

CENTRAL PROCESSING UNIT That portion of a computer that fetches and executes instructions. It consists of an arithmetic and logic unit (ALU), a control unit, and registers. Often simply referred to as a processor.

COMPUTER INSTRUCTION (ANS) An instruction that can be recognized by the processing unit of the computer for which it is designed. Synonymous with machine instruction.

COMPUTER INSTRUCTION SET (ANS) A complete set of the operators of the instructions of a computer together with a description of the types of meanings that can be attributed to their operands. Synonymous with machine instruction set.

CONDITION CODE A code that reflects the result of a previous operation (e.g., arithmetic). A CPU may include one or more condition codes, which may be stored separately within the CPU or as part of a larger control register. Also known as a flag.

CONDITIONAL JUMP (ANS) A jump that takes place only when the instruction that specifies it is executed and specified conditions are satisfied. Contrast with unconditional jump.

CONTROL REGISTERS CPU registers employed to control CPU operation. Most of these registers are not user visible.

CONTROL STORAGE (IBM) A portion of storage that contains microcode.

CONTROL UNIT That part of the CPU that controls CPU operations, including ALU operations, the movement of data within the CPU, and the exchange of data and control signals across external interfaces (e.g., the system bus).

DIRECT ADDRESS (ANS) An address that designates the storage location of an item of data to be treated as an operand. Synonymous with one-level address.

EMULATION (ANS) The imitation of all or part of one system by another, primarily by hardware, so that the imitating system accepts the same data, executes the same programs, and achieves the same results as the imitated system.

EXECUTE CYCLE That portion of the instruction cycle during which the CPU performs the operation specified by the instruction opcode.

FETCH CYCLE That portion of the instruction cycle during which the CPU fetches from memory the instruction to be executed.

FIRMWARE (ANS) The program instructions stored in a read-only storage.

GATE An electronic circuit that produces an output signal that is a simple Boolean operation on its input signals.

GENERAL-PURPOSE REGISTER (ANS) A register, usually explicitly addressable, within a set of registers, that can be used for different purposes, for example, as an accumulator, as an index register, or as a special handler of data.

---

*Based on Glossary in *Computer Organization and Architecture, Second Edition*, by William Stallings, Macmillan, 1990.

GLOBAL VARIABLE (IBM)   A variable defined in one portion of a computer program and used in at least one other portion of that computer program.

IMMEDIATE ADDRESS (ANS)   The contents of an address part that contains the value of an operand rather than an address. Synonymous with zero-level address.

INDEXED ADDRESS (ANS)   An address modified by the content of an index register prior to or during the execution of a computer instruction.

INDEXING (IBM)   A technique of address modification by means of index registers.

INDEX REGISTER (ANS)   A register whose contents can be used to modify an operand address during the execution of computer instructions; it can also be used as a counter. An index register may be used to control the execution of a loop, to control the use of an array, as a switch, for table lookup, or as a pointer.

INDIRECT ADDRESS (ANS)   An address that designates the storage location of an item of data to be treated as the address of the operand, but not necessarily as its direct address. Synonymous with multilevel address.

INDIRECT CYCLE   That portion of the instruction cycle during which the CPU performs a memory access to convert an indirect address into a direct address.

INSTRUCTION ADDRESS REGISTER (ANS)   A register from whose contents the address of the next instruction is derived.

INSTRUCTION CYCLE   The processing performed by a CPU to execute a single instruction.

INSTRUCTION FORMAT   The layout of a computer instruction as a sequence of bits. The format divides the instruction into fields, corresponding to the constituent elements of the instruction (e.g., opcode, operands).

INSTRUCTION REGISTER (ANS)   A register that is used to hold an instruction for interpretation.

INTERRUPT (ANS)   A suspension of a process, such as the execution of a computer program, caused by an event external to that process, and performed in such a way that the process can be resumed. Synonymous with interruption.

INTERRUPT CYCLE   That portion of the instruction cycle during which the CPU checks for interrupts. If an enabled interrupt is pending, the CPU saves the current program state and resumes processing at an interrupt handler routine.

LOCAL VARIABLE (IBM)   A variable defined and used only in one specified portion of a computer program.

MAIN MEMORY (ANS)   Program-addressable storage from which instructions and other data can be loaded directly into registers for subsequent execution or processing.

MEMORY ADDRESS REGISTER (ANS)   A register, in a processing unit, that contains the address of the storage location being accessed.

MEMORY BUFFER REGISTER   A register that contains data read from memory or data to be written to memory.

MEMORY CYCLE TIME   The inverse of the rate at which memory can be accessed. It is the minimum time between the response to one access request (read or write) and the response to the next access request.

MICROCOMPUTER (ANS)   A computer system whose processing unit is a microprocessor. A basic microcomputer includes a microprocessor, storage, and input/output facility, which may or may not be on one chip.

MICROINSTRUCTION   An instruction of a microprogram. Each instruction specifies one or more micro-operations. Execution of the instruction by the control unit causes the control unit to issue control signals to perform the required microoperations.

MICRO-OPERATION   An elementary CPU operation, performed during one clock pulse.

MICROPROCESSOR   A computer processor (CPU) all of whose components are on a single integrated-circuit chip.

MICROPROGRAM   A program, consisting of microinstructions, that is executed by the control unit.

MICROPROGRAMMED CPU   A CPU whose control unit is implemented using microprogramming.

MICROPROGRAMMING LANGUAGE   An instruction set used to develop microprograms.

OPCODE   Abbreviated form for operation code.

OPERAND (ANS)   That which is operated upon. An operand is usually identified by an address part of an instruction.

OPERATION CODE (ANS)   A code used to represent the operations of a computer. Usually abbreviated to opcode.

ORTHOGONALITY   A principle by which two variables or dimensions are independent of one another. In the context of an instruction set, the term is generally used to indicate that other elements of an instruction (address mode, number of operands, length of operand) are independent of (not determined by) opcode.

PROCESSOR (ANS)   In a computer, a functional unit that interprets and executes instructions.

PROCESSOR CYCLE TIME   The time required for the shortest well-defined CPU micro-operation. It is the basic unit of time for measuring all CPU actions. Synonymous with machine cycle time.

PROGRAM COUNTER   Instruction address register.

PROGRAM STATUS WORD (IBM)   An area in storage used to indicate the order in which instructions are executed and to hold and indicate the status of the computer system. Synonymous with processor status word.

RANDOM-ACCESS MEMORY Memory in which each addressable location has a unique addressing mechanism. The time to access a given location is independent of the sequence of prior accesses.

READ-ONLY MEMORY Semiconductor memory whose contents cannot be altered, except by destroying the storage unit. Nonerasable memory.

REGISTERS High-speed memory internal to the CPU. Some registers are user visible, that is, available to the programmer via the machine instruction set. Other registers are used only by the CPU for control purposes.

SCALAR (ANS) A quantity characterized by a single value.

STACK (ANS) A list that is constructed and maintained so that the next item to be retrieved is the most recently stored item n the list (i.e., last-in-first-out (LIFO)).

UNCONDITIONAL JUMP (ANS) A jump that takes place whenever the instruction that specified it is executed.

USER-VISIBLE REGISTERS CPU registers that may be referenced by the programmer. The instruction set format allows one or more registers to be specified as operands or addresses of operands.

Section 9: List of Acronyms

ALU	Arithmetic and Logic Unit
CISC	Complex Instruction Set Computer
CPU	Central Processing Unit
DMA	Direct Memory Access
HLL	High-Level Language
HP	Hewlett-Packard
IAR	Instruction Address Register
IBM	International Business Machines Corporation
IC	Integrated Circuit
I/O	Input/Output
IR	Instruction Register
LSI	Large-Scale Integration
MAR	Memory Address Register
MBR	Memory Buffer Register
MMU	Memory Management Unit
MSI	Medium-Scale Integration
PC	Program Counter
PROM	Programmable Read-Only Memory
PSW	Processor Status Word
RAM	Random-Access Memory
RISC	Reduced Instruction Set Computer
ROM	Read-Only Memory
ROMP	Research/Office-Products-Division Microprocessor
SSI	Small-Scale Integration
VLSI	Very-Large-Scale Integration

Section 10: Annotated Bibliography

The RISC field is relatively new and expanding rapidly. As yet, the available literature is rather sparse. An attempt has been made here to include most of the relevant recent material. The interested reader can pursue the topic in greater depth by consulting the references listed here.

ACKE87   Ackerman, M. and Baum, G. "The Fairchild Clipper." *Byte*, April 1987.

A detailed description of the Fairchild processor, which attempts to incorporate the best features of RISC and CISC.

AGRA 87   Agrawal, A.; Brown, E.; Petolino, J.; and Peterson, J. "Design Considerations for a Bipolar Implementation of SPARC." *Proceedings, COMPCON Spring '88*, March 1988.

Whereas most RISC processors have been implemented in CMOS, this paper examines the issues involved in implementing the Sun Microsystems SPARC —a RISC processor intended for implementation in a variety of logic families—in ECL.

ALLI88a   Allison, A. "Where There's RISC, There's Opportunity." *Mini-Micro Systems*, January 1988.

A survey of commercially-available RISC systems.

ALLI88b   Allison, A. "New Irons in the RISC Fire." *Mini-Micro Systems*, October 1988.

Looks at recent RISC product developments.

AZAR83   Azaria, H. and Tabak, D. "The MODHEL Microcomputer for RISCs Study." *Microprocessing and Microprogramming*, October-November 1983.

Examines the space of instruction sets containing from one to 32 instructions and concludes that instruction sets even smaller than that of the Berkeley RISC I may be superior.

BAND87   Bandyopadhyay, S.; Begwani, B.; and Murray, R. "Compiling for the CRISP Microprocessor." *Proceedings, COMPCON Spring '87*, February 1987.

Presents code generation techniques for the AT&T RISC machine.

BASA83   Basart, E. and Folger, D. "Ridge 32 Architecture—A RISC Variation." *Proceedings, ICCD 83*, 1983.

Describes the RIDGE 32 RISC-based system. Includes performance comparison with some other machines.

BASA85   Basart, E. "RISC Design Streamlines High-Power CPUs." *Computer Design*, July 1, 1985.

Describes the Ridge 32 RISC-based computer.

BELL86   Bell, C. "RISC: Back to the Future?" *Datamation*, June 1, 1986.

Places RISC in the historical context of computer development since 1948. Bell shows that the roots of RISC can be traced to the CDC 6600. He also defends the position that RISC-based machines should provide superior performance.

BERE87a   Berenbaum, A.; Ditzel, D.; and McLellan, H. "Introduction to the CRISP Instruction Set Architecture." *Proceedings, COMPCON Spring '87*, February 1987.

Introduces the AT&T RISC processor. The emphasis is on the design tradeoffs and decisions relating to the instruction set.

BERE87b   Berenbaum, A.; Ditzel, D.; and McLellan, H. "Architectural Innovations in the CRISP Microprocessor." *Proceedings, COMPCON Spring '87*, February 1987.

Provides justification for some of the novel aspects of CRISP.

BERN81   Bernhard, R. "More Hardware Means Less Software." *IEEE Spectrum*, December 1981.

A qualitative comparison of the RISC approach to recent trends toward complex architectures.

BERN84   Bernhard, R. "RISCs—Reduced Instruction Set Computers—Make Leap." *Systems & Software*, December 1984.

A brief survey of current RISC projects and commercial offerings.

BIRN86   Birnbaum, J. and Worley, W. "Beyond RISC: High-Precision Architecture." *Proceedings, COMPCON Spring '86*, March 1986.

Introduces Hewlett-Packard's new RISC-based architecture. Basic design principles are presented and defended.

BORR87   Borriello, G.; Cherenson, A.; Danzig, P.; and Nelson, M. "RISCs vs. CISCs for Prolog: A Case Study." *Proceedings, Second International Conference on Architectural Support for Programming Languages and Operating Systems*, October 1987.

Compares two experimental architectures developed at Berkeley for support of Prolog. A detailed performance analysis is included, which suggests an advantage for RISC.

BROW84   Browne, J. "Understanding Execution Behavior of Software Systems." *Computer*, July 1984.

The author suggests aspects of execution behavior to be investigated to guide the design of computer architecture.

BRUN86 Bruno, C. and Brady, S. "The RISC Factor." *Datamation*, June 1, 1986.

A survey of current RISC-based products and a discussion of their applicability in manufacturing environments.

CASE85 Case, B. "Building Blocks Yield Fast 32-Bit RISC Machines." *Computer Design*, July 1, 1985.

Describes an approach to RISC implementation using bit-slice chips. The author discusses the advantages of this non-VLSI approach.

CHAI82 Chaitin, G. "Register Allocation and Spilling via Graph Coloring." *Proceedings of the SIGPLAN Symposium on Compiler Construction*, June 1982.

It is observed that the register-allocation problem is equivalent to the graph-coloring problem in topology. From this observation, a technique is developed that was used on the IBM 801 RISC machine.

CHOW86 Chow, F.; Himelstein, M.; Killian, E.; and Weber, L. "Engineering a RISC Compiler System." *Proceedings, COMPCON Spring 86*, March 1986.

Provides an introduction to the optimization techniques used for the compilers on the RISC-based processor from MIPS Computer Systems.

CHOW87a Chow, P. and Horowitz, M. "Architectural Tradeoffs in the Design of MIPS-X." *Proceedings, 14th Annual International Symposium on Computer Architecture*, June 1987.

Examines the design of a second-generation VLSI RISC processor developed at Stanford. Topics covered include instruction cache, coprocessor interface, branches, and exception handling.

CHOW87b Chow, P.; Correll, S.; Himelstein, M.; Killian, E.; and Weber, L. "How Many Addressing Modes Are Enough?" *Proceedings, Second International Conference on Architectural Support for Programming Languages and Operating Systems*, October 1987.

Presents compilation techniques for mapping a variety of addressing modes into a single addressing mode in a target RISC processor. The target machine is the commercial MIPS R2000.

COLW85 Colwell, R.; Hitchcock, C.; Jensen, E.; Brinkley-Sprunt, H.; and Kollar, C. "Computers, Complexity, and Controversy." *Computer*, September 1985.

Reports on a large and ongoing effort at Carnegie Mellon University to assess RISCs versus CISCs. Perhaps the most thorough, objective analysis yet published.

COUT86 Coutant, D.; Hammond, C.; and Kelley, J. "Compilers for the New Generation of Hewlett-Packard Computers." *Proceedings, COMPCON Spring 86*, March 1986.

Provides considerable detail on the optimization techniques used in HP's compilers for its RISC-based machines. The paper also examines RISC-related design issues and explains how these have been addressed by the compiling system.

DAVI86 Davidson, E. "A Broader Range of Possible Answers to the Issues Raised by RISC." *Proceedings, COMPCON Spring 86*, March 1986.

A brief discussion of three RISC features (load/store architecture, few simple functional operations, and register stacks), in a variety of architectural contexts.

DAVI87 Davidson, J. and Vaughan, R. "The Effect of Instruction Set Complexity on Program Size and Memory Performance." *Proceedings, Second International Conference on Architectural Support for Programming Languages and Operating Systems*, October 1987.

Attempts to determine the effect of instruction set complexity on cache memory performance and bus traffic. The authors use a set of benchmark programs and several compilers for machines of varying instruction set complexity.

DEMO86 DeMoney, M.; Moore, J.; and Mashey, T. "Operating System Support on a RISC." *Proceedings, COMPCON Spring 86*, March 1986.

Discusses processor design features in the RISC-based system from MIPS Computer Systems that are intended to address operating system requirements. Using UNIX as an example, memory management and exception-handling are described.

DITZ87a Ditzel, D.; McLellan, H.; and Berenbaum, A. "The Hardware Architecture of the CRISP Microprocessor." *Proceedings, 14th Annual International Symposium on Computer Architecture*, June 1987.

Covers the same ground as BERE87a and BERE87b.

DITZ87b Ditzel, D.; McLellan, H.; and Berenbaum, A. "Design Tradeoffs to Support the C Programming Language in the CRISP Microprocessor." *Proceedings, Second International Conference on Architectural Support for Programming Languages and Operating Systems*, October 1987.

Discusses design decision made in the implementation of CRISP that were aimed specifically at support of C.

FITZ81 Fitzpatrick, D. et al. "A RISCy Approach to VLSI." *VLSI Design*, 4th quarter, 1981. Reprinted in *Computer Architecture News*, March 1982.

Discusses design and implementation effort of RISCs versus CISCs.

FLYN87 Flynn, M.; Mitchell, C.; and Mulder, J. "And Now a Case for More Complex Instruction Sets." *Computer*, September 1987.

In the words of the authors: "Our purpose is to evaluate and compare RISC-type designs with non-RISC instruction-set extensions using a level playing field; with similar compiler strategies, without compatibility considerations, and with similar implementation constraints." The title gives away the authors' conclusions.

FOTI84 Foti, L. et al. "Reduced Instruction Set Multi-Microcomputer System." *Proceedings, National Computer Conference,* 1984.

Reports on a very simple processor with 16-bit words, 32-bit instructions, and less than 20 operations.

FOX86 Fox, E.; Kiefer, K.; Vangen, F.; and Whalen, S. "Reduced Instruction Set Architecture for a GaAs Microprocessor System." *Computer,* October 1986.

Reports in detail on a one-year DARPA-sponsored project.

GANN85 Gannes, S. "Back-to-Basics Computers with Sports-Car Speed." *Fortune,* September 3, 1985.

The current status and commercial possibilities of RISC development are discussed.

GARN88 Garner, R. et al. "The Scalable Processor Architecture (SPARC)." *Proceedings, COMPCON Spring '88,* March 1988.

An overview of the RISC architecture developed at Sun Microsystems. The SPARC is based on the Berkeley RISC design.

GIMA87 Gimarc, C. and Milutinovic, V. "A Survey of RISC Processors and Computers of the Mid-1980s." *Computer,* September 1987.

Focuses on design and systems issues relating to a variety of commercial and academic RISC systems, and provides a comparative analysis.

GOOD85 Goodrich, P. "Simple Systems Approach Increases Throughput." *Mini-Micro Systems,* May 1985.

Describes the Whetstone XS-100 computer from Integrated Digital Products Inc. This RISC system was designed to be compatible with the Nova minicomputer.

GROS85 Gross, T. "Floating-Point Arithmetic on a Reduced Instruction-Set." *Proceedings, 7th Symposium on Computer Arithmetic,* 1985.

Current single-chip RISC processors do not support hardware floating-point operations. This paper describes a software approach implemented on the Standard MIPS. The strengths and limitations of this approach are analyzed.

GROS88 Gross, T.; Hennessy, J.; Przybylski, S.; and Rowen, C. "Measurement and Evaluation of the MIPS Architecture and Processor." *ACM Transactions on Computer Systems,* August 1988.

Reports on performance results using sets of large and small benchmark programs, run on the Stanford MIPS processor both without and with optimized compiling.

The results are used to analyze several of the organizational and architectural innovations in MIPS, including software pipeline scheduling, multiple-operation instructions, and word-based addressing.

HEAT84 Heath, J. "Re-evaluation of RISC I." *Computer Architecture News,* March 1984.

Attempts to decouple the effects of a large register file from a reduced instruction set and analyze the program size and execution time effects of the latter.

HELB89 Helbig, W. and Milutinovic, V. "A DCFL E/D-MESFET GaAs Experimental RISC Machine." *IEEE Transactions on Computers,* February 1989.

The design of RCA's 32-bit GaAs microprocessor is presented. The paper covers technology limitations, influences of the software environment, the instruction set architecture and the instruction execution sequence.

HENN82 Hennessy, J. et al. "Hardware/Software Trade-offs for Increased Performance." *Proceedings, Symposium on Architectural Support for Programming Languages and Operating Systems,* March 1982.

Makes a case for simple rather than complex machine instructions to optimize compiler writing.

HENN83 Hennessy, J. and Gross T. "Postpass Code Optimization of Pipeline Constraints." *ACM Transactions on Programming Languages and Systems,* July 1983.

A technique found in a number of RISC systems is the rearrangement of instructions at compile time to avoid pipeline interlocks. The basic problem is explored here with a detailed mathematical analysis.

HENN84 Hennessy, J. "VLSI Processor Architecture." *IEEE Transactions on Computers.* December 1984.

An exhaustive look at the relevant design issues for RISCs and CISCs, from the perspective of a RISC designer.

HIND86 Hinden, H. "IBM RISC Workstation Features 40-Bit Virtual Addressing." *Computer Design,* February 15, 1986.

A brief overview of the IBM PC RT, with an emphasis on the memory management unit.

HITC85 Hitchcock, C. and Brinkley, H. "Analyzing Multiple Register Sets." *The 12th Annual International Symposium on Computer Architecture.* June 17-19, 1985.

This study also attempts to separate the effects of a large register file from a reduced instruction set. It focuses on the effects of the former.

HOLL89 Hollingsworth, W.; Sachs, H.; and Smith, A. "The Clipper Processor: Instruction Set Architecture and Implementation." *Communications of the ACM,* February 1989.

The Clipper is a 32-bit microprocessor implemented as three chips: a processor chip and two cache and memory management unit chips. The processor is built by using

RISC principles although it has some CISC elements in its design. This paper is a detailed discussion of the instructions set architecture and the physical realization of the processor chip. The authors provide an excellent discussion of the design decisions that must be made in implementing a brand new microprocessor architecture.

HOPK83 Hopkins, W. "HLLDA Defies RISC: Thoughts on RISCs, CISCs, and HLLDAs." *Proceedings, 16th Annual Microprogramming Workshop,* December 1983.

Recommends design principles for High Level Language Directed Architectures. The paper then compares CISC, RISC, and HLLDA approaches and concludes that the HLLDA avoids the usual CISC inefficiencies and compares favorably with the RISC.

HOPK87 Hopkins, M. "A Perspective on the 801/Reduced Instruction Set Computer." *IBM Systems Journal,* No. 1, 1987.

A review and analysis of the 801 project in light of the RISC research that followed.

HUNT87 Hunter, C. "Introduction to the Clipper Architecture." *IEEE Micro,* August 1987.

A very detailed presentation of the RISC/CISC Clipper processor.

JOHN87a Johnson, T. "The RISC/CISC Melting Pot." *Byte,* April 1987.

The author looks at the Motorola MC68030 architecture. This is a "classic" CISC 32-bit microprocessor. Surprisingly, the author finds a number of RISC-like features and suggests that design techniques are converging.

JOHN87b Johnson, B. "System Considerations in the Design of the AM29000." *IEEE Micro,* August 1987.

A detailed look at the AM29000, which is a second-generation RISC system with a large register file and a simplified instruction set.

KANE88 Kane, G. *MIPS R2000 RISC Architecture.* Englewood Cliffs, NJ: Prentice-Hall, 1988.

The official architecture/instruction set reference manual for the commercial 32-bit RISC MIPS R2000 family.

KATE83 Katevenis, M. *Reduced Instruction Set Computer Architectures for VLSI.* PhD dissertation, Computer Science Department, University of California at Berkeley, October 1983. Reprinted by MIT Press, Cambridge, MA, 1985.

Contains a detailed description of the Berkeley RISC I and RISC II. Although this is a PhD thesis, it contains perhaps the best tutorial material on RISC technology.

KLEI88 Kleiman, S. and Williams, D. "Sun OS on SPARC." *Proceedings, COMPCON Spring '88,* March 1988.

Describes a Unix-like operating system implemented on the RISC SPARC. Shows how hardware features are exploited by the operating system.

KORT84 Korthaver, E. and Richter, L. "Are RISCs Subsets of CISCs? A Discussion of Reduced versus Complex Instruction Sets." *Microprocessing and Microprogramming,* August 1984.

Shows that the Berkeley RISC I instruction set can be synthesized by a subset of either the M68000 or the Z8000. The authors conclude that RISCs may offer benefits to compiler writers.

LAZZ89 Lazzerini, B. "Effective VLSI Processor Architectures for HLL Computers: The RISC Approach." *IEEE Micro,* February 1989.

An overview of the RISC approach. Nothing new, but quite readable.

LEE89 Lee, R. "Precision Architecture." *Computer,* January 1989.

The best and most detailed description of the Hewlett-Packard RISC machine available in the open literature.

LEHR87 Lehr, T. and Wedig, R. "Toward a GaAs Realization of a Production-System Machine." *Computer,* April 1987.

Looks at the use of GaAs RISC to implement a machine for expert system applications.

LUND77 Lunde, A. "Empirical Evaluation of Some Features of Instruction Set Processor Architectures." *Communications of the ACM,* March 1972.

This, along with TANE78, is one of the most influential papers on instruction execution characteristics. They have been referenced frequently in the RISC literature as providing evidence in favor of the use of a reduced instruction set.

MACD84 MacDougall, M. "Instruction-Level Program and Processor Modeling." *Computer,* July 1984.

Presents results of analysis of COBOL program execution on the IBM 370. The analysis is at the machine-instruction level.

MAGE87 Magenheimer, D.; Peters, L.; Pettis, K.; and Zuras, D. "Integer Multiplication and Division on the HP Precision Architecture." *Proceedings, Second International Conference on Architectural Support for Programming Languages and Operating Systems,* October 1987.

Describes an approach to provide reasonable performance of integer multiplication and division at little or no hardware cost on a RISC machine. The approach involves sophisticated compiler techniques.

MAGE88 Magenheimer, D.; Peters, L.; Pettis, K.; and Zuras, D. "Integer Multiplication and Division on the HP Precision Architecture." *IEEE Transactions on Computers,* August 1988.

An expanded version of MAGE87.

MANU87 Manuel, T. "The Frantic Search for More Speed." *Electronics,* September 3, 1987.

A well-thought-out look at the current role of RISC in commercial computer architecture. Includes a RISC versus CISC analysis and a look at a number of commercial machines.

MARK84   Markoff, J. "RISC Chips." *Byte,* November 1984.

An overview of RISC, concentrating on the Berkeley work.

MARS88   Marshall, T. "Real-World RISCs." *Byte,* May 1988.

Brief overview of RISC technology, together with a discussion of Motorola's MC88000 RISC processor.

MCDO87   McDonald, J.; Greub, H.; Steinvorth, R.; Donlan, B.; and Bergendahl, A. "Wafer Scale Interconnections for GaAs Packaging—Applications to RISC Architecture." *Computer,* April 1987.

Describes a high-speed, high-density, wafer scale packaging technology for the implementation of GaAs systems. The authors describe a 32-bit RISC design using this technology.

MCNE87   McNeley, K. and Milutinovic, V. "Emulating a Complex Instruction Set Computer with a Reduced Instruction Set Computer." *IEEE Micro,* February 1987.

Argues that, while GaAs is not yet appropriate for a CISC architecture, a RISC implementation with CISC emulation is both feasible and attractive.

MILL85   Miller, M. "Simplicity Is Focus in Efforts to Increase Computer Power." *The Wall Street Journal,* August 23, 1985.

Reports on prospects for commercial RISC systems.

MILU86a   Milutinovic, V.; Fura, D.; and Helbig, W. "An Introduction to GaAs Microprocessor Architecture for VLSI." *Computer,* March 1986.

Looks at the use of GaAs for implementing VLSI RISC processor chips. GaAs technology is examined in detail.

MILU86b   Milutinovic, V.; Sibley, A.; Fura, D.; Keirn, K.; Bettinger, M.; Helbig, W.; Heagerty, W.; Zieger, R.; Schellack, B.; and Curtice, W. "Issues of Importance in Designing GaAs Microcomputer Systems." *Computer,* October 1986.

Examines the architectural details of a RISC approach to the use of GaAs.

MILU87   Milutinovic, V.; Fura, D.; Helbig, W.; and Linn, J. "Architecture/Compiler Synergism in GaAs Computer Systems." *Computer,* May 1987.

The authors argue that the low chip density and long off-chip delay in GaAs systems can be overcome with a RISC design. RISC allows compiler techniques that replace hardware real estate with software cleverness. A detailed examination of compiler strategy and techniques is provided.

MOAD86   Moad, J. "Gambling on RISC." *Datamation,* June 1, 1986.

Speculation on the possible success of various RISC efforts. Analysis focuses on the Hewlett-Packard RISC-based product.

MOKH86   Mokhoff, N. "New RISC Machines Appear as Hybrids with Both RISC and CISC Features." *Computer Design,* April 1, 1986.

Discusses a number of RISC-based products, with emphasis on the IBM PC RT and HP 900/9000 series. CISC features in these products are discussed and justified.

MOUS86   Moussouris, J., et al. "A CMOS RISC Processor with Integrated System Functions." *Proceedings, COMPCON Spring 86,* March 1986.

Introduces the RISC processor from MIPS Computer Systems, based on the Stanford MIPS project. General design principles are discussed.

MUCH88   Muchnick, S. et al. "Optimizing Compilers for the SPARC Architecture: An Overview." *Proceedings, COMPCON Spring '88,* March 1988.

Describes how the compilers use the SPARC RISC architecture and discusses the design of the compilers.

NAMJ88a   Namjoo, M.; Agrawal, A.; Jackson, D.; and Quach, L. "CMOS Gate Array Implementation of the SPARC Architecture." *Proceedings, COMPCON Spring '88,* March 1988.

Describes the Sun Microsystems RISC architecture as implemented in CMOS.

NAMJ88b   Namjoo, M. et al. "CMOS Custom Implementation of the SPARC Architecture." *Proceedings, COMPCON Spring '88,* March 1988.

A companion to NAMJ88a, this paper looks at the use of custom circuitry to achieve greater performance.

NAUS87   Naused, B. and Gilbert, B. "A 32-Bit, 200-MHz GaAs RISC." *IEEE Micro,* December 1987.

Reports on a DARPA-sponsored project to develop a 100-MIPS, GaAs RISC processor chip.

NEFF86a   Neff, L. "Clipper™ Microprocessor Architecture Overview." *Proceedings, COMPCON Spring '86,* March 1986.

Introduces a microprocessor developed by Fairchild. The microprocessor exhibits RISC features. Both hardware and software design issues are briefly explored.

NEFF86b   Neff, D. "C Compiler Implementation Issues on the Clipper™ Microprocessor." *Proceedings, COMPCON Spring 86,* March 1986.

Describes a compiler designed for use with a Fairchild processor that exhibits RISC features. The compiler takes advantage of the architecture to yield high performance, but with programming constraints.

OHR85 Ohr, S. "RISC Machines." *Electronic Design,* January 10, 1985.

A survey of commercial RISC ventures.

PATT82a Patterson, D. and Sequin, C. "A VLSI RISC." *Computer,* September 1982.

Describes the most influential of the RISC systems, the Berkeley RISC I. Provides a detailed rationale for design decisions taken.

PATT82b Patterson, D. and Piepho, R. "Assessing RISCs in High-Level Language Support." *IEEE Micro,* November 1982.

Compares the Berkeley RISC I to five other processors, focusing on execution speed.

PATT83 Patterson, D. et al. "Architecture of a VLSI Instruction Cache for a RISC." *Proceedings, Tenth International Conference on Computer Architecture,* 1983.

Reports on an instruction cache developed for the Berkeley RISC II. The authors introduce several novel design features, and evaluate their effectiveness.

PATT84 Patterson, D. "RISC Watch." *Computer Architecture News,* March 1984.

Assesses the performance of the Berkeley RISC II machine by comparing it with the VAX-11 and the M68010.

PATT85 Patterson, D. "Reduced Instruction Set Computers." *Communications of the ACM,* January 1985.

A survey article. The historical background and motivation that led to the research in RISC architecture is examined. The RISC approaches of Berkeley (RISC I and II), Stanford (MIPS), and IBM (801) are compared.

QUAC88 Quach, L. and Chueh, R. "CMOS Gate Array Implementation of SPARC." *Proceedings, COMPCON Spring '88,* March 1988.

A companion to NAMJ88a, this paper focuses on the CMOS technology and fabrication issues.

RADI83 Radin, G. "The 801 Minicomputer." *IBM Journal of Research and Development,* May 1983.

Describes the first RISC machine, the experimental IBM 801. Provides a detailed rationale for design decisions taken.

RAGA83 Ragan-Kelley, R. and Clark, R. "Applying RISC Theory to a Large Computer." *Computer Design,* November 1983.

A description of the Pyramid 90X RISC machine.

RASS86 Rasset, T.; Niederland, R.; Land, J.; and Geiderman, W. "A 32-Bit RISC Implemented in Enhancement-Mode JFET GaAs." *Computer,* October 1986.

Provides technical details of a project at McDonnell Douglas.

ROBI87 Robinson, P. "How Much of a RISC?" *Byte,* April 1987.

A discussion of the state of RISC technology with speculation about future trends.

ROWE88 Rowen, C.; Johnson, M.; and Ries, P. "The MIPS R3010 Floating-Point Coprocessor." *IEEE Micro,* June 1988.

Describes a floating-point RISC chip developed by MIPS Computer Systems.

SEIT85 Seither, M. "Pyramid Challenges DEC with RISC Super-Mini." *Mini-Micro Systems,* August 1985.

Describes the Pyramid 98X and compares it to the VAX 8600.

SERL86 Serlin, O. "MIPS, Dhrystones, and Other Tales." *Datamation,* June 1, 1986.

Argues that MIPS, the conventional benchmark for comparing performance of different machines, is useless. Several other techniques are discussed. Results are presented that compare some RISC machines with CISC machines.

SIMP87 Simpson, R. and Hester, P. "The IBM RT PC ROMP Processor and Memory Management Unit Architecture. *IBM Systems Journal,* No. 4, 1987.

Provides a description of the RT processor and memory management unit chips. It also compares this commercially-available IBM product with its predecessor, the experimental 801 processor.

SIMP88 Simpson, D. "OEMs Cheer Motorola's 88000." *Mini-Micro Systems,* August 1988.

A simplified overview of the Motorola RISC processor.

STEV88 Steven, G. "A Novel Effective Address Calculation Mechanism for RISC Microprocessors." *Computer Architecture News,* September 1988.

The author describes a method for calculating effective addresses that is rapid and allows one of the pipeline stages to be removed from a typical RISC pipeline. The Stanford MIPS-X is used for demonstration purposes.

TABA87 Tabak, D. *RISC Architecture.* New York: Wiley, 1987.

This short (150 pages) monograph attempts to provide an overview of RISC architecture. It begins with a brief historical summary, followed by a concise summary of the advantages and disadvantages of RISC. Then, the Berkeley RISC machines (I and II) are examined in detail. Some comparative performance results are included. Finally, the book includes brief overviews of eight other RISC processors.

TAMI83 Tamir, Y. and Sequin, C. "Strategies for Managing the Register File in RISC." *IEEE Transactions on Computers,* November 1983.

Explains the multiple-window approach used on the Berkeley RISC machines, and analyzes alternative techniques for optimizing register use.

TANE78   Tanenbaum, A. "Implications of Structured Programming for Machine Architecture." *Communications of the ACM*, March 1978.

This, along with LUND77, is one of the most influential papers on instruction execution characteristics. They have been referenced frequently in the RISC literature as providing evidence for the use of a reduced instruction set.

TREL82   Treleaven, P. "VLSI Processor Architectures." *Computer*, June 1982.

Examines a variety of new approaches to processor architecture based on VLSI implementation, including the RISC approach.

UNGA84   Ungar, D.; Blau, R.; Foley, P.; Samples, D.; and Patterson, D. "Architecture of SOAR: Smalltalk on a RISC." *Proceedings, 11th International Conference on Computer Architecture*, 1984.

Smalltalk is a highly productive programming environment that poses tough challenges for the implementor: dynamic data typing, a high-level instruction set, frequent and expensive procedure calls, and object-oriented storage management. This paper describes a successful implementation on a RISC machine.

WALL85   Wallich, P. "Toward Simpler, Faster Computers." *IEEE Spectrum*, August 1985.

Summarizes the motivations for the RISC approach and reports on the relative merits (compared to CISC) of the approach as seen by proponents and opponents.

WATE86   Waters, F., ed. *IBM RT Personal Computer Technology*, IBM Publications SA23-1057, 1986.

A collection of papers by the developers of the RISC-based IBM RT PC. The papers cover major hardware components, microprocessor architecture, user interface, operating system design, and virtual resource management.

WEIS87   Weiss, R. "RISC Processors: The New Wave in Computer Systems." *Computer Design*, May 15, 1987.

A survey of commercially available RISC products.

WILS84   Wilson, P. "Thirty-Two Bit Micro Supports Multiprocessing." *Computer Design*, June 1, 1984.

Describes the Inmos Transputer which is a single-chip product combining processor, memory, and communication, and whose design reflects RISC principles.

WILS87   Wilson, R. "RISC Architectures Take on Heavyweight Applications." *Computer Design*, May 15, 1987.

Examines the evolution of RISC concepts; current applications of RISC concepts to superminicomputers, workstations, and embedded computers; and the likely future direction of RISC technology.

WILS89   Wilson, R. "Applications Determine the Choice of RISC or CISC." *Computer Design*, March 1, 1989.

Although recent RISC and RISC-like processor offerings appear to offer substantial price/performance advantages over CISC, current and forthcoming CISC processors continue to dominate the market. This article examines the reasons for the continued success of pure CISC machines.

Author Biography

Dr. William Stallings has been active in computer-communications and telecommunications for nearly 20 years. He is an independent consultant and president of Comp-Comm Consulting. Prior to forming his own consulting firm, he has been vice president of CSM Corp., a firm specializing in data processing and data communications for the health care industry. He has also been Director of systems analysis and design for CTEC, Inc., a firm specializing in command, control, and communications systems.

Dr. Stallings holds a PhD from M.I.T. in Computer Science and a B.S. from Notre Dame in electrical engineering. He is a frequent lecturer and author of the following books:

- *Computer Organization and Architecture, Second Edition*, Macmillan, 1990
- *Local Networks, An Introduction, Third Edition*, Macmillan, 1990
- *Business Data Communications*, Macmillan, 1990
- *A Business Guide to Local Area Networks*, Howard W. Sams, 1990
- *ISDN: An Introduction*, Macmillan, 1989
- *Data and Computer Communications, Second Edition*, Macmillan, 1988
- *Handbook of Computer-Communications Standards, Volume I: The Open Systems Interconnection (OSI) Reference Model and OSI-Related Standards, Second Edition*, Howard W. Sams, 1990
- *Handbook of Computer-Communications Standards, Volume II: Local Network Standards, Second Edition*, Howard W. Sams, 1990
- *Handbook of Computer-Communications Standards, Volume III: Department of Defense (DOD) Protocol Standards, Second Edition*. Howard W. Sams, 1990
- *Reduced Instruction Set Computers, Second Edition*, IEEE Computer Society Press, 1989
- *Integrated Services Digital Networks, Second Edition*, IEEE Computer Society Press, 1988
- *Local Network Technology, Third Edition*, IEEE Computer Society Press, 1988
- *Computer Communications: Architectures, Protocols, and Standards, Second Edition*, IEEE Computer Society Press, 1987
- *A Manager's Guide to Local Networks*, Prentice-Hall, 1983

Other IEEE Computer Society Press Texts

Monographs

Integrating Design and Test: Using CAE Tools for ATE Programming:
Written by K.P. Parker
(ISBN 0-8186-8788-6 (case)); 160 pages

JSP and JSD: The Jackson Approach to Software Development (Second Edition)
Written by J.R. Cameron
(ISBN 0-8186-8858-0 (case)); 560 pages

National Computer Policies
Written by Ben G. Matley and Thomas A. McDannold
(ISBN 0-8186-8784-3 (case)); 192 pages

Physical Level Interfaces and Protocols
Written by Uyless Black
(ISBN 0-8186-8824-6 (case)); 240 pages

Protecting Your Proprietary Rights in the Computer and High Technology Industries
Written by Tobey B. Marzouk, Esq.
(ISBN 0-8186-8754-1 (case)); 224 pages

Tutorials

Ada Programming Language
Edited by S.H. Saib and R.E. Fritz
(ISBN 0-8186-0456-5); 548 pages

Advanced Computer Architecture
Edited by D.P. Agrawal
(ISBN 0-8186-0667-3); 400 pages

Advanced Microprocessors and High-Level Language Computer Architectures
Edited by V. Milutinovic
(ISBN 0-8186-0623-1); 608 pages

Communication and Networking Protocols
Edited by S.S. Lam
(ISBN 0-8186-0582-0); 500 pages

Computer Architecture
Edited by D.D. Gajski, V.M. Milutinovic, H.J. Siegel, and B.P. Furht
(ISBN 0-8186-0704-1); 602 pages

Computer Communications: Architectures, Protocols and Standards (Second Edition)
Edited by William Stallings
(ISBN 0-8186-0790-4); 448 pages

Computer Grahics (2nd Edition)
Edited by J.C. Beatty and K.S. Booth
(ISBN 0-8186-0425-5); 576 pages

Computer Graphics Hardware: Image Generation and Display
Edited by H.K. Reghbati and A.Y.C. Lee
(ISBN 0-8186-0753-X); 384 pages

Computer Grahics: Image Synthesis
Edited by Kenneth Joy, Max Nelson, Charles Grant, and Lansing Hatfield
(ISBN 0-8186-8854-8 (case)); 384 pages

Computer and Network Security
Edited by M.D. Abrams and H.J. Podell
(ISBN 0-8186-0756-4); 448 pages

Computer Networks (4th Edition)
Edited by M.D. Abrams and I.W. Cotton
(ISBN 0-8186-0568-5); 512 pages

Computer Text Recognition and Error Correction
Edited by S.N. Srihari
(ISBN 0-8186-0579-0); 364 pages

Computers for Artificial Intelligence Applications
Edited by B. Wah and G.-J. Li
(ISBN 0-8186-0706-8); 656 pages

Database Management
Edited by J.A. Larson
(ISBN 0-8186-0714-9); 448 pages

Digital Image Processing and Analysis: Volume 1: Digital Image Processing
Edited by R. Chellappa and A.A. Sawchuk
(ISBN 0-8186-0665-7); 736 pages

Digital Image Processing and Analysis: Volume 2: Digital Image Analysis
Edited by R. Chellappa and A.A. Sawchuk
(ISBN 0-8186-0666-5); 670 pages

Digital Private Branch Exchanges (PBXs)
Edited by E.R. Coover
(ISBN 0-8186-0829-3); 400 pages

Distributed Control (2nd Edition)
Edited by R.E. Larson, P.L. McEntire, and J.G. O'Reilly
(ISBN 0-8186-0451-4); 382 pages

Distributed Database Management
Edited by J.A. Larson and S. Rahimi
(ISBN 0-8186-0575-8); 580 pages

Distributed-Software Engineering
Edited by S.M. Shatz and J.-P. Wang
(ISBN 0-8186-8856-4 (case)); 304 pages

DSP-Based Testing of Analog and Mixed-Signal Circuits
Edited by M. Mahoney
(ISBN 0-8186-0785-8); 272 pages

End User Facilities in the 1980's
Edited by J.A. Larson
(ISBN 0-8186-0449-2); 526 pages

Fault-Tolerant Computing
Edited by V.P. Nelson and B.D. Carroll
(ISBN 0-8186-0677-0 (paper) 0-8186-8667-4 (case)); 432 pages

Gallium Arsenide Computer Design
Edited by V.M. Milutinovic and D.A. Fura
(ISBN 0-8184-0795-5); 368 pages

Human Factors in Software Development (Second Edition)
Edited by B. Curtis
(ISBN 0-8186-0577-4); 736 pages

Integrated Services Digital Networks (ISDN) (Second Edition)
Edited by W. Stallings
(ISBN 0-8186-0823-4); 404 pages

For Further Information:

IEEE Computer Society, 10662 Los Vaqueros Circle, Los Alamitos, CA 90720

IEEE Computer Society, 13, Avenue de l'Aquilon, 2, B-1200 Brussels, BELGIUM

IEEE Computer Society, Ooshima Building, 2-19-1 Minami-Aoyama, Minato-ku, Tokyo 107, JAPAN